NORTH AMERICA

Fig. 1.—Physiographic Regions of the U.S.A.

NORTH AMERICA

AN HISTORICAL, ECONOMIC AND
REGIONAL GEOGRAPHY

by

LL. RODWELL JONES

LATE PROFESSOR OF ECONOMIC GEOGRAPHY
IN THE UNIVERSITY OF LONDON

and

P. W. BRYAN, B.Sc., Ph.D.

FORMERLY PROFESSOR OF GEOGRAPHY AND DEAN OF THE FACULTY
OF ARTS IN THE UNIVERSITY COLLEGE OF LEICESTER

LONDON : METHUEN & CO LTD
NEW YORK : E. P. DUTTON & CO INC

First Published October 30th 1924
Second Edition, Revised and Enlarged, November 1928
Third Edition, Revised, September 1930
Fourth Edition May 1933
Fifth Edition, Revised and Enlarged, May 1938
Sixth Edition, Revised, March 1943
Seventh Edition, Revised, January 1946
Eighth Edition September 1948
Ninth Edition, Revised, May 1950
Tenth Edition, Revised, 1954
Reprinted with a New Appendix 1957
Reprinted 1961 and 1963

10.4
CATALOGUE NO. 2/3617/10 (METHUEN)

PRINTED AND BOUND IN GREAT BRITAIN BY
BUTLER AND TANNER LTD., FROME AND LONDON

PREFACE

IN these days Geography stands for a study of physical environment in its relation to human activities. It has called for
the selection of facts significant from this point of view.
The correlation of these facts—of environment and of history—
has led to useful generalizations, and has suggested fruitful lines
of research. No subject engages to such an extent the gift of
visualization, or depends so much upon a sense of proportion.
For a just appreciation of the economic and political problems
of various peoples a knowledge of the more significant and effective environmental facts is essential. Geography is then a
citizen's subject, and as such, has now a stable place in the
curriculum of the schools.

Though a number of excellent school-books exist, yet surprisingly few works have been published in English of scope intermediate between that of the elementary textbook and that of
the University thesis. There is then sufficient justification for
the production of a continental study of intermediate standard,
and this is what we have attempted in the present work.

The arrangement of the book, in particular its division into
Historical, Economic, and Regional portions, has entailed some
slight repetition. It is for this and other reasons open to criticism.

The authors are fully aware that the more usual treatment
follows the order—Relief, Structure, Climate, Vegetation, etc. ;
and in fact such a sequence does obtain in the Regional section
of this book. The weakness of such a treatment of the whole
continent, however, lies in the fact that too big a gap is formed
between the consideration of the physical facts and that of their
economic effects. Our threefold division seemed particularly
applicable to a study of North America for the following reasons.

The peopling of the continent by European races began so
early as to suffer a very complete measure of geographical control,
yet late enough to have a detailed historical record. Above
all, it is a record *ab initio*, without the entanglements of earlier
influences. The historical geography of North America, then,
is singularly clear-cut. The successive influence of each well-
marked physiographic region upon the westward-moving peoples

v

is so definite that it has seemed best to us not to separate the description of these regions from a running historical comment.

With regard to the Economic section, we would point out that, to the Americans of the middle-west, economic development was largely a question of railways (i.e. of coal and iron) and of crops (and therefore of soils and climate). These major considerations cut across all the minor divisions—" the natural regions " of the physiographer. So, after our description of the coast lands and of Appalachia, we have in the second section of the book chapters dealing with general climate, major crops, and the fundamentals of industry.

And lastly, there is the Regional aspect. It is generally recognized that there exist regions in which man's activities—his points of settlement, lines of movement, occupations, and mode of economic development—bear quite special relation to some few and essentially simple physical characteristics of the regions themselves : characteristics not shared by surrounding areas. To a mind impatient of unrelated inconsequent fact, the study of such a region is singularly attractive, for every detail fits into a scheme. The thing may be seen whole. Examples of such complete regions are the Weald of England, and the Great Valley of California. Whether the treatment be elementary or detailed, one is brought down ultimately to the same few essential physical characteristics of the particular region studied. But though such regions exist, it by no means follows that a whole continent can be divided up into equally well-marked areas. The climatic regions of the climatologist, and the structural regions of the physiographer alike, have frequently ill-defined boundaries, and of course they seldom coincide. Indeed, the minute and complete division of a continent into regions seems to us rather an interesting exercise than a useful basis for the arrangement of the matter of a geographical treatise. Once a division is adopted it is so easy to exaggerate the significance of the boundary lines, and in the treatment of almost any economic activity we shall find few self-contained, and no self-sufficing units. Where the regional characteristics are very strongly marked, as in the Great Valley of California, the Ozarks, the New England States, etc., we have based our treatment on the region. Otherwise we have contented ourselves with pointing out the generally accepted regional divisions in our treatment of an area which may include several of them.

In actual fact, the repetition involved in our threefold division has not been serious. The sections are to some extent complementary and not complete in themselves. For this very reason the work must be viewed as a whole. A difficulty which must be felt by any who produce treatises of modern geography is to know how far questions of geological structure may be introduced with advantage. If they are ignored entirely, then in certain regions, that which gives unity to the whole geography, physical and human, is omitted. On the other hand, there is no room in a text-book of Human Geography for accounts of isolated and purely physical phenomena however interesting in themselves. Where, in broad outline, the geological history and structure can be related to the present relief and human activities of large physio-graphical units, then such an outline has been given. The names of the chief subdivisions of the Geological Record are introduced because without them any reference to geological history and structure becomes involved and cumbrous. If we except the Historical section, then the whole of the book is based on original, largely on official, sources. The maps, the geological folios, memoirs, and papers, of the United States and Canadian Geological Surveys, and the publications of the meteorological and agricul-tural offices of the two countries, have been the most important sources of material. Many articles in the " American Geo-graphical Review," the " American Journal of Geography," and the " Annals of the Association of American Geographers," have been found useful. When material from such sources has been utilized, acknowledgment is made in the text.

With regard to the Historical section, the aim of the author responsible for this has been to indicate the nature of the con-trolling geographical facts rather than to submit a connected historical survey. He trusts that this section may form a useful *geographical* basis for one reading early American history. The work here has not been carried beyond the mid-nineteenth century, for at this stage economic geography and historical geography are almost one. It is, of course, in this section of the book that most use has been made of previous treatises. The main and simple lines of American Historical Geography have been indicated once and for all in the works of Shaler, Semple, and Brigham. Save in detailed studies there is little to add. The author trusts, however, that he has been able to take an independent point of view, and in a few details to indicate the importance of some physical controls not previously emphasized.

With regard to footnote references, these need be few in a work which, if it break new ground at all, does so in the *correlation* of facts themselves undisputed. We trust we have made full acknowledgment in the case of recent scientific papers, and of geographical articles. Critical reference is occasionally made also to works which will be of outstanding use to teachers and students. In this connection, we may refer at once to the extraordinarily full and valuable bibliographies included in two publications of the Carnegie Institution, viz. " History of Transportation in the U.S.A. to 1860," and " History of Commerce and Industry in the U.S.A. to 1860." These and the works to which they are appended have been of very great assistance to the author of the Historical section.

Most of the diagrams have been specially prepared for this work. They should be regarded as forming an integral part of the subject-matter.

Finally, we would state that for the reader only a very elementary knowledge of geomorphology and of meteorology is assumed.

The thanks of the authors are due to the Editor of the " Scottish Geographical Magazine," for permission to reproduce an article therein published in July, 1923, and here forming the substance of Chapter II.

Ll. R. J.
P. W. B.

PREFACE TO SECOND EDITION

The occasion of a second edition has afforded the authors a welcome opportunity for revision and for the incorporation of a considerable body of new material. Corrections, amendments and additions occur in every chapter of this edition, and Chapters VIII, XI, XII, XXV, XXIX and XXXII are either largely rewritten or entirely new. The authors have to thank many correspondents for suggestions and corrections, and the Editor of " Geography " for permission to embody in Chapter XXXII an article which appeared in that periodical in the Spring number of 1928.

Some new diagrams have been prepared for this edition. Figs. 80 and 88 and also Figs. 91–96 (except Fig. 95, which is from an official government publication) have been prepared by Miss Hunt, B.Sc., of the London School of Economics Geography Staff. For Figs. 32 and 90 the material was selected and prepared by Miss Saner, B.A., and the drawings were made by Miss Wilford. The authors' thanks are due to these ladies for their help and for many valuable suggestions.

Ll. R. J.

P. W. B.

October, 1928

PREFACE TO FIFTH EDITION

More changes have been made in this than in any previous edition. Chapters on Soils and Soil Erosion (XII), Physiographic Provinces (XIII), the Hay and Dairying, Hard Winter Wheat, and Spring Wheat Belts (XVI), and Power Resources (XXIV), are entirely new ; while chapters XIV, XV, XVI, and XXXII are largely rewritten. The remaining chapters in parts II and III of the book have been supplemented and revised, and all statistics brought up to date.

Some maps and diagrams have been deleted and thirty new ones are included.

Our thanks are due to Mr. R. J. Church, of the Geography department of the London School of Economics, for his most useful work in preparing the new statistics, for reading much of the work in proof, and for a number of helpful suggestions.

Ll. R. J.

May, 1938   P. W. B.

PREFACE TO 1954 REPRINT

Corrections and additions have been made throughout the book.

P. W. B.

1954

PREFACE TO 1957 REPRINT

In this edition the Appendix has been entirely revised ; the statistics are the latest available ; and as far as possible they are on a regional basis.   The statistics in the text have historical value and may now be compared in most cases with those in the Appendix.

My thanks are due to Mr. K. R. Sealy, of the Geography department of the London School of Economics, for his work in preparing the new statistics and for helpful suggestions.

P. W. B.

February, 1957.

CONTENTS

MAPS AND DIAGRAMS

PART I
HISTORICAL GEOGRAPHY

CHAPTER I

THE PHYSIOGRAPHY OF THE NORTH ATLANTIC OCEAN IN ITS RELATION TO THE DISCOVERY AND EARLY SETTLEMENT OF THE CONTINENT

ON the 14th of June, 1919, near St. John's, on the Newfoundland coast, was enacted without ostentation a scene destined to become historic. Assistants had assembled some days previously the parts of the great Vickers-Vimy bombing plane, and as the wireless reports indicated that the Atlantic weather, if not wholly favourable [1] indeed, was not adverse, a little group impatiently awaited the start. The pilot and navigator [2] took their places in the machine and the sign was given. Rising slowly over a little wood, the plane was soon lost to the view of the watchers on the fog-bound coast, and headed for her 1,900 miles flight to Britain. Some sixteen hours later, and after the long riding of a severe storm, a landing was made near Clifden, in Ireland. For the first time in history, one of the great oceans was completely crossed in the air, and a new and important stage was reached in that evolution of communications which is so effectively reducing the apparent size of our globe.

It had been a great achievement, yet very really the fruit

---

[1] The actual average speed was about 120 m.p.h. The winds proved to be exceptionally favourable as regards strength (20–30 m.p.h.) and direction. This was particularly fortunate, for the clouds made observations almost impossible. See "Nature," London, June 19, 1919, p. 306.

[2] Capt. John Alcock (pilot) and Lieut. Arthur W. Brown (navigator).

of the times, and not to be regarded as an isolated effort. The men had been trained, and the design of the machine perfected, by the stern necessities of a great war. The aeroplane engine had been evolved quite naturally from the gas and petrol engines of earlier decades. The machine was equipped with many products of modern science—notably with wireless apparatus —and it was a well-charted ocean that was crossed. This is not to belittle the performance. If the greatest skill and the most modern methods had not been brought to the task, its completion would have seemed to us less admirable ; and most certainly with the fullest provision, there was not wanting that margin of unavoidable danger, so inspiriting and enticing, because so inseparable from all progress.

The occasion may serve to remind us of another yet more noteworthy Atlantic crossing. It is more than 400 years since three little ships slipped down on the tide from Palos, to make what was the first passage of which we have definite record. But how different the circumstances here. In known seas, and hugging the coast, the vessels of those days were less safe than the air packets of our own times ; but in this instance they deliberately set forth upon an unknown sea to an unknown destination, with navigation instruments so little reliable that errors in latitude of 1 to 2 degrees were frequent. The longitude estimations, based on dead reckonings, were, for considerable voyages, simply worthless. Whether we hold the traditional view that Columbus sailed west to reach the Indies, using the knowledge of the earth's rotundity common to the navigators of his day, and influenced in his estimate of the position and distance of Cipangu by the map of Toscanelli ; or whether we are convinced by the ingenious arguments adduced by Henry Vignaud,[1] which suggest that he sought New Lands of whose existence he had by hearsay special and private knowledge ; in either case, he could know so little of his route or of his destination that we must deem his voyage in the truest sense a voyage of discovery. Concerning his great work there are books without number, but they reveal little of the man or of his early life, though in all one characteristic stands clearly defined— the amazing fixity of purpose which bore up against the delays and disappointments of those long years of waiting, while he haunted the precincts of the courts of Portugal and of Spain, seeking patronage and authority for what must have seemed in truth a very dubious enterprise.

[1] "The Columbian Tradition of the Discovery of America, and of the Part played therein by the Astronomer, Toscanelli." Henri Vignaud. Clarendon Press.

But there is an analogy between these two great voyages. Each marks the beginning of a scientific era. A few years after the discovery of America, the great ocean, inviolate through the ages, was revealing her secrets to the adventurer, the settler, and the trader. By the mid-sixteenth century the western limits of the ocean appear on the maps, and with some semblance of accuracy; and custom and experience were teaching the mariner the ways of the great sea itself—how to set a course most free from storms, most favoured by fair winds. Many years were to pass before the regular scientific observations of seamen were to be systematically collected and correlated, yet already in the sixteenth century sailors were learning to master the ocean by learning of her habits. Oceanography became a science when mariners left the familiar seas of the Mediterranean and the landmarks of the Eur-African coast, and, with some misgivings maybe, confided themselves and their ships to the steady westward winds which bore them to new lands.

And the first air passage, too, is just a noteworthy episode in our gradual mastery of the air, a mastery depending upon and entailing a growing knowledge of the atmosphere, its properties and movements. At the very beginning of this geographical study we must grasp the significance of this interrelation of man and his environment—must see him first apparently the sport of chance, then with his movements and settlements largely determined by physical environment, and finally gaining a wider freedom through a fuller knowledge.

In every stage of the development of these New Lands, the shape and size, the winds and currents, of the Atlantic Ocean have been controlling factors, and it is to our purpose to study the nature and operation of these controls. We will begin with the chief of them. Every school atlas now shows, for summer and for winter, isobar maps of the world. Turning our attention to the North Atlantic Ocean, we find that a broad belt of relatively high pressure stretches almost from shore to shore with its medial line about lat. 35 (rather higher in summer, rather lower in winter), and that in winter it is continued over the continental masses, while in summer it is self-contained within the ocean area. Such simple maps are apt to be misleading unless we understand exactly what they represent and how they are obtained. We know, of course, that if for some definite instant of time (say 6 p.m. of a certain date of a certain year) it is possible to transmit, to some central meteorological station, the barometer readings of numerous and widely scattered stations on the land ; and by wireless, say, of numerous definitely located ships at sea ; then lines (isobars) can be drawn through

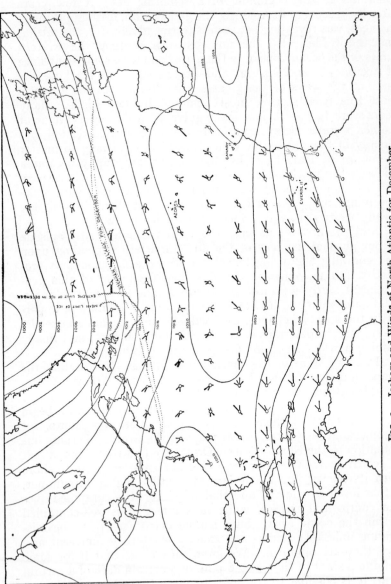

Fig. 2.—Isobars and Winds of North Atlantic for December.

The wind-roses are taken from Admiralty charts—the length being proportioned to percentage frequency.　Light winds are neglected.

places of equal selected pressure (say every two millibars), and we obtain for that moment of time the basis of the ordinary synoptic chart or weather map.[1] The isobars may show the pressure distribution to be quite irregular, or more frequently we find our maps blocked into several extensive areas of relatively high or low pressure. Theory and experience show that accompanying certain pressure distributions are certain wind systems. Thus in the Northern Hemisphere we always find (neglecting exceptions due to the friction around buildings and other surface irregularities) that, with our backs to the wind, high pressure is on our right and low on the left. So far the matter is a purely empirical relationship. The pressures are *observed* pressure distributions existing at a given moment of time, and the winds are *observed* winds.

The next point to notice is that if a similar map be constructed representing actual conditions of pressure and wind a day later, say, we should probably find—especially in our own latitudes—that though the general distribution resembled that of the earlier map, yet that there was some change in the form of the isobars themselves, and probably far more in their positions relative to longitude and latitude. The winds, of course, are in sympathy with Buys Ballot's "law" for these new positions. As certain temperature changes and the possibilities of precipitation are to be associated with certain types of pressure distribution, a forecast of to-morrow's pressure distribution is largely a forecast of to-morrow's weather. And the men who handle year in and year out thousands of these consecutive synoptic charts, in spite of the exhibition of occasional and exasperating originality on the part of the isobars, do find, in the main, that a certain pressure distribution of to-day is likely to be followed by a certain type for to-morrow.

Figs. 2 and 3 represent, not actual (i.e. synoptic), but averaged pressure conditions for December and July.

A cursory glance at the December map suggests that we have permanent high pressure at about lat. 35° and a permanent low pressure about Iceland and the Equator, undisturbed gradients between these areas, and wind everywhere in sympathy with these apparently stable conditions. This is not quite in accordance with the facts. We know, for example, that the wind does *not* blow constantly from the south-west over these islands in January, nor, indeed, in any month, though this is the *prevailing* direction of air movement. Now obviously these average condition maps can have no value unless for some areas

[1] Synoptic charts of the North Atlantic are available based on European, American, and ocean messages.

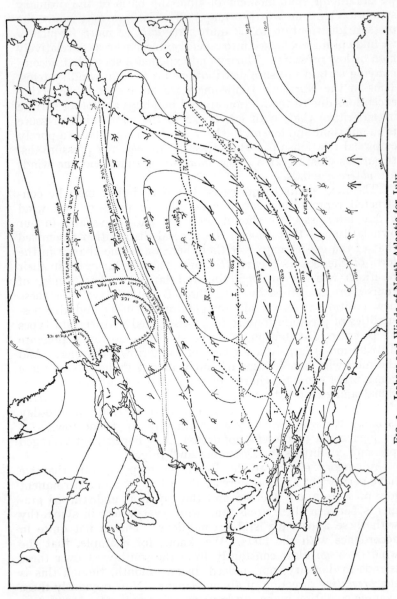

FIG. 3.—Isobars and Winds of North Atlantic for July.

Tracks of Columbus' first and fourth voyages ------ **Normal sailing route from the Channel to the West Indies and Charleston** —·—·—

they do represent permanent or semi-permanent conditions. The student should study carefully a consecutive series of the daily synoptic charts of the North Atlantic (now issued by the Meteorological Office). Then, confining his attention at first to the high-pressure belt, he will not fail to notice, that though there is nothing rigidly permanent about this belt, yet it is almost always represented by *some* marked anti-cyclone (sometimes more than one), about lat. 30°–40° N. We must think of its isobars as continually changing in shape, giving the system now more importance in the Azores region, now in the Bermudas, its form bulging and narrowing, and even dividing, after the manner of an amœba. Our average conditions here, then, have some meaning. A similar semi-permanent high-pressure belt exists in similar latitudes to the south of the Equator, and between is an Equatorial belt where at any actual moment of time the pressure is relatively low, and for which, therefore, the average isobars represent the facts correctly enough.

The three contiguous belts, then, the two high pressure, and the Equatorial low, are so nearly permanent that if we base our wind system on the average map, we shall get not merely a prevailing air movement, but one which represents generally the actual conditions for most days. We see, then, that the normal distribution of pressure, from about 35° N. to 35° S., is in sympathy with two great areas of calm anti-cyclonic weather —the Horse-latitudes—and two belts of easterly winds—the Trade winds—these last separated by a belt of Equatorial calms —the doldrums ; and that the conditions experienced in all these areas have some elements of permanence.[1]

We have still to notice that these average high-pressure systems are contained within the ocean limits in *summer* only, when there is a marked pressure gradient, not merely to the north and south, but also towards the continental masses which lie to the east and west. Thus in summer, and in summer only, the northerly winds off the Eur-African shores, and the southerly winds off the south-east coast of North America, have some degree of permanence also.[2]

On the Poleward side of the North Atlantic high-pressure belt, we come to an entirely different state of affairs. Here the average condition map, with its steady gradient slope to the

[1] A very good idea of the day-to-day permanence of the Trade Winds may be gathered by a study of the wind-roses contained in " The Trade Winds of the Atlantic Ocean," Meteorological Office Publication No. 203, 1910.

[2] A fact which was of some importance in the colonial days of the Triangular Trade, and one which is referred to in a later chapter.

marked low pressure over Iceland, entirely masks the actual conditions. Actually the daily weather maps show us that we have usually here a frequent succession of cyclones separated by wedges of rather higher pressure. The passage of each of these over any one place is accompanied, of course, by a complete veering or backing of the wind, probably, therefore, with considerable temperature changes, and usually by some precipitation. The resultant air-flow over a considerable period is undoubtedly from the west, and is a part of the general air circulation of the globe, but in reality the winds are very variable.

Bearing the characteristics of these great air zones in mind, let us try to see how they may be related both to the question of the discovery of North America and also to the earliest trade routes. One outstanding factor in the situation was the seaman's inability to determine longitude. Hence a voyager hugged the coast and trusted to landmarks. When this was impossible, or when he was temporarily deflected from the coast, he sailed to his required latitude and then held to this as nearly as possible until he made the land, the coast of which he followed to his destination. Till the latter end of the fifteenth century the known and frequented sea routes of Western civilization were confined to the Mediterranean and the Western European coasts from Gibraltar northwards. As far as the European coast is concerned, this is entirely bounded by the westerly zone or the Horse-latitude zone. Sailors had no reason to make for the west, every reason for avoiding such a course ; and if, as must frequently have happened, they were driven out of their course by occasional easterly gales, the chances were always in favour of their regaining their position by a change of wind to the more usual westerly drift. To the south in the Trade-wind belt, where the winds *favoured* movement to the west, they blew from the desert and little-known shore of North-west Africa.

There was some traffic here, however, for the extraordinarily irregular sea bottom off the African coast rises from considerable depths to bear the scattered groups of the Canaries and Cape Verde Isles. Further to the north-west and normally within the Horse-latitude calm, were the Azores rising sheer from the ocean depth. All these islands were known and mapped before the days of Columbus. They were rediscovered and colonized by Spain (Canaries) and Portugal (Azores) in the early fifteenth century, and held regular commerce with their respective mother-countries. It is quite likely that from such visits, or from the very coast of Portugal itself, a ship might be blown into the belt of the Trades, and have been carried by them to the West

Indies or the coast of South America. But the ocean is here at its widest, and such ships would usually have escaped from the Trade-wind zone into the calm and light variable breezes of the Horse-latitudes, and so slowly home without any sighting of the great New Lands lying beyond.

We see, then, what were the characteristics of the Atlantic which for so long made it a barrier between the Old and New Worlds; but these generalizations require a particular modification in the extreme north. Even the experienced are unconsciously misled by the usual Mercator projection map of the Atlantic. The true form is only really discernible on a globe, where the crowding-in of the Polar lands becomes evident. In reality, we have exemplified here the well-known geographical homologue which calls attention to the fact that the North Pole is situated in a sea surrounded by a land ring—in distinction to the South Pole, which is situated on a land mass surrounded by an ocean. In the north this land ring is broken only by the narrow, shallow, submerged Behring Straits between Asia and America; the narrow channels between the islands west of Greenland and north of Hudson Bay; and the wider space between Greenland and the Norwegian coast. This last is broken by the Shetland, Faroe, and Iceland island groups, which are the above-water representatives of a great undersea ridge stretching from Norway to Greenland—the Wyville-Thomson ridge. Let us look at the matter from the point of view of direct sailing distances.

The great circle route from the Channel to New York in the zone of the Westerlies is about 3,000 miles, or about three times the total sea distance to be traversed in a succession of journeys from Norway to the Orkneys, Orkneys to Faroes, Faroes to Iceland, Iceland to Greenland, and Greenland to Labrador; for most of these crossings are less than 250 miles. Now, when we remember that the great height of most of Western Norway renders it—in such a latitude—unsuitable for human habitation, and that the actual agglomerations of population are confined to the fiords where the inhabitants combine fishing and farming, we may realize how it comes that the Norwegian is by nature a seaman, and also that pressure of population should cause him to use this characteristic in attempts to invade and settle neighbouring and often more fertile lands. In the late ninth century, King Harold overcame the lesser princes of Norway, and the process of unification which ensued was contemporaneous with the exit of many an independent spirit in search of greater freedom in New Lands. Neglecting the important excursions of these Northerners to the south, we are concerned with the fact that they settled in the Orkneys, Shetlands, Faroes, Iceland, and Greenland—so many stepping-stones to the west.

Of their penetration even further west to the American mainland, we are told in a number of Icelandic chronicles, which form the basis of the Norse claim to the discovery of North America. These tell us, with some extraneous matter, that in 983 one Eric the Red, having had the misfortune to kill his man in a brawl, was outlawed from the Norse Republic of Iceland, then founded about 100 years. Tradition told of a land to the west visited previously by Gunnbjörn, one of the first of Icelandic settlers, and Eric determined to seek this land. Setting out with a few followers, he sailed west, and in two separate voyages explored the inhospitable coasts of Greenland. Now, the East Greenland coast is little indented, high, bare, bleak, uninviting, and usually inaccessible through pack-ice. Passing the southerly point, Cape Farewell, Eric sailed in the West Greenland current up the west coast. This is little more inviting, but it is indented with long fiord-like openings, at whose angles, and protected from the bitter wind, were patches of meadow-land where stock could be raised, and human habitation of the type with which Norsemen were familiar was not impossible. He settled in 985 eventually, and was followed by a number of colonists. These scattered colonies on the west coast of Greenland existed for some 400 years, and their existence is an undisputed historic fact. Remains of buildings, churches, some runic stones, and considerable records of trade and communication with Iceland and Norway, attest the fact.

A Danish expedition in 1924 has thrown new light on these settlements. In particular there was discovered in churchyard excavations near Ikigait a unique collection of mediaeval costumes. Vegetable roots had penetrated to the skeletons, i.e. to depths where to-day the subsoil is frozen summer and winter. There is corroborative evidence of a deterioration of climate since mediaeval times.[1]

It is different with the North American discovery. No authentic remains of Norse occupation have been found, though a multitude of " finds " originally dubbed Norse have proved to be of Indian, or even English, origin. The question of Norse voyages to the American mainland rests entirely upon sagas, passed possibly by word of mouth from one generation of professional saga-men to another. This profession must have found its occupation gone when, after the introduction into Iceland of Christianity, the trained memory and the cumber-

---

[1] " The Norsemen in Greenland," " Geog. Rev.," October, 1925.

some runes gradually gave place to the written word, so that by the twelfth century the sagas had been reduced to writing and initiated an active and illustrious literary period.

The saga versions relating to America are preserved in the Codex Flatöiensis manuscript in the archives of Copenhagen, a work completed certainly a century before the time of Columbus.[1] Briefly the tale is this. Eric the Red, after his find of a few habitable regions in West Greenland, returned to Iceland, and was so successful in inviting colonists that he set out again with twenty-five ships, for fourteen of which storm and icebergs accounted. His followers settled at Igaliko fiord and Ericsfiord, on the west coast. The son (Bjarni) of one of these first colonists, on a voyage from Iceland to Greenland, encountered foggy weather and sailed on without sight of sun or stars. Eventually he sighted lands without mountains, fiords, or glaciers, but covered with dense woods. This was evidently not Greenland, and he turned northwards for home. The story eventually comes to the ears of Leif, the son of Eric the Red. He it was who first brought missionaries from the Christian king, Olaf of Norway, to Greenland (about A.D. 1000). Hearing of Bjarni's experience, he decided to visit the lands to the south of Greenland. He passed a bare rugged coast and called it " Helluland," and then, after some days, a wooded coast, " Markland," and eventually losing sight of land for two days under a keen northeast wind, he came to low coasts in which the wild vine is abundant —" Vinland."

Leif returned to his unwooded colony with a cargo of *timber*, and successive voyages were made, probably between 1000 and 1010.

We should notice about these stories that although they contain nothing to define exactly the points reached, yet they do allude to conditions—of relief, vegetation, climate and inhabitants—which would be met with progressively on a coastal voyage from Labrador to Southern New England, and, moreover, they contain nothing unlikely or inexplicable. It is much more difficult to believe that a colony could exist in Greenland for over 300 years, than that, granted such a colony, some members of it should not at times have hit upon the American coast. Had these voyages taken place from Norway itself, they might

[1] There is now a considerable literature concerned with the Norse Discovery. Among more recent works in English, the following are recommended to the student :—Babcock, W. H. : " Early Norse Visits to North America," 1913, in Smithsonian Miscellaneous Collections, vol. 59, No. 19. Fossun, A. W. : "The Norse Discovery of America," 1919. De Costa, B. J. : " The pre-Columbus Discovery of America," 1890. " The Wineland Voyages," Halldór Hermannsson, " Geog. Rev.," January, 1927.

perhaps have aroused a more active curiosity, but they were the occasional voyages of a distant colony. More important, perhaps, as limiting contemporaneous information of the discovery, were the general conditions of Europe in the eleventh century.

Nearly 500 years later, in the days of Columbus, the Renaissance had brought with it a revival of scientific geography. Sea routes to Asia, avoiding exchange in the Eastern Mediterranean, were being consciously sought. The desert coast of North-west Africa, the deadly reefs of Cape Bojador, and the supernatural myths associated with the tropic sea, had lost some of their terrors in the voyages of Prince Henry's navigators. If Columbus had not purposefully discovered land to the west, Cabral would have done so accidentally, when, driven out of his course on the newly found Cape route, he made the coast of Brazil in April, 1500, with a fleet of thirteen vessels and 1,200 men bound to establish a Portuguese trade centre on the Malabar coast of India. He had taken a course too far to the west, and perhaps in the Equatorial belt of calm was left to the influence of the Southern Equatorial current. Or, again, although the voyage of Columbus was known in England before 1497, and almost certainly hastened the attempt of Cabot, yet the idea seems to have been present in Cabot's mind long before his actual voyage, and he would probably have discovered North-East America in any case.

It was the peculiarity of the Columbus voyages that they were immediately effective, being followed up by a period of discovery and settlement. It is quite possible that the vague stories of a land of Brazil and of the Island of the Seven Sisters had their origin in the tales of seamen who had actually had the good fortune to return, after having been driven out of their course to the shores of America. It is very probable that some made such a journey, never to return. But it is at least noteworthy that the two first Atlantic voyages of which we have definite and exact information (those of Columbus and Cabot) were both purposefully made with the very idea of discovery.

It is not our purpose to give account here of the four great voyages of Columbus ; such scraps of his journal as came to Las Casas are reproduced in a hundred books, and are interesting only when fully quoted. But it is proper to enumerate the instances of definite geographical control exhibited in these mighty adventures.

We note, then, that on his first voyage Columbus sailed south until he reached the Canaries. His reason for doing so may have been either—as is usually supposed—that he wished to reach the latitude of Northern Cipangu, as indicated on the Toscanelli map, or that, from previous experiences,[1] he realized that such a proceeding would put him well in the zone of prevailing east winds. Possibly both reasons weighed with him, and further, the call at the Canaries enabled him to take in stores and repair the *Pinta's* rudder.

From the isle of Gomera, in the Canaries, he set out westward in the full Trade-wind track, and so persistent were the winds that his sailors feared for the chance of returning, and, to lessen such fear, Columbus faked his log of the daily run. The same wish to propitiate a suspicious and unwilling crew led him to juggle with his compass, for he was going far enough to the west to demonstrate the variation of that instrument. Then it is evident, from his description of masses of floating weed, that he skirted the Sargasso Sea, that great mass of floating vegetation that has its existence in the immobile area of constant high pressure and high salinity, between the Trades to the south and the Westerlies to the north. Just in time to prevent open mutiny came sure sign of land, and a few hours before the dawn on October 11, 1492, that curious moving light seen by the Admiral himself and his two companions, so that they put by the ship and watched intently until dawn revealed the low surf-ridden shores of what must have been one of the Bahaman group of islands. After coasting Cuba and Hispaniola, and landing a small colony at La Navidad, he made for home. Here, again, he sought first his ultimate latitude, that of Southern Spain, a course rendered easy by the frequent tendency of the winds to assume almost a southerly direction off the south-east coast of North America. Thus skirting the Atlantic high-pressure area, he was brought to the southern edge of the stormy belt of Westerlies. After passing the Azores, the two remaining ships became separated in a storm, Columbus eventually reaching the Tagus, and Pinzon, Bayonne. Columbus had discovered the outposts of the New World, and, incidentally, he had followed a great natural route. To go west on the Trades and return on the anti-Trades became the usual and purposed procedure of the multitude of mariners who followed in his track.

Of the influence of Atlantic conditions in his later voyages there is little to add. On his third voyage, disappointed in his Indian Isles, he deliberately set himself to use the Trade winds until he should reach Equatorial latitude, and thence sail westward, " that he might find some other land." Such a procedure provided him with an experience of a third Atlantic weather

---

[1] He himself had sailed the North-west African coast before and visited the Canaries, and sailors from Portugal continually visited the region.

zone, for it brought him, of course, at about lat. 5° N. into the Equatorial calms ; and there he remained almost without movement under a burning sun for eight days. Then with a light breeze he steered north-west and reached the mainland about Trinidad.

His fourth voyage was another attempt to win a way past the outpost arcs of the West Indies to the mainland of the supposed Asia beyond. In it he discovered the coast of Central America and the Gulf of Mexico, and heard of a land rich in gold to the north-west—a presage of the coming Mexican rush. On this voyage, too, he had experience of the notorious West Indian hurricanes. He returned to Spain for the last time in 1504, a worn-out, disappointed old man, and died in 1506.

He had voyaged and made known the whole of the Caribbean region and the south coast of the Gulf of Mexico. Even before his death, there were permanent Spanish colonies in Hispaniola and Cuba. The natives of his newly won islands were failing in their fatal contact with a race so different ; and the gold which they wore so simply as ornament, was proving the chief incentive to settlers, who tracked it to its source from island to island, and thence at length to the more plentiful supplies of the mainland.

The growing traffic of the Atlantic was influenced by other control than that of the winds, and notably by the system of ocean currents. The movements of the ocean waters may be classed under three headings :

(1) *The tides*—these in the open sea are represented by a mere heaving of the waters, as the tidal wave of about 2′ amplitude passes by. It is the passage of a condition, and no real current movement is entailed until this tidal wave encounters the continental shelf and narrowing estuaries of the great land masses, when local tidal currents of great importance are caused.

(2) *The water movements initiated by variations in density, variations which are themselves due to the differential heating and evaporation to which various portions of the ocean are subjected.* The density of water increases with its salinity (i.e. the amount of dissolved solid matter contained per unit weight of water), and decreases with rise of temperature. Also, it increases with depth, because of the compressibility of water. Thus, in an ideal case, an increase of heat or a diminution of salinity in a certain surface-water mass tends to set up *surface* currents flowing *outwards* and *over* surrounding water masses of greater density, and *under-currents* of this denser water inwards to complete the circulation.

In actual fact, the greater heating usually goes with an increase of salinity, for it occurs, of course, at the surface and in low latitudes, and is accompanied by the rapid surface evaporation of the Trade-wind and doldrum belts, which makes for increasing surface salinity. But in fact, too, the variations in salinity are much more effective in respect of density than variations in temperature. The actual oceanic circulation resulting from these changes in density is not yet completely known. It is not in the least likely to be very simple, but probably there is a slow creeping of the deep polar waters towards the Equator, and an upper movement of warmer water from low latitudes Polewards.

The system is enormously complicated by the variations in surface supplies of fresh water, either by direct precipitation, or by the outpourings of large rivers, and also by surface-water movements originated by air movements.

(3) *Surface movements, mainly caused by air currents.* Here we consider what is probably the most considerable factor in surface movements, and the one most influential upon man's activities. We have only to remember the very great pressure of the atmosphere upon the ocean surface to realize that any considerable movement of the superincumbent air must be accompanied by a corresponding drag upon the water surface. We have evidence of this in the immediate wave-formation resulting from any accession of wind. But we have just seen that a very considerable element of permanence characterizes the wind conditions of the Trade-wind belts, and it is only to be expected that this should be accompanied by a surface-water movement, which, while tending to vary in velocity with the wind conditions, yet acquires a sufficient momentum to be somewhat independent of small and temporary variations in the air movement.

We should expect, what indeed we find, a surface movement from the high-pressure belts towards the Equator of relatively salt and warm water, though with a falling off of salinity actually within the Equatorial region due to surface supplies of fresh water from increasing precipitation and river outlet. But more important than the Equatorial trend in this surface movement is its westward tendency. As a result, steady currents (the Northern and Southern Equatorial currents) set within the Trade-wind belts towards the West Indies. A portion of this water, threading its way through the Lesser Antilles, forms the Caribbean current.[1] The water from this last appears—at any rate

[1] Between the Lesser Antilles there is a regular strong current westwards. The openings between the Greater Antilles, e.g. Monat and Windward Passage, are set parallel to and not opposite the general direction of the Antillean current. The movement in these channels, therefore, is irregular, and depends partly on the strength of the Trade winds.

as a surface current—just to enter the Gulf of Mexico, and then, piled up against the waters of the Gulf, to change its direction so that it runs to the north and finds an outlet in the narrow notch in the sea-bed which separates the great Bahama Banks from the mainland of Florida. Here it issues as the Florida current (misnamed Gulf Stream), and is joined by the even larger body of westward-driven warm water, which, as the Antillean current, has skirted the Bahama Banks to the north. The resulting northward-flowing body of warm water is at once the most considerable and, in its relation to human life, the most effective of all ocean currents.

The average velocity and temperature of the water in Florida Strait are extraordinary both at the surface and for a considerable depth, as is clearly shown in Fig. 4. Thus, off the coast of Florida, the Gulf Stream is not a surface drift merely, but a moving body of warm water of great depth and volume. The velocity is variable, and increases, as we should expect, with any increase in the development of the Atlantic High, and it is therefore greatest in the late summer, when this latter system is most clearly defined.

As a complement to this warm stream, we have the Labrador current (Fig. 5). This enters the Atlantic proper from Davis Strait (between Labrador and North Greenland), when it hugs the Labrador coast. The water movements giving rise to its emergence are somewhat complicated, but in outline the system appears to be somewhat as follows. In the first place, a surplus of relatively cold fresh water, derived partly from the Siberian river outlet, finds an exit from the North Polar Sea over the Wyville-Thomson ridge between Iceland and Greenland. This moves south as the East Greenland current. It carries with it some soft pack-ice, but few icebergs, for the great Greenland glacier tends to flow off the indented, fiord-like, *west* coast. At Cape Farewell it completely skirts the coast and follows the western shore as the West Greenland current. The current shown on some charts from Cape Farewell to the Newfoundland bank is non-existent, and the East Greenland current is unimportant as a contribution to the icebergs of the Atlantic; indeed, an increase in its flow may be related to a clearance in Atlantic ice. The northward-flowing West Greenland current continues, sometimes in the teeth of the wind, for many miles up the west coast, detaching ice from the land, and finally overcome by a stronger southward flow from Baffin Bay. The ice brought north by the West Greenland current now drifts into the southward-moving middle ice (see Fig. 5), and the combined stream eventually joins the west ice to form the Labrador cur-

rent. Between the West Greenland ice and coalescing middle
and west ice, a wedge of warm saline Atlantic water can be
detected as far north as lat. 63°, when it disappears under fresher,
but colder, polar water.

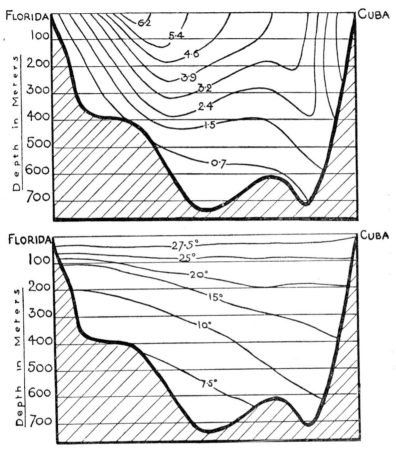

FIG. 4.—Speed in kilometres per hour and Temperature in deg. C. at various
depths of the Gulf Stream in the Straits of Florida.
(*After* Schott, in " Geographie des Atlantischen Ozeans.")

The Labrador current, bearing ice, flowing slowly over the
Newfoundland Banks, meets the Gulf Stream drift of warmer,
salter water which has been deflected to the right (as is the case
with all moving masses in the Northern Hemisphere). A considerable area of very cold water with somewhat indeterminate
currents surrounds Newfoundland and extends over the Banks

to the east and south. A portion of the Labrador current deflected to the right tends to hug the north-east coast of North America, and is perceptible in its influence upon climate as far south as Cape Hatteras. Off Newfoundland, then, on the Banks and to the east of them, we have side by side two wide belts of surface water slowly moving in opposite directions and characterized by great differences in temperature, salinity, and colour.[1] Indeed, it is just this dual difference in temperature and salinity which makes it possible for the two water bodies to maintain their identities for so considerable a period of contact. It is quite possible for a body of warm water to exist in contact with a body of cold water without relative displacement, if only the lesser density proper to the warm water in virtue of its higher temperature is balanced by a greater salinity. If this is so, then, depth for depth in the two streams, the density may be nearly the same. In the same way, it is possible for a cool fresh water to flow over warmer but salt water without marked mixing. Off Labrador the current of that name is well marked and continuous, but in the wide expanse of cold water which surrounds Newfoundland, the surface movement is very variable and depends largely on temporary wind directions. The *prevailing* movement must be to the south and south-east, and under the Gulf Stream drift.

To the east of Newfoundland there occur the most marked surface temperature gradients to be found in any ocean (Fig. 5). This is indicated by the very marked crowding together of the isotherms in this region. A notable result of this rapid decrease in the temperature of the surface as one approaches the Banks from the west is that in summer, when it is most marked, and when also air movement is more frequently from the east, warm moist air from the Middle or South Atlantic on passing over the cold seas off the Banks, precipitates some of its moisture in the form of fog.[2]

[1] Actually along the zone of contact of the two currents there is frequently some interdigitation, and warm and cold surface belts alternate for a few miles.

[2] The best accounts of the oceanography of the North-west Atlantic are contained in :—(i) " Depth of Ocean," Hjort & Murray, Chap. V ; (ii) " Geographie des Atlantischen Ozeans," G. Schott ; (iii) " Ice Observation, Meteorology and Oceanography in the North Atlantic " (s.s. *Scotia*, 1913), Government publication ; (iv) " International Ice Observation and Ice Patrol Service in the North Atlantic Ocean," Treasury Dept. U.S.A. Coastguard Bulletin, 1912, etc. These are yearly bulletins publishing the scientific records of the ice patrol vessels engaged about the Newfoundland Banks. They are illustrated by many maps and diagrams showing actual surface and underwater temperature conditions, and also the strength and variation of surface currents, and, of course, the actual observed ice conditions.

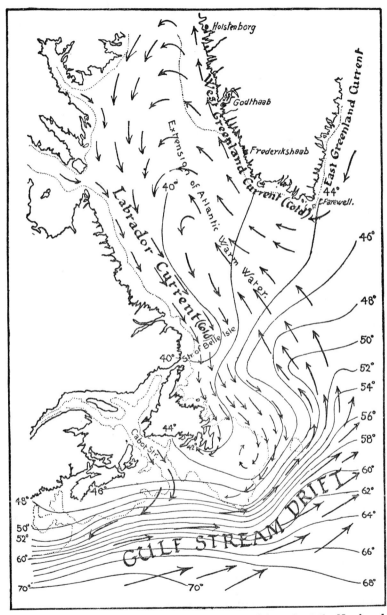

FIG. 5.—Sea Surface Temperature and Current Conditions about the Newfoundland Banks.

And then, again, the shallow water over the Banks (Fig. 5) and the presence of a marked cold current are just the conditions which seem to favour the production of large quantities of sea plankton, for they are conditions paralleled in all the great fishing grounds the world over.

Here, then, right in the track of the great circle route between New York and the English Channel, lies a considerable sea area noteworthy for its summer fogs, its icebergs, and its fish. We have already noticed how the Icelandic stories of Vinland voyagers mention all three. And the same is true of the first really authenticated crossing in this Northern Atlantic. It is said of Jean Cabot, a native of Genoa and a citizen of Venice, that he had long wished to sail westwards to discover the east, and when Henry VII gave him authority—and very little else—for his voyage, and he actually sailed from Bristol, he at any rate had the advantage of knowing that Columbus had found land to the west. Cabot sailed from Bristol, a port that for a period was to become our chief point of exchange with America. Bristol at that time had important fishing connections with Iceland, and it is often stated that Cabot, and possibly Columbus (who is believed to have visited Iceland), had heard of the Vinland tradition. If these old stories had referred to voyages but newly undertaken, this would appear likely enough, but we find it difficult to believe that a legend some centuries old, and one in which the Icelanders themselves apparently took no practical interest, should, as it were, " crop up in conversation " between a number of fisher-folk and a foreign mariner. However that may be, the voyage of the Cabots is of special interest to us as being the first Atlantic crossing to take place from a British port (it was made the basis of a subsequent claim to the mainland of North America), and as being the first successful attempt in the Northern Atlantic.

Cabot put out from Bristol on May 2, 1497. After passing Ireland, he sailed first north and then west, and such were the contrary winds and storms he encountered, that it was June 24 before he sighted what was probably the western extremity of Cape Breton Island, that is to say, considerably longer than Columbus took in making the much longer distance from the Canaries to Watling Island (33 days). Cabot's storms and contrary winds are typical of the zone in which he crossed ; they, and perhaps the prevalent fog and ice of the Newfoundland area, form the main reason why the northern narrower ocean had not been frequently crossed before. Later sailors from Bristol could certainly not subscribe to the too sanguine estimate of their predecessors who had accompanied Cabot, " who, now that they know where to go, say that it is not more than fifteen days thither, nor do they ever have storms after they leave Ireland ! " Such is the buoyancy born of successful accomplishment ! The Cabots, too, on their several voyages, noticed the fish, which they claimed stayed their vessel and could be caught by the lowering of a basket.[1] The immediate successors of Columbus were lured in quest of gold from island to island, thence to the mainland to lose their birthright in the barren heights of Northern Mexico, leaving to others the more real wealth of the great new continent. The immediate successors of Cabot were fishermen, who found off Newfoundland grounds richer and nearly as accessible as those long visited off Iceland. It is a little difficult for us to realize that more than one hundred years intervened between Cabot's voyages and the first permanent European settlement in North-eastern America, and yet that for the whole of this period, from the very beginning of the sixteenth century, every summer season from at latest 1504,[2] saw the assemblage on the Great Banks of a multitude of fishing craft representing every nation of Western Europe. The French, the Spanish, the Portuguese, the Basque, the British, and the Dutch, all came year after year, showing apparently little curiosity as to the mainland beyond that Cabot had visited, or to the coast that Corte Real had sailed in 1501 and that Verrananzo explored in 1523, or of that great gulf that Cartier made known to geographers in 1534-5.

Quite fair maps of the north-eastern coast of North America were appearing in the mid-sixteenth century, yet still the Spaniard had 100 years' clear start in the matter of settlement. He confined himself to the south, and the north was visited only by fishermen intent on their immediate business.

Even in Newfoundland itself there appears to have been no real settlement in this long period, though her harbours must have been crowded with craft in the summer months. No doubt there were seasonal settlements when fish was landed and cured, salt stored, boats built and repaired, and where a rather freer interchange of international commodities occurred than was possible in the recognized and controlled harbours of Western Europe. The importance of the British share in this traffic in the middle and late sixteenth century may be gauged by the fact that in an Act passed under Edward VI, 1548, which attempts to protect the fishermen from excessive charges of Admiralty ships, Newfoundland is mentioned along with the

[1] " Voyages of the Cabots and Corte Reals," p. 49 *et seq*. H. P. Biggar.
[2] See A. Hellot : " Le Premier armateur de Fécamp pour la Pêche à Terre Neuve," 1898.

fisheries of Iceland and Ireland. A second Act (2 & 3 Elizabeth, cap. 5) seeks to fasten a fast-day upon Protestant England as a sort of protective measure for these fisheries.

Now let us leave for a moment the consideration of these early voyages and turn our attention to the influence of the chief Atlantic factors in the development of trade routes.

A modern navigator with his modern instruments can tell exactly his latitude and his local time. The chronometer (not in *general* use till the nineteenth century) gives him his Greenwich time, and therefore his longitude, or more recently he may get his time by wireless. Thus, when observations are possible, he has no difficulty as to his exact location, and further, his course is on an ocean fully charted as to depth, prevailing winds and currents, fog and ice. This information which he daily uses could only have been obtained by organized and concerted action, and much credit is due in the first place to M. F. Maury, of the U.S.A. Naval Service, who in the mid-nineteenth century almost originated the modern science of oceanography. He saw clearly that the ocean winds and waters obeyed certain more or less definite rules ; that mariners were not making the fullest use of these rules, because their knowledge of them was not sufficiently definite ; and, lastly, that the only way to a completer knowledge lay in the pooling of the information as to wind direction and strength of currents, water temperatures, and actual courses followed, available in each ship's log.

As a result of his researches into the logs of a very large number of merchant ships, and of men-of-war, he issued in 1851 his celebrated "Wind and Current Charts " and accompanying "Sailing Directions." In these is shown the actual courses of a great number of vessels (chiefly sailing ships, of course) relating to voyages in the first half of the nineteenth century. It is rather difficult to follow the track of individual vessels in these charts, because of the great number of intersecting tracks, but from an examination of them it seems fair to make the following generalizations with regard to the North Atlantic sailing routes in the early nineteenth century. Vessels from Spain, Portugal, and the Straits of Gibraltar all came south of the latitude of the Canaries to get well in the Trade-wind belt when bound for *any* (even the northern) ports of North America. Vessels from France and the English Channel came south for the Trade winds if bound in the first instance for any port south of Charleston. Vessels from France and the English Channel bound for ports north of Charleston usually tacked across the zone of the Westerlies on direct routes. Nearly all vessels returning from America to Europe returned in the Westerlies zone.

And the southern or Trade-wind route to America was even more used in the earlier centuries. In this respect, it is interesting to read some remarks of M. F. Maury, which appear in his " Sailing Directions," and have reference to the influence of the Gulf Stream on Atlantic navigation. He points out that although the Gulf Stream was recognized by earlier navigators, it was not at all accurately mapped until the well-known map of Benjamin Franklin, and he goes on to connect this mapping of the Gulf Stream with the dwindling trade of Charleston.[1]

" Before the Gulf Stream was known to practical navigation the course of trade between England and America was such as to make Charleston the half-way house between the *Mother Country* and the New England States, including Pennsylvania and New York among the latter. At that time, the usual route of vessels bound to America was to run down on the other side of the Atlantic to Cape de Verde, and until they got the northeast Trades, and with them to steer for America. . . . This route brought them upon the coast of the Southern States, where their first landfall was generally made. Then steering to the northward, they drifted along with the Gulf Stream until they made the Capes of the Delaware, or other headlands to the north. If now, as it often happens in the *winter season*,[2] they were driven off the coast by snow-storms and westerly gales—instead of running off into the Gulf Stream, as vessels now do, to thaw themselves, they stood back to Charleston, or the West Indies, *where they would spend the winter*, and wait until the spring before making another attempt to enter northern ports. . . ."

". . . The instruments of navigation were rude, chronometers were unknown, and lunars were impracticable, and it was no uncommon thing for vessels in those days, when crossing the Atlantic, to be out of their reckoning 5°, 6°, and even 10°."

Lieut. Maury goes on to explain that Dr. Franklin presented the mariner with three pieces of information :

(a) That a thermometer would tell him when he entered the Gulf Stream from the east.

(b) That differences in water coloration would tell him when he had crossed its western limit.

(c) A map of the Gulf Stream.

This information enabled the mariner to find his approximate position when entering the Gulf Stream before the day of chronometers. It rendered the call at Charleston less necessary, and

[1] " Explanations and Sailing Directions to accompany Wind and Current Charts," by Lieut. M. F. Maury, U.S.N., 3rd ed., p. 25, 1851.

[2] Notice again (Fig. 2, p. 4) that the *winter* conditions were unfavourable for sailing northward along the U.S.A. coast.

it assisted in the development of the northern more direct sailing route between northern colonies and the Channel.

Such a statement coming from such an authority deserves
attention, but in the same article Maury makes it clear that he
does not really think the mapping of the Gulf Stream the *main*
cause for an increase in northern crossings. Probably we should
find that in the eighteenth century the heaviest traffic was not
from some one European port to some one American port, but
rather first to the West Indies or Gulf, then to Charleston, then
to North-east America, then home ; and that, as suggested by
Maury, winter stoppage at the West Indies and Charleston often
prolonged the journey. New England and Bristol slave-ships
also prolonged the circular route with an excursion to the African
coast.　But in the early nineteenth century the growing proportions and hinterland of the north-eastern ports (Philadelphia,
Boston, and New York) made it possible for them to sustain a
trade with Europe independently of the West Indies and southern
traffic ; and though in the outward journey from Europe the
winds were usually contrary, better-built ships and superior navigation made, at any rate, the *average* voyage much shorter
than those involved in the southern route.

There was also a very large, purely coastwise trade, carried
on chiefly in New England ships to the West Indies and back,
and without direct relation to the Atlantic triangular route.

A steamer can pursue its course independently (save with
regard to speed) of the wind, and its course is usually made from
point to point on great circle routes. The present-day courses
from and to Europe are slightly separate : collisions are thus
avoided in foggy weather, and for the same reason these steamer
lanes are avoided by sailing vessels. The prevalence of ice is
at a maximum in the North-west Atlantic, and under the influence of the Labrador current, especially when this is reinforced
by north-west winds, icebergs and loose floes find their way
sufficiently far south in the Western Atlantic to intercept the
usual trade routes. These are in part Great Circles, and therefore in Northern latitude a little north of the straight-line track
obtained by joining the sailing points on a Mercator chart.
Icebergs in this trade-route region are at a maximum usually
in June and a minimum in the late autumn and early winter.
They increase rapidly in April and May, and the steamer courses
are shifted a little to the south in the ice-prevalent season
(Fig. 3).

CHAPTER II

THE GEOGRAPHICAL FACTORS WHICH CONTROLLED THE SPANISH ADVANCE INTO NORTHERN MEXICO AND SOUTHERN CALIFORNIA

COLUMBUS in his four voyages made known the location of the Greater Antilles and the coastal configuration of Northern Panama and Eastern Nicaragua. By 1525 Spain had permanent settlements in Española, Cuba, Jamaica, Porto Rico, and on the mainland in Mexico and Central America. Balboa had exposed the Pacific Ocean, and Spanish sailors had circumnavigated the Gulf of Mexico in their efforts to find a passage to this new-found sea. Stephen Gomez had sailed the Atlantic coast from Nova Scotia to Florida, Cabral had discovered the Brazilian coast, and a Portuguese expedition of which Amerigo Vespucci was pilot had disclosed the southern continent to the La Plata River. Finally, the Portuguese Magellan, in the service of Spain, had discovered the straits which bear his name and had crossed the Pacific to the Philippines, there to meet his death, leaving the completion of perhaps the most wonderful voyage in history, to his comrade Elcano.

Thus in the first quarter of the sixteenth century had Spain some knowledge of the entire eastern coasts of the Americas and of the great ocean which lay beyond. Then, and for the next half-century, she was pre-eminent in Europe and might have planted her colonies in areas later occupied by the French and the English—probably without serious competition. When these later colonists appeared upon the scene, her power was already waning, and she stood committed to the protection and advancement of her original holdings. She had not then strength enough seriously to contest the Atlantic coast with the English, or the Northern Mississippi plains and the St. Lawrence with the French.

The first landfall of Columbus placed him within easy reach of the larger West Indian islands, and their size and fertility at once attracted the attention of early colonists, while for a period the Lesser Antilles remained neglected. But there was a further reason for this. The warlike and cannibal Caribs of these smaller isles, who inhabited also much of the Caribbean coast of South America, put up a much more serious resistance to Spanish occupation and exploitation than the Arawaks, those meek cultivators of the greater islands and of the Darien coast. Thus the Lesser Antilles received little attention from Spain, and fell eventually one after another into the hands of her enemies. The inhabitants of such of them as had been visited by the Spaniard welcomed any who might appear as his enemy.

The accident of early discovery, the size and fertility of the island, the relative weakness of the natives, and, above all, the fact that there gold was discovered, all served to make Española the most considerable of the Spanish West Indian possessions. Santo Domingo became the seat of Spanish rule in America. Mining camps, where the alluvial gold was washed in the stream beds, quickly sprang up. Fifteen years after this first settlement, colonies came into being in Porto Rico, Jamaica, and Cuba.

It is an error to suppose either that Spain neglected to send colonists to these early settlements, or that when sent they were entirely occupied in the exploitation of the natives in the mines. Bananas, cotton, maize, and tobacco were cultivated before the coming of the Spaniard, and he soon added sugar to the list of staple crops and cattle to the fauna. It is true that the agricultural serf of Spain was not usually among the early colonists, and the plantations were largely worked at first by the Indians, and then by imported negro slaves. At first when land was allotted to the Spaniard the forced labour of the native was included in the gift. Then, and partly no doubt from a perfectly sincere desire to better the lot of the native, he was congregated in camps, "protected" against his wish, practically forced to a nominal acceptance of the Spanish faith, and forced also to labour in the fields. Though the intention was that the native should yet remain in many matters a free man, and should receive pay for his work, the system quickly became one of virtual slavery.

There is evidence of an extraordinarily rapid decrease in the native population, partly no doubt due to the harshness of these new conditions, and partly perhaps to the virulence of European diseases among a people for the first time exposed to their attack. The natives became scarce. The negro was expensive. Plantations ceased to pay. The balance of Spanish power in America was shifted to the richer (in minerals) mainland of Mexico, leaving insufficient forces in Gulf and Caribbean waters either to protect the trade which later had to filter through the network of the Antilles,[1] or to prevent the seizure of the islands themselves by other Powers.

Let us turn our attention for a moment to the broad geographical features of this mainland in so far as they affected the problem of Spanish settlement and advance.

Cortez landed near the present town of Vera Cruz, and must have seen before him a low, sandy, swampy shore, backed immediately by a vivid fringe of tropical forest. The land rises irregularly but rapidly from near the coast, and the great snow-clad peak of Orizaba (18,000 feet high and 70 miles distant) is visible in clear weather from the shore, a reminder of the physical difficulties which confronted all who would gain the central tablelands.

For Mexico consists of a vast highland bordered by even higher ranges. The Western Sierra Madre forms a broad ridge of difficult terrain in parts more than 8,000 feet above sea-level and dividing the Sonora province from that of New Mexico; dividing, too, the northern streams of Spanish settlement to these political divisions. The Eastern Sierra is exceedingly steep and difficult about the latitude of Vera Cruz, but diminishes in height as one goes north, giving back so as to form a wider and more perfect coast plain on the Gulf than exists on the Pacific coast. The Southern Mexican tableland, with its temperate, fertile plateau-valleys and considerable populations, suffered always a considerable degree of isolation by reason of its extremely difficult approach either from the west or east coasts; for to the difficulties due to relief were added the dangers of crossing coastal belts of close and fever-ridden tropical forest.

To the far north-east, where, so far as relief was concerned, access to the plateau was relatively easy, there were broad areas of semi-desert to be crossed. Further, the Gulf coast was almost everywhere fringed by sand-bank and marsh; boats of 10-feet draught could seldom approach the shore, and no Gulf Mexican

[1] Eventually the Spaniards made use of convoys for their seasonal treasure ships. These normally entered the Caribbean Sea between Tobago and Trinidad and picked up the Northern Andean produce at Cartagena, the terminus of the land route. They then continued to Porto Bello for the Peruvian treasure (which had come by sea to Panama, and thence by mule train across the isthmus), and then to Havana. At Havana the fleet was joined by the galleons from Vera Cruz, laden with Mexican silver. These apparently circled the Gulf in their voyages to Havana, instead of sailing directly, thus avoiding to some extent the contrary Trade winds.

The assembled fleet then left Havana and reached the anti-Trade-wind zone via the Strait of Florida. They sought always to leave Havana by mid-September, before the autumn and winter storms. These routes and the constant danger from Dutch and English attack are admirably brought out in T. Gage's " A New Survey of the West Indies," 1640.

roadstead had shelter against the periodical northers of the winter months.

Detailed maps are required to show the frequently precipitous slopes of some of the southern border ranges, the narrow gorges by which they may be crossed, the obviously volcanic origin of some of the mountain cones, and more important than all, the physically isolated nature, not only of the plateau region as a whole, but of the many separate valley plains within it where alone human settlements are possible. Chief among these is the valley of Mexico City itself, which is some 60 miles long and 30 miles broad, almost encircled by mountains and—in Cortez' time —largely occupied by shallow swamp-like lakes. In such high valleys the nights are cold. There is a greater difference between sun and shade, and between day and night temperatures, than between those of summer and winter. The surrounding hills, largely treeless, deprive the valleys of precipitation. The rainfall at Vera Cruz is 69 inches, at Mexico 24 inches. Man could perhaps live more healthily than on the steaming tropical coast-lands of the *tierra caliente*, but Nature was less lavish. A greater ingenuity was demanded for the provision of the necessities of existence. Cortez found a people who sheltered themselves from sun and cold in relatively elaborate buildings of sun-baked earth, who eked out the lessened rainfall by using in irrigation works the streams which had their origin in the greater precipitation of the encircling heights. They suffered a complicated legal and religious system and had all but acquired the art of letters. Cortez was amazed by the workmanship as well as by the value displayed in the presents by which a succession of emissaries of Montezuma sought to buy his retirement.

The comparative isolation of these scattered communities meant a lack of cohesion in Montezuma's overlordship. In considering the extraordinary progress of Cortez we must remember that to the perseverance, shrewdness, and imagination which made him so outstanding a personality, was added his good fortune in finding an enemy divided against itself. The isolated and easily defended valley of the Tlascalans had never quite yielded to the dominion of Mexico City, and its inhabitants found the forces of Cortez so formidable that, after being defeated by him, they were pleased to give their assistance against the enemy at Mexico. And so also when Cortez himself had mastered the Mexican valley, he had to send out separate expeditions to the semi-independent valley states about Lake Chapala in the north-west, to the high valley of Oaxaca in the south-east, and to the upper valley of the River Panuco in the north-east.

In Southern Mexico the Spaniard found concentrated settlements of skilled labour which could be more profitably exploited than the natives of the West Indian islands. A higher social organization made the exaction of tribute a possibility. The frequent finding, and more frequently rumoured finds, of the precious metals, encouraged a more rapid survey, conquest, and exploitation of the country than would otherwise have occurred. While, and even before, Cortez was engaged in conquering Mexico, other Spanish adventurers were busy about the Gulf of Darien and in the Isthmus of Panama. Here, again, gold was the immediate attraction. The importance of these settlements lay in the fact that they led at once to Balboa's discovery of the Pacific, to the Spanish exploration of the Pacific coast for hundreds of miles to the west and south, and to the discovery of precious metals in the Pacific Cordillera of South America, and eventually in Peru.

In the sixteenth century, then, the activities of Spain in North America were distributed mainly in three distinct geographical areas.

First : The greater islands of the West Indies.

Secondly : The scattered plateau-valley settlements of Southern Mexico.

Thirdly : The isthmus region with its minor goldfields, its pearl fisheries, and its important overland route by which the treasures of Peru crossed to an Atlantic port.

Now, with reference to the second of these regions, it will be convenient to examine here the geographical factors which were limiting Spanish influence so largely to *Southern* Mexico, and preventing its extension—in any force—to the present area of the United States, and, in particular, to the Californian valley. The dominating factors here are very simple and can be clearly expressed in Fig. 6. Note first the mean annual rainfall lines, and we see that the whole of the north and much of the central plateau has less than 20 inches of rainfall. A V-shaped drought area exhibits a south-easterly extension almost to the Gulf coast just north of the Rio Grande, and the west coast north of lat. 24° is practically sterile almost to San Diego. The high mountain ranges receive a greater precipitation, sufficient, in fact, to allow of the crossing of the sterile west coast plain by a few parallel river-courses emptying into the Gulf of California.[1] Much of North-eastern Mexico—Coahuila, for instance —is a sterile area of inland drainage, and abuts on a similar area in the United States of America.

A great belt of aridity, then, stretched between the more

[1] E.g. the del Fuerte, Yaqui, and Sonora all cross an exceedingly sterile coast, but though of very varying regimes, these longer rivers do not run dry. See " Mexico," in Admiralty I.D. Publications.

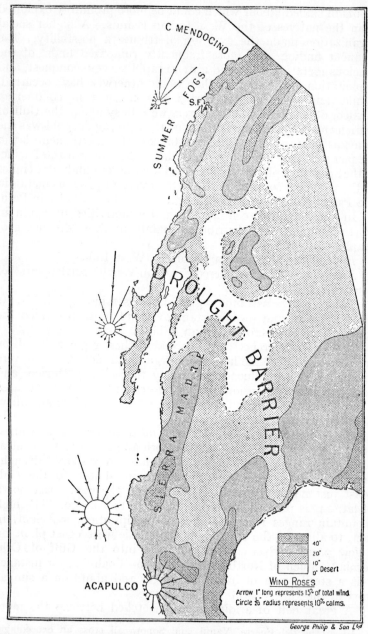

FIG. 6.—The drought barrier between Upper California and Mexico; the rainfall is in inches. The winds adverse to northern voyages are also shown.

habitable parts of Southern Mexico and regions in the present area of the United States of America where rainfall is sufficient for agriculture. Indeed, such precipitation is hardly met with in the Pacific coast lands until latitudes a little north of San Diego, and in Texas till east of long. 98°. On the mainland between these coastal limits the general aridity increases somewhat, as one goes north, to a maximum in Arizona and New Mexico. With regard, then, to northern advance by land—and, as we shall presently note, this was more considerable than by sea—it had to proceed through a country which, if not actually desert, could support only a small population which was concentrated in (1) scattered settlements dependent upon irrigation ; (2) in mining communities where the great value of the product paid for the difficult transport of supplies ; (3) in cattle ranches.

For the northward-moving Spaniard, this meant increasingly long journeys between points of possible supply, and supplies which, when obtained, could only support small trains of men. Ever he became more at the mercy of the Indian as his distance increased from the more populous, concentrated, and stable settlements of the south.

Now the motives underlying this northward expansion, though first and foremost we must place the perpetual search for precious metals, included others which varied somewhat with the period concerned. In the days of Cortez the Spaniard had met with so many marvels, so much wealth, and so much military success, that no rumour was too extravagant to be believed. Ever beyond lay fairer cities, more astounding riches. Thus, we have Cortez himself attracted by the rumour of a wonderful *island* of California to the north, of great wealth and inhabited by Amazons. Surely enough his lieutenant, Jiménez, discovered a new land in the peninsula of California, long thought to be an island, and incidentally discovered also an important pearl fishery. But Cortez acquired a more accurate conception of the Lower California peninsula, its climate and its possibilities, when, after a few months' suffering, he was obliged to withdraw the little colony which he himself had founded there at La Paz in 1535.

Mexico is notably rich in silver, however, and after much of the accumulated wealth of the southern native settlements had been acquired, the Spaniard organized and superintended labour for such mines [1] as he knew, and was continually prospecting for fresh supplies.

[1] Humboldt, in his " Essay on New Spain," vol. ii, p. 407, emphasizes the importance of the presence of the mining centres in the evolution of agricultural centres using irrigation—cf. the case of the settlement in the Western States of the United States of America.

In connection with this great mining activity, it became necessary to build roads for supplies and a series of fortified settlements to protect the treasure routes. Durango became the chief military centre of the northern area and Guadalajara that of the south-west. The mines of Zacatecas, Guanajuato, and St. Luis Potosi were among the most famous.

The seventeenth century witnessed in Europe a steady diminution of Spanish prestige. In America it saw the founding of the British tide-water colonies, the French settlements of the St. Lawrence, and that extending line of French forts about the Great Lakes and the confluents of the Upper Mississippi, which was to reach eventually to the Gulf of Mexico. Yet the same century saw a steady advance of the Spanish colonies in Northern Mexico. As has been pointed out, the Spaniard was here more at the mercy of the native, and the initial preparation and control of the latter was handed over to the real vanguard of this latter movement, the Jesuit, and (in the north-east) the Franciscan missionaries. These wonderful pioneers, whom complete faith rendered unmindful of danger, were unappalled by hardships in the pursuance of what they believed to be their duty.

At the beginning of the seventeenth century, they were founding and improving irrigation settlements in the Macarito, Sinaloa, and Fuerte valleys, and in the next three-quarters of a century the valleys of the Mayo, Yaqui, and Sonora were similarly occupied. Their sincere aim was to convert the native, and they could usually show encouraging figures of baptism. Apostasy and rebellion were, however, the usual sequels, and then the Spanish soldiery would appear in force to quell the disturbance. The successive occupation of these parallel western streams was important as representing a zone of northern advance, separated in the main from the corresponding advance on the central tableland, by the difficult ranges which form its western edge. The rainfall was less than on the plateau, and settlement was even more definitely limited to the stream beds. It must be emphasized that the actual numbers of Spaniards, of half-castes, and even of the local Indians, were very small for so immense an area—chiefly the result of the prevailing aridity. In 1768 (so says Professor Chapman [1]) there were only about 500 families of pure Spanish blood in Sonora, though the half-caste Christian population was much larger.

To the north, then, an increasingly difficult terrain was encountered, and we wonder naturally that a simpler mode of advance was not sought by sea. The geographical factors involved are worthy of some consideration. In the latter half of the

[1] " The Founding of Spanish California," by C. E. Chapman, p. 13.

sixteenth century, Spain had acquired the ascendancy over Portugal in the Philippines, but her returning galleons were subject to Portuguese piracy on the Cape route, as were her treasure ships in returning from the Gulf. It occurred to some that New Spain would form an excellent base for communication with the Philippines, and Legazpi's expedition of 1565 was undertaken with the avowed purpose of finding a convenient Pacific route. We must note that Southern Mexico and the North Central Philippines are in the same latitude (15° N.) and within the Trade-wind zone which favoured a direct route across. Return on the same track would have been difficult or impossible, and Legazpi sailed north into the stormy but usually westward-tending wind zone, and so made landfall in Northern California about Cape Mendocino, and then used the prevailing northerly winds along the coast to his South Mexican port. He initiated, that is to say, the sailing route around the normal high-pressure belt for the Pacific, as Columbus had done nearly a century before for the Atlantic.

Each year thereafter one or two galleons made the round trip, usually reaching the American coast about Cape Mendocino, and bringing their rich produce eventually to the Acapulco Fair.[1] Long before there were any settlements in what is now the American State of California, its coast was known to the pilots of these galleons.

But the Manilla galleon was making use of the normal winds and currents. To sail from a Western Mexican port *up* the Californian coast was to run counter to them ; and that alongside a coast, mountainous, without wood or water, deficient in harbours, and for long stretches uninhabited. The accounts of such early voyages as are recorded clearly illustrate these conditions. Cabrillo in 1542 reached a little to the north of San Francisco Bay, Ferraro went as far north as Cape Blanco. But more interest attaches to the voyage of Vizcaino in 1603, for the reasons for this expedition summarize the general motives underlying Spain's wish to colonize the Pacific coast. Firstly, the extraordinarily long voyage across the Pacific made it advisable to find some good port in Upper California, where the usually rotting and scurvy-ridden Manilla galleons could refit before proceeding to Acapulco. Then, since the audacious appearance

---

[1] Acapulco is one of the few good harbours on the Pacific coast, and was the Pacific port of Mexico. The arrival of the Manilla galleon gave it a seasonal activity comparable with that (described by Thomas Gage, 1635) occurring at Porto Bello (Panama), when the Spanish convoy galleons called to take up the Peruvian treasure which had crossed the isthmus by mule train from Panama.

2

of Drake on the Pacific coast in 1579, followed by the Cavendish expedition in 1586—the latter actually burned a returning Manilla galleon (the *Santa Ana*) off California—it was felt that a protective naval station was required on this coast.

Again, though the *eastern* coasts of America were by this time approximately mapped, they were not known in detail, and many gulfs had not been followed to their heads, so that people were slow in abandoning all hope of a passage-way through to the Pacific. The most celebrated of these mythical sea-ways was the Strait of Anian, which should have led to the Pacific somewhere about the latitude of Northern California. The Spaniard was anxious to forestall the Dutch and English in the command of this supposed strait.

All these voyages were made with difficulty. Monterey Bay, a poor harbour, was discovered and explored, likewise San Diego. The magnificent San Francisco Bay was unnoticed on these voyages, as also by the yearly passing Manilla galleons. No settlement was made. The direct trade between Mexico and the Philippines dwindled, and Spain was sufficiently preoccupied.

The next serious attempt was not made till the late eighteenth century, and we cannot conceive that this would have been so if the physical conditions had been as favourable as they undoubtedly were unfavourable. This expedition of 1769, entrusted to a Spanish governor, one Portola, had rather different aims. The Spanish mission stations had by the end of the seventeenth century reached to Santa Fé on the Upper Rio Grande,[1] lat. 35°–40°. Further advance here led only to the mountain plexus of Colorado. On the north-west, however, as we have seen, the Upper Sonora River had been occupied, and it was but natural that advance here should lead to the Santa Pedro and Pueblo Valley tributaries of the Gila, and by the latter river to its junction with the Colorado at Yuma. This adding of the Southern Gila basin to Spanish influence was largely the work of Father Kino, who, beginning in 1687, spent some twenty-five years in mission and exploration work. His journeys convinced him that Lower California was a peninsula and not an island. Meanwhile, the Jesuits, as though to demonstrate that no adverse physical conditions could withstand their missionary zeal, actually planted five small missionary stations on the intensely

---

[1] The settlements here were mainly mission stations about the river valley. A road is shown on a contemporary map connecting Santa Fé with Mexico City, but even at the end of the eighteenth century the New Mexico Rio Grande settlements were practically separated from the more populous southern area by the Coahuila desert, and its formidable Indians. Humboldt, "Essay on New Spain," vol. ii, p. 308.

sterile middle peninsula of California; but these would have been abandoned if Father Kino had not driven cattle hundreds of miles to the supply depot of Guaymas and shipped them across the Gulf.

In the eighteenth century, Spain, impoverished by her European struggle, was unable to render the military and financial support which her frontier mission stations required, and yet had to see the consolidation of the English in the Atlantic States and the rapid penetration of the French in the Lake and Great Plain regions. To add to her fears, and seemingly, indeed, a more imminent danger, there were the voyages of Bering across the strait which bears his name (1725 and 1740) and the consequent rush of Russian fur-traders to the Aleutian Isles.

These fears spurred Spain to last despairing efforts. The Portola expedition of 1769 was designed to establish military stations on the bays of San Diego and Monterey. These bays had been visited and explored two hundred years previously, but had not been settled. The expedition consisted of land and sea portions, that by sea being under Captain Vicente Vila, whose diary was recently published in the publications of the Academy of Pacific Coast History.[1] This diary is little more than a log, but it is interesting as giving a detailed exemplification of the difficulties in sailing *north* from any West Mexican port.

Vila took four months to reach San Diego, and as many weeks to return. On the northward journey he hung about for three weeks, while a landing party sought water on the almost desert shores. The winds were northerly and persistently contrary.[2] The land party which had come from the peninsula joined up at San Diego, whence Portola continued north by land, through the Salinas Valley and between the coast ranges to his goal, Monterey Bay. This he failed to recognize—it is indeed a poor harbour—and continued overland to discover accidentally San Francisco Bay. The winter storms off the Californian coast, the almost permanently contrary winds of summer, the sudden storms and rocky islets of the Gulf of California, are perhaps enough to explain, in part at any rate, the curiously long period (two hundred years) which elapsed between some early knowledge of the coast even so far north as Cape Blanco in Oregon, and its ultimate occupation by the Spaniard in the late eighteenth and early nineteenth centuries. Even so, what with the regular passage of the Manilla galleons, and the set expeditions to explore the coast and discover a good harbour,

[1] " Diary of Vicente Vila, Sailing Master of the *San Carlos*," in publications of Academy of Pacific Coast History.
[2] See Fig. 6.

it is an extraordinary thing that the Golden Horn and San Francisco Bay should have first been reached by a land route, and then not till 1769. Again, the explanation may be largely geographical. The almost constant (in summer) northerly winds off the five hundred miles of the Californian coast are accompanied by a markedly cold current. This, however, is limited to a relatively narrow belt of water immediately off-shore, so that a hundred miles or so out in the Pacific there is a rapid increase in surface temperature. A movement of warm, moist Pacific air towards the land and over this cold belt is accompanied by fogs which shroud the coast, but seldom penetrate into the hot, dry interior valley. Summer fogs are as constant off the Californian coast as off Newfoundland itself. We may give these factors a little more definition by the following quotation from the U.S.A. Pilot ("West Coast of Central America Pilot," 1916, pp. 34–41):

" On the coast of California, from lat. 40° north, southwards for 10° or 15°, a wind from north-west nearly parallel to the coast blows pretty steadily during the greater part of the year. . . ."

" Along the coast of Lower California, from lat. 23° to 32°, the wind is generally from between west and north, but during the winter months that coast is subject to violent gales from the south-east, which, as most of the bays and anchorages are open towards this quarter, are much dreaded. . . ."

" *Sailing Vessels.*—The only way to make a passage from any part of this coast to the northward is *to stand out to sea on the starboard tack until the variable winds are reached* in about 130° W. and then make northing. From July to January vessels may have to stand on as far as 140° W. . . ."

" *Golden Gate.*—When approaching the entrance *in fine weather* it is *difficult to imagine* that a deep channel lies ahead, so clear is the atmosphere, and so *well defined* the Contra Costa mountains behind the bay."

" *Fogs.*—In the northern part of the coast (California) they are more frequent, and at times are very dense, and have been known to extend several hundred miles seaward. They continue at *times for weeks*, rendering navigation difficult. . . ."

Average number of hours [1] per month, from a record of about nine years that the fog signals were operated at the stated light station (Point Reyes, near San Francisco) of the U.S.A.:

	1917.							1916.				
J.	F.	M.	A.	M.	J.	J.	A.	S.	O.	N.	D.	Total.
86	179	67	158	96	158	370	326	313	167	70	117	2,107

[1] See " Fog along the Californian Coast " in the " Monthly Weather Review " for October, 1917.

The Yuma massacre (1781) and subsequent trouble with the natives of Northern Mexico made it almost impossible to maintain a regular land connection between Southern Mexico and the string of Spanish mission stations which in the early years of the nineteenth century sprang up and flourished in the *coastal* districts only of California.[1] The southern great valley of California was not at first occupied—it was too dry. But by this time the Pacific was becoming better known to trading vessels. Other European countries began to send their vessels to San Diego, Monterey, and San Francisco—against the law of Spain and of the later Mexican Republic, but with the entire approval of the local settlements. Indeed, it was the physical separation from Mexico in the revolutionary period which allowed these stations to work out their own salvation in comparative peace. Still more was it the fact that at last, after centuries of struggle northwards, the Spaniards had reached a country less forbidding than the vast sterile tracts through which they had passed. The winter rains increase rapidly from San Diego northwards. The raising of crops with and without irrigation was more feasible, and the vast herds of cattle which were the main staple of these settlements could be maintained on much smaller areas.

These most northern mission stations—the Alta California of the Spaniard—throve abundantly. The neophytes were attached to the stations as cultivators, carpenters, weavers, and herdsmen, supplying all the material wants of the stations and preparing a surplus of hides and tallow for foreign trade. They were humanely treated, but remained undeveloped in a system of complete dependence. Here were the most peaceful and economically successful of Spanish missions, and if—as the contemporary Humboldt states—the monks were averse to white colonists, it was doubly unfortunate, for here at last was a land more suited to agricultural settlement than any the Spaniard had encountered in his sixteen hundred miles of arid track thither from the populous plateau-valleys of Southern Mexico.

[1] An admirable geographical account of the Dominican Missions inaugurated between 1774–1834 in the Peninsula of California, is contained in *University of California Publications in Geography, Vol. 7. The Dominican Mission Frontier by P. Meigs.*

CHAPTER III

THE GEOGRAPHICAL ENVIRONMENT OF EARLY FRENCH SETTLEMENT

THE position of the early French settlements in North America was largely controlled by the nature of the St. Lawrence and Mississippi River basins. The configuration of both these systems must have been considerably influenced by glacial action—the Great Lakes owe their very origin to such action—and a summary of the chief stages of their development seems so to emphasize features of critical geographical importance, that we shall essay such a summary here before dealing at all with the early French occupation.

A glance at a geological map will show that the north-eastern quadrant of North America consists of pre-Cambrian rocks, and that the southern boundary of these lies almost, but not quite, along the line of the Great Lakes. South of these the central interior lowlands of North America are developed on little disturbed palæozoics of Cambrian to Pennsylvanian [1] times. To the east these have undergone a somewhat complicated geological history—to be outlined in a subsequent chapter—in the evolution of the Appalachian Mountain system, but immediately to the south of the Great Lakes they outcrop in succession, with the oldest nearest the lakes.

The pre-Cambrian lands to the north constitute the Laurentian Shield, and a somewhat detailed geographical description of them appears in Chapter XXXI. All we need notice here is that they consist chiefly of granite and gneiss and of metamorphosed sedimentaries, and that they are largely soil stripped by glacial action. The soils, then, are patchy, and often marshy, and small lakes of glacial origin cover an enormous area in the aggregate. The drainage is somewhat indeterminate, the small lakes being linked up by a network of waterways often interrupted by falls. Where soil-covered, the land was forested. In general the country is hummocky rather than mountainous, though the rim of the region is raised to form a

[1] I.e. later Carboniferous.

real highland country bordering the St. Lawrence valley on the north, and about the coast lands of Labrador. There was, and is, little to attract settlement. Communication by canoe with frequent portages was possible in nearly any direction, but by canoe only.

We must notice at once that the Great Lake system is not the actual boundary between that type of country and the very different areas of the little disturbed sedimentaries to the south. Lake Superior lies wholly within the pre-Cambrian area, which indeed extends south of that lake into the

Fig. 7.—Showing Lake Plains and the Lines of the Portage, Onondaga, and Niagaran Escarpments.

T, Toronto.   **R**, Rochester.   **B**, Buffalo.   **S**, Syracuse.

(*After* Kindle and Taylor, in the " Niagara Folio of Geological Atlas of U.S.G.S.")

northern portions of the states of Minnesota and Wisconsin. The southern part of the peninsula of Ontario, on the other hand, is an extension of the central plain north of the Great Lakes, while the narrow lowlands forming the Lower St. Lawrence valley from Kingston to Quebec belong also to the same physiographic division.

Now, before the Ice Age, the major features of relief were much as at present. The most considerable heights immediately south of the lakes were those bordering Lakes Ontario and Erie on the south, and formed by the uplifting of the palæozoic rocks in the Cumberland plateau. The northward-facing scarps of this plateau set a limit to the southward-moving ice in their area. But south of the western lakes the land was, and is, low-lying, with relatively unimportant northward-facing scarps which were overridden by the ice. In pre-glacial times a river basin of mild relief occupied the present lake area.

To the south-east formidable hill-scarps, as now, limited the basin (Fig. 7). To the south there was—as now—only a very low water-parting between the St. Lawrence system and the Mississippi. The ice advanced from two centres—the

C CORDILLERAN ICE SHEET

K KEEWATIN ICE SHEET

LABRADOR DO.

FIG. 8.—To show originating centres and greatest extent of the Continental Ice-sheets.

Labrador and Keewatin ice-sheets (Fig. 8). It covered the pre-glacial St. Lawrence basin, and in the central plain spread far beyond the old water parting of the St. Lawrence and Mississippi. In the east it was held up by the northern escarpment of the Cumberland plateau. We must not think of this ice invasion as consisting of a single advance and retreat, but of a succession of advances and retreats with long interglacial intervals. The great lakes were the product of the final retreat. When the ice-sheet was to the south of the water-parting. drainage from its melting edges would be to the Mississippi via the Missouri and Ohio, which two tributaries indeed mark approximately the furthermost limits of the ice. As the ice finally retreated to the north, however, it would at length recross the water-parting, and, with further retreat, large bodies of water would be dammed between this water-parting and the ice itself. These were the precursors of the present Great Lakes, the detailed stages of the development of which were conditioned by two main factors, viz. (1) the details of the pre-glacial relief, (2) the slow and irregular tilting of the north-east of the continent itself. With the final clearance of the ice the lakes did not disappear, because (1) the land did not regain its exact pre-glacial level, (2) minor details of relief were affected by glacial deposits—moraines, etc., which have helped to impound the lakes.

The stages of development of the lakes have been worked out as the result of prolonged and detailed examination of the boundary moraines, of lacustrine deposits, of the position and inclination of old lake shore lines, and by the evidence of old outflow channels from the constantly varying ice-dammed water bodies.[1] We will select sufficient stages to indicate the general mode of evolution and to emphasize particular outlet channels which were ultimately to become routes of great historical importance.

Stage I. The ice-sheet was beyond the Mississippi-St. Lawrence water-parting, and discharge was therefore to the Mississippi in the Central Lowland Region.

Stage II. The ice withdrew to the north of the divide, and the impounded water rose to the height of the nearest depressions or cols in the divide. Very numerous small water bodies appeared and discharged by a great number of minor streams to the Mississippi. In the hilly country of Central New York impounded water found a temporary outlet to the north branch of the Susquehanna.

Stage III. A further withdrawal of the ice-sheet disclosed a part of the shallow basins of the pre-glacial St. Lawrence tributaries. These were roughly coincident with the basins of the present lakes. The ice-front then began to assume a lobate form, the major lobes being southerly extensions of the present lake basins (Fig. 9). Thus were formed what have been named Lake Duluth, Lake Chicago, and Lake Maumee, each with its notched outlet over the divide to the Mississippi system. We may notice at once the short portages which were used

[1] U.S.G.S. Monograph 53, 1915. "History of the Great Lakes," by F. Leverett and F. B. Taylor.

in French colonial days between the Mississippi tributaries and the small streams draining to the Great Lakes and along the line of these one-time outlet channels, viz. the approach of the St. Croix River to Duluth, of the Illinois to Chicago, and of the Wabash to the Maumee and Lake Erie. All these outlets were at first separate, but as the ice still further retreated a minor lobe developed in the depression about Saginaw Bay, and as the land was further uncovered the water body about this lobe found an outlet to Lake Chicago via the track of the present

D = Lake Duluth. C = Lake Chicago.
M = Lake Maumee.

FIG. 9.—Evolution of the Great Lakes, showing the beginning of the Great Lakes dammed between the retreating lobate terminals of the ice-sheet, and the water-parting to the south. (Stage III.)

Grand River (Fig. 9). About the same time the water from Lake Maumee abandoned the Wabash outlet, finding a lower outlet by skirting the Saginaw lobe to Lake Chicago also. When the ice had retreated far enough to uncover the whole of the present Lake Erie area and a part of the Lake Ontario area, yet still closed the Mohawk route, a vast water body, called Lake Warren, occupied the whole of the present Lake Erie basin and parts of the present Huron and Ontario. It extended eastwards so as to include the valleys of the present Finger Lakes of New York, and it drained, not by the Wabash, but via the Grand River outlet to Lake Chicago and the Illinois River (Fig. 10).

Stage IV. A further retreat of the ice uncovered the Mohawk-Hudson depression, but left blocked the Huron Bay-Trent River depression, and of course the St. Lawrence itself. There was a general decrease in the height of the water, and the water bodies took approximately their present outlines. A sub-stage sees Lake Iroquois (Ontario approximately) draining to the Hudson, while Erie still drained to Lake Chicago and the Mississippi. The lowering of water-level due to the opening of the Mohawk-Hudson outlet uncovered the northward-facing escarpments which mark the difference in level between Erie and Ontario.

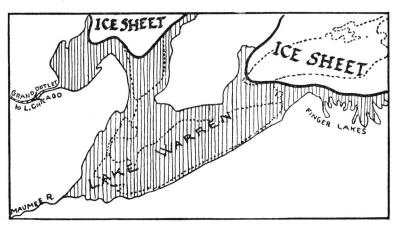

FIG. 10.—Evolution of the Great Lakes.
A later stage showing the coalescence of Lake Maumee and the water-body about the Saginaw Lobe.

Stage V. A further retreat uncovered the depression between Georgian Bay and Lake Iroquois (now followed by the Trent River system), and the general configuration of water bodies indicated in Fig. 11 was achieved.

The St. Lawrence was still ice-blocked, and the particular outlet followed by the water varied with any variation in the tilt of the land mass. Thus in the figure we see the whole water body draining via the Mohawk-Hudson route, the three upper lakes via the Trent River, and Lake Erie delivering only a small tributary stream. But a very slight tilt would deliver the water of the three upper lakes via lake St. Clair and cause the disuse of the Trent River route. In this case a very large body of water would flow from Lake Erie to Lake Ontario. Now, any stream flowing from Erie to Ontario had to fall over the Niagara escarpment; an escarpment existing, of course, in pre-glacial times, and formed by the weathering back of a shale-bed capped by a massive limestone dipping slightly to the south in conformity with the contiguous strata of this locality. Between Erie and Ontario the scarp faces north, and it soon dies out to the east. Westward it forms a great bend across the peninsula of Ontario, appears in the Manitoulin islands, and bends down again in Eastern Wisconsin (Figs. 7 and 12).

For the moment we are concerned with it only as a north-ward-facing scarp between Erie and Ontario. Now, as soon as this was uncovered, any stream between the two lakes would

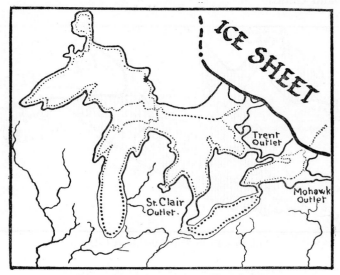

FIG. 11.—Evolution of the Great Lakes.

The St. Lawrence is still ice-blocked and the outlet is by the Mohawk and Hudson Valleys, *either* **from** the Upper Lakes via the St. Clair Lake, *or* via the Trent Outlet.

form a waterfall, which would eat its way back into the escarp-ment. The rate at which the Niagara gorge was formed, as well as its width, would vary with the volume of water taking this route, and in the form of the gorge to-day are sure indica-tions that enormous variations actually did occur, according as it was receiving the whole of the Great Lakes water, or only that from Lake Erie, or again sharing the outlet with Lake Chicago.

Stage VI. At the final clearance of ice from the St. Law-rence, and with a depression of the north-east portion of the continent, arms of the sea occupied the St. Lawrence Valley, up to and just including the present area of Lake Ontario, and also the Ottawa valley and the Hudson Mohawk gap. The tilting to the north-east allowed the now uncovered Ottawa outlet to be used, and again Niagara water was only from Lake Erie.

Stage VII. A slight uplift left the system as it is to-day, with the whole drainage through St. Clair Lake, Niagara, and the St. Lawrence. Since the first opening of the Hudson-Mohawk outlet till the present day, Niagara has varied as follows:

(i) *Big Niagara.* All water through St. Clair River, Niagara, and the Mohawk.

(ii) *Small Niagara.* Upper three lakes drain via Trent River. Only Erie through Niagara.

(iii) *Big Niagara.* St. Clair River used again, but some lake water leaves via Chicago outlet, and so to the Mississippi.

(iv) *Small Niagara.* Submergence of St. Lawrence and Champlain. Opening of St. Lawrence, and water uses Ottawa route.

(v) *Big Niagara.* Uplift and present conditions, with all the water using the St. Clair route and Niagara.

We see, then, that the lake waters are somewhat delicately poised and that very small earth movements would effect radical change of outlet channels. Lake water is actually carried to the Mississippi to-day via the Chicago drainage canal, which occupies the site of the old glacial outlet.

The above is a broad outline of the evolution of the Great Lakes, but we must remember that there were many sub-stages. It is worth while considering this evolution, for besides forming the best example the world can offer of the formation of glacial lakes, there is no one of the outlet channels mentioned but has been of great importance in the historical and economic development of the country. Thus the Great Lakes and Mississippi outlets serve to remind us of the absence of a general relief barrier to the south; of the old French portages between the Lakes and the Mississippi tributaries, and of the later canal connections along the same lines. The river Trent outlet, and its present Lake Simcoe and Trent River basin, will remind us of one of Champlain's great journeys, as well as of a modern canal route. Georgian Bay, Lake Nipissing, and the Ottawa outlet point the directest way to the west. It was followed by the French, who avoided the Iroquois of the southern lakes; by the first direct rail westwards; and has been the subject of much discussion as a deep-sea canal route. The Mohawk, Hudson, and Champlain routeways have been the chief battle-ground of the continent, and the begetter of the greatest city in America. The great Falls them-

selves have been a vital factor in the development of New York
and of Buffalo, and provide the greatest hydro-electric power
at present used in the world at one source.

* * * * *

The earliest European settlements in North-eastern America,
of whatever nationality, were singularly dependent, for some
years at any rate, upon their respective home countries. A
handful of men, often unaccustomed to agricultural pursuits,
ignorant of measures to be taken against the rigorous winters,
holding their own against the natives only by the use of fire-
arms : such required regular supply ships from the home country, and the organization of trade in some staple (e.g. tobacco,
furs, naval stores) at least to carry them over a period of complete dependence. Thus the protection and financial support
from the home government or from authorized traders were

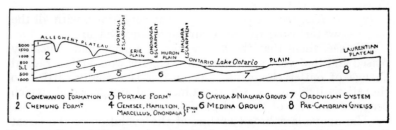

| 1 Conewango Formation | 3 Portage Form" | 5 Cayuga & Niagara Groups | 7 Ordovician System |
| 2 Chemung Form" | 4 Genesee, Hamilton, }p"" Marcellus, Onondaga }"." | 6 Medina Group, | 8 Pre-Cambrian Gneiss |

Fig. 12.—North-South Diagrammatic Section, showing relation of Lake Ontario
to the North-facing palæozoic escarpments.

(*After* Kindle and Taylor, in the "Niagara Folio of Geological Atlas of U.S.G.S.")

necessary. We have seen how, from 1504 onward, the Newfoundland Banks were visited by fishing vessels, and it is a remarkable fact that no permanent settlement was made, either on
the island or on the mainland beyond, for more than 100 years.
There was little to attract in the island itself—the trade staple
was from the sea, not from the land ; and though the fishermen
knew the Newfoundland coast well, and in fact used its harbours for shelter, for boat-repairing, and for the salting and
preparation of their fish, such harbours were mere summer stations. The great St. Lawrence Gulf lay far beyond the fishing
grounds ; its entrances—Belle Isle Strait and Cabot Strait—
were often shrouded in fog in summer, and blocked with ice
in winter. We have no record of its penetration until the voyages
of Cartier in 1535-42, voyages, be it noticed, undertaken with
government authority and with the declared purpose of discovery and colonization. The exact courses of Cartier's voyages

are not rendered perfectly clear in the "Bref Récit,"[1] but it is clear that he entered the St. Lawrence by Belle Isle Strait, that he voyaged the inhospitable western coast of Newfoundland, and contrasted it with the fertile lowland of the Magdalen and Prince Edward Isles; that he experienced the heat of a Canadian summer in Chaleur Bay, rounded the eastern end of Anticosti Island, and returned by the Belle Isle Strait to France. He thus circumnavigated the almost enclosed sea between Newfoundland and the Gaspé peninsula. His two subsequent voyages were to make known the St. Lawrence River, its marked narrowing at the Indian village of Stadacoma (Quebec), the difficult navigation between Quebec and Hochelaga (Montreal), and the rapids above Montreal. On these latter voyages, too, the crews wintered at Quebec, where to the rigours of a quite unexpectedly severe climate was added the terrible scourge of scurvy. Cartier thus made known the St. Lawrence to the then limits of its navigation at Montreal, and, considering the official nature of his voyages, it is surprising that no further attempts were made for more than half a century. Probably the religious wars of the second half of the sixteenth century prevented further interest in colonial schemes, for it was not until after the Edict of Nantes, and during the consolidation undertaken by Henry IV of France, that successful colonization took place. We must note the unsuccessful effort of the Marquis de la Roche on Sable Island in 1598, and the much more important voyage of Pontgrave and Sieur de Monts. The latter were granted a fur-trade monopoly by Henry IV. They formed a summer trading station at Tadoussac, where the Saguenay joins the St. Lawrence, typical in its location of many such stations to follow. Two years' successful fur-trading encouraged further expeditions which had the advantage of the services of that remarkable navigator, Samuel de Champlain. He was a native of Brouage (near Rochefort), where salt was extracted from the marine marshes and sold to the Newfoundland fishermen. For many years on a succession of voyages, this man exhibited his instinct for discovery, his critical observation, and his exact surveying. Whatever the official purpose of the voyage —fur-trading or colonization—he himself always contrived to engage in some work of pure geographical discovery. His detailed observation, and the extraordinary distances traversed, as also the full and accurate records which he made, place him in the very front rank of world discoverers. The account of

---

[1] "Bref Récit et Succincte Narration de la Navigation faite en 1535-6," by le Capitaine Jacques Cartier, aux Iles de Canada, etc., with Historical Introduction by D'Avezac. Paris, 1863.

his voyages is extraordinarily interesting, and fortunately readily accessible.[1] We cannot follow it in detail here, though it contains actually references to all the essential geographical features of the St. Lawrence Basin. Let us summarize the more important of these. The narratives bear witness to the summer fogs, the multitude of fish, and the presence of fishing fleets on the Newfoundland Banks, as well as to the fact that nothing was to be gained by leaving France too early in the season, for then there would be trouble with ice in the mouth of the St. Lawrence. His record of the exploration of the Gulf of St. Lawrence is much more complete than that of Cartier. Then he gives us the first detailed account of the Nova Scotia, Maine, and New England coasts ; the high tides of the Bay of Fundy, the sheltered valley scooped out of the softer rocks of Annapolis, and the fact, which he elicits from natives, that the Penobscot provides a route —as the natives understood routes—from the coast of Maine to the St. Lawrence. Again, he followed in the track of Cartier, and not finding the long-sought passage-way to north or south, had perforce to be content with the freshening waters and narrowing shores of the St. Lawrence River itself. He noted the line of bold hills to the north, bare or sparsely fir-clad, and the gaunt gateway of the Saguenay, which led—they told him—to a great lake and a salt arctic sea beyond.[2]

From Tadoussac he proceeded, in a smaller vessel, and with a boat for very shallow waters, past the falls of Montmorency to the heights above the narrows at Quebec. He noted the narrow fertile plains which border the river, with their forests of hardwood, as contrasted with the pine of the less attractive hills ; plains which to-day represent the most densely populated portions of Eastern Canada. He noted the present site of Three Rivers and its fitness for trade and settlement ; the widening of the river in St. Peter's Lake, and the entrance of the Richelieu River, up which his progress was barred by the Chambly Falls. On a separate occasion he joined forces with the Algonquins and accompanied an expedition of theirs against the Iroquois, which passed these falls and reached Lake St. George and Lake Champlain, and pointed the way to the Hudson. The skirmish here, near the very site of Ticonderoga, is rightly held significant. He was the first European to fight in this great natural routeway which was to become the chief battle-ground of the New Continent.

It is significant, too, because forming an alliance, as for very

[1] "Voyages of Champlain." Translated by Chas. T. Olis. Edited with Memoir and Notes by E. F. Slafter. 3 vols. Boston, 1878–82.
[2] Possibly a reference to Lake St. John and to the Hudson Bay.

existence he must, with the natives of his adopted country, he found himself committed to strife with the powerful Iroquois federation. These dominated then, and for long, all the country of the great three-way, Hudson, Mohawk, Champlain Gap, as also the strategic positions to the south of Lake Ontario and about Niagara. (See Fig. 18, p. 116.)

He then followed the St. Lawrence again, in Cartier's track, and, like him, was stopped at the Lachine rapids, where before returning to Tadoussac, he sounded the natives as to the country still further west, and received somewhat vague descriptions which in the light of later knowledge we see may have referred to the Great Lakes and to the Falls of Niagara. To Champlain they were so many indications of a passage-way at last to the sea of Cathay. So in yet another season he returned to the attack, and, at the instigation of the untruthful Vignau,[1] explored the Ottawa sufficiently far at any rate to convince him that it did not lead to an open sea or passage-way. On yet another voyage he again followed the Ottawa, and we have frequent references to the falls and portages on that powerful, unnavigable stream. On this occasion he left the Ottawa to follow the waterway via Lake Nipissing and Georgian Bay. Coasting the latter he returned by the mesh of waterways about Lake Simcoe to Lake Ontario, near the present site of Kingston. Crossing this lake, he and his allies unsuccessfully attacked an Iroquois fortress, probably as far south as Lake Oneida. They then retired to Lake Ontario. Champlain wintered in the Huron country and returned to the St. Lawrence in the spring. This most remarkable of all his journeys is of special interest because in it he traverses the route of the Georgian Bay canal and also the route of the present Trent River Navigation, both routes, we may remember, followed by overflow water in the period of the glacial lakes. We should notice the intention, too, of his native allies in this particular journey, which was to *round* the left flank of the Iroquois. We cannot overestimate the importance in the struggle for North America of this concentration of Iroquois from the Hudson to the south of the eastern lakes. They were consistently hostile to the inhabitants of the Lower St. Lawrence and the Ottawa valleys, and to their French allies. But for this formidable opposition, we cannot but think that the French would have penetrated and occupied the pleasant fertile

---

[1] Vignau was a young man left by Champlain to winter with the Algonquins at Allumette Island. When he again returned to Champlain, it was with tales of a Northern Sea on which an English ship had been wrecked. The whole account was a fabrication, but it influenced Champlain, who was looking for a passage to the Pacific.

Mohawk, Champlain, and Hudson valleys and preceded the Dutch at the site of New York. Or, again, they would have gained more quickly the fertile south shores of Erie and Ontario, and by the time the British penetrated the Appalachians, might have put up a greater resistance, based on a more settled population. As it was, for many years the French and their fur trade were committed to the Ottawa route, with a general environment and a staple trade little conducive to close settlement. On his return to the St. Lawrence, and on his later voyages, Champlain found frequent, but not very gratifying, evidence of the trade which had followed in the wake of his discoveries. At Tadoussac, at Three Rivers, at Montreal, the vessels of the fur-traders swarmed, and their crews were found often squabbling over the too limited supplies brought down by the Indian canoe fleets ; for these traders were not in the first instance the hunters. Initially, their activities were confined to a seasonal visitation of trading stations placed at the convergence of the canoe waterway of the Indian and the main stream of the St. Lawrence. Here they awaited the Indian canoe fleet with their fur freights, and here an exchange for spirits, fire-arms, cloth, hatchets, and ornaments was effected. Later such stations became permanent, but they were forts rather than settlements, manned by a few men, strung along the stream at strategic places of confluence or of portage, often so far separate as to be at the mercy of the Indian, unless properly garrisoned, suffering some seasonal activity but relapsing in the winter. Such stations were not symptoms of a healthy colonization, yet for the first two-thirds of the seventeenth century they represented the full extent of French settlement. Even at the consummation of the French-English struggle in 1760, permanent agricultural settlement was almost confined to the river-side stations between Quebec and Montreal. Even here population was not dense.[1] Quite apart from influences emanating from the home country—at times a too inadequate support, at others a too definite and centralized control, and the lack of all freedom of trade—quite apart from such factors, the general geographical condition obtaining in New France very largely controlled the nature of settlement.

The discoveries of Cartier and of Champlain led France to the most significant gateway of the continent. The natural obstructions to the navigation of the St. Lawrence system, to which reference has been made, did not prevent its use as the

---

[1] In 1629 and nearly twenty years after the first settlement, Quebec was so weak as to succumb to three English vessels, and was restored to the French, because it had actually been taken *after* peace had been concluded by the two home countries.

main highway of advance, but they qualified the nature of that advance. It was France's misfortune to be committed to a country, only narrow river-side strips of which lent themselves readily to cultivation ; to be committed also to Indian river routes to be traversed only by canoe, and that with frequent portages. The most formidable of Indian powers checked her use of southern routes to the Atlantic, and for a considerable period also, to the Mississippi basin, confining her to the rugged Ottawa route and rendering precarious even that semblance of a colony which existed between Montreal and Quebec. The one staple traffic—the fur trade—was not conducive to settlement. Regions quickly became exhausted, and new ones were sought further and further along the canoe routes. There was rapid ingress but little real settlement. Activities were concerned with trading for fur, and not with that settled production, which must be the foundation of a vigorous colony. The routes of Champlain were perforce the routes of the fur-traders and missionaries who followed him. They were defined in those physical changes caused by the glacial era, and are followed by the modern rail and canals of our day.

As in the case of Spanish advance in New Spain, the efforts of the Jesuit missionaries led to an advance of geographical discovery, probably as noteworthy in fact, certainly more definite in record, than that of the trader, whether gold-seeker or fur-hunter. The waterway remained the highway, and entirely controlled the siting of western mission stations and forts.

Thus in 1634, Champlain sends Nicolet once more in quest of a through passage to the China seas. Nicolet followed the now familiar Ottawa-Nipissing-Georgian Bay route, passed Sault St. Marie into Lake Superior, and reached Green Bay to hear of a Great Water some three days distant.

At this date the whole French population of New France was the merest handful—certainly less than 1,000 men—and all efforts now were needed to cope with the Iroquois, who began to advance from their strongholds south and east of the lower lakes and to encroach upon the land of the weakening Hurons. By 1659 they were menacing the very existence of the Lower St. Lawrence settlements, and a French regiment was sent out to cope with them. Thus reinforced, the settlers were able to procure peace for some years, and efforts were made by the home government to encourage colonization, which were so far successful that by 1666 the settlers numbered over 6,000.

Unfortunately, neither settlers nor traders had that freedom of initiative so necessary in the development of a new land. Trade was controlled by a succession of monopoly companies

—in turn, the Hundred Associates, the New Company, and later, the West India Company. The government was undemocratic and centralized, being in the hands of a governor appointed by the king, the head of the Jesuit Church in Canada, and a few colonists chosen by these. Down to the end of the seventeenth century, the only real areas of settlement in Canada were the strips of land bordering the St. Lawrence from Montreal to Quebec and up the Richelieu to the Falls of Chambly. This land was parcelled out in grants, each with its river frontage, among the ex-officers of the Canadian Regiment. Men of the same regiment were settled on these grants in almost feudal relationship to their landlords. Beyond these strips there was no real settlement, though the Jesuits established mission stations by 1670 at La Pointe (west of Lake Superior), where Marquette was in control; at Sault St. Marie and at Michilli-Mackinac, at the exit of Lake Michigan ; and fur-traders and *coureurs de bois* were operating west and north of the Great Lakes.

Under the governorship of Frontenac (1672) official attempts were made to investigate the Great Waters so often heard of from the Indians. They are of interest geographically as evincing the continued control exercised by the possibility of canoe movements in the French advance. In our brief discussion of the glacial origin of the Great Lakes, we referred to the low water-parting between the St. Lawrence and Mississippi systems, and to the fact that in the earliest stages, when the eastern outlets were ice-blocked, the outflow of glacial waters notched this low divide at certain points. With the restoration of the St. Lawrence outlet these notchings became areas of somewhat indeterminate drainage, and in each case the little river running to the lake comes within canoe portage distance of some angle of a Mississippi tributary. Thus the approach at South Bend on the St. Joseph River to the Kankakee tributary of the Illinois, and of the Chicago River to the Illinois itself. Note also the approach of the Fox River running to Green Bay and the Wisconsin tributary of the Upper Mississippi. Of later importance and similar origin are the portages between the Maumee and the Wabash, and between the Upper Alleghany and South-east Lake Erie. We shall see later how fundamentally important has been this absence of substantial divide between the two great water systems, in the construction of canals, in the evolution of railroad systems, and in the general economic development of the continent. Frontenac sent the fur-trader Joliet to find the Mississippi. On the way he was joined by the missionary Marquette, and these two representatives of French occupation sailed to Green Bay, took the Fox-Wisconsin portage referred to above, and sailed the Mississippi to its junction with the Arkansas.

Meanwhile Frontenac was conscious of the necessity of opening up the two eastern lakes also, in spite of the hostility of the Iroquois, and of diverting, too, the Iroquois fur trade to Canadian rather than English routes. As a first step in this direction, he planted forts near the exit of Lake Ontario (near Kingston of to-day). Associated with him in this work was La Salle, after Champlain the greatest of French discoverers in North America. The latter made three attempts before he succeeded in making known the whole course of the great river. Building his ship, the " Griffon," above Niagara, he sailed to Green Bay, and, taking the Fox-Wisconsin portage, journeyed some distance down the Mississippi and returned to Fort Crève-cœur on the Illinois. At the third attempt he left Lake Michigan by the St. Joseph River, and crossed the portage to the Kankakee and so to the Mississippi itself, which he followed to its mouth, and claimed the new country for his king. La Salle, like his predecessor, had been looking for a passage to the east. He found himself in the Gulf of the Spaniard—in a position which, if strongly held for France, would threaten Spanish power in Mexico and hold up the advance of Spanish forts and mission stations, which by this date had reached and just begun to cross the Rio Grande into Texas.

La Salle returned to Quebec by the way he came and thence took news of his great journey to France and Louis XIV. The closing years of the seventeenth century saw the approach, to the outlet of the Mississippi, of the vanguards of the three chief European Powers in North America. The English had made settlements in North Carolina and her pioneers had made journeys across the Appalachians to the Tennessee. France in a single journey had traversed the whole of the central plain and shown the ease of communication between the two most significant inlets of the continent ; while Spain, too long held by the mineral wealth of the Mexico plateau, was just advancing into Texas. The Mississippi River in its lower course had been known to Spain through the voyages of Coronado and De Soto for more than 100 years, but as far as any permanent settlement was concerned, the region was virgin ground when entered by La Salle, and with Louis XIV's keen support he set out to found there a colony. Calling first at a French West Indies isle, he re-embarked for the Gulf, and among the low, swampy, unfamiliar shores of the northern coast missed the outlet of the great river and landed in Texas, far to the west, where he planted his little colony at Fort St. Louis (1685) near the mouth of the Guadalupe River. He and a small party made several attempts to reach the Mississippi overland. Eventually he was murdered by his desperate followers. The colony was massacred by the Indians in 1689.

The immediate result of the journeys of La Salle was an increase in Spanish activity in Eastern Texas, and on the North Gulf coast. A more gradual consequence was the evolution of the definite French policy by which the military occupation of the St. Lawrence-Mississippi waterway should sever and threaten the Spanish forces of the south, and prevent the emergence of the English beyond the Appalachian barrier.

CHAPTER IV

THE BRITISH TIDE-WATER SETTLEMENTS AND THEIR PHYSICAL SETTING

THE coastlands of the Middle and Southern Atlantic States are developed on cretaceous and younger rocks. These rest unconformably upon much older material. The junction of the cretaceous belt with the old rocks is known as the Fall Line, and the country between this and the sea is called the Coast Plain. Further inland, to the west of the Fall Line, the old rocks which underlie the Coast Plain come to the surface in what is known as the Piedmont Plateau (Fig. 14). There are marked differences in surface features, drainage, and soils, between these two physiographical areas.

The Coast Plain varies in detail from north to south, but as its several beds of sand, clay, marl and pebble, all dip gently to the east, and are little disturbed and partly unconsolidated, the result is in general a low but not perfectly smooth plain, characterized by the outcropping of roughly parallel belts of varying fertility, and occasionally, too, of slightly varying resistance, so that very low infacing escarpments sometimes occur. There are many varieties of soil, but a preponderance of sandy and very light ones. The alluvium of the river flood plains is derived in part from the Piedmont and yields fertile strips of good agricultural land, though draining is often required.

Now the slope of the plain to the Atlantic is gentle, and the plain itself is continued beneath the sea as the continental shelf. Consequently, a very slight variation in level will have a very marked effect on the position of the shore line. Such variations have been frequent in recent geological time. The most noticeable recent displacement has been downwards, and the whole coast from Chesapeake Bay to the north, exhibits the characteristics of a drowned area. The continental shelf is grooved with valleys originally formed above sea-level. The

shallow Chesapeake Bay is simply the drowned lower portion of
a river system of mild relief.

But postponing for the moment any detailed description
of the coastal plain, let us concentrate our attention on certain
extremely significant features in the actual configuration of
the present shore line, resulting in part from the differential
displacement of various portions of the coast. In Georgia and
South Carolina, the coast line is separated by a broad coast
plain from the roughly parallel Piedmont edge; but in the
north the depression is relatively greater—more and more of
what was once coastal plain is submerged as continental shelf,
and consequently a narrowing coastal plain ultimately disappears entirely in New England, where the old rock formations
reach the shore line and indeed have been in part themselves
submerged. The resulting configuration of the actual coast
line is irregular, but in the main it follows three parallel north-
east to south-west lines of direction, the exact positions of
which have had interesting and important consequences in
the economic development of many of the Atlantic ports and
settlements.

The three lines in echelon to which attention is called (see
Fig. 13) are Savannah to Cape Hatteras; then from Baltimore
to Cape Cod, and finally from Boston to the Bay of Fundy.
Beside these, it is instructive, from the point of view of the historical geography of the early colonies, to place the great circle
route from Charleston to the English Channel, and to notice
its general parallelism. The importance of the fact that inter-
colonial trade was on a route parallel to that from the West
Indies to New England and the British Isles, cannot be over-
estimated.

Again, the line from Baltimore to Cape Cod is of particular
interest as marking the approach of the heads of Chesapeake
Bay, Delaware Bay, and Long Island Sound; a general configuration which, as we shall see, was to have fundamental
influence in the position and growth of some of the chief ports
of America. We may divide the coast then into four parts:
(i) From Nova Scotia to Cape Cod we have a rocky coast, studded
with rocky islets and deep harbours, having no part of the physiographical division which we have called the Coast Plain, and
backed by an irregular hilly region in which glacial drift is underlain by rocks of great age. (ii) From Cape Cod to the Hudson,
the coastal plain is less completely submerged and is represented
by parts of Cape Cod peninsula itself, Nantucket Island, Long
Island and Staten Island, the surface features of which, however, are of morainic material. (iii) From the Hudson to the

FIG. 13.—To show the Position of the Fall Line and of the Chief Towns thereon. The projection is gnomonic and so the Great Circle Route a straight line.

Chesapeake, the coastal plain emerges and is just attached to the mainland by the narrow necks of the irregular peninsulas of New Jersey, Delaware, and Virginia. In this portion, the Fall Line appears and is at or about the junction of estuarine water and river. (iv) Lastly, from Washington to the south the coast plain develops into a broad belt, till the Fall Line is 100 feet to 200 feet above sea-level, and one hundred miles and more above tide-water.

In the first division, then, there is no coast plain. In the second it is represented by islands ; in the third by peninsulas, and in the fourth by a broad belt of continuous land.

Before proceeding to see in greater detail how the coastal characteristics influenced the development of the early colonies, let us briefly enumerate these earliest settlements and see as succinctly as may be what were the general influences which led to their origin. In a work dealing with the influence of geographical environment, we must be careful not to over-state our case. Geography undoubtedly influenced the economic and political character as also the extent of early settlement and penetration. The date of these settlements, the origin of the settlers, in this instance, too, the very boundaries and original constitutions of the settlement, the amount of support available from the Mother Country : all these things were a reflection of the general political situation in Western Europe. The British colonies in North America were founded and sustained under the influence of our growing naval supremacy, and in opposition to rival claims which Spain and France had the will but not the power to substantiate. All of the long-drawn struggles for supremacy in Western Europe, e.g. the War of the Spanish Succession and The Seven Years' War, were reflected in struggles between the American settlements, and the fate of these was largely dependent upon the issue of the European wars. The Spaniard preceded us in the Gulf, the Frenchmen in the St. Lawrence, the Dutchman and the Swede in the most vital areas of the Atlantic coast ; but it was, above all, the relative support of the home countries which decided the ultimate possession of the land.

For England the Tudor period was one of conservation rather than expenditure. Her continental possessions gone, the power of the baron checked, her immediate external concern was with religious wars of Europe and the adventures of Charles V. And before we were ready to make and retain American possessions, or to put our naval power to a decisive test, our seamen of the Elizabethan period were to be trained in many an unofficial contest with the Spaniard returning treasure-laden from Central America, or in the establishment of a supremacy among the various nationalities represented on the Newfoundland fishing banks.

By the peace with Spain in 1604, we agreed to desist from trading with the West Indies—an agreement incompletely kept—and our merchants were ready to turn to colonization in the hope of preserving their carrying trade. It was but natural that the first successful colonization should be undertaken by companies. It was an age of mercantile associations. The last two decades of the sixteenth century saw the rise of the Eastland, Levant and East India Companies, all setting out to gain a large share of the trade with the Far East. From any colonies to be founded in America we might expect not a mere part, but an absolute monopoly of trade. But the great distances involved, the expense of fitting out the expeditions, and the considerable time—actually it was under-estimated—which must elapse before any returns could be looked for, these were considerations which necessitated the financial support of some body of subscribers rather than the efforts of an individual.

Thus it came about that our earliest permanent settlements in the New World were made under the ægis of two chartered companies—the London and Plymouth respectively, the first to found a settlement somewhere between 34°–41° N. lat. and the second between 38°–45°. The companies were given a monopoly of trade and for a period of years a freedom from custom dues. The subscribers made possible these earliest settlements, but they received no material advantages for their pains. So far from being supported by the colonists, they had the privilege of supporting these for the first few critical years of their existence. The richest of continents could not nourish these few strangers on her shores until they had learnt something of her nature and had achieved some measure of economic organization. There is a pitiful sameness in the stories of the first few years of each settlement. Few emigrants had agricultural experience, and none of this new land. In the northern settlements particularly, the rigours of the winters were a revelation to those accustomed to the mild climate of North-west Europe. The Jameston and Plymouth settlements were preceded by the dismal failures of Raleigh at Roanoke, and by the first attempt of the Plymouth Company on the Kennebec River. They themselves were very dependent for half a decade or so on the regular sending of supply ships.

It was soon found, too, that a complete freedom for individual initiative was vital in the early economic development of these settlements, and this was stifled by an internal attempt at communistic agriculture on the one hand, and by the over-regulation of trade which resulted from a company monopoly on the other. But not for long—Communism and the Companies both went by the board. The settlements very early came under the dual control of the Privy Council and the King. Subsequent colonies arose either through the overflow of the original settlement into new segregations for which were granted charters, or by the direct grant by the Crown of large areas to proprietors. In all cases what was looked for was a direct profit to the Crown through trading dues ; and the control of the home authority, possible and stringent in this matter, allowed considerable freedom in the internal organization in each colony. For the first few years, each and every settlement was concerned with the evolution of its own subsistence agriculture, but in a decade or so the marked differences in the general economic development of the colonies began to appear. We find that the tide-water colonies can be grouped according to types of commercial activity, and here geographical environment is all important. To elucidate this point, we will now consider in greater detail the geographical environments of certain groups of settlements, beginning with those of New England.

New England has some claim to physical unity. A relief map first of all suggests a rather irregular hill country. Closer examination shows the general north-east and south-west trend of the hills, and if the contours are carefully examined, it is found that the crest lines correspond with an old peneplain level, sloping from west to east and bounded on the west by the really serious barrier of the Berkshires. This rugged dissected peneplain is formed mainly of early palæozoic material, frequently metamorphosed and disturbed, but its drainage, soils and the details of its relief have been entirely altered by glacial action. The origin of the New England drift is such that it forms in general a rather poor class of soils—not readily yielding up its constituents to plant growth, but on the other hand actually deteriorating only slowly. Further, much of the ground is boulder-strewn. Another usual result of the ice covering has been the divergence of some of the streams from their pre-glacial course into new paths not completely graded. There are many rapids and falls often quite near the coast. The rivers generally were, and are, unnavigable, the one considerable exception being the Connecticut, which was navigable as far as Hartford for early sea-going vessels.

Some good alluvial land exists along the river plains and in lowland patches near the coast. The whole region was densely forested, white pine and spruce predominating. We have already noted the absence of coast plain proper, and the drowning of portions of the deeply dissected old peneplain has given an irregular, rocky coast line studded with rocky islets representing the crests of the submerged relief, and characterized by occasional depressions representing a drowned lower river basin. Such is Boston harbour, the arms of which represent drowned tributary streams ; and such also is Narragansett Sound. The one considerable inland plain is the broad fertile lower valley of the Connecticut developed on softer material of Triassic age. The coast is particularly bold and indented in the State of Maine as far south as Portland. There are fine harbours, but with an immediately difficult hinterland. Occasional sand spits and low stretches of glacial drift appear between the rocky portions of coast as we go south from Portland, and at Cape Cod begin some coastal characteristics which can be discerned in the whole remaining east coasts of the continent. From this point the whole coast proper is fringed by sand spits. The southern portion of Cape Cod peninsula, Nantucket Island, Martha's Vineyard, and Long Island itself, are underlaid by cretaceous and tertiary rocks and form portions of the submerged coast plain proper. The surface covering, however, is derived from glacial material. The surface relief of Long Island, for instance, is formed by two low parallel morainic hills running almost the whole length of the island, coalescing in the western half, but separating in the east to include the inlet of Sag Harbour. To the south of each slope a smooth outwash plain exists. The whole of the southern coast of this island is fringed by that tidal-marsh and sand-spit configuration which can be followed, with only the brief breaks of estuary and river mouth, right round to Mexico. The soils of Long Island are sandy and infertile and the market gardening so characteristic of the western end to-day must be related directly to the great centres of population adjoining and to the modern accessibility of fertilizers. Of enormous importance to early communications was the East River and Long Island Sound water passages, giving a comparatively sheltered communication between the coastal New England settlements, and between these and settlements in East New Jersey and the Hudson River. Weeden says : " Perhaps the largest single factor in their physical conditions was Long Island Sound, the sole medium of communication between the important colonies in Connecticut and the eastern district of Massachusetts."

Of great significance, too, are the large fishing banks situated off the coast of New England. less extraordinarily productive perhaps than the corresponding bank off Newfoundland, but

nearer. Finally, as to climate, we must note that New England has a longer and more rigorous winter—a more even distribution of precipitation throughout the year, with much winter
snowfall, and a shorter growing season than any of the other
Atlantic regions.

Here, then, was a land with nothing to attract, and no facilities
to promote, an interior development. No lowland routes, no
navigable ways, no mineral wealth, no extraordinary fertility,
led the early settlers inland. On the contrary, the best agricultural land, the mildest climate, the very possibilities of trade
with other colonies and with the Mother Country, combined
to keep them to the coasts. Owing much to a certain sturdi-
ness of character reinforced by the intensity of their religious
convictions ; bringing with them from their home-land some
predisposition to social organization and discipline, they yet
followed a mode of economic development almost completely
controlled by their geographical environment.

For the first few years, the few miserable folk in the settlements at Plymouth, in Cape Cod Bay, had enough to do to find
shelter, to learn the possibilities of maize production, and to
reinforce their meagre supplies with fish from the immediate
coasts. They soon learnt enough, taught by the Indian, to
develop a subsistence farming, and a proportion of them were
learning to be seamen in their fishing expeditions. Thus issued
the sequence common to so many coastal peoples. The fishermen required boats. The virgin forest stretched right to the
harbour. The harvest of the sea provided a commodity ex-
changeable in the southern colonies, in the West Indies, and
even in Southern Europe. The colonist became fisherman,
boat-builder and trader. This was but the normal evolution
to be expected. The *Mayflower* settlers established themselves in Plymouth and Cape Cod Bay, the Massachusetts Company in Salem, and such were the losses through sickness that
the first decade shows little increase in population. In the
second decade, such increase was rapid, but we must not regard
the further settlements altogether as overflows from these two
areas. In 1629 the " Governor and Company of Massachusetts
Bay in New England " sent five ships to the site of Salem and
in the next few years there was a very rapid increase in the
number of immigrants under the ægis of this company, and
under the pressure of Archbishop Laud's activities against
the Nonconformists in the Home Country. In 1634 there were
4,000 people in Massachusetts scattered in shore settlements
between Cape Ann and Plymouth (e.g. Salem, Lynn, Charleston,
Boston, Dorchester, Weymouth and Hingham). Of a different

nature was the planting of the first settlers in Providence (R.I.) (1636), for a non-geographical factor enters largely into the redistribution of these coast settlements. The earliest settlers had suffered for their religious opinions. They knew little of the larger tolerance born of a less certain faith. They could not bring themselves to join in the discussion and arrangement of town affairs with those who disagreed with them in religious matters, for their Council Chamber was their Meeting House. To be a citizen one had first to be a sectarian. Thus Providence (R.I.) was settled by the separatist followers of Roger Williams, who denied the authority of magistrates in the church. So also at Portsmouth and Newport (R.I.), Mrs. Hutchinson led a little body pledged to the Covenant of Grace. From Narragansett Sound it was a natural step to the Connecticut Valley. Here the Dutch had erected a fur-trading station 45 miles up the river, and at the head of sea-going navigation. Above Hartford there is in places only 3 feet of water and that when the river is not low. As has been already noted, for agricultural settlement this is the most attractive valley of New England, and there was soon a steady movement going on from the eastern settlements to this broad fertile plain. Ignoring the Dutch, settlements were made at Fort Saybrook at the mouth of the river. Then in 1638 came the Rev. John Davenport and Theophilus Eaton, and planted theocratic settlements at New Haven, Guildford, Milford and Stamford. "In Connecticut," says Professor Johnson,[1] " town and church were but two sides of the same thing, and as there would be differences of opinion in church as well as in town matters, every religious dispute gave rise to a new town until the faintest lines of theological divergence were satisfied."

Thus the divergence of religious views, as well as the pressure of population which occurred on the sites best suited for the almost amphibious pursuits of the New Englander, were responsible for the scattering of town settlements, almost all of which were on the navigable portion of the Connecticut, or around such drowned depressions as Narragansett Sound (R.I.), Cape Cod Bay and Boston Bay. (See Fig. 14.)

This growth of population is to be associated with an economic development in which to a very large extent everything in the physical environment of New England combined to make her production and services complementary rather than competitive to those of the other American colonies. Had her trade been limited to the British Isles, it would not have amounted to very much. Some furs she sent—in early colonial days—and also

[1] Quoted in McGrady's " History of South Carolina," p. 6.

timber for naval use ; but not very much, for the Baltic continued to yield the main supply for British use. Her exports to Great Britain did not nearly cover the value of her imports from that country. On the other hand she could provide for many of the wants of the southern colonies, and of the West Indies, and, above all, could build ships and carry on trade for them. To them and also to Spain and the Canaries, she sent salted fish and sawn timber. The poorest quality of fish went for the slaves of the Barbados,[1] better qualities to the Catholic populations of Southern Europe. Her chief shipbuilding yards were at Dorchester, Boston, Gloucester and Salem.

Her merchants often sold both ship and cargo. It is estimated that at the time of the Revolution 30 per cent. of British ships were New England built.[2] As we shall see presently, the plantation system of the middle and southern colonies and West Indies did not lend itself to town growth or manufacture, but towards the Revolutionary period and immediately afterwards, the surplus town population, and the water-power, often quite near the coast, gave New England manufacturing facilities in advance of anything the southern States could offer. Her manufactured articles then were exchanged for the sugar, molasses, rum, indigo, and rice of the southern colonies and thence she took some products of the South in her ships to Europe. The later Corn Laws of Great Britain shut out the grain of the middle colonies, and this also her traders carried to the West Indies. This trading contact with the South enabled her to take a large part in the slave traffic, for which she built and manned many boats. She then took her part in the great triangular route of the Atlantic, mentioned in our first chapter, and the very configuration of the Atlantic coast of North America favoured her traffic. But in addition to her part in the triangular European route, she had an even larger bulk of traffic directly to and from the West Indies and southern colonies.

The Navigation Acts of 1650 and 1663 were a stimulus rather than a deterrent to her trade, for they permitted colonial carrying and debarred Dutch and other foreign competition. Also the clause insisting that the shipment of tobacco, indigo, and rice should in the first instance be made to England or Ireland, made little difference in the actual sum of trade, though it undoubtedly restricted the development of trade with other countries. These Acts, as also the Treaty of Breda, 1667, which confirmed the passing of New York and Delaware settlements

---

[1] Weeden, " Social and Economic History of New England," p. 245.
[2] P. 73, " History of Domestic and Foreign Commerce of the United States." Carnegie Institute, Washington, 1915.

to the English, and by which the English gained important slave-trading facilities, mark stages in the diminution of Dutch maritime power.

We now come to the tide-water settlements of the Hudson, and here we have to consider a very different environment from any obtaining in New England. We have already noted in an earlier chapter how at certain stages of the glacial period, the Great Lake overflow intensified the most marked of all the Appalachian passage-ways, viz. that running from Oswego to Albany, and then by the present Hudson to New York, and joining this route to the Albany-L. Champlain-St. Lawrence route. In any exposition of the historical geography of North America, the extraordinary significance of these well-marked routes must receive full attention. This was the only natural route to the interior at all comparable with that provided by the St. Lawrence system for the French, and nothing is more eloquent of the influences which kept our colonies to the coast for so long a period than the fact that this route belt was little occupied in the seventeenth century, and became a through route only in the nineteenth century.[1] The Englishman, Hudson, sailing a Dutch ship, discovered the river in 1609. He was attempting a north-west passage to the East for the Dutch East India Company, and naturally he sailed the Hudson River to the limit of its navigation for sea-going vessels, i.e. to Albany. From this date until 1623, when the first Dutch colonists appeared, the New Netherland Company's agents explored the Hudson and Connecticut and Long Island districts, and planted fur-trading stations at Albany (Fort Nassau, later Fort Orange) and other centres. In 1623 colonists settled at New Amsterdam on Manhattan Island, and from this date until 1664, when the Dutch lost the colony to Great Britain, the chief points of settlement were New Amsterdam, Fort Orange (Albany) and Hartford on the Connecticut. We shall have to give some rather detailed attention to the site of New York in a later chapter, but just at this point certain main features in the environment should be mentioned.

The Hudson off Manhattan Island forms a broad sheltered roadstead available for the largest ships at any state of the tide (only about 4 feet here). Just above New York an exposure of basaltic trap gives the actual river-bed the appearance of a gorge in the well-known palisade area, but to the north of these the river as far as Albany is bounded by a narrow fertile plain between the unproductive and difficult heights of the Catskill Mountains on the west and the Berkshire Mountains

---

[1] For a relief map of the Hudson, see p. 116, Fig. 18.

3

on the east. There was not room for a large agricultural population here. There was more room and better lands for expansion in the Mohawk Valley and towards the Great Lakes, and with the site of Albany so naturally and so early occupied, this land would soon have been taken up, but for one reason and that a non-geographical one. Barring the way from Albany to the Great Lakes and from Albany to Lake Champlain and Montreal, was the most powerful of all Indian Confederacies. It would be difficult to over-estimate the importance of this one fact in American history. Albany was a sort of advance post of the Dutch in Indian territory, and for many years was simply the fortified place of transhipment from the fur-laden Indian canoes to the Dutch vessels. The through route factor, then, so properly emphasized in elementary geographies, meant nothing to the early development of New York.

But besides being a fine harbour, New York has a certain coastal nodality of its own which was effective immediately. Apart from the Hudson gap altogether, its early traffic concentrated in three routes, viz. (i) direct access to the ocean ; (ii) by East River and Long Island Sound to the New England coast settlements ; (iii) to the settlements of East New Jersey and Raritan River, and thence across a low and short waterparting to the Delaware at Trenton.

The immediate result of this last factor was to make the little overflow Dutch settlements from New Amsterdam about the present Jersey City (Bergen, Orange, etc.), together with the settlements of New Englanders upon the Raritan (Port Elizabeth) mere feeders of New Amsterdam. Thus, initially, there were two New Jerseys, an East New Jersey based on the Raritan and Newark Bay settlements, and closely related to New Amsterdam in its early evolution ; and a West New Jersey based on the Dutch and Swedish settlements of the Upper Delaware estuary (i.e. between the present sites of Trenton and Wilmington).

It is anticipating matters somewhat, yet perhaps not out of place, to emphasize here the importance to New York of the mere *coastal configuration* which brings the heads of the Chesapeake, Delaware and Raritan inlets together ; an importance evidenced by the early canal connections, and to-day by the enormously heavy railway traffic on the line, Baltimore, Philadelphia, Trenton and New Jersey to New York.

The semi-feudal land system of the Dutch patroonships was not attractive to colonists, and the chief interests of the early settlers were concerned with the fur trade. The colony suffered from the hostilities of the Indian, especially in the period 1643–45, when the Dutch of Albany had to retire to New Amsterdam. By the middle of the seventeenth century, they found themselves hemmed in between extending settlements of British or New England origin, in Connecticut, in the east of Long

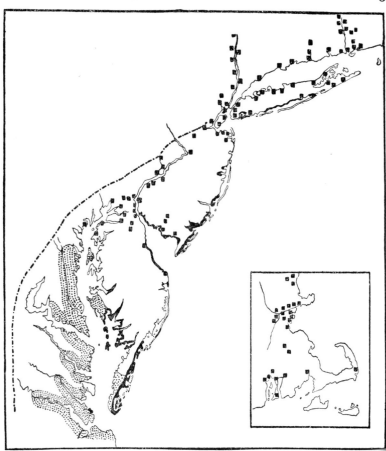

FIG. 14.—The British Colonial Settlements at the end of the seventeenth century (except the Carolinas). Boston Bay and Narragansett Sound (inset).

The coastline has been generalized from the U.S.A. pilot maps. The most considerable marine marshes are blackened in. The town and village sites are derived from a number of late seventeenth and early eighteenth century maps (Moll, 1720; Lea, 1690; Seller, 1666; Thornton, 1680, and others in the B.M.). Note the approach of settlements along the Baltimore, Philadelphia, New York line and their absence on the coast proper.

—.—.—. Fall Line. ⬛ Town Site. ::: Plantations.

Island, and in New Jersey. Finally, in 1664, at the close of the Dutch-English war, New Netherland was ceded to the British, but for many years after this the majority of New York inhabitants were of Dutch origin. Further, the Hudson region continued to suffer in competition for colonists through its system of land holding and the strength of the Indian in the Upper River basins.

With regard to the next settlements to the south, it is important to note that the whole of the Atlantic coast of New Jersey (from Sandy Hook to Cape May), like the south side of Long Island, is bounded by sand spits and tidal marshes. It was difficult of access[1] and did not attract settlement, which naturally followed the Delaware inlet, though here again the marshes of the east side of the lower estuary were so extensive as to forbid settlement. Further, as the Delaware above Trenton and the Schuylkill above Philadelphia both cross the Fall Line belt and become unnavigable, it is not surprising that the earliest settlements were confined to both sides of the river from about the present site of Trenton to the mouth of the Brandywine Creek. At this last point was the earliest settlement of all, Fort Christine, made in 1638 by the Company of New Sweden. The first settlers on this north-east to south-west part of the Delaware were Swedes and Dutch. They here occupied fertile lands and proved themselves good colonists and expert agriculturists. Their weakness lay in lack of home support— particularly in the matter of the encouragement of emigration. The Swede had first submitted to the Dutch, and their lands were included in the Dutch transfer to the British colonies in 1664.

For a long period peninsular New Jersey, save just along the Delaware, was little occupied, for besides the coastal marshes, to which reference has been made, much of the peninsula has too light and sandy a soil to be attractive. As in the case of the Long Island market gardens of to-day, it is the proximity to great centres of population and the modern possibilities in the way of fertilizers which are the determining factors in its present agricultural development.

The boundaries of the separate states even to-day reflect the entire ignorance of the physical characteristics of the continent displayed by the Home Authorities. They are a symptom of the newness of the country. The usual plan was to fix on northern and southern latitudes and on the Atlantic coast as three boundaries, and to hope for the best in the matter of a western. But when Penn got his grant in 1681, the coast

[1] " Between Sandy Hook and Cape Charles (Chesapeake Bay), the only sheltered anchorage for vessels, if over 6 feet draught, is inside Delaware Bay entrance." U.S.A. "Pilot." The largest marsh areas are shown in Fig. 14.

to the east being occupied by New Jersey, the river Delaware formed a boundary till it cut the 42° lat. N., and after a squabble with the earlier settlement of Maryland, the southern boundary was fixed on the present line. The settlers on the west of the lower Delaware estuary having quarrelled with the settlers of the river Delaware itself, formed ultimately the State of Delaware. Finally, Pennsylvania was left with its narrow estuary front from Trenton to just above Wilmington. It is not to be supposed that in drafting the original boundaries of Pennsylvania, the authorities realized that they were including the most valuable anthracite and bituminous coal-fields of the world, a north-eastern region where the relatively fertile Piedmont took the place of the sandy belts of the other tide-water colonies, and a region further west, where the fertile limestone valleys of the Appalachians were most accessible from the coast. Pennsylvania was peculiarly fortunate, too, in her first proprietor, who, while providing an asylum for his earnest industrious co-religionists, yet was in favour at the Court. There was an unusual wisdom and restraint in his dealing with the Indian, at whose hands the early Pennsylvania suffered less than most of the colonies. The prosperity of the colony was reflected in the growth of its port. Philadelphia—from the first a well-planned city—was laid out in 1682 on the narrow tongue of land between the Schuylkill and the Delaware, at a concave bend of the latter stream, to which swung the deep-water channel. It quickly grew in competition with the other and earlier Delaware River ports, and soon came to be the collecting and distributing centre of the estuary. Later canal and rail connections with New York lost to it some portion of its natural modern development.

Now the tide-water colonies based on the Hudson and the Delaware, i.e. New York, Pennsylvania, New Jersey and Delaware, had an economic development of a type transitional from that of New England to those of the Chesapeake Colonies. They had a milder winter and a longer growing season than New England, but they could not have produced rice or cotton as did the Carolinas. They included (in Pennsylvania) large areas of the moderately fertile Piedmont soils as well as an area (in New Jersey) of coastal plain, denied to New England. They were generally better suited to agricultural settlement than New England, but they contained a much greater area devoted to small farms and mixed agriculture than did Virginia, where large plantations and specialized culture (tobacco) prevailed. They availed themselves of slave labour, but to a much less extent than the southern colonies. They built some of their own ships and did some of their own carrying and were thus less dependent upon New England traders. Like New England, they shipped furs, and some timber to the West Indies, but in smaller quantities, and they added farm produce such as salted meat, pork and grain.

Chesapeake Bay is a larger, longer and more irregular edition of the Delaware. Corresponding to the New Jersey peninsula we have that enclosing the great inlet to the east divided in its northern, widest part between Delaware on the east and part of Maryland on the west, and with a sandy finger-like extension to the south—it may be compared to Cape May in the case of New Jersey—which belongs to Virginia. The whole of the Atlantic shores of this great peninsula is fringed by a belt of marsh and sand spit strictly comparable to that of New Jersey and entirely unconducive to settlement. We may find another analogy in that a belt of marshland situated on the eastern shores of Chesapeake (about 37° 30′–38° 31′ N. lat.) corresponds to the marshy eastern shore of Delaware Bay. To the western margin of the Chesapeake Bay come the larger estuaries, the deeper rivers, the better soils, the more considerable hinterland (Fig. 14). It would be difficult to select a better example of the drowned estuary than that exhibited by the Chesapeake. " The bay from its entrance to the mouth of the Susquehanna is about 170 miles long ; the lower half has a width varying from 10–20 miles ; the upper varies from 2¾ to 10 miles. The prevailing depth in the lower part of the bay is 4–10 fathoms." " From a point a little above the Rappahannock River a long, narrow deep channel, following the general course of the bay, extends to within a few miles of the mouth of the Patapsco River " (on which lies Baltimore). " In this channel the depth is 10–26 fathoms. Towards the head of the bay the channel shallows gradually to 12 feet abreast of the North-East river." [1] Although the bay is shallow for its size, it has from the Patapsco River to its mouth a depth of over 35 feet. The irregular shallow marshy inlets of the eastern shores have never borne much traffic, and are unimportant in this respect to-day save for that connected with the oyster fisheries. It is quite otherwise with the western shores. Here the Susquehanna, the Potomac, the Rappahannock, the York and the James Rivers have their lower courses changed into estuaries and their junction with the old bed of the Chesapeake obliterated, by the general depression of the land. The junction of coastal plain and Piedmont passes through the very mouth of the Susquehanna at its entrance to the bay, thus ruling that fine stream out of the navigable

[1] U.S.A. Pilot.

system and operating against the development of any large centre on its lower course ; the line then passes just above Baltimore (Jones Falls), so that the Patapsco is unimportant above that port. Vessels of 30 feet draught can now reach Baltimore. The Potomac was and is navigable to Washington just below the Fall Line as exemplified at Little Falls. So far the Fall Line has been practically at tidal water. But in the Rappahannock, the next big river to the south, the draught shallows gradually to the Fall Line which intercepts the river at Fredericksburg, where there is 10 feet of water. The York River, whose broad straight estuary terminates at West Point (22 feet of water), is here fed by two rivers as distinct from estuaries, the Pamunkey and the Mattaponi, which are navigable for barges (and small river steamers in the lower courses), to the Fall Line some 40 miles inland.

The James River is navigable to the Fall Line at Richmond, where there is now 17 feet of water, and its chief tributaries, the Appomatox and Chickahominy, will take big barge traffic, the former having 9 feet to Petersburg (11 miles), and the latter 8 feet for 23 miles. These depths, which represent modern conditions, are in part due to dredging, which has been chiefly concentrated upon the port terminals and the sandbanks which most of the rivers have as they enter the bay. On the other hand, the vessels of sea-going colonial days were seldom more than 200 tons. The majority were 100 and under, and drew only a few feet of water. Further, the prevalent forests before deforestation gave a more regular regime to the rivers. The Fall Line was the effective limit of river navigation in colonial days, though later it was crossed by canals on the lower Potomac, Susquehanna and Delaware.

Tide-water Virginia was then essentially a series of narrow, parallel peninsulas running roughly north-west to south-east and separated by broad navigable estuaries. The soils in the coast plain province of Virginia are often sandy and light, and such areas were originally occupied by pine forests. There was an alluvial cover, however, along the river sides, and the soils here were originally excellent, though apt to become quickly exhausted and often, too, of no great depth. Most of the rivers flow in well-defined flood plains (not so definitely marked as in the case of the Carolina streams), and since these were often marshy, importance would attach to those spots where the river was undercutting its bank and thus approached firm ground at a low bluff. Here were the landing wharves of the early plantations. The whole of the coast plain is low but not absolutely level : the shore perfectly flat and bordered by sand spits. From the Atlantic the only elevations to be seen are the occasional high sand-dunes, e.g. those about Cape Henry, which are over 80 feet high. The whole country was originally forested, and though the coast plain soils—as noted above— were in general sandy, yet areas of heavier soils were formed in a larger proportion of the whole than in the Carolinas, and these heavier soils were occupied by deciduous trees. The pine belts of Virginia were less extensive and less continuous than those of the more southerly Atlantic colonies. Early representatives of the London Company sent home information that pitch, tar, and resin could not become staples of Virginia because the pine belt was too scattered, though of course these articles became of very great importance in the Carolinas.[1]

Here, then, between the wooded sandhills of Capes Charles and Henry, came the first permanent settlers of British North America. They attempted a way into Hampton Roads and eventually found the deep-water channel which hugs the North- ern shore at Point Comfort—indeed the channel was so narrow and so near the Cape that it could be defended there by the short range Sacre. Considerable strategic importance attached to the twin capes Charles and Henry which guarded the narrow entrance to a whole series of river settlements, for each and every tide-water settlement of North America might be attacked and wiped out by any considerable naval force (cf. the West India settlements).

Captain Smith, the leader of these earliest British colonists, sailed the *James* to its limit of navigation at Richmond, but not before actual settlement had taken place much further down the river at Jamestown. The place had the advantage of deep water close in. The ships could be tied to trees! Also it was an island and therefore less liable to Indian attack. It had no other advantages and was a marshy and unhealthy spot. This was in 1607. In 1675 it sheltered only some twelve to fourteen families "who obtained a living chiefly by keeping houses of entertainment."[2] To-day it is no more than a name on the map. The first year or two of this first colony tells the familiar tale of wretchedness and complete dependence upon supply ships, but in a few years subsistence farming had suffi- ciently advanced to keep the colony in food-stuffs. In 1612

[1] " Economic History of Virginia in the Seventeenth Century," Bruce, vol. I, p. 89. Note that the coast plain forests, particularly the pine belts, were entirely open and free from undergrowth. It is incorrect to think of them as being in any sense impenetrable, though forests with under- growth deserving such an epithet were found by the early pioneers who attempted to penetrate the upper Piedmont and Appalachian ridges.

[2] Quoted in " Economic History of Virginia," Bruce, vol. II, p. 545.

began tobacco planting. The climate, and the river bottom soils, were found peculiarly suitable. Large profits were made and settlers attracted. Penetration of the country was facilitated by the great navigable estuaries, and caused by a rapid increase of colonists requiring new lands, and by the fact that as tobacco was cultivated without rotation, and the soil peculiarly liable to exhaustion, planters were continually taking up fresh lands. The possibility of water transport, and of a landing wharf, were, after the fertility of the soil, the chief desiderata in these new plantations. Colonial Virginia consisted merely of river and estuary bordering plantations. Often the sea-going vessel could come right to the plantation wharf some 30–40 miles inland. Towns and even villages were non-existent (contrast New England). The unit was the plantation—often very large—and there was none of that point concentration of population which favours industry and trading activities. British and New England merchants carried the Virginian traffic and arranged its business. The type of agricultural land holding lent itself to slave exploitation, and Virginia soon received large numbers, at first via Barbados and the other West Indies, and later direct. Her outstanding staple was tobacco. The quality varied very much with soil; perhaps the very finest varieties were grown on the peninsula between the James and York Rivers. In spite of an at first rapidly increasing market, there came a time before the end of the seventeenth century when prices fell through over-production. Planters were then limited to a certain *number* of plants per acre. Since a much fuller growth, and therefore weight per acre, took place on virgin soil, here was another reason for the constant movement to fresh plantations.

Of the seventeenth-century tide-water mainland colonies, the most southerly and the latest were those of the Carolinas. Here again we have the usual concurrent circumstances—the gift by the Crown to proprietors, in this case to a board of proprietors. Then we have the usual little groups of people, adventurous or discontented, or both, willing to take advantage of the opportunity of starting afresh; in this case the Royalists from the Barbados and some of the other West Indian isles; the Huguenots, who settled in South Carolina; and the group of New Englanders and Virginians in North Carolina. And finally we have the coastal geographic factors controlling the actual areas of earliest settlement; usually some bay of entry and escape from the predominant salt-marsh and sand-spit coast. Thus Albemarle Sound became the nucleus of North Carolina, and at the tide-water junction of the Ashley and Cooper rivers was Charleston, all that the seventeenth century saw of a South Carolina.

This division, however, into a North Carolina based on Albemarle Sound, and a South Carolina based on the Ashley-Cooper inlet, was subsequent to a single unsuccessful effort in the neighbourhood of Cape Fear, which, instituted by Sir John Yeaman in 1665, was abandoned in 1667. In 1669 vessels with ninety-two colonists for Carolina left England, and at length arrived at Port Royal—an inlet in South Carolina—after a journey via Barbados and Bermuda. They moved almost immediately to Old Charleston on the Ashley River. Port Royal was again used as a site of settlement by a party of Scots in 1683. Meanwhile, as early as 1653, a party of Virginians had settled on the Chowan River in Albemarle Sound and formed the nucleus which was to become North Carolina, this river being within the original Carolina grant, though in sympathies and effective distance it should properly have been classed with Virginia. And here we must lay stress on the great distance between these original southern settlements. Charleston is more than 250 miles from Albemarle Sound. The journey was a difficult one. Here was no transverse line of communication such as that presented in the general trend of the Chesapeake and Delaware and Raritan systems. The rivers were at right angles to the coast. In the coastal plain they were wide, winding, and set in wide, marshy flood-plains that offered few conveniences for crossing. The coastal salt marsh was even more marked a feature than in the middle colonies. For many decades Charleston was the most isolated (as far as land routes are concerned) of our mainland colonies. Communication by land with the middle colonies was extraordinarily difficult. Even at the end of the eighteenth century it is said that the news of the Declaration of Independence reached Paris ten days before it arrived at Charleston.

Because of this isolation and because also of its historical connection with the Barbados, South Carolina (Charleston) was much more akin to the West Indian settlements than to the other mainland colonies. " When Eden Randolph, the collector of the King's Customs, proposed in 1694 a re-arrangement and consolidation of the colonial government for the better control and collection of the King's revenues, he recommended that the proprietary governments be set aside and that South Carolina and all the Bahamas islands should be put under one government, under His Majesty's immediate authority; that North Carolina should be annexed to Virginia, Delaware to Maryland, W. New Jersey to Pennsylvania,

E. New Jersey and Connecticut to New York, and Rhode Island to Massachusetts, thus reducing the number of colonies to about six."[1] Such a grouping would indeed have been in accordance with the essential geographical facts. The Albemarle Sound settlers had environment and activities like to those of the Virginians. The Charleston settlement had characteristics arising from three main factors. Firstly: its intimate relations with the Barbados, Bahamas and West Indies generally. Secondly: it represented the only point of call and of refilling between the West Indies and Virginia. Thirdly: the southern temperature made possible the cultivation of rice.

With regard to the first point, we may notice that very many of the earliest Charleston settlers came from the Barbados, at, or just after the period of the Restoration, when their loyalty to the Crown had met with indifferent reward. At this period the Barbados was one of our most important colonies. Though only as large as the Isle of Wight, it contained by 1762 some 18,000 white settlers and 70,000 negroes. It is noteworthy, too, in being almost the only considerable West India island which has never changed hands. It was started by Sir William Courten in 1625. It was one of the outer girdle of lesser islets which the Spaniards had ignored and which falling into the hands of rival nations served as naval bases from which her shipping was attacked. Blessed with fertile soil and a healthier and more temperate climate than obtains on the mainland of Central America, or on the larger islands, it quickly attracted colonists and produced first tobacco, and then sugar, on great slave-manned plantations. It soon became the first point of call for European trading vessels (particularly Dutch and English) taking the southern or Trade-wind route to America, and also for the slave vessels from Africa. Thus for many of the slaves required in the southern mainland colonies the Barbados was a kind of half-way house.

The slave economy and plantation system were transplanted, then, bodily to Charleston. So, too, was the semi-military social organization of the Barbados. And this last was developed in Charleston, for the extreme isolation of the little colony laid it open to the attack from Indian by land and from the Spaniards by sea. The leading citizens of New England were pillars of their respective churches; those of Charleston were of military rank, and military titles abounded in this colony a century and a half before the Civil War made them common in all States.

Then as to Charleston's position on a great trade route,

[1] " History of South Carolina," McGrady, p. 7.

as also its sub-tropical climate, these two factors interact. Some point of call, of shelter and of refitment was required between the West Indies and the middle and northern colonies, particularly as in winter the winds are frequently unfavourable to a northward-sailing vessel.[1] Ships on the great trade circle often wintered at Charleston and proceeded in the following spring. As we noted in the opening chapter, vessels bound for the Chesapeake colonies would often cross the Atlantic in the Trade-wind belt and would make for the coast (because uncertain of their latitude) before proceeding northwards. They would thus have to pass the site of Charleston. And then Charleston had characteristic products to offer to such vessels. Her slaves, her swamps and her climate made for the production of rice. Indigo was another staple. The pine forests of the Carolinas were less intercepted by deciduous trees than those of the middle colonies and more adapted to the production of turpentine, resin and tar than those of New England. In the early eighteenth century Charleston became the most important trading centre on the mainland south of Philadelphia.

[1] See Chapter I.

(For unit dot population maps of 1760 and 1790, see Fig. 17B, opposite p. 83, and Fig. 17C on p. 114.)

CHAPTER V

THE APPALACHIANS AND THE FRENCH AND BRITISH STRUGGLE

DURING the seventeenth century, purposes of trade and defence kept the colonists to tide-water. They looked back to Europe rather than forward to the West. Only in the Chesapeake and Delaware groups was there a rather rapid ingress, and this but followed the sea arms to the Fall Line, where estuary met river. But early in the eighteenth century the fur-trader, whose traffic demanded virgin grounds, and the adventurer, impatient of the restraint pertaining to a settled existence, followed stream and Indian trail ever further west, discovering routes to be followed later by the farmer. By the mid-eighteenth century, the Appalachian Mountains at their weakest (i.e. in Pennsylvania) had been crossed, and the head-streams of the Ohio reached. But by this time, too, the agents of the French King had reached the same region via the St. Lawrence and Lake Erie portages, and before we can understand the great struggle ensuing between England and France for the possession of the continent, we must know something of the form of the Appalachian Mountain system itself. Though the character of relief here did not, of course, decide the result of the struggle, yet it controlled the plans of campaign of both parties and determined the points of effective contact.

In this chapter, then, we shall essay a description of the Eastern Cordillera of the continent—especially of that part lying to the west and south of the Hudson. The highlands of this area have been divided by geographers into definite physiographical regions and these—in a broad review—are so simply related to the geological history of the whole system, that a brief résumé of this history should help us to realize and to remember the leading characteristics of the various regions enumerated. The limits of these physical units to be considered are shown in Fig. 1.

The Piedmont region—in the main[1]—is an exposure of some of the oldest rocks of the continent and represents one of the

[1] It bears, however, some narrow lowland strips of Triassic deposits.

great positive areas of North America. Twisted, contorted and rent by later intrusions, it has throughout geological times been, in the main, above sea-level. It represents the stumps of a great continental mountain system, the denudation of which has contributed deposits which went to the formation of the rocks of the central plains. From Cambrian to Upper Carboniferous (i.e. Pennsylvanian) times, then, we must conceive of a mountain land of continental proportions whose western shore line occupied—very roughly—the western limits of the present Piedmont region.

From this shore line, over nearly the whole of the area of the present continent to the west, lay a great sea, which received deposits from this mountain land, as also from that other great positive area, the Laurentian Shield, to the north-east. West of Appalachia, then, and south of Laurentia were laid down the whole sequence of rocks from Cambrian to Pennsylvanian times. After Carboniferous times there was an emergence of the mid-continent which never after suffered complete submergence, so that the surface rocks of the central States are of Carboniferous age (Mississippian and Pennsylvanian), and no later rocks occur until we go far enough west to approach the High Plains and Rocky Mountain systems, or far enough south to meet the great embayment of the coastal plain about the lower Mississippi. Rocks *older* than the Carboniferous do occur, however :—

(i) On the margin of the Archæan masses owing, in part, to a gradual rising of the land, so that later deposits were made further and further from the original shore line ; and, in part, to the denudation of younger deposits at these margins. Thus the whole sequence pre-Cambrian to Pennsylvanian occurs on the line, say, Ottawa to Pittsburg, or, again, Washington to Pittsburg.

(ii) Where in anticlinal areas of the mid-continent the later formations have been completely denuded, exposing rocks of pre-Carboniferous age, e.g. in the Ozark region and in the Lexington and Nashville uplifts.

Now, we may suppose that the rocks of this central sea were originally laid down horizontally, and in much of the area they remain nearly so to-day. The formations, however, do not maintain their thickness over the whole area. In general they are thickest near to the old continental mass of Appalachia and thin out to the west. Many of the thickest deposits of the east are of shallow water origin and, therefore, we must presuppose a gradual sinking of the sea-bottom as deposits thickened upon it, especially in the region immediately to the west of Appalachia.

Towards the close of the Carboniferous period, conditions over much of what is now the Central Plain of North America favoured the production of coal seams. The rock surface was alternately just above swamp level and covered with a luxurious vegetation, and just below water level where such vegetable remains would be hardened and consolidated under layers of mud and sand. Thus were built up the coal measures of Pennsylvanian times. At the close of the Carboniferous period, however, were initiated movements of a much more comprehensive order. Great lateral pressure and consequent movement from the east, not only raised and further contorted the Piedmont area, but induced also complicated series of north-east to south-west folds in the thick deposits immediately to the west (Fig. 15). These folds became progressively less acute with increasing distance to the west and almost died out in the area now designated Cum-

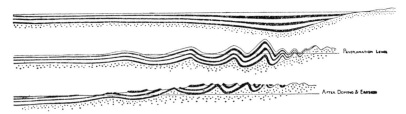

Fig. 15.—Diagram to show the effect of folding, peneplanation and uplift on sedimentaries originally nearly horizontal. The dark lines represent the more resistant strata.

berland Plateau. There were thus upraised, then, three great parallel strips of country :—

(i) The most westerly, consisting of horizontal stratified rocks.
(ii) The central strip of intensely folded stratified rocks.
(iii) An eastern strip of pre-Cambrian unstratified crystalline rocks.

For the whole period Permian to Cretaceous times, denudation was active and the great mountain area was reduced to a peneplain, the most considerable residual heights being in the south-western portions of the pre-Cambrian strip. This peneplain received Cretaceous deposits and then the whole threefold system was domed up along the old north-east to south-west line of weakness and denudation was again active on the upraised mass, removing much of the Cretaceous cover but producing very different effects in the three main areas of the uplift. Thus in the west, though surface strata had been lost in the original denudation to the peneplain stage, yet the underlying strata were also mainly horizontal, and where these were raised to form the western slope of the dome, denudation was active over great areas having the same lithological character. The drainage here, then, was independent of differences of surface resistance, for over large areas these differences hardly existed. The rivers flowing to the Mississippi maintained the irregular directions of the peneplain stage and merely deepened and enlarged their valleys. In the central strip, forming the summit of the dome, conditions were very different. Here the original denudation of intensely folded strata had resulted in almost a plain, it is true, yet a plain in which rocks of very varying resistance were exposed in narrow north-east to south-west belts. When this area was raised then, and denudation again became active, the drainage soon conformed to the lines of less resistant rock and the area became dissected into a great number of roughly parallel narrow valleys, developed by subsequent streams on the outcrops of lesser resistance and separated by intervening ridges of resistant rock. Where the original east and west stream direction has been maintained, deep and narrow gaps occur in the parallel ridges, so the whole drainage of the area assumed a curiously rectangular character, noticeably different from that obtaining in the western strip. The whole central strip, then, assumed the form of a wide valley plain partially filled up by narrow ridges, whose derivation from an uplifted peneplain is betrayed in their common summit levels.

The third strip, that formed by the eastern arc of the dome, is different again. Firstly, because the original peneplanation was here much less complete, particularly in the south, so that it was an already irregular surface which was again exposed to increased erosion. Then its component rocks were unstratified and though of very varying resistance, yet arranged quite irregularly. Thus the drainage of the eastward flowing rivers quite lacks the almost geometrical design characteristic of the central strip. A final marked uplift in tertiary times has resulted in the rivers cutting narrow valleys within their wider, older valleys.

From Cretaceous to recent times the relative level of sea and land has been such that a coast plain of Cretaceous and later deposits has partially covered the eastern and southward sloping Piedmont.

Fig. 16 represents diagrammatically a very simplified ideal section across the Eastern Cordillera, south of the Hudson, from west to east. We should recognize the following divisions. Notes are appended.

(i) *Cumberland Plateau.* Deeply eroded. Dentritic river system. Developed on horizontal or gently swelling strata.

(ii) *Appalachian Valley.* Parallel valleys. Narrow resistant ridges. Gridiron drainage. Developed on closely folded, peneplained and uplifted strata.

(iii) *Blue Ridge and Piedmont Plateau.* Irregular mountain masses in west, to gently rolling relief in east. Developed on uplifted mass of crystalline pre-Cambrian rocks with igneous intrusions.

(iv) *Fall Line* at junction of coast plain and Piedmont.

(v) *Coastal Plain.* Generally level. Strata dip gently seawards with occasional slight infacing escarpments. Often unconsolidated beds of sands and clays. Belts of very light soils (pine belts). Navigable rivers with marshy flood plains. Sand-spit and sea-marsh coast line.

(vi) *Continental Shelf.* Continuation of coast plain beneath sea. Evidence of recent depression in submerged river channels.

(vii) *Continental Slope.*

(viii) *Oceanic Abyss.*

We must now see what are the actual limits of these major physiographical divisions and what qualifications we must add to our very generalized explanation and description (Fig. 1).

Cumberland Plateau. One is naturally disposed to ask upon what criteria are based the limits of this region. Fig. 17 should make this point clear, for it is a simplified actual section. Note that at the junction of roughly horizontal strata, and folded strata, there is a particularly precipitous eastward facing scarp. This major scarp is not, of course, continuous throughout the

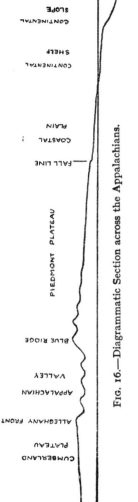

FIG. 16.—Diagrammatic Section across the Appalachians.

Appalachian system, yet it is characteristic. This criterion, indicating the rapid change from gently swelling to closely folded strata, is usually a sufficient index to the eastern edge of the Cumberland Plateau, but it cannot always be applied.

In the south the intense folding of the Great Valley becomes a series of broad swellings further west. The domes of these latter have been eroded and it becomes difficult to say which of two east-facing scarps forms the real Alleghany Front and eastern limit of the Cumberland Plateau region. We should notice that the Cumberland Plateau is particularly well developed in Western New York. The strata here are smoothly swelling rather than horizontal, and over most of the surface are of Devonian age. The most resistant of these forms massive escarpments overlooking the Mohawk to the north and the Hudson to the east. Notice that the general height of this northern extremity of the Cumberland Plateau gives way a little in the neighbourhood of the Finger Lakes, which are of glacial

FIG. 17.—Generalized section of a part of the Eastern Cumberland Plateau (almost horizontal strata), and Western Appalachian Valley (folded strata).

origin, and note also the approach of the Upper Susquehanna (Chemung tributary) and Lower Seneca, marking one epoch of the Great Lake glacial overflow. In Pennsylvania and Virginia, the Alleghany Front is well marked and in West Virginia reaches its greatest height. Indeed, it is sufficiently high, steep and free from gaps in Pennsylvania and West Virginia to present a real barrier, though in general it was the Cumberland Plateau itself, rather than its eastern edge merely, which constituted the historic barrier. The very name plateau gives an incorrect impression here, save in reference to the equal summit levels, for the ground is dissected by deeply-trenched streams. Irregularly distributed, these as often form a barrier as an aid to communication. Much, too, of the higher ground was infertile, and all was forested.

The Cumberland Edge is 2,000 feet in Maryland, 3,000 feet to 4,000 feet in West Virginia and Kentucky, and becomes lower in the south, being 1,600 feet at the Cumberland gap.

The Great Appalachian Valley. This occupies the area between the pre-Cambrian massifs to the east and the less folded plateau to the west. About 50 miles wide and 800 miles

Arching of Fall Zone peneplain and its Coastal Plain cover: regional superposition of southeastward-flowing streams

Arching of Schooley Peneplain

uplift and dissection of Somerville peneplain to give present conditions

Appalachian Plateau *Newer Appalachians*   * Older Appalachians *Coastal Plains

ALLEGHENY FRONT ⌐ * ⌐——— RIDGE and VALLEY BELT ⟶*⟵GREAT⟶*⟵READING⟶*TRIAS *⟵PIEDMONT⟶*
                                              VALLEY PRONG LOWLD

FALL ZONE   FALL ZONE

FIG. 17A.—To illustrate Stages in the Evolution of Appalachia subsequent to the original Folding and Major Peneplanation.
(After "Geomorphology of the Central Appalachians." "International Geological Congress Guide Book." No. 7.)

FIG. 17B.—Population, 1760.

From an article by H. R. Friis. Courtesy of the " Geographical Review " (July 1940), published by the American Geographical Society of New York.

long, it is characterized by a number of roughly parallel ridges having sharp sides and even crests—the remains of the original peneplane. In the north there are the broad valley plains of the East-Shenandoah, Cumberland, and Lebanon, while between these and the Appalachian plateau to the north-west, is a region crowded with narrow ridges and with very little lowland, a region sometimes referred to as the *ridge and valley* province.

These ridges are usually narrow and if the intervening valleys were filled up, the whole country would assume the characteristic of a nearly featureless plain—its condition immediately preceding the Cretaceous uplift. Now, with respect to the original folding of the strata, we have to remember :—

(i) Folding was not perfectly regular. The axes of folds pitched, and inclined, giving after peneplanation and uplift, zigzag hill ridges and valleys.

(ii) Canoe and cigar-shaped ridges were developed according as the underlying strata were part of a syncline or of an anticline.

(iii) Consequent streams cutting the resistant ridges do so in narrow gorges, where rapids are often developed. Subsequent streams flow in the broad valleys developed on the less resistant strata. The whole system lends itself to extensive river capture, with resulting deep water gaps and high level wind gaps. These are of the greatest importance for purposes of east and west communication.

(iv) The valleys are frequently floored by limestone and have fertile soils. Some were particularly broad and fertile, e.g. the Shenandoah in the north-east and those of the Holston and Tennessee in the south-west.

The Appalachian Mountains and the Blue Ridge. This name is usually given to the first distinct mountain range to be met with in passing from the Piedmont to the Appalachian Valley. Structurally, it usually forms simply the most upraised extreme western portion of the Piedmont and is formed of similar unstratified material. The distinction, then, is chiefly that of relief.

In North Carolina and East Tennessee, the Appalachian Mountains are the most considerable in the Eastern States and here we have a mountain mass more than 50 miles wide and over 6,000 feet in height. This is the only true *mountain* barrier in the Eastern States, south of the Hudson. Starting at Grandfather Mountain (lat. 36° 30') two great chains diverge to the south—the Blue Ridge of great height but smoothed contour and developed on igneous rocks, and the Bald, Great, Smoky, and Unaka Mountains, of sharper relief, developed on metamorphic rocks. These enclose between them a great intermont region seldom less than 4,000 feet in height and of smooth but very irregular relief. To the west are the broad flat cultivated plains of the South Appalachian Valley, to the east the gently rolling and usually cultivated Piedmont. Between, rises this wedge of rugged, forested, mountain mass, with few inhabitants and few means of communication. Only three railways cross for a distance of 300 miles to the south of Grandfather Mountain. To the north the Blue Ridge is represented by a series of single ranges, viz. the Blue Ridge of Virginia, Catoctin Mountains (Maryland), and South Mountains (Pennsylvania), and by the Highlands of New Jersey. Topographically, they are the easternmost of the Appalachian Valley ridges, structurally the westernmost heights of the Piedmont. They are frequently crossed by wind and water gaps and the prevalence of these, combined with the relatively low altitudes, *make the Great Appalachian Valley particularly accessible from the Piedmont in Pennsylvania and Maryland.*

The Piedmont Plateau is completely misnamed. It has none of the characteristics of a Piedmont alluvial plain, and few of of those of a plateau. Seen from the real mountains of the Blue Ridge, it has the aspect of an undulating plain. From the foot of the Blue Ridge it slopes gently eastwards at the rate of 20 feet per mile, i.e. from about 1,000 feet to 1,200 feet on the west, to 400 feet to 500 feet on the east.

Its low rounded summits have a common elevation and represent a tilted peneplain. Above this general level, however, especially in the south, are numerous residual heights and irregular ridges testifying to the absence of complete peneplanation. The tertiary uplift has intensified the action of the streams, and in the mid-Piedmont these are frequently in deeply dissected valleys, and as frequently obstructed by falls.

This is the real remnant of the ancient continental mass and it is composed mainly of gneisses, gabbros, schists, quartzites, etc., with intrusions of granite. These are of different hardnesses, but being irregularly distributed have not led to a regular drainage scheme. Since the uplift, the master streams have maintained their courses across bands of varying resistance, developing wide valleys in the less resistant rocks and narrow ones in those of greater hardness. A slight monoclinal flexure and a series of faults with eastern down-throw mark the limit now reached by the most western extension of the coast plain deposits, and most of the streams develop rapids at, or within a few miles of, this junction.

Over large areas the characteristic rocks, soils and relief

of the Piedmont are entirely masked by the presence of sand-stone, shales and thin limestone beds deposited in Triassic times. These were accumulated in narrow trough-like depressions in the Piedmont. In regions of rugged relief such as obtains in the hard crystalline rocks of Nova Scotia and New England, the relative softness of the triassic material has led to valley development and we get the sheltered Annapolis and Connecticut valley lowlands. Further south a complete peneplanation has bevelled the Triassic series to the same level as the surrounding crystalline masses, and the presence of the beds is evidenced by a greater general fertility rather than by very marked topographical differences.[1]

Let us briefly summarize some of the controlling factors in this great system of relief south of the Hudson. The northern rivers, e.g. Susquehanna, Potomac, and their tributaries, rise just east of the Cumberland Plateau and flow to the Atlantic, while in the south, the Kentucky and Tennessee tributaries rise in the Great Valley and flow to the Mississippi. The New River rises near the Blue Ridge and cuts right across the highest part of the Great Valley ranges and of the Cumberland Plateau, to the Mississippi drainage. The Great Valley, then, in the north (Pennsylvania, Maryland and Virginia) was most accessible from the east by water and wind gaps in the Blue Ridge. In the south it was most accessible from the west via the Cumberland and Chattanooga gaps in the Cumberland Plateau Front. The great mountain masses which represent the Blue Ridge in the south entirely blocked access from the east. The easiest movement and most fertile lands were in the parallel north-east to south-west valleys of the Great Valley itself.

North of the Hudson the mountains of New England, of the Canadian Atlantic Provinces and of Newfoundland, represent a continuation of the Appalachian Province. Much of this country, too, consists of Palæozoic rocks which have been closely folded, uplifted, peneplained, and raised again. The folds generally were on the same north-east to south-west axis as those to the south of the Hudson and the result is shown in the general trend of the valleys and of the headlands and gulfs, e.g. of Nova Scotia. It is much more difficult, however, to relate the main present relief and drainage to the outstanding events of the geological history, for the following reasons :

First of all, the period of folding began more early in the

[1] For a physiographical account of the Appalachians, see " The Northern Appalachians," by Bailey Willis ; and " The Southern Appalachians," by C. Willard Hayes, in " The Physiography of the United States."

north than to the south of the Hudson. The Carboniferous rocks of Nova Scotia and New Brunswick are little disturbed, yet south of the Hudson the chief disturbances were post-Carboniferous. Then the disturbances were accompanied by igneous intrusions and by metamorphism, which are not paralleled in the south. Finally, glaciation has greatly modified the drainage. The folded yet unresistant rocks of the Hudson and Richelieu passage-way may properly be considered a continuation of the Great Appalachian Valley—here limited to a single valley—and the Taconic Mountains of New England, and the inclined peneplain to the east of them, represent a physiographic continuation of the Blue Ridge and Piedmont respectively (for relief, see Fig. 85, p. 358).

Such in general outline are the Eastern Cordillera. Less extensive, less really mountainous than those in the west, they were of far greater historical significance. In the eighteenth century they provided a wholesome check to a too rapid development of the young body of the British colonies, a check making for consolidation of strength, and one preventing the dissipation of energy and liability to disease apparent in the stooping form and sprawling limbs of the French colonial growth.

The seventeenth was the century of the tide-water colony. The eighteenth saw the occupation of the Piedmont and of the Northern Appalachian valleys, and the first half of the nineteenth that of the middle-west. This advance was not the outcome of a continuous and peaceful penetration. For much of the eighteenth century, Europe was the scene of destructive and interminable wars. Victims of religious persecution and refugees from devastated lands alike sought the asylum of the New World, only to find themselves embroiled in the quarrels of their respective mother countries. Indeed, the virgin country with its incitement to the lust of possession, provided its own occasions of dispute. International struggles in the New World were not strictly coterminous with the actual European outbreaks.

The entry of the French via the St. Lawrence and the lines of communication afforded by the Great Lakes and Mississippi systems, resulted in their occupancy of the country beyond the Eastern Cordillera, and postponed for some decades the inevitable struggle. And when at length this came, the strategy of either side was directed, as was that of the later Wars, of Independence, of 1812, and of the Civil War, by certain major physical features of the Appalachian system. So, also, in the intervals of peace, the positions of settlements, the lines of advance and of trade communications, were largely controlled by these same physical features.

That we may understand this, let us examine a little what was the general nature of the French advance in the late seventeenth and early eighteenth centuries, and turn then to the contemporary progress made by the English colonies. We have already noticed how La Salle's great journey to the mouth of the Mississippi indicated alike the line of French advance, and the geographical factors controlling that advance. But the seventeenth century saw few real settlements, apart from the river border farms of the *habitant* from Quebec to Montreal, and the Annapolis Valley colony. For the rest, there were small military ports and fur-trading stations at such strategic points as Fort Frontenac, Fort Michillimackinac and Fort Miami. But in the whole of the seventeenth century there were never more than a few hundred Frenchmen to the west of Montreal, though individual traders, *coureurs de bois*, and missionaries had made prodigious journeys over the great water system of the Central plains of North America. Indeed, in the decade (1680–89) preceding the War of the Palatinate—King William's war as it was known in America—the French colonies were in a very bad way. They suffered from a too rigid control by the mother country, a corrupt officialdom, and from the weak rule of La Barre and his successor Denonville as governors. We have already noticed how the traditional animosity of the Iroquois had diverted French influence to the Ottawa and Lake Superior routes westward, and away from the nearer and more obvious Ontario, Erie and Ohio country. In the decade under consideration the Indians grew yet bolder ; Fort Frontenac was given up and the country between the Ottawa and St. Lawrence itself was rendered dangerous to the French. The European War of 1689–93 had of course its counterpart in America and at the outset the French were fortunate in recovering the firm control of Frontenac as governor of Canada. He re-established Fort Frontenac, sent a post to Michillimackinac —note the obvious strategic importance of these—and set about a plan for attacking the British colonies. At this date, and in contrast to the later French-British struggle, there were no French in the Ohio region and no British in the Great Appalachian Valley, so that the only lines of effective contact were :—

(i) Hudson-Lake Champlain, or Hudson-Mohawk-Oswego routes, to the St. Lawrence system.
(ii) The sparsely settled border country between Nova Scotia and Maine.
(iii) Strategic points at the mouth of the St. Lawrence.
(iv) The islands of the Caribbean Sea.

Thus Frontenac in 1689 sent out three parties—the first

from Montreal to the Upper Hudson.   This surprised Schenectady, but then retreated before a British force from Albany.   The
second went from Three Rivers and attacked Salmon Fall on the
border and then, joining the third party from Quebec, captured
and destroyed the frontier stations of Casco Bay.   So also in the
counter-blows of the British.   Delegates from New England
colonies at New York—note this first feeble essay at co-operation under the stimulus of external menace—met to determine
upon a common military policy.   Their plans included a land
expedition via the Hudson-Champlain route to Montreal, and
an expedition by sea to take Quebec.   The first reached the
southern shore of Lake Champlain, was decimated by sickness
and retreated.   In the second Admiral Phipps on an advance
expedition with seven vessels took Port Royal (Acadia) in 1690 ;
but on a second expedition with thirty vessels, took two months
to reach the Upper St. Lawrence, there only to suffer a reverse
below Quebec.   Further, we lost all Hudson Bay stations but
one, and had distinctly the worst of it in the Maine border raids.
Meanwhile, small islands were changing hands in the Caribbean.
By the Treaty of Ruyswick, however, captured places were
restored.   So far, Great Britain had had the worst of it, and
this was a symptom of the naval power which enabled France
to put forces at the disposal of her colonies, and not at all of
the relative strength of the settlements in America.

In a few years the growing power of France and especially
her dominance of Spain, led to that attempt to regain a balance
of power in Europe which we call the War of the Spanish Succession.   In America the British colonies found themselves
confronted with hostile Spanish forces in the south and those
of France in the north.   Lack of effective settlement on either
side of the Appalachians still prohibited a point of contact directly
across the barrier.   The Maine border was again the scene
of ruthless raids of the French and their Indian allies.   These
reached as far as Deerfield in Connecticut and within a short
distance even of Boston.   The importance of the St. Lawrence
outposts is indicated by the successive attacks and final capture
of Acadia.

Once again, too, the British plans consisted of a twofold
expedition against Canada—one via the Hudson-Champlain,
directed against Montreal, and one by sea against Quebec.
The latter was really quite a major operation and Admiral
Walker, General Sir John Hill, seven of Marlborough's veteran
regiments and 1,500 colonials entered the St. Lawrence in August,
1711, only to be wrecked on the reefs and shoals of Egg Island.
In view of this disaster, the Hudson expedition was abandoned.

All this on the northern frontier. To the south there was— at this period—little penetration in the great triangle of country between the Gulf and Atlantic coast plain, yet the Spanish and South Carolina coast settlements were mutually accessible to sea raids. A Charleston raiding naval force burnt St. Augustin in Spanish Florida (1702). A return attack on Charleston was unsuccessful. Both sides here, as on the northern frontier, continued to enlist the services of the local Indians. There were, further, the usual trials of naval strength in West Indian raids. The Treaty of Utrecht initiated a period of comparative calm in North America. The chief terms affecting subsequent developments were the granting of Acadia, Newfoundland and certain Hudson Bay territories to the English ; of the strategic- ally important Cape Breton Island guarding the mouth of the St. Lawrence to the French ; and the Asiento, giving England an exclusive slave-carrying right to Spanish possessions for thirty years. Also one vessel might trade yearly with Spanish- American ports.

Meanwhile, the French had begun an occupation of the Mis- sissippi valley. We have not space here to follow this out in detail, but in outline we perceive a definite French policy to separate the Spaniard by driving a wedge of settlement down the Mississippi to the sea and at the same time to prevent the emergence of the British beyond the Appalachians. The succes- sive Canadian governors, Iberville and Bienville, were the lead- ing spirits. Thus in 1702, Iberville explored the lower Missis- sippi and planted French stations on the Gulf, viz. Bilexi and Fort Louis. Bienville built Fort Toulouse, whence furs were floated to Mobile Bay. Still avoiding the nearer lakes, the French continued to use the Lake Superior and Michigan port- ages, and about the junction of the Missouri and Ohio with the main stream, a number of fur-trading, and also of actual farm- ing settlements grew up in Illinois. These Illinois settlements, together with those of the lower settlements (Louisiana), were handed to one Crozat, as proprietary governor, and he, making nothing by them, surrendered his patent in 1717. After a brief period of company [1] management, the whole great area became a royal province. New Orleans was founded in 1719 and at once ensued the tiny beginnings of what was to become a great stream of river traffic from the central states to the Mississippi mouth.

Peltries and even grain were sent in this period from the Illinois stations, and the division between St. Lawrence and Gulf fur trade came, as we should expect, at the line of low-water

---

[1] John Law and his *Compagnie des Indes.*

parting between the Great Lakes and the head-stream of the Mississippi system. In the period 1720–1740 many new French stations appeared at strategic points on the Mississippi River system. They show at a glance the dependence of French advance on waterway and canoe traffic and low and short portages, as also the general character of their occupation with its slender lines of isolated forts—its mere handful of people strung out over enormous distances.

In 1743 there were only 3,200 French and 2,000 slaves in the Louisiana district and 1,500 French in Illinois. The whole system had extensions to the west along (i) the complicated system of waterways occurring in the glaciated country west of Lake Superior and comprising the Lakes Rainy, Winnipeg, Winnipegosis and their connecting links—a line of easy advance for fur trade and canoe traffic, (ii) the Missouri Red River and Arkansas tributaries of the Mississippi, an advance which ultimately threatened the Spanish in New Mexico. Yet down to 1740 the French had not any station in the Iroquois country south of Erie and Ontario, or on the Upper Ohio.

Meanwhile great progress had been made by the British to the east of the Appalachians. At the end of the seventeenth century the population was about one-quarter million ; by 1740 it had increased to 1,000,000. Where there is an abundance of the necessities of life, and work and welcome for each new pair of hands, the birth-rate is high, yet much of this increase was due to immigration. Such immigration was encouraged, for the home government was quite aware of the striking progress of the French since the Treaty of Utrecht. At the end of the seventeenth century the better estuarine lands (i.e. apart from marsh lands and sand belts) were taken up as far south as Albemarle Sound. Then came 200 miles of unoccupied country and then the isolated settlement of South Carolina. To protect these from Spanish raids from the south, the government granted a charter to Oglethorpe in 1732 for lands between the Savannah and Altamahah Rivers. Oglethorpe's altruism took the form of a penchant for the debtor class, and it was partly of these that the original Georgia was formed. In 1733 Savannah was founded. By 1737 the river had been followed to the Fall Line and there Augusta was made an Indian trail and trade centre. By the early eighteenth century, too, a series of retaliatory raids had put an end to any serious Indian menace in all the coastal states. For many years to come there was to be a constant possibility of Indian trouble on the frontiers of settlements, but after King Philip's War (New England), the Susquehanna War (Virginia), the Tuscarora War (North Carolina), and the Tennessee War

(South Carolina) an organized and serious opposition to advance was not to be expected.

When we come to examine the rapid growth of the colonies in the period 1700–60, we see that apart from the quota due to natural increase, it took place under the influence of certain definite stimuli which may be enumerated as follows :—Firstly we have to remember that a very large part of the early colonists were indentured servants. That is to say, they were paying for their transport from England and their keep, by a period of servitude of from five to seven years. As these in time became free men, they sought homesteads of their own on the cheap unoccupied country further inland. Again, as we have already noticed, primitive methods of farming led to a rapid deterioration of land and a tendency to take up virgin lands further inland. These two are, of course, factors of extension rather than of increase in population. The increase of the eighteenth century and late seventeenth can be ascribed very largely to the great German and Scots-Irish streams of emigration. Thus from 1680–1700 we have a stream of German persecuted sects, seeking the shelter of Penn's hospitable colony and founding settlements, each with its distinctive tenets. More numerous bodies arrived after the devastation of much of south-west Germany in 1707. London became full of German refugees and these were passed on to the colonies. Some of them remained at tide-water, but the majority were passed inland. They settled on both banks of the Hudson and to a greater extent on the Mohawk. But the greatest stream of all made for Philadelphia and were distributed in Pennsylvania. The leasehold land system of New York did not appeal to the colonist who, if landing there, would usually pass on to Pennsylvania. It is just in this colony particularly that entrances to the Great Appalachian Valley are most numerous and least difficult.

The middle Susquehanna basin was soon occupied, and settlers followed the trend of the Great Appalachian Valley to the south through Maryland into Virginia. By 1740 the fertile Shenandoah was occupied with a string of settlements and the northern half of these were largely German. So great was the influx of Germans into Pennsylvania that the preservation of the English language was at this period a matter of some concern. Smaller numbers entered the Meuse and Trent settlements of North Carolina, and others again founded Ebenezer and Frederica in Georgia.

Hard on the heels of the Germans came the Scots-Irish. These had a multitude of grievances in the oppressive measures affecting Irish trade, and in particular, after 1714, in the very general increase in Irish rents. All colonies received them, yet again the greatest number sought Pennsylvania. They were usually passed through to the frontier and the penetration of the Scots-Irish goes a stage further than that of the German. But it was on the same lines. They completed the occupation of the Piedmont in Pennsylvania and swarmed over the narrow ridged gaps into the Great Valley. They followed the German through Maryland into the Shenandoah, overtook him in the valley, and using the notches in the Blue Ridge, made their exit back to the Piedmont again in Virginia and Carolina, there to be slightly augmented by new-comers direct from tide-water. They thus followed the natural south-west trend of the fertile Appalachian valleys and avoided the endless swamps and transverse streams which added so much difficulty to any movement parallel to the coastline on the coast plain.

In general the Scots-Irish belt extended further south and further west than that of the German. It became the frontier zone *par excellence*. By 1750 the Piedmont of Pennsylvania and Maryland was almost completely occupied, and the eastern Appalachian Valley to the southern Shenandoah. The Piedmont of Virginia was loosely settled and scattered settlers had appeared on the Yadkin and at various other points of the Carolina Piedmont.

This great Piedmont belt of settlement entering mainly via New York and Philadelphia and inserted, as it were, behind the middle and southern tide-water colonies, evinced certain characteristics arising from its mode of origin and of advance ; characteristics which gave it a kind of unity of political sympathies often in opposition to the older tide-water populations to the east. For in the first place, the Piedmont settler was often of different race—German or Scots-Irish. He was usually poor and acquired a portion of ground small in comparison with the southern tide-water plantations. Above tide-water and therefore cut off from easy trading communications, he became more self-sufficing than his brother colonist of the coastal plain. He engaged in subsistence farming and eschewed the staple farming for export. He grew and manufactured his own wool and linen. In the southern Piedmont particularly the extent of unoccupied land provided ample room for his herds of cattle and of swine—the one product which could transport itself. The southern Piedmont was the eighteenth-century representative of the modern western ranch lands. Individual material progress was so obviously the result of initiative, resource, and hard work that the Frontiersmen became, at the same time, intensely individualistic, democratic and adventurous.

Their position in the frontier zone made them most alive to danger from the Indian and from advancing French settlement. Their position above tide-water emphasized the need for means of communication for the exchange of commodities with the coast plain region.

Politically, then, there was apt to be a line of kindred sympathy striking across the western halves of the colonies and giving a certain unity to the people of the Piedmont, and a division between east and west, tide-water and Piedmont, in each colony.

We must envisage the French-English struggle as having its immediate cause in the steady advance of the two populations —as something inevitable and casually independent of the relations of the mother countries, though, of course, the seasons of its most active prosecution coincided with the period of actual European warfare. In the mid-eighteenth century were two such periods, that of the War of the Austrian Succession, 1743–48, and the Seven Years' War, 1756–63. In reality the inclusive period 1740–63 may be looked upon as one of armed struggle as far as America was concerned. Here we may discern two main common motives. First, the old one : the desire to gain an exclusive diversion of the fur trade to the St. Lawrence by the French, and to the Hudson by the English. Secondly, the struggle was consequent upon the almost simultaneous appearance of the French and English in the Ohio country—the French having overcome, in part at any rate, the Iroquois barrier and wishing to develop the Lake Erie-Ohio route westward—and the bulge in the advance of the English mid-colonies having brought the frontiers of these to the upper waters of the Ohio. The outcome of this actual struggle was largely determined by (a) the relative vulnerability of the French long and weak chain of settlements, (b) the relative support which could be afforded by the home countries, and this again largely depended on the question of naval supremacy. The strategy and the zones of contact were a matter of pure geography. What were these zones of contact ? Well, first there were the two main naval areas. The West Indian Islands settlements were often in themselves vulnerable, especially to raids, and some of them provided also naval bases. Success or failure here, except in so far as it was accompanied by considerable naval losses, was not likely to affect the campaign vitally. Then there was the St. Lawrence itself considered either as a passage-way for direct attack on the chief French settlements, Quebec and Montreal; or in respect of the importance of naval bases at the mouth commanding the supply ship route from France.

On land, too, there were two main contact areas. First,

the ever-important Hudson-Mohawk gap providing (a) a route for direct attack on the St. Lawrence settlement via Lake Champlain by the British, or on New York by the French, (b) a route via the Mohawk by which the British might seek to sever the French chain of lake communications at strategic points such as Oswego, Frontenac or Niagara. Secondly, there was the Upper Ohio district. Here the student should examine both the relief and drainage carefully. He will notice that the south fork of the Susquehanna, the Youghiogheny, and the Potomac, after traversing a portion of the grid-like formation of the Appalachian Valley, lead up to the difficult country of the Alleghany Front, which, if crossed in the head-water basins of these streams, leads to a portion of the Cumberland Plateau included within the two arms of the Upper Ohio—the Allegheny and the Monongahela Rivers. However the pioneer crosses the Appalachians in this zone, he must fall within the embrace of these great streams, both—from the point of view of pioneer movement —navigable. A further point to notice is the short portage between Presqu' Isle, French Creek and the Upper Allegheny. In fact, we have here the shortest and most easterly of the whole series of low-water partings between the Great Lakes and Mississippi systems, and a route which would have been used much earlier by the French but for the Iroquois occupation. The merest enumeration, and it is for this only we have space, of the moves, counter-moves and engagements which took place, will indicate very clearly the strategic importance of these areas.

We have seen that the British had occupied some of the Mohawk Valley by the beginning of the eighteenth century. In 1727 Governor Burnett of New York planted a fort at Oswego, hoping to divert more and more of the fur trade to New York. During the war of the Austrian Succession, the French fortified Louisberg on Cape Breton Island (1744) and throughout the struggle great importance attached to this place. Thus it fell in 1745 to 4,000 New England volunteers, but was among the places returned to France at the peace of Aix-la-Chapelle. But by far the most effective results of this war were those attained by the British Navy. In 1745 Admiral Rowley destroyed a considerable French force in the West Indies. In 1746 storms prevented the operation of a French fleet endeavouring to recover Louisberg and Acadia. In 1747 Warren and Anson intercepted and completely defeated a second French fleet bound for Louisberg; this time off Cape Finisterre. Later in the same year a French convoy fleet was captured in the West Indies.

With her much smaller colonial population, her greater

dependence on home supplies, and her scattered holdings, it was vital that France should have uninterrupted communication with the St. Lawrence, and these naval catastrophes were the prelude to her final overthrow. When Louisberg was restored at the peace, France immediately set about strengthening it and added another St. Lawrence fortress in Beausejour, on the isthmus connecting Nova Scotia and New Brunswick. To strengthen the position against an unsympathetic Acadia, the British gathered some hundreds of emigrants and founded Halifax, thus again emphasizing the importance of naval stations on the great circle route to Europe and at the mouth of the St. Lawrence. Meanwhile the British had been diverting more and more of the fur trade to New York, had improved their standing with the Iroquois and were just beginning to send their fur traders to the Upper Ohio, which they had received in grant from the Indians.

The French replied with a fort at Rouillé (site of Toronto), another at the Niagara portage, and strengthened Detroit and Sault St. Marie. So far there had been no real contact in the Ohio region. Neither party had any real settlers within many miles of the Alleghany Plateau, but the preparations of each were made known by Indians and fur traders, and every move had its counter-move. So we have the French governor of Canada in 1749 sending Céloron de Bienville by the natural portage route, Lake Erie to Lake Chautauqua and the Upper Allegheny and thence down the Ohio to return via the Wabash portage and Fort Miami. A chain of forts here would have completed the French occupancy of all the Great Lakes and Mississippi portages. De Bienville in default of forts left something less substantial in the inscribed tin sheets and sunken leaden plates, by which he attested the claims of his King to the region. In 1753, however, Governor Duquesne seriously set about the task of holding this region for France. Fort Presqu' Isle (later Erie) was erected, a road built over the portage to French Creek and a fort planned at the junction of the Allegheny and Monongahela —a point of immense strategic importance. And all this soon came to the ears of the Governor of Virginia, Dinwiddie. Virginia, jealous of the western extension of Pennsylvania, had followed up the Iroquois grant of the Ohio country with the formation of an Ohio Company to stimulate trade and settlement. Christopher Gist surveyed the country, followed the Ohio to the rapids of Louisville and reported favourably. A trail was blazed from the site of the present town of Cumberland to the Monongahela. Dinwiddie at once sent Washington, guided by Gist, to the forks of the Ohio and up the Allegheny

4

to Fort le Bœuf, to inform the French of the claims of Virginia to the region and to request their withdrawal. This was firmly refused and from this moment we may date (1753) the outbreak of hostilities in America, though the actual European struggle between France and Great Britain did not open until three years later.

On his return, Washington was again immediately sent to occupy the Ohio forks. A few backwoodsmen were sent in advance to build a fort. They were captured by the French, who immediately built Fort Duquesne (Pittsburgh later) for themselves and despatched thence a force which completely defeated Washington's little squad at Fort Necessity. And now we see the beginning of union among the states under the influence of this external menace. The colonies were exceedingly jealous of their individual independence, entirely taken up with their own concerns, impatient of the responsibilities and restraints inevitable in any scheme of confederacy. And, indeed, it was uphill work for Virginia to get any support from her sister colonies until they themselves had realized the danger. In 1754, a meeting of representatives of New York, Pennsylvania, Maryland and New England colonies was held at Albany and failed to agree on any plan of union, even for purposes of war.

The home government took the matter up more seriously and despatched the ill-fated Braddock with two regular regiments in 1755. Braddock summoned the state governors to meet him in council, and it is interesting from the geographical point of view to note his plan of campaign. He himself would take a force against Fort Duquesne, other land forces were directed under Johnson to Crown Point (Lake Champlain route) and under Shirley to Niagara (Mohawk route). Lieutenant-Colonel Moncton was to attack Fort Beausejour from the sea. Factors of relief and waterway decided that these should be the points of contact, but it would probably have been wiser of Braddock to have made sure of cutting the French communication at Niagara and of commanding the Lower St. Lawrence in the first instance. If this had been done, Pittsburg and the Lake forts would have fallen through lack of supplies. Only perfect timing could have resulted in the success of his fourfold scheme.

Actually he himself was killed and his force severely defeated in an ambush just short of Fort Duquesne. The French could then send forces from Fort Duquesne to reinforce Niagara. They also sent large reinforcements to Fort Frontenac, and Shirley, who reached Oswego, felt himself unable to proceed. Johnson defeated a French force at Lake St. George, but did not follow up his success. Only at sea were we successful, for

Moncton landed his force and captured Fort Beausejour. The French in Acadia refused the oath of allegiance and the ugly business of their deportation was undertaken. The arrival of Montcalm added stimulus to the French efforts and while the colonists fumbled with their plans, he captured Oswego, our one Lake fort, and obliged Loudoun to withdraw from the Ticonderoga attack. Next year Montcalm's forces were successful at the southern end of Lake George and he was within striking distance of the key town of Albany. The success which came to the British in the later stages of the war was entirely due to the steady preparations made under Pitt's rule in the home country. The navy made it difficult for the French to reinforce her colonies ; Abercrombie superseded the unsuccessful Loudoun as commander-in-chief in America ; and considerable reinforcements of regular troops were despatched.

Naval forces used the new settlement of Halifax as a rendezvous and proceeded to the successful attack of Louisberg in 1758, where thousands of French soldiers were captured. This gave the British the most commanding position in the St. Lawrence Gulf. Amhurst, however, lost to the French under Montcalm before Ticonderoga and retired to Lake St. George again. But in default of reinforcements from France, Montcalm had been obliged to weaken the Lake forts and Fort Frontenac fell to a large force under Bradstreet. Communications with Erie and the Ohio were thus cut and the now small garrison of Fort Duquesne scattered at the approach of large forces under Forbes. Only the Lake Champlain route now remained to be forced, but before this was further pressed the command of the lower St. Lawrence was used to support a direct attack on Quebec. Wolfe and a large flotilla with some 18,000 men advanced directly on Quebec and for long could make no impression on the French fortifications. All the world knows with what success he moved much of his force to a point above the city, the while feigning a major attack below. In spite of desperate efforts to recapture it, Quebec remained with the British. The major French forces were hemmed in between Quebec and the British forces holding lower Ontario and upper Lake Champlain. Successful advance from all three directions led to the fall of Montreal, and the end of French dominion in America. The terms of the Treaty of Paris which applied to America, ceded Canada to England, and also all of Louisiana east of the Mississippi.

CHAPTER VI

EARLIEST SETTLEMENT IN KENTUCKY

WE have seen that for some years before the actual outbreak of the Seven Years' War, France and England
had been brought into conflict in North America by
the progress of their pioneers on three separate frontiers, viz.
the Northern Maine border, the Hudson-Mohawk passages, and
the Upper Ohio tributaries. The British outlying settlements,
which had just begun to attain the Monongahela, the Greenbrier, and the Holston rivers, were withdrawn during the war.
At the Peace of Paris, 1763, the way was left more open for a
general advance westward, but there were still obstacles. In
the first place, Louisiana (then practically the whole region west
of the Mississippi, but including New Orleans) had been ceded
by Louis XV to Spain in 1762—a vast area sparsely populated
in a few river forts, and mainly by Frenchmen. True, there
was first a revolt of these French against the rule of their new
governors, but after the foolish attempt of Spain to limit New
Orleans trade to Spanish shipping had failed, a fairly rigorous
rule was established, and the trade from New Orleans became
considerable. The danger from Spain was literally more remote
than had been that from France, yet it existed. More immediate obstacles to British advance were the attitude of the home
government on the one hand, and of the Indian on the other.
Signs had not been wanting—even before the war—of a small
but growing spirit of independence among the colonists. The
French conflict, if it proved how complete was the dependence
of the colonies of that period upon the home forces, yet in its
successful conclusion led to some feeling of interdependence
among the colonies themselves, for before the close of the war
large bodies of colonial troops had been engaged and under a
unified command. The colonies were beginning to feel their
strength. If the townsman or farmer in the stable conditions
of the tide-water regions had little understanding of, or sympathy with, his fellow-colonist of the western frontier, how
much less was to be expected from a government distant 3,000
miles! The military plans for the preservation of the new war

lands, as well as the Proclamation of 1763 providing for their government, alike betrayed the attitude of the home country. As things were, so they were to remain. The colonies must realize their dependence on the mother-country; were to be protected against the Spanish and the disaffected French; and that this might be the more easily done, were not encouraged to enlarge their boundaries.

The newly won St. Lawrence, from the lakes to the sea, with its 60,000 French inhabitants, became the Province of Quebec; Spanish Florida became East Florida, and the old French country between the Appalachicola River and the Mississippi, and extending to lat. 31°, became West Florida. Otherwise, the whole of the middle-west, i.e. between lat. 31° and the Great Lakes, and between the Appalachians and the Mississippi, was reserved as Crown lands for the use of the Indians. Incidentally, a vast portion of this area to the south of the Ohio was not settled regularly by any Indian tribe, but had long been a great hunting preserve visited by various tribes both from the north and the south. The home government then looked for no immediate expansion.

Again, though the French-English struggle naturally was concentrated mostly in the eastern and more populous region, isolated French forts on the middle and western lakes and Upper Mississippi, though nominally given over, were actually unoccupied by British troops. Pontiac, the Ottawa chief, combining with the Algonquins of the lake region, and with the disgruntled French of those western posts, rebelled against the British rule, and for a period (1763-5), though the British managed to keep Detroit, Fort Pitt (Pittsburg), and Niagara, the lakes and the Upper Mississippi were closed against them. This was the last organized and very considerable resistance of the Indians, and was overcome—partly by negotiation—in 1765. For many years the frontiersman went in danger of his life from the Indian, but attacks were sporadic, unorganized and on a smaller scale.

Now, both immediately before and immediately after the war, stray hunters and trappers had travelled beyond the Appalachians, but the only significant journeys were those made for the definite purpose of survey and report. Prominent among these we must include those undertaken by Dr. Thomas Walker and by Christopher Gist. It is significant of the interest already (1751) taken in the near west that these gentlemen journeyed each as the representative surveyor of a land company. Johnson's " First Explorations of Kentucky "[1] contains the journal of

[1] Filson Club Publications, No. 13.

these expeditions and a map of the routes. Briefly, we may point out that Gist, taking the Potomac route westward, passed through Old Town, Fort Ligonier, Pittsburg, and Logstown, crossed the Muskingum at Coshocton, and thence via the Scioto to the Ohio (near Bolivar), which he followed for over 100 miles. Then leaving the river and proceeding southwards from Pilot's Knob (near Clay City, Powell County), he caught a glimpse of the fine park-like Blue Grass country which a few years later was to prove such an attraction to immigrants. It was but a glimpse, however, and then he turned south-eastward to his home on the Yadkin, crossing much high and difficult, and some sterile, country of the Cumberland plateau, before his recrossing of the Appalachians. He had seen splendid land in Northern Ohio, and had had a glimpse of the most fertile areas of Kentucky, and but for the outbreak of war, the Ohio Company would have soon been sending settlers. Walker's report was less favourable. His journey was interesting chiefly because he in part followed a route which was to become historic —that followed later by Boone to the Cumberland Gap—and because he was the first to give an account, however incomplete, of that difficult, relatively sterile, country which forms so much of the eastern part of the Cumberland plateau. Entering the Shenandoah valley, his party moved southward, crossed the New River, passed westward to the Holston valley, over Walden and Powell ridges, and so to Cumberland Gap. So far they were much in the line of the later Wilderness Road of Boone, but instead of following thence the Indian trail which led north-west to the Blue Grass region, they turned north too soon, and got among the head branches of the Kentucky River in a poor and hilly country, until they concluded "there was no good country in the west." Then then took an easterly course "over the worst mountains and laurel thickets in the world." The reader is asked to notice at once this early reference to the prevalence of difficult, high, infertile country which characterizes the eastern half of the Cumberland plateau,[1] especially in the centre and south, and which separates the fertile strips of the Great Appalachian valley from the extremely attractive Blue Grass areas further west in Kentucky. And at this stage let us look a little more carefully at the geographical control evinced in this trans-Alleghany westward movement. In Chapter V we summarized the main structural features of the Appalachians and concluded that the division between the physiographical

[1] Cf. "Kentucky," by N. S. Shaler, p. 27. "West of Pine Mt." (i.e. part of Cumberland edge) "was a region 50 miles in width, where the soil was lean and of little worth to the pioneers."

units known respectively as the Appalachian valley and the Cumberland plateau, was really a zone rather than a line—a zone in which, more or less rapidly, the extreme structural folding of the valley gave way to the gentle swelling of the strata characteristic of the plateau, with consequent results in denudation which have led to the present surface relief. At some points this slab of roughly horizontal strata which is the Cumberland plateau terminates in a great escarpment overlooking the most westerly of the Appalachian parallel valleys ; at others the intense folding characteristic of the valley region gives way more gradually to a series of gentle swellings, and the dissection of the resulting low anticlines has led to narrow straight-edged valleys separating broad belts of plateau ridge. It is characteristic of the Alleghany Front through much of its length to be a line of severe faulting. Settlers or travellers entering the Shenandoah through the many gaps in the northern Blue Ridge at once came under the directive influence of the whole Appalachian valley system. The easiest relief, the best watered and most fertile lands kept them ever moving south-west with the general trend of the system. True, even the valley later begins to reach considerable heights towards the centre of the system where a marked structural uplift on an east and west axis has caused the greatest heights of all the Great Valley ridges about the New River system, and the Upper Kentucky and Tennessee. The same uplift has caused an emergence of the land giving a coastal extension of the continent about Cape Hatteras. Here in crossing the New River system the traveller passes from streams whose course, after leaving the Great Valley, is to the Atlantic, to those which ultimately reach the Mississippi. The great masses of high irregular relief formed by the Unaka and Smoky Mountains now turned the traveller a little to the west, towards the valleys of the Clinch, Powell, and Holston.

". . . this valley is formed by Cumberland Mountain on the north-west, and Powell Mountain on the south-east, and appears to bear from north-east south-westwardly, and is, I suppose, about 100 miles in length and from 10 to 12 miles in breadth. The land generally is good, and is an exceedingly well-watered country, as well as the country on Holstein River, abounding with fine springs and little brooks. For about 50 miles, as you travel along the valley, Cumberland Mountain appears to be a very high ridge of white rocks, inaccessible in most places to either man or beast, and affords a wild, romantic prospect." [1] This escarpment, backed by the unpromising lands

[1] From an early itinerary quoted in Thomas Speed's " Wilderness Road," pp. 18–20.

of the Cumberland plateau, barred the westward exit from the Great Valley until the Cumberland Gap was reached.

If we look at a geological map of the area just to the west of the physiographical region of the Cumberland plateau, we notice that the surface exposure of carboniferous (Pennsylvanian-Mississippian) rocks which form most of the surface is interrupted by inliers of Devonian, Silurian, and Ordovician rocks in the north, about the Cincinnati bend of the Ohio, and in the south, about Nashville.

These are two dissected domes which have suffered a sufficient denudation to expose the older, underlying Silurian and Ordovician formations. Structurally, they are not disconnected, for the two domes were simply the extremities of a great axis of uplift running from Cincinnati to south of Nashville, i.e. in a north-east to south-west direction, an uplift originating perhaps as early as Mid-Ordovician times. A sagging in this ridge has given denudation less chance in the middle region, and here the carboniferous rocks remain and form a belt separating the two regions. Relatively soft materials have been exposed within these domes, and the two areas have a noticeably lower and smoother relief than is exhibited in the surrounding plateau country. In these districts and covering large areas are many soils residual from the decay of great masses of limestone. Where there is a sufficiency of clay in the soil to prevent leaching, we get a loam notably rich in lime and in phosphates. Now by the mid-eighteenth century the colonial pioneers had been dealing with virgin soils for some 150 years. They had acquired much empirical accuracy in their estimate of a soil, an estimate based on the natural vegetation—the quality and kinds of the grasses and the timbers. Such men were quick to notice the splendid grasses and fine timber growth of the Lexington and Nashville areas, and to realize that here were better lands than any lying between them and the rather similar soils of the Appalachian valley bottoms. Elsewhere on the Cumberland plateau, altitude, intricacy of relief, and the frequent capping of hard sandstones, or a covering of a thin—too pure—limestone soil, presented a relatively unattractive terrain.

As we turn over the decennial population maps of the U.S.A. Census, the first of which is dated 1790, we can almost watch the steady movement of people to these two areas, leaving for long untouched the eastern plateau lands ; and even to-day the relative value of the land in the Nashville and Lexington Blue Grass districts is indicated in the crop density and value of farm holdings maps of these areas.

Yet, as Shaler says, speaking of the Cincinnati anticline,

" but for its uplifted back, Kentucky would have had no soil to tempt the early settlers to their new home." As we have seen, these attractive lands were made known by Gist and others, and, but for the intervention of the French war, would have been occupied sooner. Their existence was remembered, however, and schemes were soon again on foot for their acquisition. Undoubtedly the Proclamation of 1763 practically forbidding settlement west of the Appalachians delayed matters somewhat, yet there were not wanting influential men even in England who favoured its revision, and it certainly had no lasting effects. After Pontiac's failure the Indians ceded their hunting grounds between the Ohio and Tennessee, and this cession was confirmed in the Peace of Stanwix, 1768. The policy of the home government was now to regulate the taking up of the near western lands and to ensure that a gradual, protected, and orderly advance was made. Actually the matter was largely in the hands of the pioneer—the man on the spot.

From 1770–3 there was a succession of prospecting and surveying expeditions—the most noteworthy being those of Washington and of Boone. Several of these crossed the Appalachians to Pittsburg, and sailed the Ohio to the Falls (i.e. rapids at Louisville), turned south across the Blue Grass region and home via the Cumberland Gap and Great Appalachian valley —a round route which was to become characteristic of early Kentucky communication with tide-water. Boone [1] (after one unsuccessful effort) led a little colony down the Great Valley to the Cumberland Gap, and thence striking an Indian trail to the north-west, emerged in the Blue Grass region and founded the station of Boonesborough. He was of the first few of a multitude who followed over the same trail—Boone's Wilderness Road, a track eloquent of the geographical controls at work. Boone founded a permanent settlement at Boonesborough in the Blue Grass region, and from this date till the outbreak of the revolutionary struggle in 1778 there was a growing stream of settlers. The region was attained—before the opening up of the Lake Erie route—by two main trails, and the physical conditions were such that both were indirect and, even so, were difficult. The two routes were via the Ohio or via Boone's trail and Cumberland Gap, and at first glance we might have expected that the Ohio would have proved the more easy. That this was not so is evidenced both in early descriptions of the Ohio journey, and by the fact that for some decades Boone's road

---

[1] Acting for Henderson, a North Carolina land speculator, who paid £10,000 for land between the Kentucky and Cumberland River to the Cherokees—with what official authority is not clear.

was the more used. For the first few years those taking the Ohio route made for Brownsville on the Monongahela, and then by boat to Pittsburg, or direct to Pittsburg by road. This meant a considerable detour to the west, and soon pioneers began to embark at Wheeling (and Lower Wheeling) on the Ohio below Pittsburg. Now, the Ohio has a rather irregular regime, and is subject to floods. The pioneers found it forested to the banks and abounding in timber snags and sandbanks. There is abundant evidence that the earliest pioneer found the route a difficult and dangerous one. Boone's road route, too, once the settlements of the Upper Shenandoah were passed, was a lonely trail with detached settlements at increasing distances until the way crossed over the stark edges of the plateau front to the difficult and completely unsettled Laurel Wilderness country. The constant danger from the Indian is evidenced in the way in which intending pioneers arranged to make the journey in large armed parties. The revolutionary period saw a partial cessation of both streams, and it will be better to defer a further account of the western movement until we have dealt briefly with the geographical factors concerned in the conduct of the revolutionary and the 1812 wars.

CHAPTER VII

GEOGRAPHICAL FACTORS IN THE WAR OF INDEPENDENCE AND WAR OF 1812

GEOGRAPHY had its part in both the causes and conduct of the War of Independence. The greatest cause of the war, and the greatest difficulty in its prosecution by Great Britain, was constituted by the 3,000 miles of ocean which separated the two countries, and that at a period in the world's history when the oceans were more effective barriers than in these days of steam and wireless. Man's requirements, opinions, and sympathies are apt to vary with his environment, and by the end of the eighteenth century the American colonist and his stay-at-home cousin had developed societies on very divergent lines. The period of the revolution saw in Great Britain the titled landowners at the summit of their influence. Government was by a succession of cabinets of great Whig or Tory families. The limitations of the franchise, the decayed condition of many boroughs, made of each parliamentary election a mere struggle between the parties of great landowners; a struggle in which the common folk had little effective voice. It was a system legitimatized and generally accepted. Meanwhile for two centuries the American Citizen was being evolved in an environment in which initiative, foresight, and hard work were readily and obviously effective in attaining individual advantage. To the pioneer who owned his land, built his own home, grew his own crops, and arranged his own commerce, any control was abhorrent, even that of his own state legislature, still more that of a distant government.

The divergence of interests, and consequent lack of understanding exhibited between Great Britain and her American colonies, have been paralleled in the frequent struggles between older stabilized settlements and newer pioneer settlements in America herself, throughout her history; struggles which at times nearly resulted in definite separation.

At the time of the Revolution, in each colony the governor and council represented the British authority, and theoretically possessed a veto on the doings of the state assembly. The

105

latter was freely elected on a democratic basis. Actually the home authority was interested not at all in the internal affairs of the various colonies, and the external affairs—foreign commerce and relationships—were willingly left to Great Britain by colonists who were quite ready to be protected in time of war, or to ignore Acts of trade when these—as in the case of the Molasses Act, 1733—threatened to be really irksome. In general, the Navigation Acts—as we have pointed out—did not at first militate against what was the natural flow of trade, and they were of real assistance to New England trading and shipbuilding.

The administrative machinery for the internal affairs of each colony was at a minimum, and none existed for uniting and organizing the various colonies for puposes of war, policy, or commerce. Up to the time of the French-English war, the colonists had borne the evil—if evil it was—of the home government's control somewhat easily. It is true that a governor, conscientiously attempting to enforce the letter of the various trade restriction Acts, soon got into difficulties; but in general his complaints received only an indifferent attention at home, and he naturally took the line of least resistance. A longer period might have elapsed without a break but for the sequelæ of the war of 1756–63. This war found the several colonies entirely and selfishly independent. It left them with the glimmering idea of the advantages to be derived from union in face of a common danger. It certainly did not leave them united, however. Not till some years after the Declaration of Independence was there a government of the United States which really possessed and exercised some powers of control over all and each of the states.

But the war was an eye-opener to the home government as well. They had been forced to take a more detailed interest in the general economy of the colonies. They noticed that the commercial regulations were being constantly infringed, and that even in time of war certain colonists had not ceased to trade with the enemy. Above all, they realized that the protection of the colonies was an expensive business, and they sought a scheme by which the colonies should contribute toward that expense. The means adopted were unfortunate. It was not beyond the bounds of possibility that the colonial assemblies should have agreed to tax themselves in contribution to a sort of Defence fund. What the home government actually did was to tighten up the trade restriction Acts, to attempt to prevent smuggling by the use of naval vessels, to put duties on foreign sugar (a large quantity of which went regularly from the

French West Indies to New England), and on Spanish and Portuguese wines, and to use the duties definitely as revenue earmarked for the defence of America, and not solely as protective trade measures. Further, as we have seen, they presumed in the 1763 Proclamation to control the Indian policy by giving the middle west—temporarily, at any rate—as an Indian reservation. As a final exasperation there was the Stamp Act of 1764, with its duty on legal documents, newspapers, and pamphlets.

However, it does not at all belong to our purpose to follow here the details of the dreary stages by which a number of largely independent, but generally loyal colonies were transformed into so many bitterly hostile societies prepared to unite to shake off what they were beginning to regard as a tyranny. For a moment there was hope of reconciliation, when a change of government, the eloquence of Pitt, and the support of the British merchants, led to a repeal of the chief causes of offence ; but almost immediately Townshend carried on where Grenville left off, and revenue-raising duties (e.g. on tea) were again attempted. Further, the Massachusetts assembly was forbidden to meet until they had agreed to pay for the quartering of soldiers. There resulted a new uproar and a not unsuccessful attempt to boycott British goods. The American question now became a party question at home. The Whigs and Chatham took the part of the colonists, not because they had previously exhibited any great interest or sympathy with them, but chiefly in opposition to the Tories. The Tories allowed dislike of the Whigs to darken counsel which might otherwise have led to relations with the colonies less entirely wanting in sympathy and understanding. Again the duties were withdrawn save only the tea tax, and all the world knows how in 1773 the Boston folk dumped the tea of the East India Company in the harbour rather than pay duty on it. The British Government now took measures which were purely punitive—Massachusetts in particular being treated like a naughty schoolboy. Boston harbour was closed, the Massachusetts legislature was insulted, while at the same time, and as if to point the moral, the Quebec Act showed unusual consideration to our new French subjects in Canada, and incidentally encouraged their settlement north of the Ohio by adding this region to the jurisdiction of Quebec. New England vessels were forbidden the fisheries and could trade only with Great Britain.

By 1775 the colonists were virtually independent, for the governors were powerless. Colonial assemblies voted delegates to a continental Congress, Washington was appointed continental commander, and the armed struggle began.

We see, then, that by the spring of 1775 the colonies were in open revolt. The administrative connection with Great Britain had broken down. Of British forces in America there were few, however. Gage, at Boston, first came into contact with armed colonials in sending a few men to capture arms and materials which were being collected at Lexington (a little north of Boston). His men had to withdraw. A second Congress in Philadelphia now took the precautionary measure of appointing Washington Commander-in-Chief, and arranged to pay a continental army by bills of credit redeemable by the united colonies.

In June, the trained troops of Gage met with unexpected resistance and heavy losses in their frontal attacks on Bunker Hill, which they gained only at the third attack. During the summer and autumn of 1775, Washington was collecting an army, and when he was prepared to take the field about Boston in March, 1776, the British force there sailed to Halifax.

In the late autumn of '75, too, the colonists arranged a raid in Canada. Montgomery used the Hudson-Champlain route and took Montreal, and then made east to join Arnold, who had come through Maine, in an attack on Quebec. Their forces were insufficient for this purpose, but they maintained a blockade of the city till it was relieved by a British expeditionary force. The numbers engaged in these operations were insignificant.

In December the British forbade trade with the colonists, and colonial sailors were liable to impressment. All this before the Declaration of Independence and before considerable forces had reached America. In July, 1776, came the Declaration, and almost immediately serious engagements with considerable forces. The chief difficulties of the ex-colonials were their lack of funds and of munitions of war, together with the risk of a blockade which would prevent the accumulation of either. Further, the hastily improvised early Congresses had neither the legal power nor the administrative machinery for a rapid and stable organization of the colonial forces. And again, such forces as could be prevailed upon to fight away from their homes, lacked training, experience, and discipline. The difficulties of the British lay in the facts that the war was unpopular with quite half the country, that the area to be subdued was of such vast extent, and the distance from home supplies so great.

Without attempting to enumerate the details of the engagements, we will try to indicate the geographical control which in part determined the zones of conflict.

It is clear that any land attack must be through Canada, and that if the Hudson-Champlain-Mohawk zone were held by the British in sufficient force to maintain communications, then the northern colonies would be divided from the southern. If, further, the British navy were strong enough to enforce a practical cessation of trade with Western Europe, then it would only be a matter of time before the Americans submitted. Actually this was attempted. The British sent a considerable naval force which speedily rescued the St. Lawrence valley from its tiny blockading army. It despatched Admiral Howe with a still greater force to Halifax with the object of later sailing to New York and joining up with the Canadian forces who were to advance by the Champlain route. Howe allowed Washington to escape to New York after defeating him in Long Island, and then pursued him into New Jersey, leaving insufficient forces on the Hudson to make sure of the Canadian connection. Meanwhile the British attempting the gaps from the north were held up by Arnold with a few gunboats on Lake Champlain.

During the winter of 1776, Washington withdrew beyond the Delaware, but using his small forces with great tactical skill recrossed and effected a surprise on the Hessian mercenaries at Trenton, and later, in January, 1777, on British supporting troops at Princeton. He passed the remainder of the winter at Morristown. Howe merely retired into winter quarters at New York. In the spring of next year a similar plan was unfolded. Burgoyne was to descend from Canada via the Champlain route ; St. Leger to support him down the Mohawk route ; and Howe to make contact up the Hudson. Actually, St. Leger only got as far as Fort Stanwix and retreated. Burgoyne, even without his aid, was very nearly successful. He took Ticonderoga and marched to the Hudson. Here he waited too long for reinforcements and supplies from Canada, and for the junction with the St. Leger force. Meanwhile a much larger force of New England militia had been collected, and marched to oppose his advance to the Lower Hudson. Burgoyne made a fine effort to pass through these superior forces, but was overwhelmed, the only help he received from New York being a small raiding force under Sir Henry Clinton (which never got near him), instead of the whole weight of Howe's army, which a proper co-operation would have entailed.

He and his force surrendered at Saratoga in October, 1777. The result was of the utmost significance. With the entry of France and Spain into the war, the British were too heavily committed defending their possessions in India, Gibraltar, and the West Indies to attempt to send large forces via the St. Lawrence to effect a union with the New York garrison.

Meanwhile Howe, obsessed with the idea of capturing Philadelphia, made two unsuccessful sorties by land, and then decided to move by water. Forts at the mouth prevented his access by the Delaware, and he decided to enter the Chesapeake in an attempt to gain the important Chesapeake, Delaware, and New York route from the south-west. He defeated Washington at Brandywine Creek, but did not follow up his success. He cleared up the Delaware forts and was able to enter Philadelphia for the winter, Washington meanwhile remaining near by in Valley Forge.

Since the outbreak of the war, America had received help from France in the matter of supplies, and at the defeat of Burgoyne, France felt justified in coming in openly. Her navy had much improved since the French-English struggle of the mid-century, and the new alliance was so formidable in its world-wide commitments that Great Britain was obliged to adopt a different mode of attack. Any attempt to subdue the country by major land operations was given up, and the policy was adopted of holding one or two larger ports, and thence sending raiding parties to harass coastal towns. The British withdrew from Philadelphia to New York. In this phase the war dragged on for three miserable years. The French navy, too occupied in acquiring West Indian islands to co-operate properly with Washington, yet prevented the British from establishing anything approaching a complete blockade of American trade. The Americans were raided on all coasts, while from the old French Lake forts, brutal Indian raids were organized against the mid-west pioneers. There were many occasions when they were near to giving up the struggle, and they could certainly have done so on terms granting independence in everything but name. During this period Charleston and Savannah were occupied, and one large land force under Cornwallis passed north into Virginia, keeping near to the coast.

It is significant that a decisive victory for the Americans came only with the first real co-operation of the French navy. Cornwallis, with his force reduced to 7,000 men and having received no help from Virginian loyalists, was able to reach Yorktown. The most considerable British holding besides this was at New York, where Clinton still maintained a garrison. For the maintenance of such positions naval supremacy was vital. Washington now asked and received the aid of the French Admiral De Grasse. The French fleet defeated an English fleet at the Chesapeake entrance, and Washington could send supply ships round by sea. De Grasse was able to land French infantry, and the garrison of Cornwallis at Yorktown was without supplies or naval support. Meanwhile Washington, feigning an attack on New York to keep Clinton busy, moved his army through

Philadelphia, south-west to the head of the Chesapeake. The French and American troops then closed in on Yorktown, which Cornwallis was forced to surrender.

This was the last serious engagement by land, though De Grasse suffered a serious defeat by Rodney in West Indian waters, 1782. But it was too late, and though Peace negotiations were protracted, at the final agreement of 1783 the United States of America became an independent Power.

Summarizing, then, we note that the struggle may be divided into three stages :

(i) The attempt by the British to separate the colonies by holding the Hudson Gap. Armies advanced from Canada via the Mohawk and the Champlain, and should have made connection with the forces landed at New York. Such a scheme, for its success, entailed perfect timing, and the individual success of each advancing force. Howe's main force was engaged in New Jersey just when it was most wanted up the Hudson.

(ii) The entrance of the French, and the limitations of the armies which Great Britain could supply for extensive North American campaigns, caused the home command to adopt a " wearing down " policy. The big ports were held and coastal raids attempted.

(iii) The first real co-operation of the French navy in American home waters led to the defeat of the chief British forces on the mainland, and the war virtually ended.

It had been badly bungled by the British in the initial stages. Better managed, it is easy to conceive that it might have ended in victory for them. Such victory would have been but temporary. A new and extraordinarily rich, yet distant country, an entirely fresh order of environments, had set their impress on a New Nation.

*   *   *   *   *

After the close of the weary struggle for Independence, the Americans quickly regained prosperity in an era of peace. There was a positive horror of being drawn into any further European struggle, and so rapid was development that between the close of the War of Independence and the War of 1812 the population was doubled. So, too, was the territory. The vast area west of the Mississippi to the Rocky Mountains, incompletely delimited and much of it little known, was returned by Spain to France in 1800. The river, its outlet, and the territory to the west— all seemed desirable to the increasing settlers of Ohio, Kentucky and Tennessee, hampered by the Appalachian to the east and with their most obvious outlet down-stream to the Gulf. Eventually they might expect little opposition from Spain ; but France and England both at the back and side doors would have established a different circumstance.   Fortunately for America, Napoleon after disaster at San Domingo was in no mood to shoulder further trans-Atlantic responsibilities.   The American representative in Paris with authority to offer a price for New Orleans, found that his country could advance to the Rockies for little more.   The Louisiana purchase was completed in 1803.

The Northern Atlantic states were taking an important share in the world-carrying trade.   It was just this last fact which proved the difficulty.   The subjection of half Europe by Napoleon had left the U.S.A. the one important neutral.   The Britisher had to see French produce carried, and France herself supplied, by the American marine, and this though Trafalgar had left Great Britain superior to all avowed enemies at sea.   British carrying languished, for most ports were enemy ports.   The American shipper enjoyed thus a form of protection, and supplied our enemies at the same time.   They even took French sugar from the West Indies to an American port and forwarded it as American produce to undersell our West Indian planters in the English market.   Thus it came about that we searched American ships off their own ports for contraband and for the impressment of sailors of presumed—too readily presumed—British nationality.

Napoleon's Berlin decree of 1806 would close all European ports to Great Britain and prevent all neutral trade with her. The counter-measure—the British Orders in Council—would prohibit all neutral trade except via Great Britain.   America must side with one or other Power, or her ships were to be the prizes of both.   It was because of this interference in her trade, and to protect her sailors from impressment, that America declared war in 1812.

The war was supported by the frontiersmen of the new midwest, more particularly by such of them as cast jealous eyes on the little-populated lake peninsula of Ontario.   It found favour also with the Southern states.   It was bitterly opposed by the New Englander, who preferred impressment and interference to an entire lack of external commerce.

Britain's naval supremacy allowed her to make a fairly effective blockade of the American ports.   There was almost no American navy, though the few frigates which existed defeated several British ships in single ship actions, and many merchant vessels were lost to American privateers.   In maintaining her blockade, the position of the British naval bases at Halifax and in the West Indies were all-important.   The British army was fully occupied on the continent.   Only the tiniest forces were available for America, and though Baltimore and New Orleans were raided, and Washington, the capital, actually occupied for a short period, there was no considerable land campaign. But if the British could not get beyond coast raids, the Canadian border lay open and unprotected save for tiny forces throughout its length. It seems almost inconceivable that Canada should not have fallen to the Americans almost at once. So it would if the war had been a few years later. In 1812 the American population, though more than 7,000,000, hardly occupied at all the area immediately south of the Great Lakes, which was still virgin forest. The trans-Appalachian roads were incomplete, the Erie canal was not yet constructed.

The British loyalist in Canada was as near his war base—as effectively near his home country—as was the American soldier at Detroit. Then, again, the war lacked the sympathetic and financial support of the wealthiest of the states.

At the outbreak of war, the U.S.A. had almost no regular army. The forces ultimately sent for the invasion of Canada were small, ill-trained, ill-organized, and reluctant to fight. Moreover, they were constantly harried by the Indian allies of the British.

If in the light of the present importance of Canada the outcome of the struggle assumes importance, yet, at the time, neither nation afforded large forces for the contest, and no engagements on an impressive scale occurred. But once more, and for the last time, the geographical control of the St. Lawrence and trans-Appalachian route-ways was exercised in an armed struggle. The Americans attacked. Canada was only populated at all in the lake side of the Ontario peninsula, and in the St. Lawrence valley. The complete control of navigation of Ontario and Erie by the U.S.A. would mean the severance of Upper Canada. The land attacks about the obviously strategic position of Detroit and Niagara were feeble attempts only, but the improvised fleet of Perry on Lake Erie at length gained control of the lake for the Americans, and the struggle became concentrated on Lake Ontario and—by land forces—about Niagara. The British and American navies built against each other on Ontario without either achieving a notable supremacy, and neither was willing to submit to the test of a major engagement. It was not till late in the war, when in 1814 British troops were released temporarily from the continental struggle, that they made use of the Richelieu-Champlain route. Here, again, the control of the lake, and therefore of the route, went to the Americans with their naval victory on Lake Champlain.

But though they prevented the British invasion, they were

not strong enough to use the route themselves. With the strengthening of the British forces in Canada, and with but half-hearted support at home, America was ready to make terms with Britain, whose carrying trade had been dislocated, and whose mercantile marine had suffered severely at the hands of American privateers.

Peace was concluded in December, 1814, but the order for the cessation of hostilities did not reach the south in time to stop the one serious attack by the British in the Gulf. Here General Pakenham with 16,000 Peninsular veterans landed and attempted to advance on New Orleans. This force was completely defeated with very heavy losses while attempting a foolish frontal attack on entrenched positions.

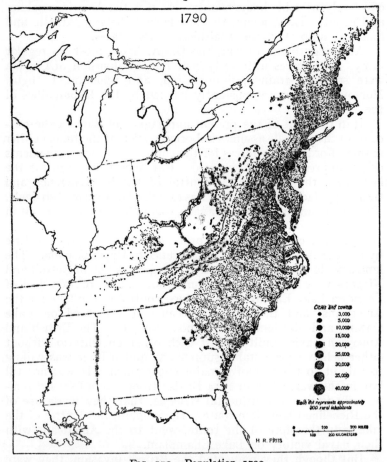

FIG. 17c.—Population, 1790.

From an article by H. R. Friis. Courtesy of the "Geographical Review" (July 1940), published by the American Geographical Society of New York.

CHAPTER VIII

THE WESTWARD ROUTES

THE close of the War of Independence saw only a few settlers west of the Appalachians, and these chiefly distributed in the fertile lowlands about Lexington and Nashville. They were largely Virginian in origin, and were at once augmented by ex-soldiers who came to take up the military land grants. These districts were at first attained by the Ohio River and Cumberland Gap routes, to which reference has been made in Chapter VI.

The post-war advance was subject to control both political and geographical. By a series of treaties from 1768 to 1785 land was acquired from the Indian up to the lakes, but this land was not readily taken up. We have once more, and for the last time, to emphasize the political and extra-geographical considerations which from the time of the tide-water colonies to the opening of the Erie canal, had hindered the settlement by Europeans of the lower lakes (Erie and Ontario) and of the Mohawk zone. The enmity of French and English, the buffer state of the Six Nations, and the wars of 1760, 1775, and 1812, all helped to retard settlement in this region. Yet it was open to entry via the Ohio as well as by the lakes. The Scioto, Muskingum, and Maumee were all navigable for canoes, and all connected by short portages with Lake Erie. In the valleys of these rivers were bottoms as fertile as any land to the south.

For a brief period we have an Act of Congress operative in a manner comparable to that of King George's Proclamation of 1763. Just as the latter sought to regulate the settlement of the mid-west, so the former was designed to control entry into the region between the Ohio and Great Lakes. For some years, indeed, a line of government forts on the Ohio prevented forcefully the northwards crossing of the river by settlers. In 1787, by a deal with the Ohio Land Company, Congress again permitted a regulated settlement north of the Ohio. Compared with the Kentucky regions then, we must note its late beginning, its greater proportion of New England and New York elements (coming in by the lake route), and its better survey of estates

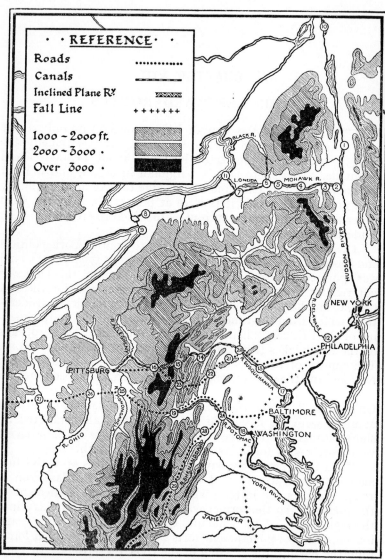

FIG. 18.—Map showing the Hudson-Mohawk-Champlain Route-way and the early Roads and Canals to the Mid-West. The number references occur in the text.

prior to disposal to settlers, whereby the conflicting claims consequent upon irregular surveys, frequent in Kentucky, were largely avoided.

In the early nineteenth century the portage tracks, Indian trails, and military ways, leading from the Atlantic states to the middle west, by a process of selection and improvement, became limited, as far as heavy traffic was concerned, to four main routes. Each of these was engineered, like the canals and early rails which followed, under the interstate competition of the great representative ports of New York, Philadelphia, and Baltimore, and in competition, too, with the Montreal and New Orleans outlets. The student should refer to Fig. 18 in what follows. The numbers in the text correspond to those on the map.

(1) *From Philadelphia* we have the *Lancaster Pike* to Lancaster (near Columbia, 13), thence to Middleton (near Harrisburg, 20) on the Susquehanna. Here we may notice that though the Susquehanna is interrupted by falls just above its mouth in Chesapeake Bay, yet the upper river, at high water, was navigable for canoe and very small boat traffic right up into Western New York. An improved road to Middleton then could take to Philadelphia farm produce of Central New York State, which had been floated down to this point. Thence the road passed by a highland interfluvial route via Carlisle, Shippensburg (21), Chambersburg (22), Bedford (23), and Johnstone (16), to Pittsburg and the Ohio. This was the Pennsylvanian route. Notice how Philadelphia gained by the obstruction on the Lower Susquehanna, which has no big town at its mouth.[1]

(2) *Cumberland Road*.[2] In this case we should notice that below Cumberland (19) the Potomac was navigable for stretches which were interrupted only by rapids at Harper's Ferry (24), and in the Great and Little Falls just above Washington. From Cumberland also there was improved road communication with Baltimore. From Cumberland the trans-Appalachian road passed through Unionstown to Brownsville (25). Passengers for Pittsburg, and for the Ohio, would often take to the river (Monongahela) here. From Brownsville the road was continued almost due west to Wheeling (26) on the Ohio, which quickly became a considerable river port, boat-building, and refitting centre; for by taking to water here, the bend of the river route through Pittsburg was avoided. By 1818 there was a regular mail coach route from Baltimore to Wheeling, and in the next twenty years the road was continued in a straight line to St. Louis on the Mississippi, and for this period served as the chief entrance

[1] Havre de Grace (17) remains to-day only an unimportant place.
[2] Not to be confused with Boone's Cumberland *Gap* road.

into the territory between the lower lakes and the Ohio. It passed through Cambridge, Zanesville (27), Columbus, Springfield, Richmond, and Indianopolis—most of them at the crossings of the northern tributaries of the Ohio. This was the route of Baltimore and Washington, i.e. of Maryland and Virginia.

(3) *The Genesee Road.* At the conclusion of the War of Independence, interior New York State was practically unsettled and but little explored. One hundred-ton vessels could approach Albany, but further navigation was limited to very small boats, and was subject to certain definite interruptions involving portages. Thus on the Mohawk, just above its junction with the Hudson, we have Cahoes Falls (2), so that any traffic from the Mohawk valley had to be transhipped at Schenectady (3). Still further up the Mohawk valley is Little Falls (4), with a halfmile portage. Above this point the river was navigable to Utica (5), where traffic for the Finger Lake country or for Buffalo would leave it. Traffic for Lake Ontario would take the portage to Lake Oneida and the river Oswego (11), the latter interrupted by falls before its entrance into the lake. An alternative portage route was to the Black River and Lake Ontario. From Albany to Montreal direct there was a portage from the Hudson below Hudson Falls to Lake St. George. Further on the Chambly Falls (10) interrupted the Richelieu River, so a short portage was made from above these falls to La Prairie, opposite Montreal on the St. Lawrence

Now, at the beginning of the nineteenth century, very little of this gap zone above Albany was occupied. There was practically no traffic via Lake Erie, and the Lake Ontario and Montreal route competed successfully with that of the Mohawk River and New York, for such traffic as existed from the Upper Mohawk and Finger Lake district. The Genesee road was built from Utica to the river Genesee in 1794, with the definite intention of developing the Genesee country, and of making it more definitely tributary to New York. It was not till later that it was continued to Buffalo, and traffic was never heavy to the lakes and Upper Ohio country until the opening of the Erie canal.

(4) *Boone's Road via Cumberland Gap* (considered in Chapter VI). Before the improvement of the Pennsylvanian and Cumberland pikes, and before the settlement of the Upper Ohio, this route, difficult and roundabout as it was, proved preferable to the earliest Kentucky pioneers.

To sum up, then, we have in the first quarter of the nineteenth century a large and growing population in the middle-west, subsisting on agriculture, holding cheap and fertile land, and having an excess of agricultural produce. Yet the most characteristic thing about this new area was its relative isolation. Until the days of railways it hardly paid to take agricultural produce from the middle-west to the Atlantic states. This economic isolation had the twofold effect of protecting middle-west industry—the woollen and iron work of Western Pennsylvania soon became important—and of concentrating agricultural export on the one natural avenue leading from the region, i.e. on the Mississippi River system. Here it is important to point out that after the Louisiana purchase in 1803, an increasing number of southern planters took up land in the Lower Mississippi basin, and cultivated cotton for the rapidly growing Western European markets. Now, just as the middle Atlantic colonies with their varied crop system and mixed farming had been able to supply the West Indies and southern colonial plantations with food-stuffs, so now the Kentucky and Ohio country could float down its corn, wheat, beef, and bacon, to the one-crop (cotton) plantations of the Lower Mississippi. We are dealing here with one of the really extensive natural navigation systems of the world. It is actually of little importance to-day, save perhaps with regard to coal traffic on the Upper Ohio—but for nearly half a century it meant everything to the middle-west. Brownsville, Pittsburg, Wheeling, Cincinnati, Louisville, all attained importance as boat-building centres, and boats of all sizes and shapes were turned out—the canoe, the pirogue, the barge, and the flat-boat ; keels which would penetrate even small tributaries of the Muskingum, the Scioto, the Miami, the Cumberland, and Kentucky rivers, and covered flat-boats which would take 20 to 30 tons of freight down the Mississippi itself.

The most considerable interruption of the main stream of traffic occurred with the rapids at Louisville, and these were passable with special pilots and at high water. With the coming of steam traffic the necessary transhipment gave some importance to the place. The Upper Ohio, too, suffered from snags, sandbanks, and falling timber, and was not always navigable by the bigger flat-boats. An exporter or pioneer might have to wait for a freshet. This might come at any time, but with the melting of the snow in spring, and with the autumn rains, there was usually plenty of water. For the first half of the nineteenth century—until, indeed, the trans-Appalachian railway era—the whole middle-west was tributary to the Lower Mississippi and to New Orleans, to an extraordinary degree. The only other outlet which avoided the Appalachians was that via the St. Lawrence, and this was little used, because (a) of its seasonal closing ; (b) its many portages—those between the Mississippi and lake systems, Niagara itself, and the series of rapids between

Ontario and Montreal ; (c) there was no market to compare with the southern plantations ; (d) the relatively late peopling of the district *north* of the Ohio.

We have evidence of the expense of trans-Alleghany freight-age in the fact that before the railway era, eastward traffic was largely confined to hogs, which did the journey on their feet and to such condensed traffic as whisky !

A characteristic of the Mississippi and Ohio traffic was that it was practically all down-stream. This for the twofold reason that ascent against the current was a long and arduous business, and also that the south had little which was wanted in the Ohio country. It was customary for the boat-owner to get rid of his craft at the plantation where he sold his produce, or at New Orleans. Frequently it was broken up at these places and the timber used for other purposes. The late owner would then fre-quently take passage for the middle Atlantic states from New Orleans, investing his takings in raw cotton or in manufactured articles at Baltimore, Philadelphia, or New York, and return by road to his middle-west farm. In 1817 steamers made their appearance on the Mississippi system. For these the falls at Louisville were a serious obstacle, and they were circumvented by a canal in 1828. Up-stream traffic was more feasible with steam power, and became of some importance, but the up-stream freight was never more than a small fraction of that carried down-stream. The Pittsburg coal-field supplied coal, iron, and machinery. The middle Atlantic states witnessed this increasing importance of Mississippi traffic with some concern. They were anxious to sell to the middle-west their manufactures and their imports, and would have exchanged these for farm produce, yet the Appalachian barrier forbade a direct exchange.

The same reasons that encouraged New York, Philadelphia, and Baltimore to urge the Genesee, Pennsylvania, and Cumber-land roads respectively, directed their support to the Erie, Penn-sylvania, and Chesapeake and Ohio canal systems. Each was a bid for trans-Appalachian traffic from the middle-west. Certain canals had proved a great financial success in England, and state propaganda ignored alike the greater distances and diffi-culties involved in trans-Appalachian construction. As events proved, there was only one route by which canal traffic could possibly be expected to succeed—that of the Erie canal. This connected Buffalo and Albany, avoided the portages of Cahoes and Little Falls, and opened up a through way to the lakes. Later, branches followed the Oswego and Black rivers route to Lake Ontario. There was considerable hesitation on the part of its promoters as to whether it should be built to Buffalo, gaining the Erie plain by a flight of locks at Lockport, or whether the easier route to Oswego on Lake Ontario should be taken. The objections to the second route were that Erie traffic would then have either a portage or expensive canal to round Niagara, and another canal avoiding the Oswego Falls; probably two transhipments would take place as between lake and canal vessels, and nothing would have been done—indeed, quite the reverse— to divert traffic from Montreal. Ultimately, these reasons prevailed and the canal was constructed to Buffalo and opened with much ceremony in 1825. It proved an immediate success. Prices of farm produce rose on the canal-side farming regions and in the middle-west, and fell considerably at New York City. It quickly became a favoured medium for western settlers, and helped to people Ohio with a predominantly northern stock. Only with the building of this canal did the geographical nodality of New York display its full significance. Previously the Pennsylvanian, Maryland, and southern routes had borne the bulk of western movement, but now the natural advantages of New York triumphed. In an earlier chapter we have already emphasized the coastal nodality of this great city as accounting for its earliest growth.

The relative accessibility of New York for coastwise and ocean traffic gave her advantages over Baltimore and Philadelphia, where north-trending estuaries necessitated a long voyage with little real ingress. By road and canal (as later by railway) she made these rival ports her tributaries along the direct line cutting through the necks of the Chesapeake and Delaware peninsulas. With the opening of the Erie canal these converging traffic streams were linked up with the one transAppalachian route which crossed with a summit level less than 500 feet, and led direct to lake navigation. If coastal configuration and the Hudson-Mohawk Gap made New York, Niagara was responsible for Buffalo, the Lake Erie terminus of the canal. Even the building of the Welland canal did not divert much traffic to Ontario, for the later big lake carriers could not use this canal, and Buffalo remained the eastern terminus of the heaviest lake traffic.

Little need be said about the Pennsylvania and the Chesapeake and Ohio canals. They preceded the railways by too short a time ever to succeed in a terrain not adapted to water traffic. Indeed, the Baltimore and Ohio Railway was built pace by pace with its Potomac rival, leaving it eventually at Cumberland, beyond which the canal, though *planned* to reach the Ohio, was never constructed. The Pennsylvania canal, built in the interest of Philadelphia, attained the Susquehanna valley at Columbia, and then proceeded via the Juniata to the base of the Alleghany Front at Hollidaysburg (15). Here was an obstruction to daunt the most sanguine of canal propagandists, and not to be circumvented by lock or tunnel. Eventually, a series of inclined planes and railways were engineered to take the canal boats over the Alleghany Front from the Juniata system to that of the Conemaugh at Johnstown (16), and thence to Pittsburg. This canal was effective in diverting Chesapeake traffic to Philadelphia, and though the Chesapeake states made a counter-move in building a canal to avoid the falls of the Lower Susquehanna, this was in part neutralized, from their point of view, by the Chesapeake-Delaware canal, which tended to make even the *mouth* of the Susquehanna tributary to Philadelphia. Finally, there was the Delaware-Raritan canal making for the importance of New York at the expense of both of the southern ports. To the east of the Blue Ridge these canals maintained for some time a heavy traffic by breaking through the Fall Line and its background of Piedmont country, but as trans-Appalachian routes they never achieved much importance, and were quickly superseded by railways.

Along these routes settlers passed through the Appalachians and occupied the lands thence to the Mississippi. Yet not evenly. The Census map of 1840—at which date no railway had crossed —shows broad patches of unoccupied country within these limits. Thus much of the relatively infertile Alleghany and Cumberland Plateau are blank, as also a broad belt between the southern end of the Appalachians and the Gulf—the land of the Creeks and Cherokee Indians. In Canada the character of the Laurentian Shield country confined settlement to the St. Lawrence and the southern part of the Ontario peninsula, where a considerable body of Loyalist settlers formed a nucleus. The opening of the Erie canal gave access to Lake Erie and thence by portage and later canal routes to the country north of the Ohio River as well as to that river itself. About the Mississippi itself settlement was considerable at the nexus of navigable ways converging on St. Louis and the lower Illinois. Up to the Mississippi most settlement had been on clearings in, or of, hardwood forest. The frontier man wanted water and timber, and gauged the land by the character of the latter. The prairies seemed to have neither and were difficult also to break with the means then in vogue. The Western Lake Huron and Michigan had not yet come into their own as lines of settlement, though the portage routes were used by occasional traders and Chicago (as Fort Dearborn) was a Government military post. In 1836 the latter was connected by a steamer line with Buffalo and the prairie lands to the south of Lake Michigan came more into the picture.

The lands about Lake Superior and the northern half of Lake Michigan were part of the northern coniferous forest of the continent—much of them typical Laurentian Shield country and nearly all providing poor soils on clearing. The densest settlement in 1840 was still in the Cincinnati and Nashville areas. Steamers had been in use on the Mississippi since 1817, and the traffic increased up to the time of the Civil War, and the river formed the major outlet for the farm products of the whole mid-west. The Lake routes to the east were not fully operating, the rail routes non-existent, the great export of American farm produce yet to be begun. Rapid settlement in the Mississippi basin had stimulated farm production beyond its market and it was partly discontent at low prices that encouraged movement still further west. The western frontier could not advance upon an even uninterrupted front. Already the Appalachian had broken it into mere connecting threads, but well to the west of the Mississippi was a greater barrier. Long before the Rockies are reached the average precipitation dwindles to less than 15″ and a broad belt of fair ranch, but poor agricultural land has to be crossed before the mountains are reached. This belt is crossed by the great tributaries of the Mississippi, useful in stretches for the canoes of the trappers, and later to provide water for the caravans which paralleled them. Only the Missouri was navigable by steamer for considerable distances. Fort Benton could be reached at high-water on this river. And beyond the semi-arid high plain came the enormous barrier of the Cordillera ; too mountainous for extensive settlements, save in the great interior plateaux, and there too dry : even to-day a land of irrigated valley and mountain fringe settlement. More attractive were the coast valleys beyond—the Great Valley of California and the Willamette valley of Oregon. Here were less severe climates, and—except in the southern part of the valley of California—heavier rainfall. But in 1840, the former was Mexican territory, and the latter was by agreement (from 1818–46) open to British and American alike.

The semi-arid land east of the Rockies and with its eastern limit on a line actually not far from that of the 15″ Isohyet, was established between 1835–41 as an Indian Reserve—a brief asylum for the westward-driven tribes. To the south-west, all that are now the Central and Southern Cordilleran States, as well as Texas, were a part of Mexico, which country had cut itself free from Spain in 1824. All this vast area actually acquired for the U.S.A., technically by the war of 1848, was, in general, even before that war, in easier communication with the States than with the government of Southern Mexico itself. American settlers under Austin were the chief influence in the movement which cut off the Lone Star State of Texas from Mexico ; a proceeding that Mexico was too weak seriously to combat, and one which made ultimate annexation by the U.S.A. inevitable.

Until the nineteenth century communication with the Cordillera country was confined to that resulting from the activities of the great Fur Companies, and to the commerce between New England and Southern California via Cape Horn. Settlements, apart from the missions of South California and those on the Rio Grande about Santa Fé, were confined to the forts of the fur companies set at strategic points on the passes and valley routes of the Cordillera.

Importance attaches to passes connecting the approaches of the eastern and western drainage systems—to the headwater passes between the Saskatchewan and Missouri to the east and the Colombian system to the west, and again between the Platte and Arkansas to the east, and the Colorado and Humboldt to the west.

Between 1820 and the coming of railways to the west, regular trading and immigrant caravan routes to some extent displaced and shortened the more definitely water lines of the fur traders. These were the Santa Fé, the Oregon, and the Californian Trails, and they did not achieve importance quite at the same date.

That to Santa Fé became of importance when American traders made a definite attempt to capture the Santa Fé market, up till then supplied by the South Mexican provinces via Vera Cruz. The first big expedition of traders took the route in 1824. Josiah Gregg, a trader writing of his own experiences, says that the caravan usually left Independence (in steamer connection with St. Louis and the Ohio, etc.) in early May. His own in 1831 consisting of nearly 100 wagons, some 200 men (all armed) and two small cannon ! Encounters with the Indians led to this amalgamation of proprietors, and each passenger had to take his turn at the watch. The route after leaving Independence proceeded directly to the bend of the Arkansas (long. 98° 30"), crossing every few miles in the moister part of the journey a number of small creeks, the head-waters of the river Osage and river Neosho. The river Arkansas was followed to long. 100° 30' and then the route turned directly towards Santa Fé and crossed the mountain border by the approaching tributary valleys of the Pecos and Rio Grande.

Santa Fé was connected with the sea at San Diego by a trail via the Gila River.

More important as affecting Pacific settlement were the Oregon and Californian Trails. The Columbia with its tributary the Snake, spread a wide embrace for the westward fur traders who had approached from the Canadian and American Rockies. The 1818 boundary of Canada was settled at the 49° N. lat., only as far west as the Rockies. Thus from California (then Mexican) to lat. 54° 30' the Cordillera was left open to settlement by either country until the final agreement of 1848.

For farm settlement the most attractive portion of the whole of this vast area (now British Columbia, Washington and Oregon) was the Willamette valley. This was better watered than the interior plain and plateau, and had better and less forested lands than the Puget Sound region. Settlement once initiated here proceeded southwards through more hilly country to the attractive northern Sacramento Valley, more particularly with the opening of the Californian gold rush.

The earliest American fur-traders connection with the Oregon country was by the Missouri and thence by the Clark or the Snake valleys. The Oregon trail which followed, after leaving Westfield or Independence, paralleled the Platte to the mountains, crossed the Rockies by South Pass and then attained, by an intricate valley system, the Beaver River of Utah. This was followed to its great northern bend where the route branched; the Oregon route going north-west to the Snake and Columbia; the California, following the Humboldt across arid Utah and Nevada, crossing the Sierra Nevada and so to San Francisco. The two routes branched rather to the north of the Mormon Salt Lake settlement, and that to California was not much used till the gold rush of 1849. Mining activity immensely stimulated the early Willamette, Salt Lake, and Californian settlements; for there was a great demand for farm produce and services.

As we have seen, Mexican California was physically separated by a vast arid area from the Mexican Government, and the increasing discontent of American settlers found some sympathy with many of the Mexicans themselves. American influence was beginning to predominate when by the conclusion of the Mexican War the whole vast region passed to the States in 1848.

Such were the front lines of large scale movement through the mountain and desert barrier before the railway era.

In Canada was a different and even greater barrier, for though the Great Lakes form a magnificent route westward they serve the two countries very differently. The Laurentian wilderness of rock and water comes right to the Canadian border of Huron and Superior and indeed continues 300 miles west of Lake Superior before giving way to the Red River Valley plain. Lake Michigan, on the other hand, safely attains the Prairies at Chicago.

There were some difficulties in driving a caravan route across the High Plains from St. Louis westward. It was impossible to drive one over the Shield country west of Ottawa, in Canada. For decades after its initiation in 1811, Lord Selkirk's little colony of the Red River was stagnant—without an outlet until settlement in the U.S.A. came up to meet it from the south, and it expanded into the prairie provinces only with the building of the C.P.R. in 1883.

Until this date, and apart from this settlement, Western Canada was given over to the fur-traders, and later (1858) to the gold rush of the Caribou district of British Columbia.

CHAPTER IX

THE GEOGRAPHICAL SETTING OF THE CIVIL WAR

IN every war geography has conditioned the larger strategy and determined the zones of vital contact. In most it has provided, too, the underlying economic motives. Especially is this true of a *civil* war in which the original motives were cleared of the complications due to international interests; and of a war, further, between two geographical divisions, of which the common boundary zone lacked all homogeneity in cutting clear across many very varied physiographic provinces.

How is geography concerned in the causes of the war? It may be argued that the conflict had its origin in the objection of certain states to the veto, by Congress, of the practice of slavery in the New Territories, i.e. in Western lands not then admitted into the Union,[1] and that there was originally no intention of Congress legislating as to the domestic affairs of any existing states. The Southerner knew well enough that a control of slavery in the Territories would be but the thin end of the wedge; and indeed before the end of the struggle the emancipation of the slave had become the generally recognized motive and adopted policy of the North. Or, again, one may regard the war as being a demonstration of the right of secession; yet the very wish to secede was determined by the attitude of the North towards slavery.

Whatever the immediate and formal cause, the actual conflict arose from the fact that the Southerner owned many slaves and sincerely thought a continuation of the system vital to his economic existence. The Northerner owned few, and the system did not even appear to be necessary. Climate, the course of the triangular trade, and geographical propinquity, all had assisted in the extension of the vicious West Indian slave plantation system to the south. The rice swamps of Carolina and the Mississippi cotton bottoms were hardly attractive enough to compete with the Central and Northern states for the virile immigrants of North-west Europe. In 1860 the Northern states, including for the moment Kentucky, West Virginia, and Mary-

[1] I.e. all to the *west* of Minnesota, Iowa, Missouri, Arkansas, and Texas.

land, had a white population of about twenty-two millions, and less than a million negroes. The Southern states had five million whites and nearly four million negroes. Manufactures and mixed farming had developed rapidly in the North. The South was dependent upon the North, and upon imports, for manufactures, and for any variety in her food-stuffs. The Southerners cultivated cotton, corn, and little else. Cotton was their sole article of external commerce, and it was exclusively slave-grown. Land was cheap and quickly used up. It was then deserted and new districts exploited. Penetration—once the Louisiana purchase had been made, and Indian trouble had been overcome—had been easy by the Mississippi and its tributaries, and round the base of the Appalachians. The plantations of the Southern states then were spread thinly over an enormous area. The extraordinary thing is not that the South should have deemed slavery necessary to their economic existence, but that they should have imagined that they had resources at all sufficient to carry a war with the North to a successful conclusion. Almost as extraordinary was the resistance they actually put up.

It seems clear that in 1860 the Southern politicians had not sensed the significance of the changes in geographical values which had occurred since 1840. At the latter date the Appalachian barrier was still effective in keeping the Ohio and Upper Mississippi states tributary to the Mississippi. The Mississippi steamer service was rapidly developing to its maximum. The South hoped to carry these Northern trans-Appalachian states and territories with them. Yet in these two decades the Northern Appalachians had been crossed by three lines of rail which connected up with quite an elaborate network in Ohio, Illinois, Iowa, and Indiana (Fig. 19). At once the geographical control of the Appalachian system was seriously qualified. The Civil War broke sharply the economic connection between the Northern and Southern Mississippi system, but already the link was weakening.

For some time before the outbreak of war, the Democrats, exceptionally strong in the South, and with considerable support, too, in the North, had been the dominant part in Congress. Threats of the secession of the South split the party into Northern and Southern camps, and it was on such a split vote that Lincoln came into office. He disavowed a policy of interference with the system of slavery in any state in which it existed, but maintained the right of Congress to legislate as to New Territories. Above all, he denied the right of states to secede. In the sphere of home events, at any rate, he regarded the Southern forces, not as armies of a hostile Power, but as rebels within the

American *Reich*. In 1861 the confederate states of Texas, Louisiana, Alabama, and Mississippi proclaimed their secession, and were quickly joined by North Carolina, Virginia, Tennessee, and Arkansas. North of these was an east-west zone of doubtful sympathies. Quite apart from the underlying motive of slavery, even the Northern states contained many very jealous of the rights of states as opposed to the authority of Congress. Maryland, too, had always been something of a plantation state, and contained more slaves than the Northern states generally. Lincoln made sure of her by rushing troops beyond her southern border of the Potomac. These same troops had a somewhat hostile reception in passing through Baltimore. Similarly, an early exhibition of Northern force had a determining influence in the case of Missouri.

The distribution of parties in Kentucky and Virginia had a very definite geographical basis. The early Kentuckians were simply Virginian pioneers, or agriculturists with Virginian sympathies ; but later, with improving transport, there had been an influx of immigrants from the Northern states. Even on the better lands and large farms of the Blue Grass lowlands, though these were predominantly Southern in sympathy, there was considerable difference of opinion. But between these fertile lowlands about Nashville and Lexington and the similarly fertile valley bottoms of the Great Appalachian valley, stretched a wedge of the *accidenté*, often infertile, land of the Cumberland plateau—the hill-country of West Virginia and Eastern Kentucky. Population was here relatively sparse. It was poor, non-slave-owning, often Northern in opinion and in sympathies. Thus the Central and Southern Cumberland plateau represented a wedge of Northern opinion thrust between the Southern partisans in the Great Appalachian valley and the Kentucky lowlands. At the very outbreak of hostilities, when Virginia proclaimed her adherence to the South, West Virginia seceded from the parent state and declared for the North. Kentucky at first strove to hide her disunion in a futile assertion of independence.

In spite of the proclaimed secession of the Southern states, Lincoln was anxious to avoid striking the first blow. Hostilities actually broke out in connection with the anomalous position of *United* States fort garrisons situated in Southern states. These states naturally claimed the immediate evacuation of the congressional troops with the handing over of munitions to the state authorities. Fort Sumter in Charleston harbour was made a test-case. Here Lincoln did not authorize the withdrawal of the garrison, and the South Carolina folk, hearing that he was actually despatching supplies, precipitated matters by attacking the fortress. It was weakly defended and quickly fell. From this episode dates the outbreak of actual hostilities.

We have seen that geographical factors largely determined the distribution of parties. They were equally effective in determining the zones of conflict. The North and South dividing-line cuts right through each of those physiographic divisions which we have elsewhere enumerated, and each exercised its characteristic control in the larger strategy of the war. Through-

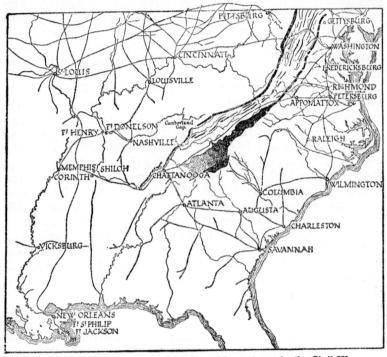

FIG. 19.—Diagram to illustrate points of importance in the Civil War.

Note N.E. and S.W. gaps from the Appalachian Valley, also the superiority of the North in railway development.

out the struggle physical circumstances forced the operations into seven well-marked zones, which may be tabulated as follows (Fig. 19):

(a) *The Mississippi River System.* This provided a downstream route for the Northern armies, and by means of such largely navigable tributaries as the Cumberland, Kentucky, and Tennessee, a means of lateral penetration into Southern territory. The Northern military forces quickly grasped the significance of control here, and at once occupied Cincinnati, St. Louis, and

Louisville with garrisons. We should here note again the network of rail which served the Northerner in Ohio and the Upper Mississippi states. The South had simply the line parallel to the Mississippi from St. Louis down to Mobile, and the one trans-Appalachian line Richmond-Chattanooga-Nashville-Cairo.

(b) *The Middle and Lower Cumberland Plateau.* This, as mentioned above, drove a northern wedge into southern districts. As events turned out however, Northern troops were soon in possession of North Kentucky, which is of the same latitude as West Virginia itself, and was Southern in sympathy. Mountainous West Virginia, however, served to provide a hostile flank to the Shenandoah valley region of Virginia, which, like the rest of Virginia, was for the South. The terrain of West Virginia was difficult for the passage of troops. Probably both armies attached altogether too much importance to its control. The Southern Cumberland plateau is broken by such well-known roads as that at Cumberland Gap, and, much more important, by the rail route at Chattanooga. Here were routes by which the Southern armies of the Appalachian valley, or the Northern armies descending through Kentucky, could each attempt outflanking movements.

(c) *The fertile Great Appalachian Valley,* providing a granary for the South. Accessible through weaknesses in the Cumberland plateau in the south-west (Cumberland Gap and Chattanooga), and in the Blue Ridge in the north-east, e.g. at Harper's Ferry, and at the many wind-gaps, e.g. Snicker's and Ashby's. By means of the great valley the South could project forces threatening to outflank the Northern army about the Potomac.

(d) *The Southern Mountain Barrier* (Blue Mountains, Unakas, Smoky Mountains, etc.), which forced all communication between Virginia and the Lower Mississippi via either the Richmond-Chattanooga-Cairo Railway (i.e. via the Great Valley), or, south of the Appalachians altogether.

(e) *The Piedmont and Coast Plain.* Here the rivers (Potomac, Rappahannock, James, etc.) served in turn and at various stages of the war as defensive lines difficult to penetrate. This was particularly so in the coast plain province, where the streams were often bordered by extensive and marshy flood plains.

(f) *Chesapeake Bay.* This (cf. the Mississippi in the extreme west) formed, in its north and south extension, a means by which Washington might outflank Richmond, or vice versa. Particular importance, then, was attached to its domination by either fleet, and to the possession of the forts at its entrance.

(g) *The Atlantic.* Here a blockade of Southern ports would effectively prevent the one great source of Southern wealth—the export of raw cotton : a blockade to be applied, however, to some 1,500 miles of coast-line.

Before proceeding to a brief résumé of the most important engagements developed in these well-marked zones, let us emphasize the disparity in numbers and material existing between the opposing parties. In 1860 the white population of the North was between four and five times that of the South. Manufacture was highly developed in Pennsylvania, New York, and New England. The South had almost none. They were dependent upon the North or upon imports, for textiles, iron, and machinery. Financially, they were at no less a disadvantage. Prolonged resistance appeared for them impossible unless they could market their cotton in Europe regularly and receive munitions of war in return. Against the possibility of their doing this were the facts that much of their trade was normally done in Northern vessels ; that shipbuilding was almost confined to the North ; and the U.S.A. navy, built and manned by Northerners, was entirely under Northern control. Lastly, communications—roads, canals, and rails—were much further developed in the North than in the South. Of many of these difficulties the Southern leaders were aware. They could hardly have realized at first the full weight of such adverse factors.

Let us turn back now and see what were the outstanding geographical controls in the main zones enumerated above, and rather than attempt a complete and chronological list of engagements, we will content ourselves with a summary of the significant events occurring in each physiographical zone. In the three long years of war there were, of course, numerous exchanges of troops among these zones ; yet to a surprising degree, and for long periods, the Trans, Cis, and Inter-Appalachian army groups, on both sides, preserved their independence. Let us turn our attention first, then, to the eastern zone of contact. Here on the Fall Line were opposed, at 200 miles distance, the rival capitals of Washington and Richmond. The capture of either would have had a popular significance out of all proportion to its strategic value. Defending both, then, throughout the war, were the greatest armies engaged. At the very outset Lincoln occupied Washington with large numbers of troops, and nervousness as to the safety of the capital caused him to maintain there a greater garrison than the military necessities demanded. In advance of the Washington garrison was McClellan's big army of the Potomac. Facing this and in defence of Richmond was the army of the Southern general, Beauregard. Between the armies were wide, flood-bordered, navigable rivers. Flanking, and to the north of these opposing forces, Johnston held the Shenandoah valley for the South almost to Harper's Ferry, and large Northern forces were detailed to prevent his emergence eastward.

The initial engagement took place at Bull Run, July, 1861, about 25 miles from Washington, when Northern forces were routed, but the attack was not followed up. McClellan was then placed in command of the army of the Potomac, which he organized and prepared through the summer and autumn of 1861. He planned to attack Richmond by a campaign up the York peninsula, his right being supported by ships in the York River estuary. After Ericsson's *Monitor* had overcome the Southern armoured frigate—the *Merrimac*—the James estuary also was open to the Northern ships supporting McClellan. The latter would probably have succeeded in his campaign but for the fact that his full forces were depleted to provide armies against the flanking threats of Stonewall Jackson from the Shenandoah. As it was, he proceeded with care up the York peninsula and became engaged ultimately in the great Seven Days' struggle (June 26th to July 2nd, 1862) with Lee's forces before Richmond, in a wooded and difficult terrain. From this engagement McClellan was able by a skilful manœuvre to withdraw his army to a fortified base at Harrison's landing on the Potomac. He suffered less loss than Lee, and, if supported, might have successfully reached Richmond via Petersburg had his plan to that effect been approved. He had been too slow to convince the public and the politicians, however, and he and his army were withdrawn to the Potomac again in July, 1862.

Lee was then free to effect a raid into Maryland where he hoped to gain recruits as well as territory, and to destroy the railway bridge over the Susquehanna at Harrisburg. He received little support in Maryland, and after reaching Hagerstone was compelled to come south again or have his communications cut by McClellan. He was defeated in the considerable battle of Antietam (September, 1862), but managed to extricate his army and recross the Potomac into Virginia. The successors of McClellan made little progress in this Piedmont and Coast Plain region, where much of the terrain was second-growth forest, and every stream was a line of defence for the South. At Fredericksburg (December, 1862) on the Rappahannock, and at Chancellorsville (May, 1863), the superior ordering of the Confederate armies under Lee gained for them victories over the more numerous forces of the North.

In June (1863) Lee again raided the Appalachian valley as far north almost as Harrisburg in Pennsylvania. His communications threatened, however, he moved south again to

Gettysburg, which controlled the roads to the Potomac. Here Meade held him in the grim encounter of July 2-4, 1863, in which nearly 200,000 troops were engaged. Lee was defeated but managed to retreat via the Shenandoah valley to the south of the Potomac.

Thus in the eastern theatre the war was degenerating into one of attrition, for large numbers were engaged and heavy losses sustained with little decisive action. Ground was gained more quickly in the Middle West. Here there were three lines of defence for the South. First there was the Ohio—but the Northerners were beforehand here. Cincinnati, Louisville and St. Louis were quickly occupied by them. Kentucky was only partly sympathetic to the South, and this line of defence was never reached, except in raids, by Southern troops.

Then the Cumberland and Tennessee rivers, with Nashville as a principal base, formed a second line. The mouths of these rivers were quickly in the hands of the North, but Forts Donelson and Henry barred penetration by these streams. These fell to the North, however, in February, 1862, and Nashville was occupied without a fight. Thus the South had to retire to their third line—the Memphis-Corinth-Chattanooga railway. The eastern portion of this line was cut to prevent reinforcements from the Appalachian valley via the Chattanooga gap.

Northern troops also approached this line by the Tennessee as far as the great bend just north of Corinth. Here, in April, 1862, near Pittsburg Landing (Shiloh), their troops met those of the South in one of the greatest engagements of the war. Once again the Southern forces retreated, abandoning the railway line and Memphis, and opening the way for an attack on Vicksburg in the west and Chattanooga in the east.

The Northern fleet had meanwhile passed the delta forts of the Mississippi, and a Northern garrison had occupied New Orleans (April, 1862). Only the portion between that city and Vicksburg remained to be cleared to open the whole of the great river to the Federal boats. Vicksburg, with its intricately dissected and characteristic river-bluff terrain, put up a great resistance. Federal troops, however, crossed the river well below Vicksburg and attacked from the south and east, supported by armoured river boats. The town suffered a siege for nearly three months and surrendered with 37,000 troops on July 4, 1863—an even more decisive success for the North than Gettysburg of the same date.

In September, 1863, Federal troops of the army of the Ohio entered the Appalachian valley of E. Tennessee, and occupied Knoxville, thus cutting partly across one of the main lines of communication connecting the armies of the Confederation. Meanwhile the Federal army of the Cumberland advanced on Chattanooga, but not, however, via the Tennessee valley from Knoxville. Instead, they crossed the river from the west, below Chattanooga, lost touch in the ridges south of the town, suffered defeat at Chickamauga, and extricated themselves only to be almost besieged within Chattanooga (September, 1863). A road for supplies was opened, however, and they emerged in November, 1863, to defeat the Confederates decisively about Missionary Ridge and Look Out Mountain.

Grant took over the Northern command in the east, and in the summer of 1864 moved the army of the Potomac to the James River with the intention of concentrating on the strategic road and rail centre of Petersburg from the east and thence attacking Richmond. He was held by Lee, however, until the following spring. Meanwhile in the south-west, after Chattanooga, the Northern general, Sherman, prosecuted a long and difficult campaign which culminated in the taking of Atlanta in September, 1864. In November he cut himself from his base and began his hazardous march through Georgia to the sea at Savannah. He met with little resistance, and the gigantic raid seemed to damp the waning courage of the civilian Southern population. He destroyed the one railway in Southern territory which then connected the coast and the Mid West. The taking of Savannah (December, 1864) put him in touch with Northern naval forces, and ensured another base for the difficult work of blockading Southern ports. Sherman's further journey north, up the coast plain to take the main Southern force in the rear, was more difficult. The weather was bad and the rivers, all transverse to his path, were flooded. Progress was made, however, and with the fall of Wilmington, January, 1865, Southern blockade-running ceased from Nassau (Bermudas), and from the West Indies. In December, 1864, the Confederates, under Hood, were decisively defeated by Thomas at Nashville. In the spring of 1865, Grant's forces were closing in around Richmond and Petersburg. In April, without hope of further reinforcement and with his area of supply most seriously curtailed, Lee relinquished both towns and was retreating towards the Appalachians when overtaken at Appomatox. Further resistance was useless and his surrender ended the war.

PART II
ECONOMIC GEOGRAPHY

CHAPTER X

CLIMATE

WE are concerned in this chapter only with the *major* facts of the climates of the continent. Some further detail, when it is significant, will find a place in the later part of this book, which deals with the chief regions of the country.

Every type of climate, save only the Equatorial, is exemplified in the continent ; yet all may be related in the first instance to a fairly simple scheme of pressure and temperature distribution and to a few major systems of relief. In the first place, let us examine what there is of climatic significance in the very world position, shape, and major relief of the continent. North America is roughly triangular in shape, and so placed on the world's surface that much the larger part of its area is in the temperate zone. But it is precisely in the temperate zone that great land masses suffer seasonal extremes of temperature. Here we have in completeness examples of all that is meant by that rather unfortunate term *continental climate* ; a term which could not possibly be applied, e.g., to the major land mass of the continent of South America, which lies in Equatorial regions. A further result of this distribution of the land of the continent is that only the southern half of Mexico comes within reach of the Equatorial rains, and that only in the summer months. Then with regard to relief, any modification is attended by some climatic change—indeed, variations in relief are the chief causes of local variations in climate. In a consideration of the climates of the whole continent, however, we are concerned only with the effect of the very outstanding systems of relief. These are the Pacific Cordillera, the Great Central Lowlands and Plains, and the Appalachian system. *The Pacific Cordillera* exhibit usually the following well-marked units of relief :

(i) The Coast Ranges—usually between 1,500 feet and 2,500 feet in height, but rising to 8,000 feet in Mount Olympus (Washington), and continued in a line of islands (Vancouver, Queen Charlotte, etc.) off the shores of British Columbia, but merging into a great peninsula in Lower California. The coastal margin, then, is everywhere mountainous, and from a climatic point of view these mountains are not high.

(ii) East of the Coast Ranges and running the whole length of the continent to the latitude of the tip of the peninsula of California, we have a great Pacific valley forming the straits of Georgia, Hecate, Clarence, etc., off British Columbia, Puget Sound, and the Cowlitz and Willamette valleys in Washington and Oregon, the Great Valley in California, and the Gulf of California off the coast of Mexico. The whole of this valley is in the rain shadow of the Coast Ranges and somewhat separate, too, from the cooling effects of the ocean.

(iii) Immediately to the east of the Pacific valley comes a topographically—but not structurally—continuous belt of very high mountains, usually over 5,000 feet in height, and often over 10,000 feet. It is represented by the Coast Range of British Columbia, the Cascades of Washington and Oregon, the Sierra Nevada, San Gabriel, and San Bernardino ranges of California. These form a real barrier to precipitation further inland. The marked winter rainfall maximum so characteristic—as we shall presently describe—of the whole Pacific coast from British Columbia to the latitude of Northern Mexico, ceases to be *very* perceptible East of this great system of ranges.

(iv) Between the belt just indicated and the Rockies on the east is an enormous area of high plateau and irregular mountain masses. This includes the interior of British Columbia, the Snake and Columbia River Basin of Washington and Oregon, and the Great Basin of Nevada and Utah. The region is largely barred from Pacific influence from the west and from Gulf and Atlantic from the east. The precipitation is everywhere very small. It is better distributed throughout the year than immediately either to east or west, and tends to a spring maximum in the north and to an early autumn maximum in the south.

(v) The irregular and very high mountain belts which enclose these plateau areas on the east are designated the Rocky

Mountains. These, in virtue of their height, receive a heavier precipitation than the high plains to the east, or the great basins to the west. It is heavier, too, in the north than in the south.

The Central Lowland of North America, if considered only from the climatic point of view, may be construed to mean the whole of the rest of the continent, save those portions which are included in, or lie to the east of, the Appalachian Mountains. Much of this area is neither central, low, nor plain. The rolling High Plains rise to 4,000 feet, and sometimes even 5,000 feet, before the foothills of the Rockies are reached. The even plains of the centre are interrupted by the irregular and extensive, if modest, heights of the Ozarks, Ouachita, and Witchita Hills.

The Canadian Shield area is hummocky, irregular, and really mountainous in the extreme north-east. All this variety has its effect on local climates, but in our present consideration the fact to be emphasized is that between eastern and western continental cordillera exists a great area of relatively even relief where no considerable barrier lies in the way of free surface air movement from the Arctic to the Gulf. In the centre and north centre it has the true continental climate, but everywhere, in Arctic regions as on the borders of the Gulf itself, great variations of temperature are liable to occur with the passage of deep and extensive pressure systems. Much of the summer rain of this area extends freely from the Gulf. An important climatic factor in the north is the presence of the great water bodies of the Great Lakes, and of the very considerable total body of water represented by the innumerable lakelets and marshes of the Laurentian Shield.

The Eastern or Appalachian Mountain systems are not high enough or complete enough to prevent direct movement of Atlantic moisture to the central lowlands, and of course they leave these entirely open to influences from the Gulf and from the Great Lakes.

Now, the whole relief system of the continent thus broadly summarized is set among certain prominent areas of low and of high pressure, themselves the product of the differential heating of the earth's surface.

Broadly, we have to consider five pressure areas :
(*a*) The Aleutian and Icelandic Lows.
(*b*) The Pacific and Atlantic HIGHS.
(*c*) The Alternating (summer LOW and winter HIGH) of the land mass. (Figs. 20 and 21.)
These represent *average* conditions. The student will notice

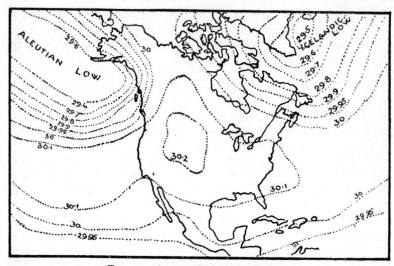

FIG. 20.—Average Isobars for January.
Note extension and intensity of the Icelandic and Aleutian Lows.

that in winter the Aleutian and Icelandic Lows are at their fullest development, and present sharp pressure gradients to the continental HIGH. In summer, on the other hand, they retreat to the north, and the dominant systems are the Atlantic and

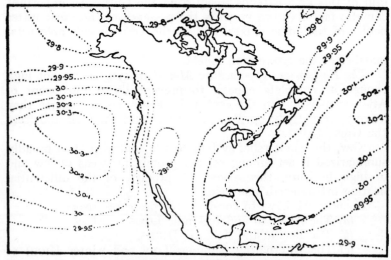

FIG. 21.—Average Isobars for July.
Note weakness of Aleutian and Icelandic systems.

Pacific HIGHS, now separated by a deep continental Low. We must be very careful to insist that such maps only represent *average* monthly conditions ; that, for instance, the Aleutian and Icelandic Lows are both the seat of origin and the areas of passage of many separate cyclonic systems, and do not at any moment of time correspond to the simple pressure curves of the map. Then, again, with regard to the continental winter HIGH, relative high pressure is shown here because large anticyclones form and are nearly stationary for weeks at a time over parts of the continent in winter. Yet extensive cyclonic systems move from west to east across the continent, usually keeping well down over the Mississippi lowlands and leaving the land mass along the line of the St. Lawrence. Such a passage—if the cyclone is deep and extensive, as it often is—will be accompanied by complete changes in wind direction and therefore in temperature, and usually by precipitation, either rain or snow. In winter, the Trade winds, i.e. the winds in sympathy with the southern portions of the oceanic HIGHS—which, by the way, in this season are joined rather than separated by continental conditions—in winter these Trade winds dominate the Mexican and West Indian areas, giving rains on the mountainous windward coasts. In summer the Equatorial Low moves north of the Equator and gives rain over the whole of Central America and the southern half of Mexico. In this season the oceanic HIGHS are self-contained, and sympathetic winds, southerly off the South Atlantic states, northerly off California, are semipermanent in character.

We shall now give some examples of the actual and average conditions of temperature and rainfall in different parts of the continent. This is best done by the use of average isotherm and isohyet maps, and after a consideration of these we will discuss, as a sort of corrective, the limitations attending the use of any such average maps for obtaining a real idea of the climate. The isotherm map for January (Fig. 22) shows the expected dip down of the lines over the continental mass.[1] The 32° line comes as far south as St. Louis over the centre of the continent, so that the whole of Canada—save the actual coasts of British Columbia—the whole of New England, New York, most of the lake states, the Dakotas, Montana and Wyoming and the eastern portions of Washington and Oregon, are usually well below 32° average temperature for this month. The line is of some significance, for within it snow is apt to be long on the ground and waterways to be blocked by ice.

[1] This dip is apt to appear exaggerated on most projections because of the curvature of the lines of latitude.

Then notice that the isotherms dip much more steeply on the west coast than on the east. Proximity to the sea has little climatic significance if the air movement is predominantly from the land. And this is the case in the north-east of the continent in winter when cold north-west winds are prevalent. Even when these are temporarily checked by cyclonic movement, incoming air from the east suffers some cooling in its passage over the reservoirs of cold water brought down by the Labrador current and occupying the Newfoundland and New England coastal seas. In corresponding latitudes on the west the coast ranges received the full influence of the prevalent damp

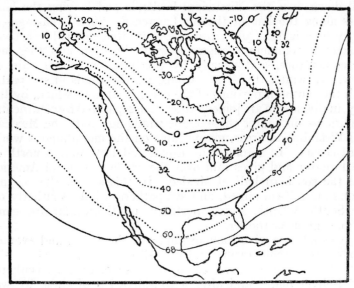

FIG. 22.—Sea-level Isotherms for January.

westerly winds and the harbours of Southern Alaska are open even in winter. But this modifying influence is closely confined to the coast lands, and this to a degree more obvious than in the corresponding area of Europe. Hence the steepness and crowding of the isotherms in the west. Another illustration of the January temperature distribution may be obtained by taking the *actual* (i.e. not corrected for height) average temperatures for a number of places about the same latitude (41° N.) across the continent. Here note particularly the extraordinarily low mean annual temperature range of the Pacific coast—and of the coast only ; the high summer temperature and considerable range of even the extreme north of the Great Valley of Cali-

fornia ; and the low winter temperature and great range of everywhere to the east, even including the Atlantic coast. The latitude is that of Oporto in Europe.

	Pacific Coast.	Great Pacific Valley.	Pacific Plateau.	Great Plains.	Central Lowlands.	Cumber-land Plateau.	Atlantic Coast.
July .	55·3	82·1	76·2	76·5	75·4	74·7	73·5
January	46·9	45·4	28·8	21·2	23·1	31·0	30·2
	Eureka, Cal.	Red Bluff, Cal.	Salt L. City, Utah.	Lincoln, Nebraska.	Peoria, Illinois.	Pitts-burg, Penn.	New York City.

Then for the whole of the western half of the continent the
average January map gives an entirely wrong impression by
reason of reduction to sea-level temperature. As a corrective
here we will use a killing frost map of the U.S.A. (Fig. 23). In
the climatic records of the U.S.A., the term " killing frost " is
applied to a diminution in temperature which actually causes
considerable damage to the staple crop of the district considered.
It is represented by rather different temperature figures in
various parts of the country. From actual past records, and
quite empirically, then, it is possible to construct maps showing
for different parts of the country the average frost-free period
between the last killing frost of spring and the first one of the
fall. There are, however, great variations in the dates of first
and last frosts, and the period actually at the disposal of the
farmer who wishes for reasonable safety is considerably less than
the *average* frost-free period ; e.g. Chattanooga has an *average*
frost-free period of 200 days, but this means that the period
may be shorter on the average every other year. If the farmer
reckons for only 170 days, past records show him to be safe in
four years out of five. A map constructed on these lines, however, does give an indication of the time available for agriculture
in various regions, and, since it refers to actual figures, does cor-
rect the erroneous impressions made by an isotherm map constructed on the basis of temperature reduced to surface level.

Consider now the July temperature conditions. If we have
always in mind the variations between day and night, and from
day to day ; if we realize, too, the effect of reduction of temperature to sea-level, then the corrected isotherms of Fig. 24
are not uninstructive. Greater heat is now over the continental
mass and the isotherms bend up over the great land mass. It
is very important to notice, however, that this great bend is

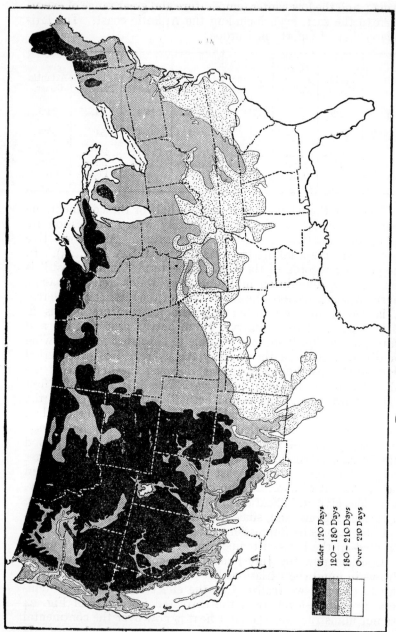

FIG. 23.—Frost-free Periods in the U.S.A.
(*After the* " American Atlas of Agriculture.")

Under 120 Days
120 — 180 Days
180 — 210 Days
Over 210 Days

not set symmetrically to the general shape of the continent, but is most pronounced west of the median line in the north. Here is a great extension of summer warmth to the north between the Rockies and the Great Lakes and Hudson Bay water bodies. Latitude for latitude, places in the prairie provinces reach a higher temperature than places in Eastern Canada.[1]

The highest temperatures of all are reached in the arid southwestern interior. The crowding of the isotherms on the Pacific coastland is due to the effect of the sea, and is particularly noticeable in the coastal towns of California, which suffer remarkably constant northerly winds, and cold currents, and much

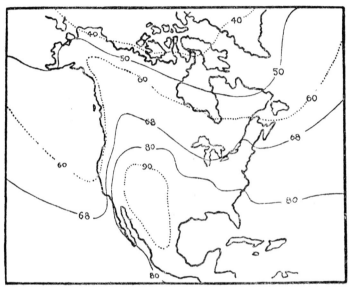

Fig. 24.—Sea-level Isotherms for July.

summer fog. This influence, however, extends little beyond the coast ranges, and the towns of the Great Pacific valley have a summer temperature many degrees higher than coast towns of the same latitude. On the middle Atlantic coast, on the other hand, the winds are southerly, the current warm, and oceanic influence therefore slighter.

So far we have been concerned merely with the average isotherm and isohyet maps. Considered by themselves, they are apt to be misleading. In the first place, they exhibit the

[1] This is more particularly noticeable in April and May—months in which the temperature changes are very rapid. It is the longer growing period rather than the summer maximum which is important.

limitations inseparable from any system of averages, e.g. day and night and other temperature variations within the month are masked. How variable is the actual rainfall distribution, how far from the smooth curve of the average distribution, may be exemplified by one very typical key example shown in Fig. 29, and an example of actual variation in temperature is illustrated in Fig. 28. We may best appreciate the physical phenomena by a consideration of climate from another aspect, viz. that of actual weather conditions. The main elements of what we call weather are actual temperature and precipitation conditions, and these are found to vary in periodic and non-periodic modes ; e.g. the day and night and summer and winter variations are periodic ; the temperature changes incident upon the passage of a Low are mainly non-periodic. Actual weather conditions are a kind of algebraic sum of the periodic and non-periodic elements. Any account of climate, then, which ignores the effect of daily pressure variations is apt to be entirely mis-leading. The student is familiar with the surface air movements attending the movement of a self-contained well-marked Low —the Low of the ordinary textbook. If the weather conditions attending one of these were the same whatever its position over the continent ; if the Lows themselves followed perfectly defined tracts and were of equal intensity, then both weather forecasting and climatic facts would be much simpler than they actually are. What we must emphasize, however, is that an area is said to be subject to a Low when its actual pressure is lower than that of surrounding areas. A point is traversed by a Low with every trough of its barograph, although some of the pressures recorded by these troughs may actually be higher than those of the crests of succeeding conditions. It is the *relative* pressure which defines the HIGH or the Low. On the whole, we may say that the most intense, most extensive, most rapidly moving, and most frequent Lows of the continent are those of the winter season—yet this is the season of which the average isobar map (see Fig. 20) would indicate high continental average pressures ![1]

Then we must remember that the temperature and precipi-tation phenomena associated with either HIGH or LOW vary not only with its relative size and intensity, but with its posi-tion and with the season in which it occurs. For instance, the air movements of which a Low, in winter, say, on the North Pacific coast, is but a symptom, are concerned with rather warm, humid air, the adiabatic expansion of which is attended by very

[1] See " Monthly Weather Review," Supplement No. I : " Types of Storms in the United States and their Average Movements."

heavy precipitation and slight temperature variations. The Low as a pressure condition may perhaps be traced right across the Pacific Cordillera to the High Plains. It is now concerned with different bodies of air much of which may be very cold and of low humidity. There will be less, sometimes no precipitation, consequent upon its passage. The temperature changes may be very great. Or it may be traced right across to the Atlantic, where it will be attended by heavier precipitation again, and that in a different quadrant.

It is these non-periodic variations of the climatic element which defy the analysis of averages ; yet, though irregular in character and in incidence, they are susceptible to certain broad

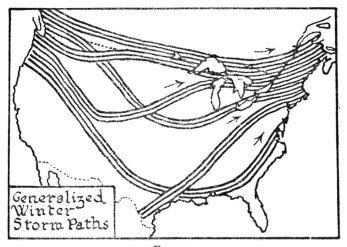

Generalized Winter Storm Paths

Fig. 25.

classifications which may be indicated here. In the first place, HIGHS and LOWS alike move from west to east across the continent—not always directly by any means—but always or nearly always, with an easterly component in their velocity. They are named according to the locality of their apparent origin ; e.g. Alberta, North Pacific, and Texas Lows, are terms used in the official meteorology, but we need not trouble with this classification in an elementary summary. It is sufficient to state that the majority first appear in the north-west coastal area, and move thence across the continent. A minority appear first in Texas, in the Gulf, or even off the South Atlantic states. The Lows are most extensive, deep, swift-moving, in the winter months ; that is, in the season which shows the greatest southern extension of the Aleutian Low itself. The movement of those (the great majority) which first appear in the north-west, though very irregular, can be classed along two main tracks—a northern circuit, which follows roughly the international boundary and leaves via the St. Lawrence valley ; and a southern circuit, on which they first move south-east across the High Plains almost to the Gulf region, and then loop up rapidly to the St. Lawrence exit (Fig. 25). Frequently the southern and longer transit is

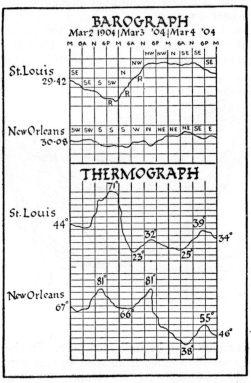

FIG. 26.—Showing characteristic changes due to the passage of a Low over the Central Plains in winter. To illustrate non-periodic changes.

(From U.S.A. Dept. of Agriculture, Weather Bureau Bull. Q, 1906.)

made in as short a time (usually about four days) as the northern one. The passage of these deep winter cyclones, either with their accompanying intervening wedges of high pressure, or around areas of somewhat stable high pressure, may be attended by very great temperature changes, particularly in winter. This is especially so in the interior plains of the continent, where the front of the cyclone may be the area of the northward flow of warm Gulf air, and the rear of the cyclone be accompanied by a southward-moving current of cold air. The diagrams (Figs. 26 and 27) will illustrate typical day-to-day changes consequent upon the passage of these Lows followed by a HIGH in winter.

Now, it is in the winter season that with decreased insolation the diurnal (periodic) control is at its minimum, and, as we have seen, the cyclonic (non-periodic) at its maximum. The temperature changes consequent upon pressure conditions entirely outbalance the diurnal effect. The larger Lows and HIGHS of winter "import wind and weather from a distance."[1] This non-

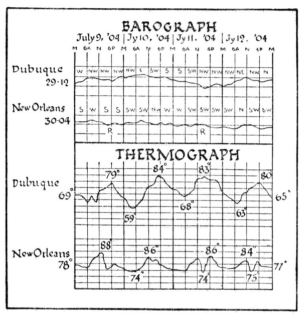

FIG. 27.—To illustrate typical summer conditions in the Central Plains. Day and night temperature changes (i.e. periodic change) are here more important than those consequent upon pressure change.

periodic cyclonic control of the weather is at its maximum in the north-eastern parts of the continent, and decreases to the south. It is at its minimum in the south-western states (Arizona, New Mexico, Western Texas, and South California), where uniformly warm "settled" weather prevails. Even so, deep Lows on the southern circuit are often followed by northerly winds giving killing frosts even as far south as the Gulf coast lands.

[1] "The Weather Element in American Climates," by Robert de C. Ward, in "Annals of the Association of American Geographers," vol. iv, 1914. Students are recommended to read this valuable and suggestive article.

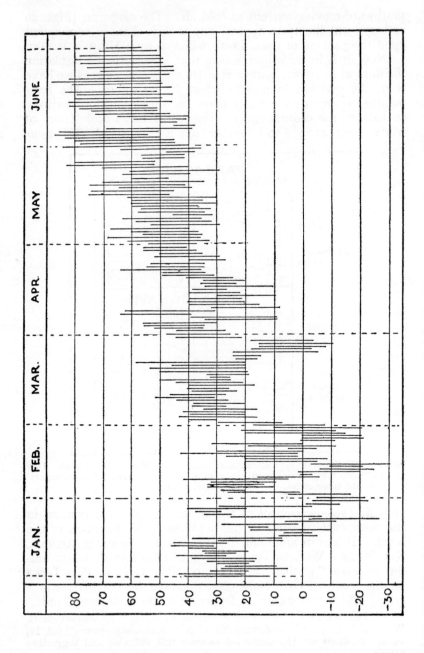

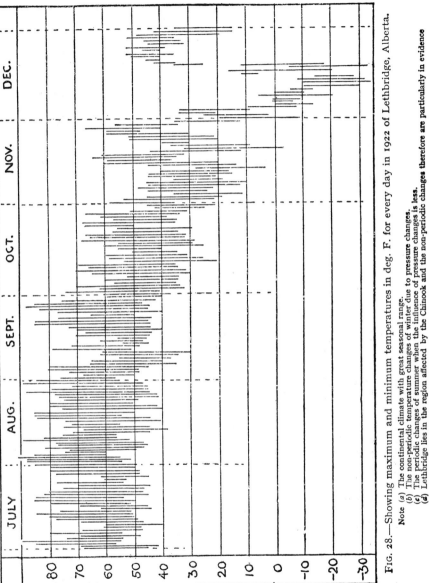

FIG. 28.—Showing maximum and minimum temperatures in deg. F. for every day in 1922 of Lethbridge, Alberta.

Note (a) The continental climate with great seasonal range.
(b) The non-periodic temperature changes of winter due to pressure changes.
(c) The periodic changes of summer when the influence of pressure changes is less.
(d) Lethbridge lies in the region affected by the Chinook and the non-periodic changes therefore are particularly in evidence

In summer the significant temperature changes are diurnal, indicating the return to periodic control. The Aleutian Low is diminished, the cyclones crossing the continent do so on more northerly tracks. They are more usually shallow and slow-moving and give rise to less temperature change than in winter, though they may be accompanied by considerable precipitation. In this season there would appear to be a steady influx of air from the Gulf, unaccompanied by extensive pressure changes, but attended by a multitude of local convectional currents giving daily rains of the thunderstorm type.

It remains to deal with the question of precipitation, which so far has received only incidental mention. Here the total amount and its distribution throughout the year are the important facts.

Factors making for heavy annual precipitation are :

(i) Frequency of Lows and nearness to extensive water-spaces, so that some of the air-streams concerned in the Lows may be of high relative humidity before their ascent and adiabatic cooling.

(ii) The precipitation accompanying the Low is everywhere increased in hilly or mountainous country.

Regions, then, may have a low rainfall if pressure variations are slight, i.e. if they are off the usual cyclonic paths (e.g. as in the south-western states), if they are in the rain shadows of mountains (as, e.g., in the intermontane plateaux of the Pacific Cordillera), or if they are at great distances from water areas. It would appear that the summer cyclones, though slightly less numerous and considerably less intense on the average than those of winter, are more effective rain-bringers in the interior, for the continental interior has a marked summer maximum. In the centre and south, however, much of this is due to local convectional thunder showers. Winter and summer alike, the Lows are effective precipitation-bringers in the St. Lawrence valley, and where nearing the Gulf or Atlantic coasts, or even running parallel to these coasts, as do some of the winter Lows on the southern circuit.

Broadly, we may state that precipitation east of the Rockies decreases from east to west and becomes more markedly a summer rainfall in the same direction. Perhaps the most important single climatic feature in the whole continent is the line, or rather narrow zone, which separates the eastern half of the continent, where precipitation is sufficient for agriculture, from

the western half, where—save in the north-western coast lands
—it is usually insufficient. It is not, of course, susceptible to
exact definition, for modern methods of agriculture, e.g. dry
farming and seed selection, tend to shift it slightly to the west.
Nor does it coincide with any actual isohyet, for more rain is
required in the south, with its greater evaporation, than in the
north. Heavy wheat production takes place in North-west
Dakota with a rainfall of barely 15 inches. The production of
Kansas and Oklahoma is mostly in areas having more than
20 inches. However, a line from about long. 97° on the Texas
Gulf coast to long. 101° at the boundary between the Dakotas
and thence swinging westward with the 15-inch isohyet into
Canada, divides roughly the agricultural lands of the east and
central states from the arid lands of the high plains. East
of the main valley of the Mississippi and of Lake Superior,
the rainfall is pretty well distributed through the year, and,
apart from irregularities due to relief, decreases from south to
north and from east to west. From the Mississippi line to the
Rockies, the precipitation decreases and becomes more markedly
a summer rainfall.

Turning now to the Pacific coast of the continent, we find
that precipitation may be related to the positions of the pressure
systems—the Aleutian Low dominant in winter, and the Equatorial Low swinging northwards in summer. The change-over
from a winter to a summer maximum takes place in the latitude
of the nearly rainless regions of the mid-Californian peninsula.
From about lat. 29° precipitation increases both to the north and
to the south—but to the north with a winter maximum and to
the south with a summer maximum. The Pacific coast ranges
and Great Valley are usually divided from north to south into
regions as follows :

(a) To lat. 42°. Well-distributed rainfall.
(b) To ,,   34°. Mediterranean climate.
(c) To ,,   25°. Arid belt.
(d) South of lat. 25°. Region of summer rains.

The division is well enough if one remembers that the change
is everywhere *very gradual*. The British Columbia coast knows
no regular summer drought, though there is a very marked
winter maximum. The Cowlitz-Willamette portion of the Pacific trough has from one to two months' summer drought ; the
Great Valley of California from four to five months' summer
drought, and that with a temperature high enough to be classi-
fied as a region of Mediterranean climate. Throughout the

whole Pacific coastlands the precipitation in any latitude varies with relief, being heaviest on the western side of the Sierra,

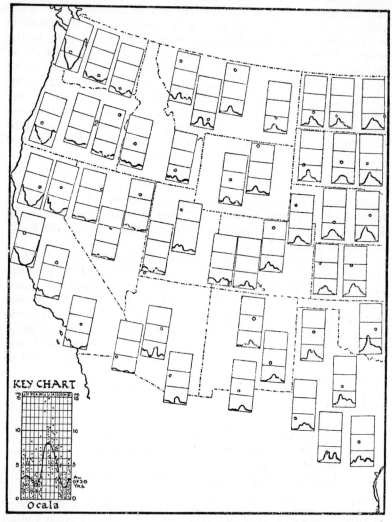

KEY CHART

Ocala

FIG. 29.—Shows average distribution of

then on the western slope of the coast ranges, and least in the Great Pacific valley.

Students should examine very carefully the rainfall curves of Fig. 29. It is far and away the best method of realizing both the distribution of precipitation throughout the United States and throughout the year. It will be seen that on the basis of

rainfall throughout the year in selected localities.

(*After* " Atlas of American Agriculture.")

such curves the U.S.A. can be divided into precipitation distribution divisions such as those indicated in Fig. 30. The particular lines shown are those adopted by Kendrew in his " Climates of the Continents."

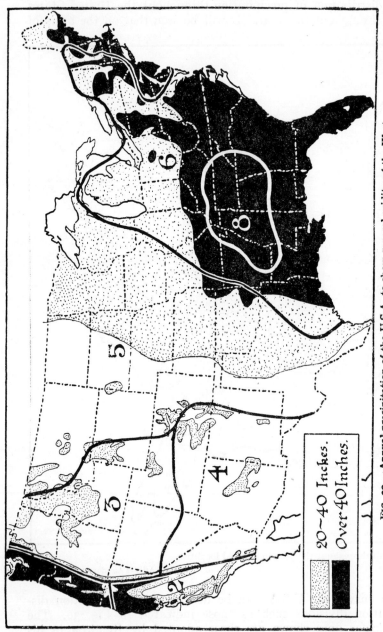

FIG. 30.—Annual precipitation of the U.S.A. to show general aridity of the West.

Rainfall Regions are those adopted by Kendrew in the " Climates of the Continents." The boundaries should be considered zones rather than lines everywhere save along the Sierra Nevada-Cascade system. The unshaded area has less than 20 inches.

20–40 Inches.

Over 40 Inches.

Notes on the divisions.

(1) Abundant rainfall with tendency to drought in July and August. Marked winter maximum.

(2) Rainfall diminishing to the south and summer drought increasing.

Total precipitation depends on position ; on coast range, Pacific valley, or western sierra.

(3) Rainfall small. Greater in winter six months with slight spring maximum.

(4) Rainfall small. Greater in winter six months but with an early autumn sub-maximum.

(5) Rainfall with distinct midsummer maximum. Arid in the west.

(6) Rainfall everywhere well distributed and sufficient for intensive agriculture.

(7) Well distributed but with autumn and early winter maximum.

(8) Fairly well distributed but with early spring and summer maximum.

Fig. 31, showing the number of days under snow for various areas, is interesting, and may be related to farm practice, e.g. the snow protection of fall wheat and the winter housing of cattle.

We have already noted that afternoon thunderstorms are a periodic feature of the south-eastern states in summer. They are accompanied by heavy rainfall, and their frequency and wide distribution make them important contributors to the precipitation of the country. More local and much more intense are the tornadoes. These are defined as " violent windstorms accompanied by rain, hail, thunder, and lightning, in which air masses whirl with great velocity about a central cone, while the whole storm travels across-country in a narrow path at a considerable speed." These storms have a destructive diameter of from a few hundred feet to a half a mile, and sometimes more. When seen from a distance, the tornado has the appearance of a dense cloud-mass with one or more funnel-shaped clouds which may or may not reach the earth. They occur almost invariably in the south-eastern quadrant of a Low. They travel from south-west to north-east, and seldom persist as destructive storms for more than 25 miles. These storms are confined to the continent east of the Rockies but south of lat. 48°. They are most frequent in the summer months, but occur only in the Gulf states in winter. They are most frequent in the West Central states.

In our discussion so far we have made use of what are the most accessible and compact body of data, viz. mean monthly

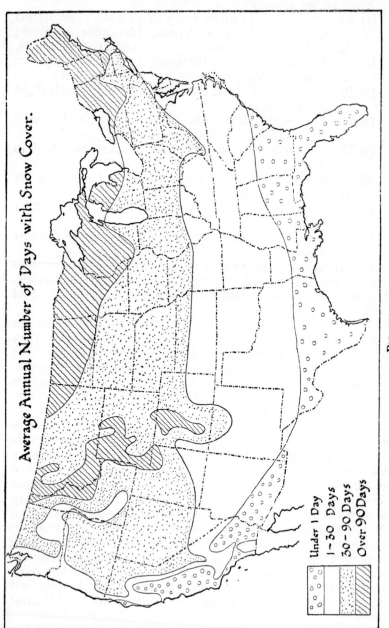

Average Annual Number of Days with Snow Cover.

Under 1 Day
1–30 Days
30–90 Days
Over 90 Days

FIG. 31.

temperature and precipitation figures. Caution and experience are necessary if such are not to be very misleading. Apart from the masking of both periodic and non-periodic variations inseparable from this use of averages, it is questionable whether the simple arithmetical mean is the best summary indication available. In this connection we would refer the student to a suggestion for the use of medians rather than averages in the presentation of precipitation data.[1]

In geography we are concerned with the biological importance of climate, and here precipitation and temperature act not separately but together. It follows then that the most significant index of climatic influence must be found neither in the one nor in the other, but in some function of both. In relating precipitation to crop production we require to know, not only its distribution throughout the year, but also its relation to evaporation, and therefore to temperature.

Perhaps the two best known systems which combine both temperature and precipitation data are those of Köppen and of Thornthwaite, and these, and particularly that of the latter, can at once be correlated to the major zones of natural vegetation.

In detail, no manipulation of shade temperature and precipitation data, actual or average, separate or combined, can give a complete index of vegetative cover. Much of plant growth is on and in the ground, and not only at the height and in the shade of a Stevenson screen. It is subject to soil conditions which are seldom homogeneous within a climatic province.

Official meteorological and climatic data are contained in the following publications :

" *Climatic Data of the U.S.A by Sections.*" The monthly volumes contain daily maxima and minima temperatures for the month, and also daily precipitation for all stations in the U.S.A. The annual volume gives the averages for the months and for the year and the departure of these averages from the normal. The volumes are wholly statistical.

" *The Monthly Weather Review.*" This is an official meteorological and climatic periodical, and contains abstracts and contributions of home and foreign origin. It contains many articles which are essential for a detailed study of American climates.

The U.S.A. Dept. of Agriculture : " Weather Bureau Bulletin Q, 1906." Is a whole volume on the climatology of the United States by A. J. Henry. It summarizes the climatology of the country in a long article, and contains a great number of averaged data.

The U.S.A. Dept. of Agriculture : " Weather Bureau Bulletin L, 1903." Is a climatology of California.

The U.S.A. Dept. of Agriculture publishes the " Atlas of American Agriculture, 1936," which contains map folios showing climatic elements (precipitation, frost, and growing period, etc.) in map form. Compiled

---

[1] "Scottish Geographical Magazine," March 1933: "The Analysis of Rainfall Probability" by P. R. Crowe.

using the most recent material. The maps are beautifully finished and are exceedingly valuable to the student.

The Department of Marine and Fisheries Central Office, Toronto, Canada, issues the " Monthly Record of Meteorological Observations." These give the temperature, humidity, precipitation, wind, cloudiness, conditions *day by day*. Unfortunately, normal values do not always accompany these actual monthly records. More and better equipped stations must be provided in the unoccupied regions before reliable climatic maps of Northern Canada can be made.

Geog. Rev., xxi, 1931, pp. 633-55. C. W. Thornthwaite. "The Climates of North America according to a New Classification."

CHAPTER XI

NATURAL VEGETATION

IN this chapter a summary account will be given of the *original* distribution of the major types of grass lands, scrub lands, and forest lands in the U.S.A. The forest belts of Canada are dealt with in Chapter XXXII.

By original distribution we mean the distribution (as far as may be reasonably surmised) at the time of the coming of the Europeans. Since that date much forest land has become crop land. Much has been cut over, or perhaps burnt over; reverting to forest, but not necessarily, or immediately, to the original type. Grass lands and scrub lands have been over-grazed and the original character of the vegetation altered. However, the natural vegetation of the country is of special significance to the geographer. Indeed, Nature herself is here the geographer, for she has coloured the continents with distinctive belts of vegetation, each the index of a synthesis of topographic, climatic, and soil influences. In an undeveloped country the natural vegetation is often the best indication of the climate and of the value of the land.

In the brief summary that follows the student will find it necessary to have constantly in mind the major climatic and topographic divisions of the continent. The vegetation map (Fig. 32) has entailed so much simplification that certain definite reservations as to its use should be noted at once.

(i) The map refers to *original* vegetation. Thus e.g. most of the eastern hardwood forest areas are now occupied by farm lands.

(ii) The divisions are so broad that many very different types are included in one division. This is particularly so when sudden changes in elevation, aspect, soil, etc., introduce—sometimes within small areas—very various types.

(iii) In the case of some of the forest belts, the names of certain dominating species are introduced—more especially when these refer to timber of economic value. It must not be thought, however, that very many others do not occur. Pure stands over considerable areas are exceptional.

Fig. 32 shows that in the U.S.A. we have great eastern and western forest belts separated, except in the extreme south, by a grass belt. The eastern forest was predominantly hardwood, but passed to predominantly coniferous (a) along the Canadian border, (b) along the sandy belts of the coast plain.

The grass lands occupy a broad belt almost from the Western Gulf to the Canadian prairies, north of which the east and west continental forest belts coalesce in a northern coniferous forest. The western forest belt in the U.S.A. differs from the eastern in being almost wholly coniferous (except for the stunted hardwoods of the Chaparral Belt) and in being mainly developed on the outstanding mountain masses, the vast intervening plateaux, basins, and plains being covered with a semi-arid grass vegetation or arid desert shrub type. The well-watered lowland of the Pacific Valley of Washington was densely forested however.

THE WESTERN FORESTS. These are all mainly coniferous and all (except in the Puget Sound, Willamette and Cowlitz Valley region) confined to the chief mountain masses. The divisions shown on the map will require considerable subdivision and qualification. These divisions are :

(a) Forests of heavy rainfall. (Pacific Wet.)

(b) Forests of light rainfall (fairly well distributed). (Pacific Dry.)

(c) Forests of light rainfall with prolonged summer drought. (Chaparral.)

(a) *Western Forests of Heavy Rainfall.* These contain areas of the densest and most valuable stands in the continent.

Further subdivisions are essential. Thus (Fig. 32)—

(i) The Coast Range, Pacific Valley and Western (i.e. wetter) slope of the Cascades in Washington and Oregon.

Here are large areas of pure Douglas Fir, and large ones of mixed stands with Western Red Cedar, Douglas Fir, and Hemlock, predominating. In the higher parts of the Cascades, Firs are predominant. These western forests of Washington and Oregon form dense stands of large structural timber, and are the most valuable reserves of the U.S.A. Even so, much of the most accessible timber has been cut, and much burnt over.

(ii) The coast range of California as far as the Golden Gate and the western slope of the Sierra Nevada. Here in the main we still have dense stands and big timber, but the timber line rises in the southern Sierra, and forest here favours the wet southern slopes. From these great belts we may detach (ii, a)

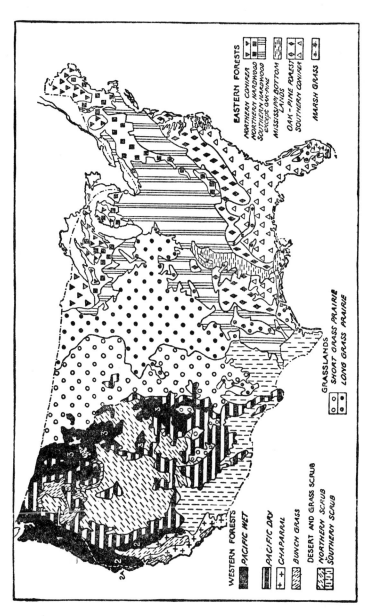

Fig. 32.—Vegetation Zones in the U.S.A.

the Redwood Forest, a belt 400 miles long and 20 miles wide, from the Oregon boundary to Santa Cruz. The Redwood forms pure stands on the flats and river benches, but is usually associated with Douglas Fir and Western Hemlock. Apart from the Redwood Forest this great area has mixed stands of Sugar Pine, Western Yellow Pine and Incense Cedar, with Douglas Fir in the more northerly wetter areas. In the Western Sierra Nevada the lower forest line rises as we proceed southwards.

(iii) The mountain masses of the Rockies in Idaho, W. Montana, W. Wyoming and in Colorado. The higher timber land here (7,500 feet–11,000 feet) is occupied by Engelman Spruce and Alpine Fir. Surrounding these and often invading Engelman Spruce areas which have been fired, are the most valuable of the Rocky Mountain forests—those in which the Lodge Pole Pine predominates.

(b) *Western Forests of Lighter Rainfall.* Between the forests already mentioned and the great semi-arid grass and scrub lands of the interior plateau, are forest belts which in general receive less moisture and occupy lower or more southerly hill masses. Such forests occupy the eastern (i.e. drier) slope of the Cascades and Sierra Nevada, and the western sides of northern Rockies. They surround the high mass of the central Rockies, and cover the highest land in Arizona. In the northern and higher areas of the southern parts of the belt, Western Yellow Pine is the predominant species, forming sometimes pure stands and sometimes mixed with Douglas Fir, Sugar Pine or White Fir. In Utah, Nevada, New Mexico, Arizona and Colorado this forest degenerates at lower levels into an open south-western woodland of mixed small pines and Juniper. The Western Yellow Pine forests are open forests of big trees with no underbush, but usually with grass underneath. The timber is valuable and the open forests afford good summer grazing.

(c) *The Chaparral* of the south coast ranges and mountains of California is a mixed forest of stunted hardwood and shrubs occupying positions similar to those of the pinus-Juniper woodlands, but in a climate where dry (summer) and wet (winter) seasons are quite definite.

THE EASTERN FORESTS. The Eastern States have in general a heavy and well-distributed rainfall, and west of the Appalachians when this becomes somewhat lighter it shows also a slight summer preponderance. Under these conditions hardwoods tend to occupy all but an area of relatively short growing season in the north, or areas of high altitudes, swamps, and sandy belts in the south, where coniferous forests are apt to occur. Of the million square miles once occupied by forest in the Eastern

States only one-quarter remains. Originally hardwood forests covered the greater area, but since they occupied also the best farm land the remaining eastern forest is almost equally divided in area between hardwood and softwood.

In Fig. 32 we have distinguished the following divisions :

(a) *North-eastern Coniferous Forest.* This occupies much of Maine and the Adirondacks, the Michigan Peninsula, and the land about Lake Superior, and occurs also in high altitudes of the Appalachian Uplands. Here Black Spruce and Balsam Fir, Norway and Jack Pine, and White Pine, are predominant trees with Black Spruce and Tamarack predominant in swampy localities. In the Michigan area dense, extensive, and almost pure stands of the valuable White Pine once formed the forest.

(b) *The Northern Hardwood Forest* of widely varying composition. Sugar Maple and Yellow Birch predominate, but the Beech and Elm are important constituents, with Hemlocks and Spruce on the less fertile areas.

(c) *The Southern Hardwood Forest* can be divided into :

(i) Oak-Chestnut forest, occupying much of the area between the Appalachian and the Ohio and Middle Mississippi. Oak, Chestnut and Yellow Poplar are predominant, but the forest is the richest in species of any in America.

(ii) Oak-Hickory forest. West of the Oak-Chestnut forest and lying between it and the prairie is a forest where Oak and Hickory predominate, with Ash, Elm and Elder as other frequent species.

These hardwood forests, which originally occupied some of the best land of the States, have been largely cleared.

(d) *The Oak-Pine Forest.* This essentially mixed type occupies a belt of country which includes much of the Piedmont, the north half of the Eastern Gulf States, and much of Arkansas. Various Oaks and the Short-leaf, Loblolly, and Scrub Pine are the chief species.

(e) *The South-east Pine Belt* is a very valuable coniferous forest occupying the light soils of the Coast Plain of the South-eastern Atlantic and Gulf States. Long-leaf, Loblolly and Slash Pines are the dominant species. The forest is open in type with a coarse grass and low brush undergrowth.

(f) *The Mississippi Bottom Forests* and the *Florida Everglades* were, and where undrained are, occupied by forests of Swamp Cypress and Tripela Gum in the more permanently wet areas, and a great variety of hardwoods on less moist areas.

(g) *Mangrove thickets* occur in the warm, salt, quiet, coastal creeks of Southern Florida.

Of the eastern forests most of the best land (i.e. best from the point of view of general situation, topography and soil, has become crop land. Much of the pine belt, too, has become agricultural land, but even more remains as cut-over land of small present value.

THE GRASS LANDS

The greatest area of original grass land in America lies between the original eastern forests and the Rockies. As one proceeded westward across Indiana, say, one left the Oak-Hickory forests approximately at the western border of that state and entered the prairie state of Illinois. Even here the river flood plains and terraces were followed by narrow belts of forest, and similar belts extended far to the west across the grass lands up the right-bank tributaries of the Mississippi–Missouri. This river border forest is general in the grass lands, but to avoid complication is not shown in Fig. 32. Proceeding north-westward across the tall grasses of Illinois and Iowa into South Dakota one would have found, were the profile examined from time to time, that with the decreasing precipitation, and the increasing summer proportion of that precipitation, one reached a zone where not enough rain fell to effect a junction between the periodically wettened surface soil and the ground water-table. Along this line a layer of calcium carbonate appears in the soil, and as one proceeds westward this increases in thickness and approaches the surface. Frequently where this salt accumulation is first perceptible the soils become black in colour. Proceeding westwards with still diminishing precipitation the lime layer approaches within 2 feet to 2 feet 6 inches of the surface; there is less room for root development and short grass species compete successfully with the long grasses. Usually, too, the black soils give place to dark brown soils along this line. We see then that in e.g. Illinois, the tall grass prairies extend far to the east of the line where a lime accumulation begins, and appear to have encroached upon areas where hardwood forests might reasonably have been expected.

The change from tall to short grass takes place always somewhere between long. 99°–101° and is usually accompanied by (i) a change from black to brown soils, (ii) an approach of the lime layer to within 2 feet to 2½ feet of the surface.

This western limit of the black soils, which, as stated, often coincides with the eastern limit of short grasses, forms by far the most important economic dividing line of the states. The humid lands, and possibly the true forest lands, may be considered to be limited westwards by the incoming of the *lime belt*, but the *long grass-black soil* belt between this line and the eastern boundary of the short grasses, though sub-humid, contains some of the most important grain areas of the continent. Once in the short grass area, however, the lands are semi-arid. Farming is limited to special crops (e.g. grain sorghums) and to dry-farming methods, or the land remains in permanent pasture.

Pacific Grass Lands (Bunch grass) occupied chiefly the eastern and southern, i.e. the higher moister parts, of the Lava Plains of Washington and Oregon, and much of the Great Valley of California. Originally a very valuable grazing area and now much used in dry-farmed crops, e.g. the Palouse wheat area of Washington.

Desert Grass and Shrub Vegetation

Northern Desert Shrub. This occupies the western portion of the Washington Lava Plain, the greater area of the Great Basin [1] and the Laramie Plains, and much of the Colorado plateau lands. Cacti are absent and there is a monotonous cover of sage bush and other silvery grey shrubs. This type pushes in places into the Juniper-Pinon woodland already referred to. The rainfall is all less than 15 inches and often less than 10 inches. All the area is grazed, especially in winter, but much of the forage value lies in relatively inconspicuous or secondary species of grasses and other forage crops in the interspaces of the dominant shrubs.

The Southern Desert Shrub. Here the heat is greater, and the precipitation even less. The characteristic plants are creosote bush and mesquite, and in parts yuccas, cacti and spiny shrubs are predominant features. In western Texas the shrub grass is interrupted by a savannah-like cover of small trees (mesquite predominant) and thorn bushes.

[1] The numerous narrow, parallel ridges, rising 1,000 feet to 1,500 feet above the great basin, are covered with a Juniper and Small Pine woodland, not shown on the map.

CHAPTER XII

SOILS AND SOIL EROSION

THE characteristics of a soil are not only reflected in its vegetation ; they are, in large part, the product of that vegetation. A mature and virgin soil may support a particular group of plant associations over a considerable period of time ; but in the establishment of this natural vegetation, there has been a gradual change of plants from those suited to the earlier condition of the soil, to those more suited to the soil as modified by this earlier cover.

We should not regard the soil as some static reserve of plant food, changing only to the extent to which it is depleted in giving nutriment to our crops. Rather we should consider it as a sensitive, vital, and dynamic whole, having characteristics, functions, and possibilities in relation to crop production, which are certain to be changed by man's interference, and which, too often, are thereby altered for the worse.

Thus the sequence in our studies—climate, vegetation, soils and crops—is a logical one ; and with climate lies the initiative. Nor should we consider only the surface layer of the soil, though this may be its most important portion, and in the growth of many crops, the one most intimately concerned.

An obvious and important soil characteristic is that relating to the size of the particles ; and since, in general, a sample from any horizon will contain both large and small particles, what we are really concerned with is the proportions of these at various levels. In the soil literature of the United States, particles of over 2 mm. are classed as stones ; of between 1 and 2 mm. as gravel ; of between ·05 and 1 mm. as sands ; of between ·005 mm. and ·05 mm. as silt ; and of less than ·005 mm. as clays. Decomposed organic matter seldom has particles of as much as ·005 mm., and is classed as clay.

In any one sample all these will be mixed, and thus *sandy soils* are defined as those having less than 20 per cent. silt and clay particles, *loams* as having between 20 per cent. and 50 per cent. silt and clay particles, and *clays* as having at least 30 per cent. of clay particles only. Unless otherwise stated this refers to only the top 8 inches of the profile.

But the texture, though of great importance, is not the only effective characteristic ; and that this may be the clearer we will consider briefly the interrelation of plant and soil.

In the ultimate analysis of a plant the chief constituent by weight will often prove to be water. In the living plant this fills out the cells of the plant, and without a sufficient supply, wilting begins. The water is derived from soil moisture, and enters the plant through the root system, circulates to the leaves, supplying nutriment in solution in its passage, and is evaporated from the leaf stomata. The rate of this evaporation, though in part controlled by the plant, is also dependent upon the temperature, humidity, and movement of the surrounding air. In general, in a warm climate, a crop will require a heavier precipitation than that which would be necessary in a cooler climate.

But a consideration of precipitation in relation to evaporation is not enough. The plant takes nutriment in solution most effectively from a colloidal complex of clay-sized mineral particles and organic matter, or humus. It is this same complex which has the property of retaining moisture, and of effecting the integration of soil particles into granules.

Ultimate analysis of the dry material of a plant would show that carbon, hydrogen, oxygen and nitrogen made up the larger part. The hydrogen and the oxygen are supplied by the water, and some of the oxygen also from the air. The carbon is partly supplied from the organic matter in the soil, but mainly from the carbon dioxide of the air by the photosynthetic action of the chlorophyl in the green parts of the plant. The next most abundant element is nitrogen. This is mainly supplied from the humus, in which its presence is partly due to the decay of plant material in the soil. Certain soil bacteria, too, have the property of taking up nitrogen from the air. Leguminous plants have the property, through bacteriological action, of fixing very considerable quantities of atmospheric nitrogen in nodular-like excrescences of the root system. Certain other elements, such as phosphorus, potash and calcium, will also be present. These, again, are in part present in the soil, because of the decay there of former vegetation ; but in part they are obtained from the parent rock material. Water, containing carbon dioxide and various organic acids obtained from the humus, gradually breaks down this parent material of the sub-soil ; and soluble parts of it are then brought up to the surface by circulation through the root systems. Upon the decay of the plant some of these substances remain in the upper layers of the soil.

In the natural condition, as a plant decays and another takes its place, most of the constituent dry materials return to the soil ; though in humid climates some of them may subsequently be leached beyond the reach of plant roots. As a rule, however, in a virgin soil, there is an excess of decayed organic material (humus) already available in the soil, though the amount and condition of this varies enormously with the conditions under which the soil has developed.

Once soil is brought into cultivation, however, large parts of the plant, and often particularly those parts richest in certain plant foods, are not returned to the soil. The excess of plant food in the humus is more or less rapidly used up, and the demand for soluble nitrogen and other elements becomes greater than their very gradual regeneration in available form.

Resort must then be had to natural and to artificial fertilizers. A crop rotation, with grasses and leguminous plants in the system, may help to retain fertility and to keep the soil in good tilth. One of the main advantages of mixed farming lies in the manure which becomes available. Chilean nitrate, and ammonium sulphate (a by-product wherever coke is produced) and nitrogen fixed chemically from the air (often as ammonium sulphate) are among the most used mineral sources of nitrogen fertilizer. Calcium and phosphorus are obtained by the treatment of bones, or of mineral phosphates. Basic slag, a by-product of the basic steel process, provides also both these elements. Potash fertilizers are usually obtained from a treatment of kainite deposits. In soils which had originally but a small storage of available plant food, continued crop production soon necessitates either the use of fertilizers, or a dwindling, and ultimately a very low yield.

We emphasize above all, then, in any estimate of a soil, the importance of the presence of organic matter in available colloidal form, not merely as the immediate source of much of the plant nutriment, but because of its physical and bio-chemical characteristics, characteristics which result in water retention, soil granulation, effective delivery of nutriment to the plant, resistance to erosion, and healthy bacteriological action.

If we inspect a fresh section of some mature soil in a humid region, we can often discern a series of layers, at once distinguishable either in colour or in texture or in both. Laboratory analysis confirms and defines the existence of layers of different texture and of different mineral and organic content.

In humid climates soils are leached. Fine particles of mineral matter and of decomposed humus become detached from the surface layer, and tend to accumulate in what becomes a horizon of finer texture some few feet or inches from the surface. Soluble matter, both organic and inorganic, is also leached from the surface layer. Thus the soil scientist calls the surface layers from which material has been leached the A horizon of a soil, and the succeeding horizon, which receives this transferred surface material, is termed the B horizon. The fragmented parent material below is known as the C horizon.

All soils of humid regions, however different otherwise, have such characteristics and are known as *Pedalfers.*

Thus these cover the eastern part of the continent, a great continuous area in which the relation of precipitation to evaporation is high. The western half, however, if we except the wet coastal regions of the north-west, and a northerly belt in Canada where evaporation is very low, has only just enough precipitation to support its various types of vegetative cover. Except in mountain ranges, there is little run-off to the rivers, and most of the water soaking into the ground is returned through the vegetation in the process of plant transpiration. A little below the root system of the plants the ground may be permanently dry, and at about this level will occur a layer impregnated with mineral salts which could be carried no lower.

Soils, however different otherwise, developed under such moisture conditions, are known as *pedocals,* and thus are predominant in the western half of the continent. The boundary line between pedalfers and pedocals comes along the eastern limit of the great Black Soil belt. On either side of this line the two major soil groups are represented by their most fertile members, the black soils to the west, and the prairie earths to the east, each of them, be it noted at once, developed under a grass cover, but the black soils with a lesser precipitation and consequently a layer of carbonate accumulation. The classification of soils on the basis of the chemical, physical and organic content of the various horizons in the whole soil profile, is a work of recent years, and one requiring an army of experimentalists. In the United States many hundreds of soils have been distinguished, and anything approaching an account of this work would be quite beyond the scope of this book.[1] All the types, however, fall into a major classification of less than a dozen groups, and the characteristics of these we will now indicate briefly. (Their distribution is shown in Fig. 33.) All the *pedalfers* have developed under a forest cover, except only the *prairie earths,* which occupy an anomalous position in that although having a natural grass cover, they yet receive enough moisture to support a forest cover.

The remaining pedalfers are grouped respectively as *podsols, grey brown earths,* and *red and yellow earths.*

[1] For a full account of the soil of the U.S.A. see " Atlas of American Agriculture." United States Department of Agriculture. 1936. Section on Soils.

The Podsols. These occur throughout Canada (except in the western prairies, the Ontario Peninsula and the drier parts of British Columbia) and the north-eastern United States ; areas of cool summers, of small evaporation, and of fairly well distri-

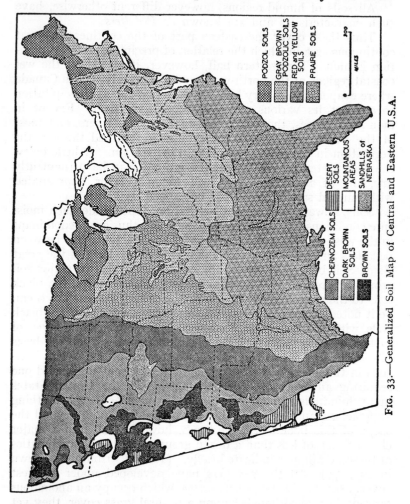

FIG. 33.—Generalized Soil Map of Central and Eastern U.S.A.

buted precipitation. The prevailing forest cover was coniferous, with an undergrowth of acid-loving plants. Hill country, or sandy belts, tend to extend these soils in patches into the next soil province to the south.

In general the soil profile is as follows. At the surface is a brown layer of largely undecomposed forest debris, acid in reaction, and without structure. This raw humus is succeeded, often quite suddenly, by a white or grey leached band of a thickness varying from a mere film to a foot or two. This light-coloured portion of the A horizon is found to be coarser in texture than the brown or coffee-coloured B horizon which lies beneath, and which usually contains, too, more aluminium (but less silica) and more calcium, iron, and bases generally than the A horizon. The B horizon is sometimes indurated, and grades usually into a lighter-coloured C horizon of the parent material. The podsols represent the poorest major group of soils in the continent. The soils are over acid, often badly drained, leached of soluble mineral bases, and with surface forest waste incompletely broken down. Much of the area concerned is mountainous, or of a topography and drainage unsuitable for agriculture. Extensive areas remain as forest or cut-over land. Farming, where possible, remains subsidiary to forest industry except in the vicinity of considerable urban centres. Dairying and the raising of potatoes and oats are typical farming activities.

The Grey Brown Earths. These pedalfers succeed the podsols to the south. They have, then, a heavy well-distributed precipitation, but a higher temperature. The original vegetation was forest of hardwood, i.e. of broad-leaved deciduous character. The forest cover and undergrowth yielded a larger amount of organic matter ; the higher temperature ensured its more complete disintegration. Leaching remains a characteristic, and finer soil particles and soluble bases have been transferred to the B horizon. The soils still have an acid reaction. The surface humus is more decomposed. The succeeding light-coloured leached layer is less defined, not so light in colour, and has more decomposed organic matter in its upper layers than is the case in the podsols. The B horizon is not usually indurated. The chief active differentiating factors have been the higher temperatures and the broad leaf forest cover.

Most of the hardwood forest has been cleared, and most of the land is in farms. Compared with the prairie earths which adjoin this soil region to the west, there has been more leaching, and there is a smaller store of plant food available. Thus, though often good as virgin soils, they quickly lost fertility, and required some form or other of fertilization. The local exceptions within the major province are very considerable, and we can instance at once such relatively rich soils as those developed in the Lexington Blue Grass region or in the Great Appalachian Valley. But these are exceptional. The area as a whole was early occupied and has been long farmed. Mixed farming predominates, with a tendency to dairy farming to supply the great industrial populations.

Red and Yellow Soils. These succeed the Grey Brown Earth province to the south. The rainfall of the province is even heavier, and occurs with a greater proportion of summer thunderstorms. The natural vegetation was again broad-leaved forest. with, however, the major exception of the great south-eastern pine belt of the coast plain. The summer temperatures are subtropical and the frost season very short. Under these conditions leaching has gone further than in the Grey Brown Earth province. The texture difference between the A and B horizons is very marked, the latter being often a stiff clay. The actual surface is usually greyish and contains a small store of humus. This is succeeded by red or yellow layers. The latter are especially prevalent if the water table is, or has recently been, high.

As a whole this great south-eastern soil province has soils of fertility intermediate between that of the podsols and the Grey Brown Earths. Again, there are very great local differences, and one may instance especially the very poor soils of much of the sandy coast plain belt. A very rapid deterioration on cultivation is characteristic. Special cash crops grown with slave labour dominated the whole area, and as the soils were quickly impoverished, much land fell out of cultivation, and new land was quickly taken up farther and farther westward. The dominant crops, cotton and maize, are intertilled, and soil without vegetation cover is particularly liable to erosion. To-day more than half this province is forest or cut-over land. Yet the long growing season allows of a great range of crops, and often of the early ripening of vegetables and orchard fruits. Thus, side by side with much poor farming on impoverished and eroded soils, are areas of specialist production of crops of such a nature that they can bear a heavy fertilizer expenditure.

The Prairie Earths. This soil province is unique. Like the pedocals its soils have developed under a grass cover, but with a precipitation and temperature which would have allowed of a hardwood forest. Only to a minor extent are its typical soils (many are not typical) pedalferic. Thus as normally represented on the flat undissected portions of the prairie plains, there has been little leaching, and the texture of the B horizon is little if any heavier than that of the A. Normally the surface 8 inches or so are dark brown or nearly black in colour, very rich in organic matter, and have bases so little leached that only the actual surface is at all acidic.

Towards the rivers, where the land is more dissected, areas of more podzolic character occur. The difference between this province and that of the grey brown earths is due most largely to the accident of its grass cover. Grass vegetation is peculiarly designed to bring leached material back to the surface, and in particular, if lime is so brought back, it will help to stabilize the colloid complex, and so preserve the flocculation of the soil into a granular tilth.

Some of the soils in this group are among the most productive in the country, combining the large reserves of plant food of the *Black Earths*, with a moisture condition which allows of more intense production than can be obtained from these. The northern part of the province occupies a considerable portion of the Corn Belt, and the southern portions contain the better cotton lands of Texas and Oklahoma.

The Pedocals. These are all developed under sub-humid, semi-arid, or arid conditions, and the generic characteristic is the accumulation of carbonate at the base of the soil profile. Their place is taken by pedalferic soils in the western half of the continent only in regions of low temperatures, as in western Canada north of the prairies ; or in regions of high precipitation, as in the Rocky Mountains and the coastal ranges and valleys of Washington, Oregon and British Columbia.

In general as the precipitation decreases, the grass cover gets thinner, short grasses take the place of long grasses, and eventually scrub and desert vegetation, the place of grass. Thus in all the pedocals there is little leaching, and the amount of organic matter depends on the density and nature of the vegetation cover. With decrease of organic matter the colour becomes lighter. Thus, between the *pedalferic* soils of the east and the Rocky Mountains we have a series of soil bands running from north to south, and with colour changing from black in the east to light brown or grey in the west. Actually, and in detail, some of the soils become a little darker again just before one reaches the Rocky Mountains.

The change is gradual and the soils have been grouped respectively as Black Earths, Dark Brown Earths, Brown Earths, and Grey Earths.

The Black Earth or Chernozem Zone. This occupies the Red River Valley in Canada, and widens into the great north–south belt shown in Fig. 33.

The natural vegetation consists mainly of long grasses, though short grasses usually just begin to predominate towards the western limit of the belt. An almost black A horizon is exceptionally rich in organic matter. This is succeeded gradually downwards by a dark brown horizon of much the same texture, but with less humus. The carbonate accumulation may come in at a depth of 30 or more inches. Even if, as in many of the northern soils of this group, the parent material be a highly calcareous glacial drift, the soil surface will be almost neutral.

The zone of carbonate accumulation is usually readily distinguishable from the parent material below.

This Black Earth belt forms one of the richest agricultural areas of the continent. The abundance of plant food stored in the soil, its physical condition, and the large areas of flat or gently undulating land available, allow of large-scale extensive farming, over a long period of years, without either the use of fertilizers or the adoption of much diversification. On the other hand, high yields cannot generally be taken because of the low rainfall, and as one proceeds westwards, a larger proportion of the land must be in summer fallow to preserve moisture, and such land is peculiarly liable to wind erosion. Even these fine soils are gradually deteriorating. In this belt lie much of the most specialized wheat farming of the continent, of both spring and winter varieties.

The Dark Brown Earths. In these is slightly less organic matter—hence the lighter colour—and a carbonate accumulation layer rather nearer to the surface than in the case of the black earths. The soils would be only slightly less valuable than those of the black earths, were precipitation sufficient and regular enough for general arable farming. Leaving the black earths for the brown earths, one finds an increasing proportion of the farm land in pasture, a decreasing proportion in crops, and these of a more drought-resistant nature. The vegetative cover is short grass only. A series of humid years have sometimes flattered the possibilities of crop production in this zone, only to be followed by a dry series and general crop failure. Ranching and the growing of drought-resistant fodder crops is indicated.

The Brown and Grey Earths. These were either covered, or partly covered, with short grasses, in which case there has been humus storage to the extent of rendering the soil brown ; or with desert vegetation, resulting in grey soils. The carbonate accumulation is often only a foot from the surface, and the soils are very thin. Agriculture without irrigation is impossible, and land utilization should be limited to pastoral occupation with care to prevent overstocking.

We have introduced here this very brief and generalized account of the distribution of the major soil types, both because implicit in it is the predominant influence of climate in soil evolution, and also because in a very general way it does serve to delimit some of the more productive, as also some of the most unproductive, areas of the continent. The generalization, however, is enormous. So far from there being any homogeneity in any one of these soil provinces, each one of them contains a very great number of distinguishable soils. And, again, the principles of soil evolution which are implied in the demarcation of these major provinces become applicable only to such parts of them as are characterized by mature soils. In the many areas where denudation is very active mature soils are not formed, nor are they in the regions of recent accumulation.

Thus only in an exceedingly general way may these major provinces be correlated to the agricultural use of the land.

Soil Erosion

We have emphasized the sensitive nature of the soil complex, and the fact that any artificial interference with the natural vegetation initiates changes in soil character, sometimes quickly, sometimes more slowly. If either forest land or grass land is broken by the plough for agricultural purposes, however fertile it may first prove—and the accumulation of humus in a virgin soil is its chief virtue—this fertility invariably diminishes. Continuous crop production uses up the plant food, particularly the nitrogen. The various devices of crop rotation, use of leguminous crops, use of chemical fertilizers, etc., can, under various conditions, mitigate or entirely prevent this deterioration. There is ample proof in many old agricultural countries, that an agricultural system, proven by experience, may maintain an almost unchanging productivity. Under certain conditions, however, the lack of productivity is the result not so much of soil exhaustion as of the actual removal of a part, or even the whole of horizon A, a soil complex which may have taken many centuries to evolve.

This removal of the surface layers of the soil is called soil erosion, and may be the immediate result of rainfall, or of wind. Its dreadful effects are clearly visible in the gullying of ploughed land, or may be only discernible in the earth-laden nature of water running from fields in times of heavy precipitation. In the latter case it is called sheet erosion. Fallow land in a dry country may lose much of its finer particles by a wind-induced drift. In any case, it must be appreciated that a loss of any of the top soil is a loss of a vital something which it has taken nature very many centuries to accumulate for man's use, and for which there is no easily prepared substitute.

Erosion takes place most readily, if the soil is bare of vegetation, if the slope is considerable, if the original humus content is low and precipitation intense, and in relation to the physical and chemical qualities of the type of soil concerned. Thus the original nature of the soil itself is a very considerable factor in the liability to erosion, but that granted, erosion will proceed according to the incidence of the conditions indicated.

It follows, too, that the liability to erosion will vary with the nature of the agriculture. It will be great if, perhaps to conserve moisture, much of the land is left fallow for long periods ; it will be greater during the periods when the land is occupied by inter-tilled crops than when it is occupied by grasses and cereals.

The evil has assumed enormous importance in the U.S.A. and has latterly been the subject of elaborate investigation. We in north-western Europe are apt to be startled by the damage revealed, for most of us are not conscious of this particular evil on a large scale in our own countries. It has been pointed out, however, that apart from differences, and these are considerable, in the major soils concerned, western Europe has not been sub-jected to the agricultural treatment meted out to large areas in the States, either by nature or man. Much of the farm land of the U.S.A. suffers a greater intensity of thunder rain than is at all common with us. Much of it was deforested, used again and again for the same crop, and that often an intertilled crop like corn, cotton, or tobacco ; and then as fertility decreased, aban-doned to the elements.

As to the importance of this evil, we cull a few figures from a recent survey of the Soil Conservation Service. This shows that, apart from the arid western region, some 44 million acres of formerly cultivated good soil has been essentially destroyed, and over 87 million additional acres have been seriously injured.

The evil is very widespread, and among some of the largest continuous areas are central and eastern Oklahoma, much of the southern Piedmont and of the upper Tennessee Valley, parts of the interior plateaux of Kentucky and of Tennessee, the older glacial till about the southern border of Iowa, and the loess-covered lands beginning just to the east of the Missouri in the same state. The loessal bluffs which border the lower Mississippi to the east have also suffered much. In the drier western ranch lands erosion is the result of both deforestation and of over-stocking.

Effective remedial action is already far advanced. Much semi-arid western plain land has been withdrawn from cultiva-tion after the terrible " dust bowl " experiences of 1933–4, and has been restored to controlled ranching. Erosion in the humid south-east is being checked by the infilling of gullies, by the use of check dams, by the reforestation of slopes which should never have been cultivated, and by contour ploughing and strip cultivation. Impoverished soils are being ameliorated by the use of phosphates, followed by the introduction of leguminous plants.

CHAPTER XIII

PHYSIOGRAPHIC PROVINCES OF THE INTERIOR

BETWEEN the uplands of Appalachia to the east, the Rocky Mountains to the west, and the little occupied Laurentian Shield to the north, lies an enormous area of relative lowland, the settlement of which has been a matter only of the last one and a half centuries. Agricultural population is denser in the east than it is in the west, and greater in the north than it is in the south ; while the Industrial population, consequent upon the exploitation of the North Appalachian coalfield, and the growth of cities and industries on and between the Ohio and the Great Lakes, has intensified a preponderance of population in the north-east.

As far as rural population is concerned, itself a market for industry, the dwindling which sets in well to the west of the Mississippi is consequent upon decrease of precipitation. Possibly the western verge of the Black Soil belt (Fig. 33) is, from this point of view, the most significant division which could be made ; and its position, like that of the zone dividing long grass from short, with which it so nearly coincides, is an index of effective rainfall. West of this line more land is required for the same standards of living ; a larger proportion of each farm is in permanent pasture ; and farming is necessarily less intensive than it is to the east.

So, too, if we are looking for a line by which to divide north from south, probably the limit of the Wisconsin (i.e. most recent) glaciation, would be as significant as any other. In a very general way we may say that topography and soils are more favourable to agricultural pursuits to the north of this line. Though the growing season is shorter, the value of farm products per unit of area are greater to the north than they are to the south, and the percentage of woodland, cut-over land, and waste land, is less.

Such divisions are, however, altogether too general. The whole interior of the continent, though relatively low, is by no means without topographic and structural interruptions which affect land utilization ; and that we may the better understand this, the chapters which follow on the great agricultural belts are here preceded by a brief account of the major physiographical

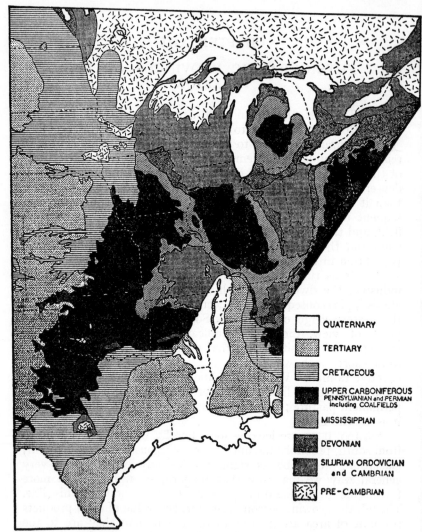

QUATERNARY

TERTIARY

CRETACEOUS

UPPER CARBONIFEROUS
PENNSYLVANIAN and PERMIAN
including COALFIELDS

MISSISSIPPIAN

DEVONIAN

SILURIAN ORDOVICIAN
and CAMBRIAN

PRE-CAMBRIAN

FIG. 34.—Generalized Geology of Interior.

divisions. Let us look first, however, at a very generalized map of the solid geology (Fig. 34) and compare this with the physiographic regions indicated in Fig. 1 (frontispiece). From these we see that much of the interior lowland is floored with rocks of Palæozoic age, and that this cover of old rock extends, as it were, in two long arms embracing the Laurentian Shield ; the one to the east, along the line of the St. Lawrence lowlands, and that to the west, along the Lake Winnipeg lowland. To the south and west these Palæozoic rocks are covered with material of Cretaceous and Tertiary age ; in the Gulf Coast Plain to the south, with its great embayment northwards as far as Cairo, and in the Great Plains to the west. Over much of the central plains the Palæozoic rocks are little disturbed, though there are notable exceptions. In general peneplanation has levelled a series of broad warpings. Thus the high-standing syncline which is the Appalachian Plateau (see p. 81) is succeeded to the west by a parallel anticline along which erosion has uncovered rocks of Ordovician and Silurian age in the Lexington and Nashville eroded domes. Parallel to this again is a synclinal axis along which the younger Palæozoics are preserved in the coalfields of Michigan and Illinois. Farther west again an anticlinal axis has stripped south-central Wisconsin of its younger Palæozoic cover, the successive outcrops forming a great U about the pre-Cambrian which occupies the north of the state.

Erosion has exposed the older Palæozoics, too, in the doming of the Ozarks of Missouri, at the core of which even the pre-Cambrian is exposed, and in the central area of Texas.

The several structures above indicated serve to break up the general evenness of the central lowlands of the continent, and to some extent correspond to the classical division of the physiographical regions.

South of the Laurentian Shield, east of the Rockies, and west of the Appalachian plateau, the following major physiographical regions are generally recognized (see Frontispiece). The Great Plains, the Gulf Coast Plain, the Interior Lowlands, the Ozarks with attendant Boston and Ouachita Mountains, and the Lexington and Nashville domes.

We will note some of the more geographically significant features of each of these, for each of them interposes characteristics of soil, or of topography, or of both, which serve to interrupt what would otherwise be a simple zoning of the Interior of the continent based on climatic data.

The Great Plains (Fig. 35). This is the term popularly applied to much of the land between the long-grass prairies and the Rockies, and distinguished from the former by greater height, less rainfall and shorter grass. The eastern boundary is not easy to define on either a geological or physiographic basis. The region is wholly developed upon Cretaceous and Tertiary rocks, but the latter extend eastwards beyond the region usually designated Great Plains. The eastern boundary adopted by Fenneman is here indicated, and in places, e.g. in the Dakotas, it does

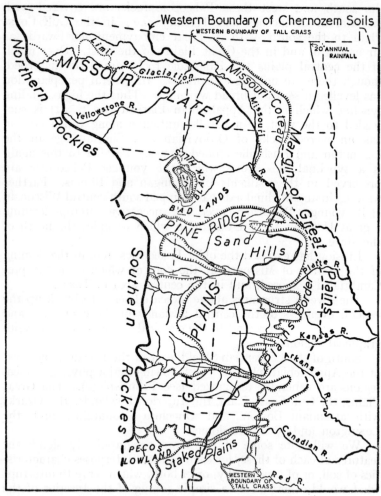

Fig. 35.—Diagram of the Great Plains Region.

correspond to certain significant changes in land utilization. For this purpose, however, it is generally of much less value than limits based upon the natural vegetation, or upon the character of the soil. Much of the fall from 4,000–5,000 feet at the foot of the Rockies to 1,000–1,500 feet at the eastern boundary of the province, is in gradual slopes, but in places it is accentuated in the east-facing escarpments of the more resistant sediments, some of which (e.g. the Côteau de Missouri, the Blue Hills of Kansas) serve to form a discontinuous eastern boundary of the region. Southwards of the north-facing escarpment of Pine Ridge, there is, over vast areas, little dissection. Few rivers, save those rising well back in the Rockies, can maintain any continuous flow, and these large streams, e.g. the Platte, the Arkansas, and the Canadian, flowing in broad aggraded flood plains between well-marked but dissected bluffs, divide the intervening plateau into blocks of gently rolling to quite flat country. There is little topographic break, save in an occasional residual butte or mesa, and much of the scanty rainfall sinks into the soil without the development of surface drainage.

This higher and little dissected portion of the Great Plains which lies to the south of Pine Ridge is given the name of High Plains, to distinguish it from the usually lower and more dissected portions of the Great Plains in the Dakotas, Wyoming, and the Prairie Provinces of Canada, which together form the Missouri Plateau. The High Plains are floored for the most part with fluviatile material derived in Tertiary times from the mountains to the west, and formed by the merging of alluvial fans ; and their monotonous evenness is best exemplified in the el Llano Estacado of Western Texas. The eastern topographic boundary of the High Plains is formed by an almost continuous but ragged escarpment, popularly called the " Break of the Plains." In the extreme south they terminate in the Balcones fault scarp, and westward a narrow belt of dissected country sometimes separates them from the Rockies.

An outpost of the Rockies occurs in the Black Hills of Dakota, an eroded uplift which exposes a rugged core of pre-Cambrian rocks surrounded by a concentric area, of infacing scarps. Greater altitude has led here to higher precipitation than occurs in the surrounding plains, and the highest portions are forested.

To the south of the Black Hills, about the White and Cheyenne rivers, erosion of finely grained strata in an area of considerable altitude, aridity, and short-rooted vegetation, has induced one of the most considerable distributions of " bad-land " topography to be seen on the continent. To the south of Pine Ridge, and so in the High Plains province, much of the centre of the state of Nebraska is covered by deposits of wind-blown sand-dunes, dimpled with lake-bearing hollows, and covered with long grass which here makes a great incursion westward.

A further significant division arises from the fact that glaciation invaded the Canadian portion of the Great Plains, and just o'er-topped the Missouri Côteau upon which, set some distance back from the slope, is the Altamont moraine.

The larger portion of the Great Plains, and the whole of the High Plains, are included in that great semi-arid region which stretches to the east of the Rockies.

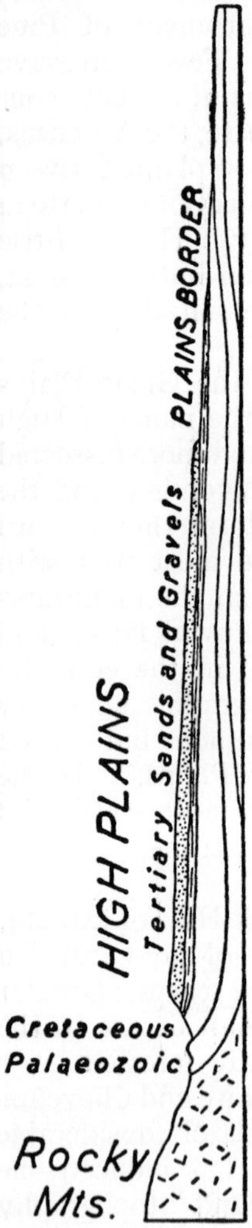

The rainfall is more effective in the cooler north than it is in the south, but everywhere the province witnesses the change from humid farming to dry farming and ranching, and in fact vegetation and soil belts form more significant boundaries than any structural phenomena. In Fig. 35 we have inserted the generalized western boundary of the Black Soil belt, and of the long-grass area, and have inserted also for purposes of comparison the line of 20 inches average annual precipitation. The significance of these will be further emphasized in subsequent chapters on agricultural distribution.

In the state of Texas (Fig. 37) terminate three of the great physiographic provinces of the interior. Here the younger rocks of the Great Plains make contact with the younger rocks of the Gulf Coast Plain, and the Palæozoic rocks of the Central Low Plains are exposed in the angle between the two, and indeed, in the eroded dome of the south centre of the state, crystalline pre-Cambrian rocks are exposed in what is still called the Mineral Area.

In the west of the state the characteristics of the High Plains are continued and thoroughly exemplified in the amazing evenness of the semi-arid el Llano Estacado, which presents a ragged but very well-marked escarpment both to the arid Pecos lowlands on the west, and to the humid and sub-humid interior low plains on the east. The el Llano Estacado plateau, surfaced with Tertiary material, continues without topographic break into the

FIG. 36.—Generalized section from west to east across the Great Plains.

HIGH PLAINS

Tertiary Sands and Gravels

PLAINS BORDER

GREAT PLAINS

Cretaceous
Palaeozoic

Rocky
Mts.

Cretaceous limestone surface of Edwards Plateau to the south, which overlooks the western coast plain of Texas in a well-marked fault scarp—the Balcones scarp. To the south of this zone of faulting, the cretaceous formations are covered by the Tertiary cover of the Coastal Plain. The timbered, rugged, dissected escarpment is 1,000 feet high near the Rio Grande, but dies out eastward to terminate, as a topographic feature, near Austin.

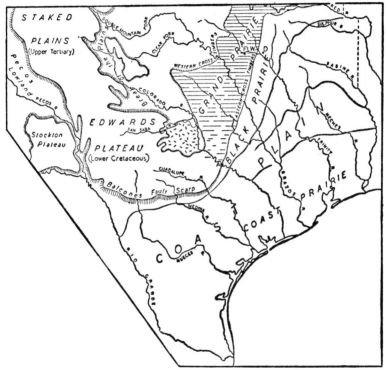

FIG. 37.—Diagram to show the relation of the High Plains, Interior Lowlands, and Coast Plain in Texas.

A, Austin. Ft. W, Fort Worth. D, Dallas.

It forms the southern limit of the High Plains. Structurally the Edwards Plateau is continued westward in the Stockton Plateau, from which it is only separated by the Pecos river trough. Uplift and erosion has separated the Cretaceous limestone cover of the Edwards Plateau from that of the Grand Prairie, the infacing, timbered, low, and irregular scarp of which may be looked upon as the inner boundary of the Gulf Coast Plain in eastern Texas. Between this and the eastern escarpment of the High Plains (the

" Break of the Plains ") are exposed the young Palæozoic (Upper Pennsylvanian and Permian) of the Central Low Plains, dipping to the west in a country of relatively uneven relief, which becomes sharper as the crystalline mineral region is approached.   It is convenient to class the Red and Black prairies, developed on Cretaceous rocks which dip gently towards the gulf, as parts of the Gulf Coast Plain.   A narrow sandy formation divides the two in a timber-belt—the Eastern Cross timbers.   These two marly prairies, like the correspondingly situated Black belt of Alabama, were originally grass lands set among forest, and have been highly cultivated.   The three of them, together with some of the better lands of the Mississippi flood plain, originally represented the most fertile regions of the south.

South-eastwards of the Black Prairie, the more sandy Tertiary formations of the Gulf Coast Plain dip gently to the sea, with the occasional development of cuestas.

Cutting right across these structural divisions of the state comes the north-south zoning of vegetation, and of land utilization, consequent upon decreasing precipitation.   Cultivation with dry farming methods has a precarious hold upon the eastern margin of the High Plains, but the west is arid.   The southern pine belt, " cut-over " or not, gives out on the coast plain west of the Colorado river, and a little farther west agriculture becomes impossible, until the irrigated plain of the Rio Grande itself is reached.

The Gulf Coast Plain East of Texas.   This is a continuation of the Atlantic coast plain, and like it, extends inland to the limit of Cretaceous or younger sediments.   These dip gently to the Gulf.   Sandy sediments are predominant, but there are some areas of limestone, and the more resistant formations give marked cuestas of moderate relief, e.g. in Alabama and in Texas.   As in the case of the Atlantic coast plain, seawards, the region is usually bordered by sand-spit, lagoon and salt marsh.   Much of the sandier portions of the coast plain remain uncultivated, as forest and cut-over land, remnants of the great south-eastern and southern pine belt.   Only in western Texas does the Gulf Coast Plain extend sufficiently far west to become semi-arid.

The Gulf Coast Plain extends in a great embayment as far north as Cairo.   This embayment is traversed by the infilled valley of a precursor of the Mississippi.   Borings here show only sands and gravels to a depth of some hundreds of feet, with a veneer of recent fine alluvium, the work of the present stream. This great flood plain is often over 50 miles in width and is usually distinctly bounded by bluffs of Tertiary sediments which are especially marked on the east, where they are often topped by loessal deposit. The boundary is less clearly defined and continuous on the west, and remnants of the Tertiary cover, entirely surrounded by alluvium, remain, e.g. in Crowley's Ridge. Of some of the physical attributes of the great river we shall be treating in a later chapter. In flood, the stream brings down an enormous amount of solid material, and the flood plain is diversified by a complex pattern of natural levee, and abandoned meander, and is continued almost imperceptibly into the finger-like extensions of the delta, which interdigitate with marsh and lagoon.

The Central Lowland Plains. Between the Laurentian Shield and the Gulf Coast Plain, and again between the Appalachian Plateau and the verge of the Great Plains, lies a vast area over almost the whole of which the map of solid geology shows only the younger Palæozoic rocks. As far south as the Missouri-Ohio line these, though gently inclined and peneplaned, are for the most part little disturbed, but they are covered up with a variable and sometimes very thick mantle of glacial drift. South of the limit of glaciation, uplift and erosion have exposed the older Palæozoic formations in the Ozarks and along the Cincinnati anticline, and have introduced a more *accidenté* topography. South-westwards the younger Palæozoic rocks extend into Oklahoma and central Texas.

The area north of the Ohio-Missouri line (glaciated) and this extension south-westwards (unglaciated) form together the Central Low Plains.

The Central Lowlands (strictly speaking, of course, in reference to the whole continent, they are *east*-central rather than central) are generally of lower altitude and smoother topography than any of the surrounding provinces. They nevertheless comprise in detail considerable diversity. Limiting our attention for the moment to the glaciated area, we may notice first of all that though the Ohio and Missouri form the general limit of the greatest glacial extension, they do not do so precisely (Fig. 38). The six southern counties of Illinois were never glaciated, though they lie to the north of the rivers. Nor, although in this case surrounded by the ice, was the " Driftless Area " of south-western Wisconsin. On the other hand, glaciation extended *beyond* the River Missouri in north-western Kansas and in eastern Nebraska.

As in the case of the European Ice Sheets there were a number of advances of the ice, which alternated with considerable interglacial periods. The limits of the various sheets were not coterminous. The last great advance, that of the so-called Wisconsin glaciation, stopped far short of the limit of the earlier sheets. We have thus areas of earlier (Kansan and Illinoian) and areas of later (Iowan and Wisconsin) glacial drift. Obviously the over-

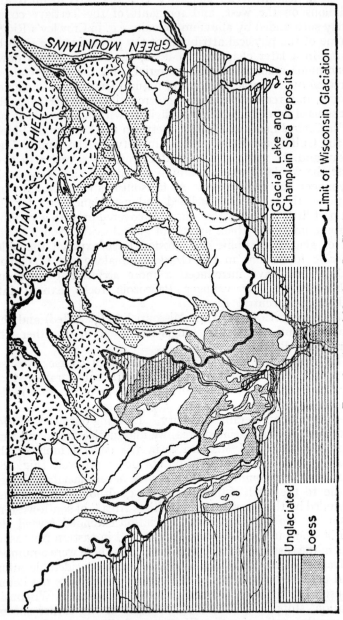

FIG. 38.—Area of Northern Ice Sheets.

riding of an earlier till by subsequent ice extensions obliterated, to a large extent, the former glacial topography ; while areas of the older ice sheet which were not later re-invaded by ice, have a drift cover more dissected, weathered, and generally modified, than that of areas of recent glaciation. Thus the smooth topography of the undissected interfluves, as well as, in places, the clearly marked terminal moraine, and esker, are alike characteristic of the younger drift ; as also are those several and large areas (we may instance those of western New York, east-central Wisconsin, or again an area immediately east of lake Simcoe in Ontario) where for miles the whole surface is billowed with drumlins. In the older drift these phenomena are hardly in evidence, dissection is more mature, and soils are relatively leached.

Such portions of the younger till as are level, are very level ; and in a very general way it is true to say that for agricultural purposes the younger drifts are more valuable than the older both in respect of topography and of soil. There are areas, however, on the younger drift in which extensive drainage was a prerequisite to any land utilization. Over the whole of this glaciated region the main streams have bitten well-marked bluff-bordered flood plains into the generally flat surface, and intricate dissection, in this young topography, occurs in proximity to these. In the original vegetation the hardwood forest (now largely cleared) extended to the western borders of Indiana, but only the dissected river valleys of Illinois were wooded, the rest of the state being originally long-grass prairie.

Besides this division, into areas of young and of old glacial drift, we may distinguish further those areas of lacustrine deposit which surround, in margins of various width, the great lakes ; and of marine deposits of the late glacial Champlain sea, which cover the St. Lawrence Lowlands below Lake Ontario. There are also the lake deposits of glacial Lake Agassiz which cover so much of the Red River plain in Manitoba and North Dakota.

One further important drift deposit remains to be noticed. In the central states, but not in the more humid east, a cover of loess frequently borders the older till, especially in extensive patches lying just to the east of some of the more important river valleys, including that of the Mississippi itself. A yellowish unstratified deposit, it probably represents wind-strewn portions of parts of the older ground moraines. It is calcareous, and often its presence gives rise to favourable soils.

On the whole the glacial central lowlands represent the best farm land of the continent, and this in spite of much badly drained land, and of, in the aggregate, a large area of terminal moraine, esker, and drumlin, some of which is unsuitable for agriculture. Yet, on the whole, the most productive land is limited to the ground moraine of the more recent ice sheets. As we indicate in our note on soils in Chapter XII, much of this area falls within the major soil provinces of the Prairie Earths and the Black soils; but in detail the value of the soils of these glaciated plains is by no means independent of parent material.

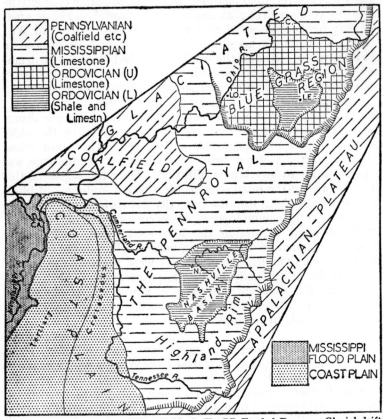

PENNSYLVANIAN (Coalfield etc)
MISSISSIPPIAN (Limestone)
ORDOVICIAN (U) (Limestone)
ORDOVICIAN (L) (Shale and Limestn)

MISSISSIPPI FLOOD PLAIN
COAST PLAIN

FIG. 39.—The Lexington (LE) and Nashville (N) Eroded Domes. Glacial drift extends as far south as the Ohio River.
C, Cincinatti. Ca, Cairo. Lo, Louisville.

Other things being equal, the presence of unleached calcareous drift, or of loessal cover, is relatively advantageous (Fig. 38).

The unglaciated south-westward extension of the Central Low Plains to form much of eastern Kansas, Oklahoma, and central Texas, lies wholly in the prairie region, and much of it is to-day valuable grain-farming country, though soil erosion has destroyed much good land, particularly in Oklahoma.

It remains to note those physiographic regions draining to the Mississippi and to the Gulf which owe their distinguishing characteristics to the denudation of marked foldings or warpings in the Palæozoic cover.

The Lexington and Nashville Eroded Domes of the Cincinnati Anticline (Fig. 39). The upraised syncline of the Appalachian Plateau presents a sharp formidable escarpment to the lake plains on the north, and a generally less marked one—sometimes hardly apparent—to the west. On this side it is succeeded by the Cincinnati anticline, with a north-east–south-west Appalachian

FIG. 40.—Plan of the Ozarks and Adjoining Regions.
S, Salem. **S.L,** St. Louis. **Sp,** Springfield. **K,** Kansas City. **M,** Memphis.

trend, which exposes older rocks (Ordovician) in two terminal eroded dome-like structures separated by a sag in the anticline. These are respectively the Lexington and Nashville domes. Together these were the first areas of trans-Appalachia to undergo considerable agricultural settlement (see Chapter VI). Mississippian limestone formations surround these inner areas to form a region of fair farming value, in what is known as the Highland Rim, but the best soils have been developed upon the phosphatic Ordovician limestones about Lexington and Nashville respectively.

The Ozarks, Boston Mountains, and Ouachita Mountains (Fig. 40)

7

form a group of structural regions which bears comparison with Appalachia.

Thus the parallel even ridges of the Ouachita Mountains rising 1,000–2,000 feet above the surrounding plains, correspond to the ridge and valley province of the great Appalachian Valley. These Ouachita hills are separated from the Ozark Province proper, by the broad valley of the Arkansas, a valley interspersed with a few ridges of relatively resistant material. In both the Ouachita Province and the Arkansas Valley the sedimentaries have been folded. The Ozarks proper (the Boston Mountains, the Springfield structural plain, and the Salem Plain) were all concerned in the same broad doming, peneplanation, and rejuvenation. The Boston Mountains, with undisturbed strata of Pennsylvanian age, deeply dissected, but with accordant summit levels, is comparable to the Cumberland Plateau, and presents a ragged dissected escarpment which overlooks the Springfield structural plain to the north. The Boston Mountains terminate somewhat sharply also to the south, where in a much-denuded monoclinal fold they overlook the Arkansas Valley lowland. The Springfield structural plain, much denuded to the south where it adjoins the spurs of the Boston Mountains, has a more even surface to the north and west. It is floored for the most part with a limestone of Mississippian age, which forms a well-marked escarpment overlooking the Salem Plain. On the latter the erosion of a former cover of very cherty limestone has left an excessively chert-strewn topography, devoid of elements of major relief, but threaded with aggraded chert-filled valleys. This land, difficult to cultivate and in some ways even to traverse, divided the major streams of westward movement and settlement, and it still remains somewhat negative

FIG. 41.—Generalized section along line a—b in diagram of the Ozarks (Fig. 40).

agriculturally, and is backward in development. The Burlington escarpment separates this Salem Plain from the Springfield Plain, and the latter may be compared in the way in which it partially surrounds this eroded dome, to the Highland Rim, which similarly overlooks the Lexington and Nashville domes. The doming was asymmetric, and differential, and the apex appears in the crystalline core of the St. Francis Mountains, a sharp, rugged little group of hills lying to the north-east of the province as a whole.

Essentially, then, the Ozark region is an asymmetric eroded dome surrounded by successive cuestas of progressively younger material ; but the dying out of some of the escarpments, the glacial cover to the north, and the Cretaceous cover of the coast plain embayment to the south-east, mask the structure on these sides

STATISTICAL SUMMARY OF LAND USE IN THE U.S.A.

Total Area (Continental) .	. 3·022	million square miles
Forest Area and Cut Over .	. 0·980	,,
Crop Area	. 0·502	,,

ACREAGE OF CERTAIN MAJOR CROPS IN U.S.A.

(in millions of acres)

	1933–42 av.	1943	1944
Wheat	. 53·9	50·7	60·8
Maize	. 91·8	94·6	97·4
Cotton	. 25·0	21·9	20·4
Oats	. 34·5	38·3	39·5
Alfalfa Hay . . .	. 13·7	14·9	14·3
Soy Beans . . .	. 3·8	10·8	10·7

CHAPTER XIV

THE GREAT AGRICULTURAL REGIONS. THE COTTON BELT. THE HUMID SUB-TROPICAL BELT

AS in the topography and structure of a physiographic region we may discern a stage in the conflict between land-building and land-destroying forces ; as in a type of natural vegetation we are presented with a synthesis of the climate-soil controls of vegetative growth ; so in an agricultural landscape, is there the physical expression of one way in which the farmer has chosen to come to terms with his environment. We say *one* way, for, in general, the natural environment gives, within certain limits, much scope for choice ; and we may suppose that a man adopts that system of farming which, he believes, will yield to him most profit under the natural and economic conditions obtaining.

The choice, if not free, is considerable ; but it is conditioned by the farmer's cognizance of technique, and is apt to be influenced by tradition.

It is important to bear in mind that a farmer does not so much produce a certain crop, as follow an agricultural system in which the production of that particular crop is interrelated with the other activities of the system. He may obtain his cash by selling cream for butter making, and, say, pork ; but his crops may then include grain corn to supplement skim milk for his hogs, and to provide corn ensilage for winter feed of his dairy herd. They may include oats as feed for his work animals, and clover and sown grasses, for hay and pasture. And the whole must be organized in respect of the area devoted to each crop and to pasture, and in respect of the availability of labour. Further it must be arranged so as to maintain his land in good productive condition.

Agricultural geography, then, is concerned with the distribution of crop systems.

So various and complex are the systems actually adopted that map distributions of particular types can only be shown on very large scale maps of land use, and would be altogether too detailed and complicated to be summarized here. Map mosaics, resulting from account being taken of every detailed variation, do not, in fact, easily build up into simple, large scale, and easily apprehended patterns.

Probably a more practical method in the case of areas of continental dimensions, is to select as criteria certain characteristics common to the farming of quite large regions ; and to indicate, and, as far as may be possible, account for, the quite outstanding variations within the major region.

For this purpose we cannot do better than adopt the broad agricultural divisions associated with the name of O. E. Baker, to whose work and method every writer on economic geography is indebted. His agricultural regions, like the physiographical provinces which they so frequently transgress, are become a part of American Geography.

Between the Arctic and the Gulf, and again between Appalachia and the arid High Plains, lies the great interior lowland of the continent. An almost absolute limit to agriculture is set by aridity on the west, and by the Laurentian Shield in much of the north. Very large-scale topographic breaks are wanting, and the major physical factors concerned with agricultural production are those resulting from an increase of summer temperature, and in the length of the growing season, as we proceed from north to south. This tends to produce east–west trending belts of farming systems. And then, some distance west of the Mississippi, comes that diminution of precipitation which tends to modify the types of farming in the western segment of each belt.

In so far as the soils have been influenced by glaciation, the effect is rather to emphasize the east–west belting ; but the major belts traverse, and are locally modified by considerable variations in soil and in topography, occasioned by the occurrence of various physiographic elements, the distribution of which is unrelated to climate, and therefore to the alignment of the major agricultural belts.

We will, in the next few chapters, adopt Baker's divisions in our consideration of the agriculture of the interior of the continent, leaving a more explicit discussion of other parts of the continent to the specifically regional portion of the book.

We should notice first of all that Baker's regions are outlined on a statistical basis ; being based, as for example, in the case of the corn belt, upon the intensity of the production of some characteristic crop ; or, as in the case of the cotton belt, upon the relative importance in terms of value, of one characteristic form of production. In any case it is statistical. It is thus subject to change.

For example, adjustments may well be needed along the western semi-arid boundary in view of the retreat of crop land because of the recent droughts, and as a measure against further erosion.   Or again, diversification in the spring wheat belt has proceeded farthest in its more humid eastern portions, and the margin between this and the hay and dairying belt may need adjustment.

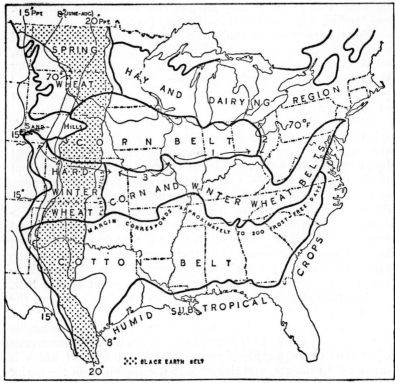

FIG. 42.—The Agricultural Regions of the U.S.A.

Along the margins of the Corn Belt: **1.** Limit of Wisconsin Glaciation. **2.** Western limit of Appalachian Plateau. **3.** Northern margin of Ozark country. **4.** Hot dry summer winds become unfavourable to corn.

On the map (Fig. 42) of these belts is inserted the area of chernozen soils as an indication of the passage zone, from sub-humid to semi-arid conditions so significant for all agriculture.

THE COTTON BELT

Cotton is still the most important (by total weight and by value) of the textile raw materials, and this in spite of an enormous increase in recent years in the use of rayon manufactured from wood pulp. The United States produces normally between a half and two-thirds of the world's cotton, and nearly all of this comes from the relatively warm and humid south-eastern quadrant of the continent.

An examination of a map of the district (Fig. 43) shows us that there are two relatively old masses of highland projecting southward into the region. That to the west consists of the Ozark Mountain country, while that to the east is the southern end of the great Appalachian system. Lying around the ends of these two old masses and extending eastward, to the waters of the Atlantic and southward to the waters of the Gulf, is a very extensive area of lowland consisting for the most part of young and soft sands, clays, and limestones mostly of Tertiary and Cretaceous age. These rocks dip gently away from the old masses towards the sea, yet with a dip, which, in general, is greater than the seawards slope of the land. Thus are exposed in succession a number of outcrop belts paralleling the coast line, and having occasional infacing escarpments. This cover of younger material constitutes the coast plain, and in the gulf region it makes a great embayment inland as far as Cairo. From Cairo southwards it is traversed almost due north and south by the flood plain of the lower Mississippi, often over 50 miles in width, and lying between well-marked bluffs. Except in portions of western Texas and Oklahoma cotton growing is almost confined to the Piedmont and Coast Plain, but within these huge physiographical provinces cotton production—as indeed agricultural production generally —becomes intensified in the areas of better soils. The distribution of these is by no means entirely independent of the distribution of parent material, and thus the better agricultural areas have some rough relation to the alignment of outcrops.

The raw cotton of commerce consists of the fibres surrounding the seeds of a shrub of the genus *Gossypium*, the species now usually cultivated being *Gossypium herbaceum*. The flower only lasts a day or two, and is followed by the fruit, or " boll," as it is called. This boll opens and displays the seeds surrounded by the mass of lint or raw cotton. About two-thirds of this mass by weight is seed, and the remaining third is the lint. Cotton is a very exhausting crop to the soil, and it is into the seed that the bulk of the valuable plant-food material goes, hence the very great value of cotton-seed cake as a fertilizer. All cotton fibres are not of the same length, the average length of the fibre, or staple, as it is called, of *G. herbaceum*, which was first brought from the East to the United States, varying from $\frac{7}{8}$ inch to $1\frac{1}{3}$ inches. *Gossypium barbadense*, better known as the famous Sea Island cotton of the West Indian Islands and the islands of the

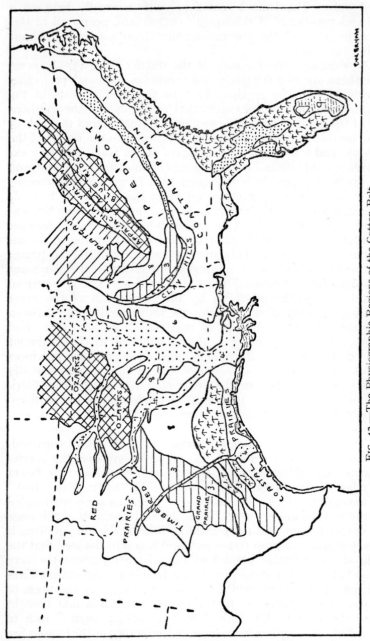

FIG. 43.—The Physiographic Regions of the Cotton Belt.

1. Flatwoods, Swamp and Marsh. 2. Sandy Belts. 3. Black Prairies. 4. River Bottom Lands. 5. Tidal Marsh. 6. Mississippi Uplands. 7. Tennessee Uplands. 8. Inner Coastal Plain. 9. Everglades. The Highland regions are shown by the cross-hatching.

coasts of Georgia and the Carolinas, has a staple which may be as long as 2½ inches, although the average length is about 1½ inches.   It is fine and silky, and used to be in great demand for the manufacture of the very finest type of cotton goods.   Now production of this type has dwindled almost to nothing.   At the other end of the scale, from the standpoint of quality and length, come certain of the Indian cottons, which have a poor, harsh fibre of less than ½ inch in staple.   Between these extremes come many cottons ranging from Egyptian, which stands next to Sea Island in length of staple, through long-stapled and short-stapled Upland, which forms the great bulk of the American crop, to the better-class Indian types, which, with improved methods of cultivation, now play an important part in the world's supplies.

Cotton is a sub-tropical plant.   A hard frost kills it.   Therefore the greatest limiting factor in relation to cotton cultivation, apart from an adequate water supply, is that there should be a freedom from killing frost for a long enough period to enable it to mature its fruit.   This period is generally regarded as being 200 days,[1] hence the northern limit of the Cotton Belt in the United States is very well marked by a line south of which, on the average, there are 200 days without a frost hard enough to kill the young plant in the spring, or to destroy a large percentage of the unpicked bolls in the autumn.   This period of 200 days is an average period, and is equivalent to a period of about 170 days absolutely frost free four years out of five.   North of this line, of course, cotton will grow if it escapes the spring frosts, but the autumn frosts will on the average destroy such a large number of unpicked bolls, that cotton ceases to be a commercial proposition in competition with the larger crops grown on more favourably situated land farther to the south.   Sometimes in the more extreme parts of the area, as in Texas, cotton is planted before all probability of a killing frost has disappeared, and the whole crop may be destroyed through the coming of a late frost. This happened in Southern Texas in the spring of 1922, and led to extensive replanting throughout this area, and also to the farmers turning to other crops because of the scarcity of seed cotton.   Sowing in the Cotton Belt begins, therefore, in the south about March 1, and extends northward till the north edge of the Belt is reached about April 21 (Fig. 48).   This north limit of the Belt starts at the mouth of Chesapeake Bay, and runs south-westward along the junction between the Piedmont and the foothills of the Blue Ridge.   Then swinging around the southern end of the Appalachian Mountains, it runs in a general

[1] Cotton is now grown in parts of the U.S.S.R. (e.g. north of the Black Sea), where the frost-free period is between 180–190 days.

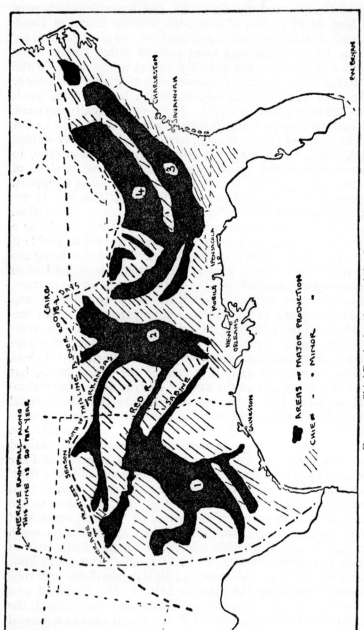

FIG. 44.—Chief Producing Areas of the Cotton Belt.

1. Black Prairie Region of Texas.
2. Mississippi Flood Plain, including the Delta Area.
3. The Upper Coastal Plain Region.
4. The Piedmont Region.

north-westward direction, with some slight bends to the north
to include river valleys such as the tributaries of the Tennessee,
and similar bends to the south over the higher ground, to the
position of Cairo at the junction of the Mississippi and the Ohio.
From this point its course is south-westward around the Ozark
massif in a loop which continues north-west almost to the Oklahoma border, and then strikes south-west across Texas.

A sub-tropical crop, cotton requires a fairly high temperature,
increasing during the growing season when it is storing up food
material. During this period both days and nights should be
warm, although, once it has completed its vegetative growth,
cooler nights are favourable to the production of fruit. The
average temperature during June, July, and August should not

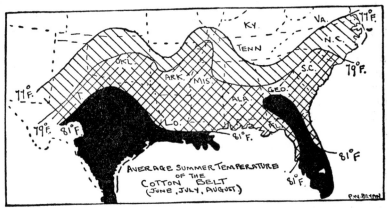

FIG. 45.—Temperature and the Cotton Belt.

fall below about 77° F. An examination of the temperature
curves for any typical areas (Fig. 45) within the Cotton Belt
will show the steady rise of temperature to a maximum in August,
which is for much of the area the end of the growing period,
and the sharp drop in temperature during September and October,
when the bulk of the cotton is maturing. There are usually at
least three pickings, the first one dealing with the lower bolls,
which are the first to ripen, the second with the middle bolls,
and the third with the upper bolls, or top crop, as it is commonly
called. Much of this top crop, especially on the northern edge
of the Belt, may be lost through early autumn frosts.

Evaporation in the cotton states, particularly in the western
parts of the Belt, is much higher than in the northern part of
the United States ; hence it is found that a rainfall ample for
wheat or corn in the north is quite insufficient for cotton in the

south. As has been explained in another part of this book, the rainfall of Texas caused by indraft from the Gulf of Mexico diminishes rapidly as one moves from east to west. A study of the rainfall map in connection with that showing the distribution of cotton, will bring out the fact that the western limit of the Cotton Belt is approximately indicated by the line of about 20 inches annual rainfall (Fig. 44). An exception to this general statement is to be found in that high north-western part of Texas known as the Staked Plains where a rainfall of 17 inches is found to be adequate.[1] This zone is further of great interest since the severity of the winter and the absence of woodland, etc., in which the boll weevil can hibernate means low weevil infestation, though this advantage is partly counterbalanced by a lower yield. There was, for this reason, a rapid extension of the cotton area here and in western Oklahoma in the period 1921–5, but the world depression of the early thirties, and recent serious droughts in an area of marginal and very variable rainfall, have led to some recession. Along the southern edge of the Belt, especially in the south-east, the rainfall rises to over 60 inches, and this fall is generally regarded as too heavy for good cotton, as it causes a rank growth under which vegetative development of the plant takes place at the expense of fruit production. This is one of the main drawbacks to a wet season in the Belt. Excessive rainfall also usually means that there is a deficiency of the abundant sunshine, which is needed for ripening the crop, and that the lint is injured in autumn before picking. Over the major part of the Belt, cloudless days occur about once in every three days. The most favourable type of rainfall is that which comes in light, frequent showers with plenty of sunshine in between, and the more of the rainfall that falls during the night the better, as there will then be a higher percentage of sunshine during the day. An examination of the seasonal rainfall maps (Fig. 46) will show that the rainfall, broadly speaking, increases from a winter minimum through spring and early summer to a maximum in July and August, so providing ample moisture during the growing period, and decreasing rapidly in the autumn when the plant is fruiting. It will also be noticed that while the annual rainfall of the eastern part of the Belt in the Carolinas and Georgia is much heavier than in the west, the rainfall during the growing period, while still slightly heavier than in the west, does not show a difference of more than 2 or 3 inches. For the three spring and the three summer months the rainfall over the greater part of the Belt is rather more than 10 inches in each period, while during the three autumn months it is distinctly less than this figure.

[1] U.S. Dept. of Agriculture Yearbook, 1926.

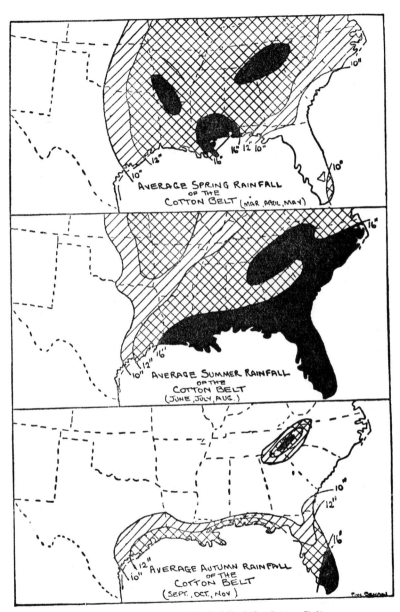

FIG. 46.—The Seasonal Rainfall of the Cotton Belt.

Summarizing, then, very briefly, the most favourable conditions, we may say that a mild, warm spring with frequent light
showers should merge into a distinctly warm, moist summer,
followed by a long, dry, cool autumn free from killing frost.
Too wet a season causes an abundant crop of very poor quality,
even if it escapes the weevils which an extra wet spring breeds
in immense quantities ; too wet a spring may cause the seed
to rot ; too wet an autumn causes dirty cotton and interferes
with the picking. Too cool a spring keeps back growth, and
thus decreases the available growing season, so that the top
crop is never harvested. Late frosts in spring kill the young
plant ; early autumn frosts injure the top crop. Within the
broad limits set out above, the vagaries of the climate of the
Belt are many. Against this must be set the fact that cotton
responds very rapidly to climatic changes, and is not permanently injured by such changes unless they are very prolonged.
In this respect cotton contrasts markedly with corn. Hence
the crop, after a spell of adverse weather conditions, will respond
quickly should the conditions become favourable. This fact is
reflected markedly in the U.S. Government crop reports, issued
periodically throughout the growing season. Most of the special
climatic conditions under which cotton is grown in the United
States arise from the fact that it is here cultivated not in its
original tropic home, but on the extreme northern margin of
the climatic zone where such cultivation is possible.

Thus the Cotton Belt is very clearly demarcated to the north
by the line beyond which there are less than 200 days free from
frost, and that to the west the boundary is set by a deficiency of
rainfall in Western Texas. What, then, are the limits to the
south and east ?   Here the edge of the area might be thought to
be the waters of the Atlantic and the Gulf. This, however, is
not so. As can be seen from the map (Fig. 44), hardly any cotton
is grown near the coast. Behind the coast lies a belt of salt marsh
and lagoon extending all the way from Virginia to the Rio Grande,
and behind that there lies, as we have seen, for the most part a
belt of sandy timbered country, which is very unfavourable from
the point of view of cotton cultivation. This region of timber
and swamp and marsh forms the real boundary of cotton cultivation to the south and east, and it is accentuated as a barrier
by the fact to which attention has already been called, namely,
the presence of an excessive amount of rainfall, particularly
autumn rainfall, to the south-east and south.

We have already seen that within this great area known
broadly as the Cotton Belt there are certain clearly marked zones
which may fairly be called areas of major production. We have
now to see what these zones are, and what are the factors

conditioning them.   The main Cotton Belt is roughly divided, both from the points of view of area and production, into two halves by the north-south course of the Mississippi from Cairo to the sea.   In each of these halves we find a highland mass projecting southwards, which is, with the exception of certain fertile valleys, void of cotton.   The Mississippi-Yazoo flood plain, centrally placed in the Belt, forms one of the major producing areas. Flanking it to the west, and linked to it by the alluvial flood plains of the Red River and the Arkansas, is the great Texan Black Waxy Prairie Region, the greatest cotton-producing region of the Belt.   In the eastern half of the Belt, between the Mississippi and the waters of the Atlantic, there are two areas of major production, forming roughly concentric curves concave to the Appalachians and convex to the Florida peninsula, having a slight projection southward into Northern Florida.   Taking, then, these two latter areas, let us see how far they are conditioned by the facts of topography, soil, and climate.   An examination of a relief map will reveal the fact that the inner of these two curving areas corresponds partly to the Piedmont Plateau lying at the southeastern foot of the Blue Ridge, and partly to the valleys of the Southern Appalachian System and Cumberland Plateau, such as the valley of the Black Warrior River and the middle valley of the Tennessee.   To the north the area is delimited by the Blue Ridge in part, and also by the line of 200 days free from frost to which reference has been made above.   To the south the boundary is marked by a region of heavily timbered, infertile sandy soils which corresponds more or less with the zone to which the rather inaccurate title of the Fall Line has been applied.[1]   The southern edge of the Piedmont section merges into the larger curving area which swings through the central parts of the Carolinas, Georgia, and Alabama, and finally peters out in North-eastern Mississippi. This area may be not inaccurately described, perhaps, as the Upper Coastal Plain Region, and of it perhaps one of the best-known section is that of the so-called Black Belt in Central or South Central Alabama.   To the south the boundary of this area is a second sandy timbered belt which forms the central part of most of the Coastal Plain, and which is now part of one of the greatest of the lumber areas of the United States, the southern zone of the long-leaf pine.   Beyond this sandy belt, as has already been pointed out, come the swamps and marshes bordering the coast.

Let us examine in a little more detail the Black Belt of South Central Alabama.   The best cotton soils are marly loams or fertile silts.   Lime in the soil is of great importance from this standpoint.   This region lies north of the Connemugga Ridge,

[1] This zone coincides with the broken country which marks the drop from the Piedmont to the coastal plain.

and forms a trough-like depression some 25 miles wide, running from the position of Montgomery at the great bend of the Coosa River in the eastern portion of the state westward to the lower part of the Tombigbee Valley near the boundary of Mississippi. Known as the Black Belt, it corresponds almost exactly with the outcrop of an easily decomposed Cretaceous limestone named the Selma chalk. It is covered with a thick residual clay, the whole forming a soil of great depth and fertility. The Belt owes its name to the dark colour of the soil, which forms a striking contrast to the light-coloured soils of most of the rest of the state. Its only drawback is that in summer it bakes very hard, while in winter it tends to become a thick mud. Throughout this area about three-fourths of the people are negroes, being in a higher proportion to whites here than in any other part of the United States, excepting only the Mississippi River bottom land, to which reference will be made in a moment. Practically all the cotton grown in the Black Belt of Alabama is the short-stapled Upland variety. This belt, like the not dissimilar Black Prairie of Texas, was originally a grass land, although surrounded by forest areas. This was one reason for the high humus content of its soil. Production here, however, has fallen off most seriously in recent years partly as the result of extensive sheet erosion. This is peculiarly active, even on slight slopes, in a region of heavy thunderstorm precipitation, and of intertilled crops. In some cases the whole of the black horizon of the soil has been removed, exposing the almost white selma chalk beneath, and much good cotton land has been degraded to poor pasture.

Extending southward from the position of Memphis on the Mississippi in Tennessee for a distance of about 200 miles to near Vicksburg, there lies an area, in shape roughly a long oval, which is bounded to the west by the main channels of the Mississippi, and to the east by the hundred-foot bluffs which overlook the flood plain of the river. It is covered with a network of waterways, the largest of which, apart from the main river, is the Yazoo, which flows close to the foot of the eastern bluffs; hence the name of the area, the Mississippi-Yazoo flood plain, or Delta, as it is frequently called. Near the water-courses the land stands higher than it does some distance away because of the fashion in which the rivers have deposited their coarser sediments in flood-time. The alluvial soils close to the streams form excellent cotton land, many parts of which have produced crops for forty years or so without the application of fertilizer and without exhausting the soil; a sufficient indication of their extraordinary fertility. The majority of the farmers are negroes, who are massed together in large numbers on plantations, the organization of which approximates more nearly to the conditions found in the Cotton Belt prior to the Civil War, than those which exist in any other part of the Belt to-day. Long-stapled Upland is the chief cotton now grown, as the alluvial soil seems well adapted to its cultivation. As in most areas which attempt to grow a higher type of cotton than that of neighbouring areas, the main difficulty with which the cotton cultivator is here faced is to keep the strain pure. The seed may be right and the other conditions may be right, but unless one's neighbours are growing the same strain, cross-fertilization from their poorer strains or shorter-stapled cotton, will result in the deterioration of one's own crop. Long-stapled cotton, the length of the fibre being from $1\frac{1}{8}$ to $1\frac{1}{2}$ inches, is in great demand for strong fine yarns, for light fabrics subjected to hard wear, for the better class of tyre fabrics, and for cloths intended for the mercerization process, which involves subjecting the fabric to a strong solution of caustic soda and also to a considerable amount of stretching. Among American cottons other than those from the irrigated regions of California and Arizona, this long-stapled Upland stands next to Sea Island, both from the point of view of length of staple and price which it commands, and for this reason, since its introduction into the Mississippi-Yazoo area, the region has become a much more valuable part of the Cotton Belt.

To the east, linking up the flood-plain region with the eastern cotton districts, are the loessal bluff lands overlooking the Delta. These lands produce fair cotton. To the west the alluvial flood plain sends long tongues up the two main Mississippi tributaries in the Cotton Belt, namely, the Red River and the Arkansas. An examination of the production map will make clear the fact, that along these two valleys there are narrow strips of heavier production which link the Mississippi-Yazoo Delta Region to the great Black Prairie Region of Central Texas.

This latter region, the Black Waxy Prairies of Texas, the centre of which between Austin and Dallas lies some 200 miles inland from the port of Galveston on the coast, is by far the greatest cotton-producing region in the world to-day. In a favourable year Texas produces some $4\frac{1}{2}$ million bales or nearly one-fifth of the total world production. Running from north-east to south-west through the state of Texas, there are a series of strata outcropping with inward-facing escarpments. Moving inland from the coast, one crosses the swamp region through a succession of timbered sandy and open prairie areas, across the last of which one rises steadily to look out from a north-west-facing escarpment across a great lowland formed by the outcrop of a clay-covered Cretaceous limestone, comparable in some respects to the Black Belt of Alabama. Unlike the Alabama area, it is separated into two regions by a sandy belt of lighter production, which is well timbered, beyond which lies the region known as the Red Prairies (Fig. 37), in which, while heavy, the production is not so heavy nor the area under the crop so continuous as in the Black Waxy Region. Within the Black Prairie Zone are found most of the important population centres of the state, if we except the ports and certain oil centres near the coast. Austin, Waco, Dallas, and Fort Worth are typical Black Prairie centres. To the south-east, as we have seen, the area is delimited by the swamps and sandy timbered belts of long-leaf pine. To the north-west the boundary depends neither on topography nor soils, but is purely climatic. It is the variable indefinite line beyond which cotton in normal years does not pay because of insufficiency of rainfall. It corresponds more or less accurately to the annual isohyet of 20 inches, and in this connection it should be remembered that this fall here is equivalent to a fall of something of the order of 18 inches in, say, Montana. As the bulk of the rainfall of Texas comes during the growing season, and as the area lies for the most part near the margin of satisfactory rainfall from the point of view of the cotton crop, it is in no way surprising that the crop of Texas tends to reflect fairly well, other things being equal, the season's rainfall. Although efforts have been made to show that the Texan crop is largely dependent on the rainfall of the preceding winter, this does not seem to have been proven, although it is easy to see that on the margin of the Belt the conservation in the soil of a part of the winter's fall might readily be the deciding factor in preserving the crop from total loss. Against such conservation one has to set the fact of the greater evaporation proper to this region. The effect of frost on the Texan crop has already been referred to (p. 199).

It has been pointed out above that cotton removes great quantities of potash and phosphates from the soil. In spite of this fact, fertilizers until quite recently have not been used to anything like the extent to which they might be used, especially in view of the fact that cotton is one of those crops which respond very generously to the application of fertilizer, greatly increasing the yield out of all proportion to the expenditure incurred. The increase in the yield from the use of suitable fertilizer is roughly about one-third. Since the bulk of the potash and phosphates extracted from the soil goes, not into the fibre, but into the seed, cotton-seed cake, which is the compressed material remaining behind after the oil has been forced out of the seed, forms one of the cheapest and best fertilizers obtainable in the Cotton Belt. Great quantities of this cake are sold as feeding stuffs for animals, many of which are wintered in the cotton-fields. Where this is not done, the fertilizer used instead is imported mineral phosphates from the great phosphate beds of Florida, which underlie a large part of the surface of the state and form nearly 50 per cent. of the world's supply. There are also considerable quantities available in Tennessee and South Carolina. Other fertilizers used are manufactured, among other things, from basic iron slag, of which large quantities are now available in the south, from fish offals, and from the refuse from abattoirs. Nitrates from Chile and potash from Stassfurt also play their part. Home production of potash has now begun from the saline brines of Searles Lake.[1] This is of special importance owing to the development of rust caused by lack of potash in the lighter soils of the Coastal Plain. Shortage of other fertilizers is directing attention to air derived nitrogen salts which possessing as much as 40 per cent. ammonia have been found to give excellent results in combination with phosphates and potash.

A study of the maps showing the cotton areas about the year 1821, the fertilizer used per acre, and the yield per acre (Fig. 47), will reveal the fact that, broadly speaking, the bulk of the fertilizer used to-day is applied to the poorer soils of the Piedmont and the eastern part of the Coastal Plain areas which have been under cultivation for a long period of time. Here the planters have been driven to apply this method of renewing the fertility of the soil to prevent its complete exhaustion. In the Mississippi-Yazoo Region, where there is normally a high yield per acre, little fertilizer is used, but this high yield is almost wholly due to the amazing fertility of the frequently renewed alluvial soil of what is rather misleadingly called the Delta.

Cotton is a crop which demands a very great amount of hand labour, and in order not to unduly enhance the cost of production, such labour needs to be both abundant and cheap. Sowing which may last some weeks is followed by a long period of very careful cultivation to ensure the best results. Picking, which may begin in Texas as early as the 1st of August, is a long process which may be, and commonly is, spread over a period of about three months. As has already been pointed out above, the cotton bolls do not all open together, but beginning with the lower bolls, the process may last from the 1st of August to early in the winter, the last bolls to open being frequently destroyed by frost. After very many years of experiment cotton-picking machines are

[1] U.S. Dept. of Agriculture Yearbook, 1928, p. 493.

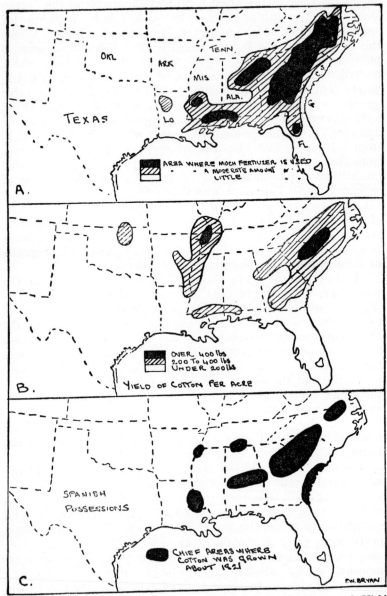

FIG. 47.—Sketch maps to show the relationship between Fertilizer used, Yield of Cotton and Early Producing Areas.

A, Fertilizer used.   B, Yield per acre.   C, Early Cotton-producing Areas.

now regularly in use. Machine-picked cotton is a little down-graded because it requires more cleaning than hand-picked cotton, but the advent of a machine picker which can be used economically will lead to very great changes in the farm-labour demands of the cotton belt.

In view of the increasing complexity of the labour problem it is interesting to note the growing practice of snapping the cotton with the boll, instead of picking the cotton and seed only. Some 4 million bales are now harvested in this fashion. Special machinery is needed to remove the parts of the boll which adhere to the seed. A further development of this method is the invention of the sled, a machine fitted in front with fingers like the prongs of a fork, only broader. This machine replaces hand snapping and thus greatly economizes labour. The disadvantages

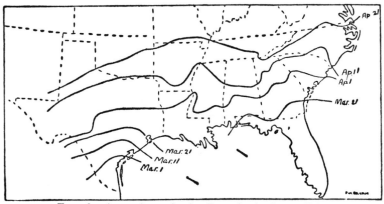

FIG. 48.—Approximate Sowing Dates in the Cotton Belt.

of this method are that the bolls are all removed at the same time, though they do not all ripen together, and the cotton is not so perfectly cleaned as when hand-picked, and the method itself can only be practised in regions like north-west Texas and Oklahoma where the cotton averages about 18 inches in height. We have here to remember, however, that the activities of the boll weevil in the wetter parts of the Cotton Belt are forcing expansion into these drier areas.

Cotton growing spread westwards with the western movement of people, gradually covering the whole of the Belt, and with the emergence of a more intensive production in specially favoured areas as already indicated. In the past three decades, however, there has been a shift in the density of the production away from the areas of long growing season, such as the lower Mississippi flood plain, and towards areas in the north and west of the Belt, having only marginal precipitation, and shorter frost-free periods. In large part this is due to the incidence of certain cotton pests. Various pests have at different times attacked the cotton plant, including the cotton worm, the cotton-boll worm, and the cotton-boll weevil. This last is by far the worst. It is a small beetle. Millions of them are hatched from eggs every spring. They attack the cotton boll before it opens and destroy it. First crossing the United States border from Mexico into Texas in 1892, the pest has spread northward and eastward year by year (Fig. 49). Reaching the Mississippi about 1907, and advancing rapidly eastward, it had by 1915 entered the state of Georgia. To-day it covers the whole of the Cotton Belt.

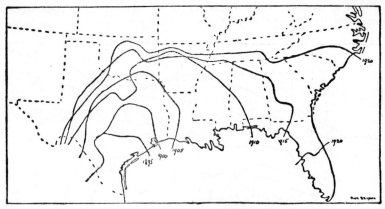

FIG. 49.—Spread of the Mexican Cotton-Boll Weevil. The black lines indicate the position approximately reached by the weevil at the end of each period of five years.

Since it lives on the cotton plant and flourishes under conditions which are beneficial to the cotton plant, its northward and westward limits seem to agree very closely with those of the Cotton Belt. Like cotton itself, it appears to have two natural enemies—the one is frost, and the other is drought. For some thirty years now the ravages of this pest have been increasing, not only in area, but in intensity. What this means can be best appreciated if one tries to realize that one pair of weevils can, it is said, produce in one year a progeny numbering about 12 millions. It is estimated that the weevils destroyed the equivalent of 6 million bales of cotton in 1921. Hard frost kills the weevils which hibernate during the winter. One of the main factors, therefore, determining the size of the cotton crop of any season, is the number of weevils which have managed to survive the preceding winter. A mild winter and a wet spring favours the weevil. Following such weather conditions, a cotton-field may average as many as four weevils to the stalk. One result of the weevil invasion has been to stimulate and extend the cultivation of cotton along the northern edge of the Belt, and also in North-western Texas, where the climatic conditions tend to be much more unfavourable for weevil propagation than farther south.[1] Another has been to encourage efforts to produce varieties of seed to suit the exacting requirements of the north and west. Liability to autumn frosts which take the top crop, and drought in Texas, reduce the yield in these areas as compared with more southerly areas under normal conditions, but this is more than offset by the partial immunity from the ravages of the pest. New varieties of seed and improved cultural methods with the object of decreasing the size of the plant and increasing the size of the crop, have been developed by the Bureau of Plant Industry.[2]

So far the only successful method on a commercial basis of tackling the boll-weevil problem has been that of spraying the plant with calcium arsenate.[3] Good results have also accrued from the cutting down in the vicinity of the cotton-fields of bushes and shrubs which form the winter quarters of the weevils.

We have referred above to the Sea Island production of the coastal islands of Georgia and the Carolinas, and also of the West Indian Islands. This Sea Island cotton, because of its very fine, silky, long staple, ranging in length from $1\frac{1}{2}$ to $2\frac{1}{4}$ inches, was in very great demand for the production of the finest types of goods. Its production has spread from the islands to the north-central part of Florida, and has now been almost wiped out by the advent of the boll weevil in all these areas, with the exception of the West Indian Islands. This cotton requires more moisture than Upland, is also more difficult to pick, and therefore makes greater demands on labour. The cotton grown in North-central Florida has not quite so long a staple as that grown on the coast, but approximates more nearly to the better strains of Egyptian.

To supplement the long-staple production of these areas, attempts have been made, which have been more or less successful, to develop the cultivation of such cottons in the Imperial Valley of California, in the Salt River Valley of Arizona, and most recently in the Great Valley of California. Here, because of the great aridity of the areas, cotton can only be grown under irrigation, the necessary water being supplied in the first case from the Colorado River, the area under cultivation lying below the level of the river, and in the second case from the Salt River, which is a tributary of the Gila. In the

[1] Much of Texas is relatively free from the weevil.
[2] U.S. Dept. of Agriculture Yearbook, 1925, p. 54.
[3] This is now done in many areas with the aid of aircraft.

Imperial Valley some difficulty has been experienced in keeping pure the strain. It is very necessary that this should be done, as the cotton grown is a variety of long-stapled Egyptian, which is 1¼ to 1¾ inches in length, it not being a paying proposition to grow here, under the additional expense of irrigation, a short-stapled cotton. This Imperial Valley area also extends across the frontier for a short distance into Mexico. The main centre of the region is at Calexico, in the Californian part of the region. Some cotton has also been grown of very good quality in the San Joaquin Valley of California, both in the northern portion of the valley and also in the vicinity of the Kern River Oilfields. The total crop from all these areas runs to about 300,000 bales,

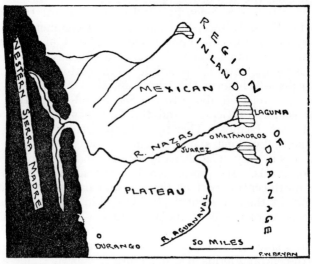

FIG. 50.—Laguna Cotton-producing Region of the Mexican Plateau. The solid black area indicates the ranges of the Western Sierra Madre.

and cultivation here has received a marked stimulus since the decline in acreage and output of the more easterly regions, but there would not seem to be much prospect that this area could ever do much more than serve to replace the disappearing Sea Island production. The main difficulties which these new areas have to face are the cost of irrigation, the scarcity of labour, and the difficulties of transport.

In Mexico, too, cotton production is almost entirely dependent upon irrigation. An extension of the Imperial Valley irrigation area over the border into Mexico is one producing area, but three-fifths usually comes from the Lagunas basin. To this the rivers Nazas and Aguanaval (Fig. 50) bring down fresh silt each year. Irrigation water is supplied by the June–September floods resulting from the heavy summer rains in the Western Sierra Madre, but this, distributed through diversion dams on the rivers, has to be supplemented by ground-water wells. An irrigation project on the similarly situated River Conejos farther north in Chihuahua is expected to yield another 150,000 irrigated acres, on some of which cotton would be grown.

In these irrigated plateau basins cotton is usually grown in rotation with wheat, and this crop with maize and alfalfa are much in demand in the mining areas, and form considerable competitors for the available acreage.

The next most important area is in the Mexicali Valley, a lowland continuing northwards into the Imperial Valley of the U.S.A. It is watered by the Colorado river canal, which the relief of the area here forces into Mexican territory for over 100 miles. The area like the Imperial Valley itself will benefit by the regulation of the Boulder dam. Cotton, wheat, and alfalfa are again the chief irrigated crops. The bulk of the Mexican production is at present consumed in Mexican mills, the larger number of which are located in the south-eastern corner of the plateau, where power is readily obtainable either directly from running water or from the hydro-electrical development which has been based on the streams of the Eastern Sierra Madre. Some of the chief centres where such power is now available are Orizaba, Puebla, and Mexico City.

In discussing the labour problem, we saw that cotton-picking is an extended process, because of the fact that the bolls open successively over a period which may be as long as six months. This delayed operation is, however, advantageous to the next process through which the cotton passes, as it ensures a steadier supply.

From the fields the cotton passes to the ginnery, the function of which is to separate the cotton from the seed, the cotton being pressed into bales of about 500 lb. each, while the seed passes to the oil-mill to be crushed. After passing through the gin, a short fuzz still adheres to the seed, and this fuzz, which is removed at the oil-mill, was in great demand during the War for use in explosives. In pre-war days it was much used for stuffing mattresses, and it has been recently very successfully used for the production of a high-class paper. From one ton of seed some forty gallons of oil are obtained. This oil is very similar in character to olive-oil, and is largely used as a substitute for it. The better the type of cotton, the less satisfactory the seed from the standpoint of oil production; hence the interests of the oil-mill owner, and of the farmer producing

for lint, have seemed at times to be opposed with not very satisfactory results from the point of view of the industry. We may
perhaps at this point usefully summarize some of the more important uses of the cotton plant. From the fibre, which is the
most important part of the plant, yarn and thread, which form the
fundamental products underlying the greatest of the textile
industries, are made. Lesser products of the fibre are batting,
wadding, and gun-cotton. Batting is used among other things
for stuffing tea-cosies. From the seed come oils which help to
make margarine, lubricating oil, and substitutes for olive oil,
and the crushed residue after extracting the oil makes feeding
stuffs and fertilizer, while the short cotton fuzz remaining on the
seed after ginning is used for batting and felt. The hulls of the
seed form feeding-stuff and paper. Even the stalk is turned to
account as feeding-stuff, paper, and fertilizer, while the root is
used for fuel, fertilizer, and certain medicinal purposes. It is
estimated that cotton and its products are now used for about
10,000 purposes.[1]

U.S.A. COTTON EXPORTS, 1936

Total Production in
the United States.
12·4 million bales (500 lb.).

Total Linter Production
in the United States (1935).
1·1 million bales (500 lb.).

Exported to :—	Thousands of bales (excluding linters).
Europe :	
United Kingdom	1,409
Germany	765
France	681
Italy	380
Spain.	207
Belgium	157
Rest of Europe	559
Asia :	
Japan	1,479
China	36
Canada	248
All other countries	49
Total	5,970
Total Linters Export	241
Total Export	6,211
Percentage of Production Exported . . .	46

Of the total of between 6 and 7 million bales which are consumed in America annually, the larger portion to-day goes to
the Southern States, the bulk of the remainder going to the

[1] U.S. Dept. of Agriculture Yearbook, 1926.

New England area, and what is left over to the Hudson-Mohawk Region and the country around Philadelphia. The rise of the Southern States to the first place is a matter of comparatively recent growth. In pre-Civil War days New England led both in the number of spindles and in the amount of cotton consumed. From that time onward there was a steady increase in the takings of the Southern States up to the first decade of the present century, when the consumption of both areas was about 2 million bales, although New England greatly outnumbered the Southern States in the number of spindles in use. In recent years, the Southern States have easily led both in number of bales consumed and of spindles.

In the Southern States the industry is concentrated on the Piedmont at the foot of the Blue Ridge in the states of North and South Carolina and Georgia, to a smaller extent along the Fall Line in the same states, and also in the valleys of the Southern Appalachians in Alabama. In these areas the industry, as in New England, was first based on the water-power available in the Appalachian valleys, the Blue Ridge foothills, and along the Fall Line. The dependence of this area on water-power is strikingly illustrated by the fact that the power companies in the vicinity of Charlotte, in the heart of the cotton region on the Piedmont in North Carolina have had at times to curtail operations because of the shortage of water, thus decreasing the output of the mills depending on it for power. Of the Southern States engaged in the industry, North Carolina is the most important, and second to it stands South Carolina, whose cotton manufacturing area is merely an extension of that of its neighbour state along the Piedmont. This southern industry has shown a very rapid expansion in the last few decades. Since 1911, it has consumed more raw cotton than the New England industry—in the last year or two it has reached one and two-thirds times as much. The South makes some fine cottons, but in general works on lower counts than New England. The proximity of raw material and the longer hours worked were probably advantages in the initial stages of the industry, but these factors count for little to-day when much of the raw cotton for the North Carolina industries, say, comes from Texas, and when the South has little advantage in the matter of child labour and labour hours. There is little to choose also in the price of motive power, whether hydro-electric or coal.

The South has, however, the advantage often of newer plant and of plant more continuously in use. At present, too, distinctly lower wages are paid in the southern industry. The actual manufacturing centres in the South are set about relatively small towns and villages of which the greatest concentration is to be found about the common Piedmont boundary of the North and South Carolinas, e.g. Charlotte and Gastonia.

Typical of the developments which have taken place in the southern area, is the growth of the industry in the vicinity of Chattanooga in the Tennessee Valley of the Southern Appalachians. In the nineties there was but one small mill in this district. To-day it ranks second in the United States as a hosiery centre, being only surpassed by the Philadelphia-Reading district.

Of the cotton which moves abroad the bulk is handled by three great ports, each of which is more or less clearly identified

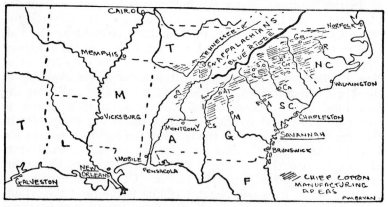

Fig. 51.—Chief Cotton Manufacturing Areas of the Southern States and Chief Cotton Shipping Ports.

A, Augusta; At, Atlanta; B, Birmingham; Ca, Columbia; Ch, Charlotte; Cn, Chattanooga; Cs, Columbus; G, Greenville; GB, Greensboro; M, Macon; R, Raleigh; S, Spartanburg. The major ports are underlined.

with one or more of the main producing areas. These are Galveston, New Orleans, and Savannah (Fig. 51). From the Black Prairies of Texas the cotton moves out by way of Galveston, which is by far the greatest cotton port in the world. Cotton forms four-fifths of the exports of Galveston, and second place is taken by cotton-seed oil, while cotton-seed cake is a good third. A small amount of the Texan crop moves out by way of Houston and Port Arthur. From the Mississippi-Yazoo Region, cotton moves out chiefly by way of New Orleans at the mouth of the Mississippi, and forms more than half the total exports in value. Cotton-seed oil and cotton-cake also are large exports from this port, which stands second to Galveston as a cotton port. A small percentage of the crop from here, and also from the Black Belt of Alabama, moves out by way of Mobile, at which port cotton again forms the main export in point of value. At the neigh-bouring small port of Pensacola a small amount also of the Black Belt cotton finds its way out, but the great bulk of the Alabama cotton moves eastward to Savannah, where it joins the cotton moving from the upper Coastal Plain and the Pied-mont, thus helping to make Savannah the third of the great cotton ports of the Southern States. Other cotton ports related to the Coastal Plain and Piedmont Regions are Charleston in South Carolina, Wilmington in North Carolina, Norfolk in Vir-

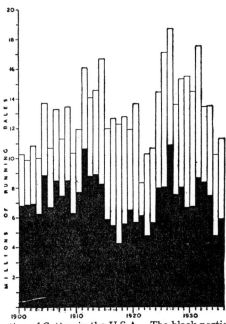

FIG. 52.—Production of Cotton in the U.S.A. The black portion of each column represents the exported cotton for each year.

ginia, and Brunswick in Georgia. Of the total quantity moving out from these various ports, part moves directly abroad, and part moves northward to the Northern Area along the coast. Of this latter movement, the bulk is for home consumption, and the remainder for reshipment abroad.

Throughout the South cotton is the chief, often the only cash crop ; and that this is so, is a direct heritage of the slave economy which prevails until the aftermath of the Civil War resulted in the freeing of the slaves and the ruin of the plantation owners. Thus emerged economic conditions which proved favourable to the development of those forms of tenancy in which rent, agricultural implements, and other supplies, are advanced on the security of a share of the cotton crop. The very characteristics of the commodity lend themselves to this system ; for cotton can be stored, and the actual production can be conveniently checked, for all of it must come to the ginning factory. On many small farms of the Old South, the tenants are habitually in debt, and the hidden rates of interest which the system actually encourages are very high. Often he has neither the means nor the inclination to maintain the fertility of the soil ; and often he shifts aimlessly from farm to farm. His poverty is in part the result of the fact that his cash crop—because of the amount of hand labour required —cannot bring in large individual returns. Partly, too, because the price is in large part dependent upon the vagaries of foreign trade—for half the crop is usually exported—and the yield of his own crop, upon the vagaries of climate and of weevil infestation.

Ruling prices—or what the farmer thinks these may be— affect very much the amount of the crop sown each year. In short his chief cash crop is peculiarly susceptible to world price fluctuations, and to the competition of cheap labour in tropical lands.

The typical cotton farm in the older parts of the Cotton Belt is about forty acres in extent, of which about eighteen may be in cotton, ten in maize, and a few acres in various vegetable and fodder crops. One or two work animals are kept—often mules— and a few hogs and chickens for farm consumption. The seasonal labour requirements of cotton, with its heavy demands in spring and autumn, are such as to compete with most other crops, and are themselves inimical to greater diversification. Less dependence upon cotton is certainly desirable, but dairy farming and mixed farming have the disadvantages that the climate makes difficult the adoption of good feeding grasses, and favours the incidence of cattle disease. Except in the drier parts of the Belt, i.e. in western Texas and in Oklahoma, where grain sorghums take its place, corn is grown throughout the Belt ; but the yield is generally much below that obtained in the Corn Belt proper, and actually the Cotton Belt is not self-sufficient in the supply of either corn or of hay. Winter wheat is important along the northern margin of the Cotton Belt, grain sorghums in the extreme west and north-west of the Belt, and velvet beans and other leguminous fodder crops in the moister south-eastern parts of the Belt.

Peanuts are locally a very important crop, particularly about the borders of South-West Georgia and South-East Alabama ; and two of the major tobacco-producing regions of the States, those of North Carolina and of Tennessee, impinge upon the Cotton Belt (Fig. 53).

It is a little unfortunate that the Cotton Belt and the South have come to be almost synonymous terms, for there are areas in the Southern states where no cotton is grown ; and where it is produced, it is not always with the same combination of crops or the same intensity. For instance, neither cotton nor any

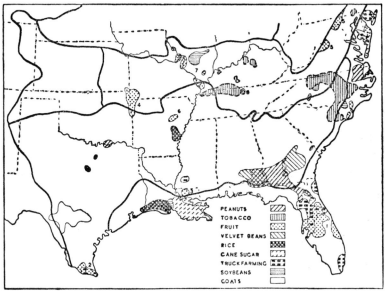

FIG. 53.—Distribution of important specialized crops in the Cotton, Corn and Winter Wheat, and Hard Winter Wheat Belts. Also area of Angora goat flocks in Texas.

Nos. of the Fruit Belts represent chiefly :
1. Florida—citrus fruit.
2. Rio Grande—irrigated fruit area.
3. Louisiana—strawberries.
4. The Ozarks (the south-western part of Missouri and adjacent sections of Arkansas and Oklahoma)— apples, peaches and strawberries.
5. Shenandoah–Cumberland Region—apples.
6. Arkansas, White County—strawberries.
7. Southern Illinois and Eastern Missouri—apples and peaches.
8. Tennessee—peaches.
9. North and South Carolina—peaches.

other crop is largely produced in the Flatlands near the coast ; and in the formerly important region of the southern third of the Mississippi flood plain, with its 250 frost-free days, cotton has retreated before the boll weevil. Yet other portions of the Belt, e.g. the El Llano Estacado of Texas, and the western portions of Oklahoma, have only been invaded by cotton in recent decades, and in tradition and development are quite at variance with the Old South. In fact, it is misleading to speak of the South. In reality there are two Souths—a South-East, including the Mississippi states and states to the east of them, and a South-West including much of Western Texas and Oklahoma. The latter differs from the former (the Old South) in having fewer negroes, larger farms, less tenancy, more farm machinery, and more extensive farming generally.

COTTON PRODUCTION BY STATES

Running bales in thousands

State	1929	1932	1934	1944
Texas	3,803	4,307	2,315	2,500
Mississippi	1,876	1,161	1,121	1,960
Alabama	1,308	934	936	950
Georgia	1,340	862	975	800
Oklahoma	1,124	1,084	330	660
Arkansas	1,396	1,326	849	1,350
N. Carolina	767	680	641	710
S. Carolina.	833	722	685	850
Louisiana	797	599	473	620
Tennessee	504	467	397	560
Missouri	221	301	230	335
California	254	124	251	355
Arizona	149	67	113	135
Others	176	76	156	168
Total U.S.A.	14,548	12,710	9,472	11,953

THE HUMID SUB-TROPICAL BELT

We have already noticed that the coastal margin of the Cotton Belt is characterized, generally, by swamp, and sandy ill-drained soils, by much poor forest and cut-over land, and by a heavy autumn rainfall ; all of which are prejudicial to cotton production and indeed to agriculture generally. In the west, however, are exceptional areas. For example, the humid eastern part of the coast belt of Texas was originally a natural prairie with relatively heavy and fertile soils. First used as a ranch land, and still maintaining some importance in this respect, much of it has now become the scene of a specialized rice-producing area. Because of the use of power ploughs, drills, and harvesting machinery, the production per labourer is enormously greater than is usual in the Far East. The production per acre is probably rather lower. Irrigation is necessary, in spite of a considerable precipitation. The water table is very shallow, and the amount pumped from shallow wells and bayous is about equal to the average rainfall. Rice is also grown in the Arkansas river flood plains and in the lowlands about the lower Sacramento in California. The U.S.A. has a low consumption per capita, but even so, on balance, is an importing country for this commodity.

Adjoining the rice region to the east—mostly on the coastlands of Louisiana—is the only region of the United States where cane sugar is produced. For this commodity the climate is distinctly marginal, and here as in New South Wales, Natal, and Southern Brazil, the crop may be damaged by frost.

Sugar has been grown here for a long time, however—often with cheap Mexican labour, and to-day production is maintained by means of a high import duty. Only very short ratoon periods are possible—two to three years at the most—and the plant has to be protected during the winter months, and the yield is relatively low. The sugar lands are held for the most part by the sugar factory companies. A few years ago difficulties of obtaining cheap labour (and harvesting is heavy hand-work) and plant disease almost brought the production here to a close. There has been some resuscitation, chiefly because of the breeding of new and more suitable varieties of cane. Apart from this production all the *cane* sugar used in the United States is imported. This area usually produces about 7 per cent. of the cane sugar used, and about 6 per cent. of the total sugar (cane and beet) consumed in the country.

Near the coast East of the Mississippi we rapidly come into a region of rather light sandy soils. These are deficient in nitrogenous material, but are warm and easily tilled. They are therefore well suited for the cultivation of early vegetables for the northern markets. Cattle are also kept and are grazed in the pinewoods and cut-over lands which occupy so much of this region. Only a small fraction of the total region is available for such use, but of that it is estimated that only about one-fifth has so far been developed. Two-thirds of the total area is under pine forest consisting for the most part of loblolly, long leaf and slash pine, and these trees supply about half the turpentine and rosin used in the United States. About one-half of the cattle grazed in the region are for beef purposes and about one-fourth are dairy cattle.

8

CHAPTER XV

THE AGRICULTURE OF THE CORN BELT, AND OF THE CORN AND WINTER WHEAT BELTS

FROM the standpoints of both acreage and production, maize or corn, as the Americans call it, is by far the greatest of the cereal crops in North America. It is essentially an American crop, as out of a total world production of some $3\frac{1}{2}$ to $4\frac{1}{2}$ thousand million bushels, the United States alone produces $2\frac{1}{2}$ to $3\frac{1}{4}$ thousand million bushels[1], or in or about three-fourths of the world total. It has been estimated that it is grown on three out of every four farms in the United States, and that it occupies a greater acreage than wheat, oats, barley, rye, buckwheat, fruit, nuts and rice all combined. It has been further estimated that roughly about one-half of the total money received for cereals in the U.S.A. is obtained for corn.

From America this grain has spread to many parts of the world. When the first settlements took place in America, they succeeded mainly because of the ease with which maize could be grown on land just newly cleared of forest with a minimum of cultivation. It was the staple cereal of the indigenous Indian population. To-day it can be regarded as the real foundation of the greater part of American agriculture, since without it to act as food-stuff for hogs and cattle, the typical economy of the average American farm would have to be of quite a different character. This aspect of the subject can, however, be more fully made clear after we have discussed the distribution and conditions of production of the crop in the United States.

Having seen something of what corn means in American agriculture, let us turn to the map of the corn regions (Fig. 54) of the United States, and let us see where the major producing areas are located. Corn, with certain minor exceptions, is grown throughout practically the whole of that part of the United States lying between the Great Lakes and the Gulf of Mexico on the one hand, and the semi-arid region of the high plains and the waters of the Atlantic on the other; in other words, throughout the Mississippi basin, with the exceptions of

[1] In 1948, 3,650 million bushels.

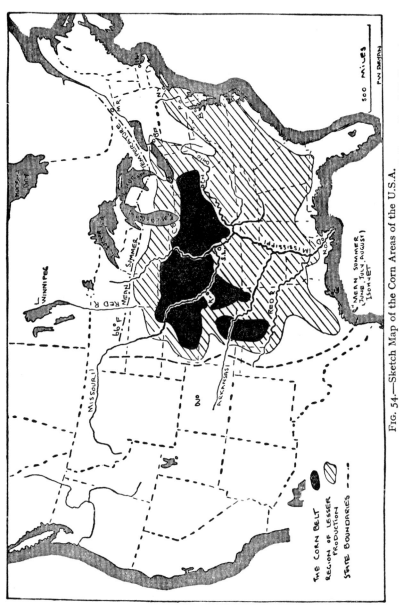

Fig. 54.—Sketch Map of the Corn Areas of the U.S.A.

B, Baltimore; BF, Buffalo; BN, Boston; C, Chicago; CN, Cincinnati; DV, Denver; G, Galveston; K, Kansas City; MR, Montreal; NO, New Orleans; NY, New York; P, Philadelphia; SL, St. Louis.

the extreme north-west and the semi-arid west, and also on the Atlantic coastal plain. While corn is grown throughout this vast area, which measures some 1,500 miles from east to west, by about 1,000 miles from north to south, there are great variations from point to point in the density of the production. These variations depend mostly on such factors as soil conditions, nature of the surface, climatic conditions, etc. Within the region there is one very marked zone of major production. It is called the Corn Belt, and lies just southward and south-westward of the Great Lakes. Beginning in Ohio, this belt runs westward through the states of Indiana, Illinois, Iowa, Northern Missouri, and peters out in Central Nebraska. An offshoot of the main belt extends southward through Eastern Kansas and Oklahoma into Texas. Within this region of the Corn Belt the areas of greatest density of production are to be found in the two states of Iowa and Illinois, lying the one to the west and the other to the east of the Mississippi southward and westward of Chicago. These states each produce about 400 million bushels, or more than twice the average pre-war wheat crop of Canada. These two states, together with Missouri, Nebraska, and Kansas on the one side, and Indiana on the other, contain nearly one-half of the acreage under maize, and rather more than one-half of the total production of maize in the United States.

Planting may begin in the Gulf states as early as February, and steadily progresses northward, until by the middle of May the Great Lakes have been reached. In the main Corn Belt south of the lakes, planting usually takes place by the 1st of May. These dates in the respective areas roughly correspond to the dates when the areas are free from killing frosts, so that by the time the young plants appear, all danger from frost has passed. The ground temperature at this time is about 55° F., a temperature which is considered suitable for successful germination. The average frostless period in the Corn Belt is 140 days in the extreme North-East to 180 days along the southern borders. These periods are of course averages and in some years, notably 1917 and 1924, the period free from killing frost was much less owing to climatic vagaries and very serious damage results to the corn crop. While this is possible, nevertheless the best corn is that which has a growing period of from 150–160 days. The succession of harvests which take place in the case of both corn and wheat are of considerable importance from the labour point of view, as labour can migrate from south to north following the harvests. This migration is of much greater importance in the case of the wheat harvest, as wheat has for the most part to be reaped immediately when ripe, because, while corn can be, and often is, left standing for months in the field, wheat, unless in a very dry, still climate, would be greatly damaged by storm and rain.

Corn grows most rapidly towards the end of the growing period, hence high day temperature and warm nights are then of great importance. An average temperature for the three summer months (June, July, and August) of about 70 to 80 degrees, and an average night temperature of 55 degrees, represent the conditions where the bulk of the crop is grown. This last condition, a fairly high night temperature in the summer, rules out the irrigated areas of part of the arid western section of the United States, as in Nevada, where the daily range of temperature is great. Very little corn is grown where the summer temperature falls below 66° F. on the average. Corn grown under those conditions, as is the case in much of Canada, is grown for fodder, and seldom matures. Cool weather in July is usually followed by a marked decrease in the crop, other things being equal. Towards the south-western part of the Corn Area, particularly in Texas, one of the limiting factors is the way in which periods of drought and dry winds dry out the pollen and the silks by means of which pollination takes place. It also has the effect of hastening the pollen and delaying the silks, so that by the time the silks are ready for pollination the pollen has been wasted.

The water requirements of the plant steadily increase until the time when maximum vegetative growth is attained in late July. Studies made by the United States Weather Bureau indicate that the most critical factor in conditioning the size of the maize crop in any year is the rainfall of the month of July. This was well shown in the year 1901, when lack of rain during July caused a serious decrease in the yield per acre. When the July rainfall of the main Corn Belt is about 4 inches, the crop is about average, that is, about 30 bushels to the acre. When under 3 inches the crop will be low, and when over 5 inches the crop will be heavy, other things being equal. For example, in the state of Ohio a fall of over 5 inches in July may give a crop of 40 bushels to the acre. It is found that everywhere in the Belt the crop, as a rule, reflects very closely the rainfall of the month of July. So close is this connection that it is also found that, should there be a deficiency in July and an excess in August, this excess does little to restore the crop. In this respect the plant offers a marked contrast to cotton, which, as we have seen, responds very rapidly to improved weather conditions. For the most part the rain in the Corn Belt comes in short showers, which, while keeping the plant well supplied with moisture, do not interfere with agricultural operations to any marked extent, and ensure the ample sunshine which the plant requires for maturing.

It will have been seen, then, that maize is the crop of a warm, moist summer area where there is sufficient rainfall to satisfy the requirements of a rapidly growing and very luxuriant crop, and that the critical month, both from the standpoints of temperature and rainfall, is that of July. It may be well to note the various combinations of heat and moisture during that month, and their probable effects on the crop. In the main Corn Belt the most favourable conditions are warm days and nights with frequent heavy showers. Next in order are cool and wet conditions. The least happy conditions from the point of view of yield exist where the weather is both warm and dry, and but little better in this respect is a cool, dry July. Dry conditions in July are always unfavourable, because of the high degree of transpiration which takes place from such a large plant.

Baker gives definition to the more intensive area of production by limiting his Corn Belt to a region within which the average production per square mile is more than 3,000 bushels (see Fig. 42). So delimited we find that the boundary lines approximate to those representing certain limiting physical conditions. Thus the eastern boundary roughly coincides with the western edge of the Appalachian plateau, the soils and topography of which are less favourable than those immediately to the west. On the south and east of the Mississippi, the boundary coincides roughly with the limit of the Wisconsin glaciation, the drift of which has in general given rise to soils less leached and more fertile than those of the older drifts which extended farther to the south.

Farther west on the southern boundary, however, it is the northern boundary of the Ozarks with relatively poor soils that sets a limit to an intense production. Still farther to the west the boundary of the Corn Belt divides prevailing corn to the north from prevailing winter wheat to the south, and the physical limitation to a further extension here to the south is due to very hot summer winds, the incidence of which increases southwards. Corn, which is much longer on the ground than wheat, is not proof against these in the late summer, at which time wheat is here harvested.

To the west the boundary of the Belt is in large part climatic, corresponding with the western limit of 8 inches summer (i.e. June, July and August) rainfall, though actually the occurrence of the Nebraska sandhills prevents the boundary here from being a simple north-south line. To the north the boundary is wholly climatic, for little corn is grown for grain north of the 70° F. summer isotherm, which on this side corresponds with the boundary of the Belt. Thus in Canada, it is only in the extreme south-west of the Ontario peninsula that corn is grown for grain, though for ensilage it is found throughout the lake peninsulas, and to some extent also in western Canada.

Within the Corn Belt, corn is invariably grown as a rotation crop, and in farms in which the production of beef and pork animals is an essential part of the farming system. Corn occupies about 40 per cent. of the crop land. The other chief crops are oats, winter wheat, and hay, each of which usually occupies between 15 per cent. and 18 per cent. of the crop land. Corn is

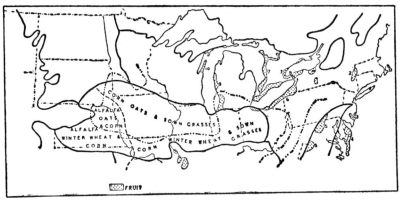

FIG. 55.—The Corn Belt.

— ·· — ·· — Oats more important than Winter Wheat to North of this line.
— — — — Alfalfa more important than Sown Grasses to West of this line.

Nos. of Fruit Belts represent chiefly :
1. Cape Cod—cranberries.
2. Hudson Valley and W. Massachusetts—apples.
3. New Jersey—peaches.
4. Delaware—early apples.
5. Shenandoah–Cumberland Region—apples.
6. Lake Erie shores—grapes.
7. Canadian shores of Lakes Erie and Huron, and the western extremity of Lake Ontario—hard fruit, especially apples.
8. Western New York and Lake Ontario shores—apples, grapes, and cherries.
9. Shores of Lake Michigan—grapes, small fruits, apples, peaches, and cherries.
10. Dore Peninsula (Wisconsin)—cherries.

usually grown in rotation with a small grain crop which is pre-dominantly spring oats north of the average winter isotherm of 23° F., and winter wheat south of this line, for in the south of the Belt, corn can be removed in time to seed the wheat. In the western and drier third of the belt, alfalfa tends to take the place of timothy and other tame grasses in the hay crop. Potatoes and peas and beans occupy considerable areas locally, but there is relatively little commercial fruit growing, or root crops. The use of soya beans as a fodder crop has increased much in recent years, the heaviest production being in the south-eastern clay pan region of poor soils in Illinois. It supplies its own needs in nitrogen and its rapid growth gives a cash crop off the ground in time to sow winter wheat. In parts of this area it occupied one-third of the cultivated land and replaced oats as the second ranking crop in 1949.[1]

To the south of the Corn Belt proper, corn remains one of the chief crops on practically every farm, even in the rough subsistence farming of the Appalachian Mountains. It gives way, however, to winter wheat and to grain sorghums in the west, and yields, generally, are less than in the Corn Belt.

Like cotton, corn has its insect pests. Of these the worst is the European corn borer which, infesting southern Ontario in 1920, entered Ohio in 1925 and 1926. Where unchecked this pest destroys from 25 to 50 per cent. of the crop. The only effective cure appears to be careful harvesting followed by the entire removal or burning of the stalks, cobs and fodder.[2]

The maize production of Mexico is of outstanding importance. Together with beans, maize in the form of the tortilla, or hot corn-cake, is the staple food of the Mexican peasants. Over half of the total Mexican production is grown under very primitive agricultural conditions in irrigated areas stretching through the provinces of Jalisco, Guanajuato, and Mexico, which lie in a line from west to east along the southern part of the Mexican Plateau. In addition to this region there is a detached region of large production in the northern part of the Yucatan Peninsula (Fig. 56). Maize is grown to some extent in almost all parts of Mexico, and, in spite of the fact that it occupies about 50 per cent. of the total area under crops, there is an annual import from the United States.

Although the staple food of Mexico, it is only in the southern Cotton Belt of the United States that maize is largely used for human food. Here it is used in the form of coarse cake, and also in the form of boiled meal. Maize does not make good bread alone, but can be used to make a coarse bread in combination with other cereals, such as rye. Maize in one form or another formed the staple food of the Confederate soldiers during the Civil War. Its production in the south is insufficient for local consumption, because of the primary demands of cotton on the soil; hence the deficiency has to be imported from the north, but there are signs that this state of affairs will not last long, and that in the near future the south will produce ample corn for its own requirements at least. The high price of corn, the activities of the boll weevil, and, lastly, the

[1] "Economic Geography," Vol. 30, No. 1, Jan. 1954.
[2] Dept. of Agriculture Yearbook, 1928, p. 108.

increasing price of meat, are all so many levers working to raise
the acreage under corn in the south.

As a human food, corn is also converted into oil, into starch
and also into glucose, a form of sugar. The oil formed from
corn is an excellent substitute for olive-oil. The bulk of the
crop raised in Illinois, within a radius of 100 miles from Chicago,
moves into that city for conversion into starch, glucose, oil, and
corn-meal, but outside that radius it is on the whole found cheaper
to market corn " on the hoof." In other words, it is fed to the
vast numbers of cattle and swine which are kept in the Corn

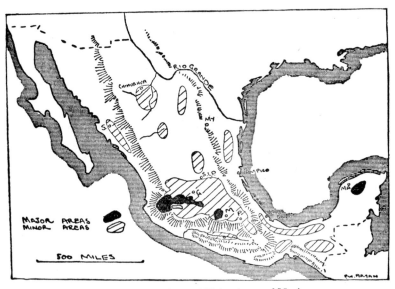

FIG. 56.—Sketch Map of Maize Areas of Mexico.
G, Guadalajara; **M**, Mexico City; **MA**, Merida; **MY**, Monterey; **P**, Puebla; **S**, Sinaloa;
SLP, San Luis Potosi.

Belt. The great bulk of the maize produced in the Corn Belt
is marketed in this fashion, and it is in this fact that we find the
most marked contrast between the distribution of maize and
of wheat. Within the area of the Corn Belt are to be found
about one-half of all the hogs and one-third of all the cattle in
the United States. There are in the United States two main
cattle-producing areas. On the great grassland of the High
Plains lying eastward of the Rocky Mountains is one of the greatest
cattle-ranges of the world. Here young cattle are kept for one,
two, or three years, pasture being cheap and particularly suited
for growing stock. Over one-third of the beef cattle of the

U.S.A. are to be found in this region. They then move east
into the Corn Belt. Maize contains more oil than any other
cereal. For this reason it is excellent for fattening stock. In
the Belt the cattle are fattened on corn, cotton-cake, hay and
silage. This last consists of the entire maize plant chopped
up and preserved in tower-like structures called silos, which
keep the food green, moist, soft, and fresh for a couple of years
if necessary. It is in this fashion that maize can be used to
give the greatest possible return in food value, and the use
of these silos is rapidly increasing, not only in the Cotton
Belt, but also in New England and in Canada, where it is
exceptional for maize to mature, but where the plant grows
with sufficient luxuriance to give ample material for storing
as silage

In the main part of the Corn Belt, cattle are fattened for
beef, and when ready move into the great packing centres, of
which Chicago is by far the largest and best known. It owes
its importance in this connection almost wholly to its excellent
position with reference to the Belt. Other centres lie mostly
on or towards the outer edges of the Belt. Of such centres
attention may be called, perhaps, to Omaha, Kansas City, and
Cincinnati. Even far south in Texas there are packing centres
at Fort Worth and Waco. At these centres cattle are converted
into beef, canned and fresh, and into the vast numbers of by-
products, ranging from buttons to fertilizer, which to-day form
such a distinctive feature of the industry.

Cattle are primarily grass-eating animals. Swine require
more concentrated food. They are essentially grain-eating
animals, and for this reason they are even better suited as a
means of marketing the corn crop than are cattle. About 40
per cent. of the corn of the United States—probably rather more
within the Corn Belt—is fed to hogs, and about 20 per cent. to
beef cattle and sheep, and about 14 per cent. to work animals.
Much is fed also to poultry. Thus as mechanized farming increases, rather less corn is required, and the same thing is true
when—as has been the case during the last decade—there has
been a large drop in the export demand for pork products and
of lard. As we have seen, the Corn Belt contains about one-half
of all the hogs in the United States. The major hog zone covers
roughly the Corn Belt with two exceptions. The area within
close radius of Chicago, which, for reasons explained above, does
not carry so much stock as the rest of the Belt, is one of these.
The other is a zone along the northern edge of the Corn Belt,
in which, because of the great amount of dairying carried on,
there is available much skim-milk, which is largely used for

feeding hogs. The fattened hogs, like the cattle, move into the packing centres. Apart from the meat products, one of the main products is lard derived from the hog-fat, of which very large quantities are obtained from the corn-fed American hog.

The basic fact underlying all this selling one's corn " on the hoof " is the concentrated food value obtained in this fashion. It has been estimated that 1 lb. of beef produced in this fashion represents about 11 lb. of corn, and that 1 lb. of pork similarly represents from 3 to 5 lb. of corn. Given similar natural advantages much depends on the efficiency with which the farm is run.[1] For this reason it is much cheaper to feed corn to cattle and hogs and even to poultry, and to transport them to market, rather than the much more bulky grain. A typical farm in Iowa would grow mainly corn and keep from twenty to one hundred or more hogs. To overcome the difficulty of harvesting corn, which, because of its size and the fact that thoroughly efficient harvesting machinery does not exist, is difficult to harvest, the practice is developing of growing a succession of fodder crops, including corn, and of turning the hogs into the standing crops and letting them do their own harvesting. In relation to corn, this is known as " hogging down corn." Where this is not done, the valuable vegetative parts of the plant are often lost as feeding stuff, and the corn-heads are harvested by hand from a wagon.

The Corn and Winter Wheat Belt (see Fig. 42, p. 196)

The Corn and Winter Wheat Belt, as defined by Baker, extends eastwards from the Flint Hills, between the Corn and Cotton Belts, as far as the Appalachian plateau. Thereafter it extends north-eastwards between the Hay and Dairying Belts and the Cotton Belt. The Flint Hills coincide almost with the 33 inches isohyet, and thus the whole Belt has humid, i.e. pedalferic, soils. Only in the extreme west, however, were these developed under grassland conditions, for over 80 per cent. of the area was at one time forested, and to-day a much greater part of the whole is in woodlots and forest than is the case in the Corn Belt. One per cent. greater in extent than the Corn Belt, it produces crops of little more than half the value ; and this for the two reasons that the larger extent of rough topography has resulted in a smaller total of crop land, and also that although soils are even more diversified, they prove on the average of lower fertility than the glaciated soils of the Corn Belt.

[1] U.S. Dept. of Agriculture Yearbook, 1926.

Soils are less lasting, more fertilizers are required, and greater areas have suffered erosion, than is the case in the Corn Belt. These are the very greatest generalizations, however, for the two chief characteristics of the Belt as a whole are its diversity of soil and of topography, and its relative homogeneity of climate. We should notice at once the variety and number of physiographic regions, parts—in some cases the whole—of which are included in the Belt. Thus beginning on the east we have the upper and more fertile portion of the coast plain of Virginia and Maryland, including with general farming an important tobacco area. Next comes the Piedmont region of South-east Pennsylvania, Virginia, and North-west Carolina, where again the general corn, wheat, and hay, typical of the whole Belt, is interrupted by very important commercial apple production on the slopes of the Blue Ridge, and about the sides of Shenandoah Valley, and by another even larger tobacco production in the Piedmont. Farther south-westwards the height and sterility of the Appalachian plateau interposes a rugged wooded area, with only small, and poor, and largely subsistence, farms.

Matters improve again on the phosphatic limestone soils of the eroded Lexington and Nashville domes, especially in the former, with its fine pasture, its traditional though reduced breeding of horses, and its great specialization in tobacco. The hilly nature of the Ouachita and Boston Mountains and the cherty thin soils of the Ozarks are again relatively unproductive, though locally fruit—apples and peaches—do well on the warm, well-drained soils of these rougher regions. Farther west again, on the rolling prairie plains of eastern Kansas, with their deep, dark, prairie soils, is a more homogeneous area of large grain and livestock farming.

In the 1,000 miles of its length only the westernmost third has a rainfall of under 40 inches. Nowhere is it less than 33 inches. Summer average temperatures range from 75° along the northern margin to 77° F. along the southern. The frost-free period is from 180 days in the north to 200 in the south. Throughout the Belt the winter average temperature is within a few degrees of the freezing-point. Frost occurs frequently, and is sometimes severe, but seldom very prolonged.

Corn, winter wheat, and hay are the chief crops on most farms, though the proportion of wheat increases to the north and west ; but in the little hillside farms of the mountainous areas wheat may drop out entirely, there being just a corn patch, some grazing land, and a few vegetables for farm use.

CHAPTER XVI

THE HAY AND DAIRYING, HARD WINTER WHEAT, AND SPRING WHEAT BELTS

HAY AND DAIRYING BELT (see Fig. 42, p. 196)

ALL of this transitional Belt was at one time forested ; all of it was covered by the most recent glaciation ; much of it was at one time occupied by the glacial precursors of the Great Lakes. The region is defined as that in which agricultural products are more important than those of forestry, and hay and pasture more important than grain crops. It is usually somewhat sharply distinguished from the Forest and Hay Belt, consisting chiefly of the Laurentian Shield, to the north, and from the forested uplands of the Adirondacks, and of the New England mountains to the east. It extends throughout the St. Lawrence lowlands. An extension southwards, caused by rougher topography, poorer soils, and cooler weather, closes in the Corn Belt along the western border of the Appalachian plateau, and thus although it marches with the Corn Belt on the south, it adjoins the Corn and Winter Wheat Belt to the south-east. Much corn is grown, particularly along the southern margin, but almost entirely for ensilage, for which purpose it is a quite common crop as far down the St. Lawrence as Montreal. Winter wheat is usual, too, along the southern border, particularly in parts of southern Wisconsin, southern Michigan, and the Upper Ontario Lake peninsula, but always in rotations, and seldom as a specialist or dominant crop. Oats are grown almost universally throughout the Hay and Dairying Belt, while the prevalence of a well-distributed light rainfall and the relatively low evaporation are favourable both to permanent and to sown pastures. Surface, or shallow well water, is usually readily available, and many of the largest of American and Canadian cities lie within the Belt. These are conditions favourable to the dairying industry, and the improved land in this belt as a whole has a greater density of dairy cattle than any other major region.

The adverse characteristics of the Laurentian Shield give a more definite northern boundary than would have been the case if climatic factors alone were concerned, and summer temperatures in relation to the fruition of corn define that to the south well enough.   To the west the belt is now definitely encroaching upon the sub-humid portion of the Spring Wheat Belt, as we shall presently see.

Within the Belt, however, are considerable areas, so sandy, so marshy, or of so rough a topography as to provide little but the rough pasture of cut-over land.   This is so in much of the Pre-Cambrian portion of northern Wisconsin, as also in the St. Peter's sandstone area in the centre of that state.   So too, the northern portion of the southern peninsula of Michigan, bereft of its fine white pine forests, and frequently burnt over, has little agricultural value at present.   Much of the borders of the Laurentian Shield, particularly in the lower Ontario peninsula is either rough or infertile or both.   Even in the St. Lawrence valley itself, particularly below Montreal, areas so sandy or so marshy as to be agriculturally useless, are by no means infrequent.   Among the winter feed crops, hay is dominant throughout, but particularly so in the cooler north-east, where silage corn and small grain is less in evidence than in the west.   Holstein cattle—a renowned breed for milk yield—are perhaps the greatest single component of the dairy herds, though, of course, there are many others.   Durhams do better in the areas of rougher topography.

The very greatest intensity of dairying occurs in southern Wisconsin, the Upper Ontario peninsula, and in the Lake Ontario plains of New York State.   In Wisconsin in particular, the industry probably owes as much to growth of a superior scientific technique, as to the fact that the law of comparative costs usually makes dairy farming the farmers first choice.   Some of the most important advances in scientific dairying have been made, and instituted in this, the first state in the Union as far as the value of dairy produce is concerned.   Throughout, there is considerable overlapping of the butter, whole milk, and cheese districts, though one can usually discern the incidence of certain principles.   Thus good communications with the large urban centres has an effect in the distribution of whole milk production, though improved communications and technique in whole milk haulage has greatly enlarged the supply area of the largest cities. Again the fact that large quantities of fluid must be moved to the cheese factories tends to limit the radius of supply, and to multiply the number of the factories, which are usually smaller than creameries.   The transport of the finished product is less urgent than is the case of milk or butter, and the regularity of the supply of milk less important.   Thus the cheese factories are often farthest away from populous centres, and often too in areas where an all-the-year-round milk supply is more difficult to attain because of the price of winter feed. Cheese is an important Canadian export and most of it comes from the Canadian portion of this Belt.

A number of locally specialized areas of farming occur within the area. Some of these are due to the ameliorating influence of the Great Lakes upon climate. Lake-side sites tend to have a cooler summer and a less severe winter than areas some miles inland. Even more important for fruit growers is the fact that the flowering and setting of the fruit trees is delayed somewhat at lake-side, and that late spring frosts are less likely, and, if they occur, less intense, than they are inland. Good air and water drainage is available on the slopes of the lake margins, and in some cases land of rather rough topography is devoted to orchard fruit. The chief commercial fruit areas of the belt are indicated in Fig. 55. The Niagaran peninsula is the only important vineyard area of Canada, and peaches are also produced there. The other Canadian areas are chiefly devoted to apples, while in the United States the borders of Lake Ontario have many apple orchards, and some vineyards, the eastern shore of Lake Michigan has a very important peach production, and the Dore peninsula, on the west shore, has cherry orchards. Potatoes are ubiquitous in the Hay and Dairying Belt, often doing well on the lighter and sometimes arid soils. Areas of intense production are the Aroostock county of Maine, the lower St. Lawrence valley, and in central Michigan and Wisconsin, where conditions of soil, or of climate, do not favour corn growing, which would be competitive in the matter of labour periods.

THE HARD WINTER WHEAT BELT (see Fig. 42, p. 196)

The belt of limestone upland with thin soils, known as the Flint Hills, interposes a narrow negative zone between the Corn and Winter Wheat Belt to the east, and the Hard Winter Wheat Belt to the west. As outlined (see Fig. 42) the latter consists of an almost square easterly portion having an average precipitation of 33 inches in the east and of 20 inches in the west, and lying for the most part in the Black Soil Belt, and two wings extending to the north-west and to the south-west respectively. These have about 20 inches in the east but extend into areas with only 15 inches. The Belt is transitional then, between the humid agriculture to the east, and the arid ranch lands of the High Plains to the west.

In spite of the fact that the western extensions of the Belt traverse the rough scarpland topography of the eastern margin of the High Plains, the Belt as a whole is of smooth rolling topography, and when cultivated, permits of the full use of large-scale machinery. We have said that the Belt is transitional, the gradually changing factor being precipitation. Thus progressively from the Flint Hills westwards the proportion of permanent pasture on the farms increases, and the corn to wheat ratio decreases, though some corn is grown in all but the extreme south-western wing. The pasture becomes of less value than the crop land, and thus larger and larger farms are required to support the accustomed standard of living. The middle and late summers become too dry for the fruition of corn, but it is warm enough to ripen wheat in June and early July ; and the winters, though frost is frequent, are not so severe as to prevent the growing and early tillering of winter wheat. As a rule winter wheat yields more largely than the spring varieties, and it is therefore grown wherever the risk of winter heaving or flooding is not too great. The western boundary is placed along the line west of which crops occupy less than one-tenth of the land area, and this boundary is found to correspond to about 15 inches precipitation along the margin of the cooler north-western wing, and about 18 inches precipitation to the west of the south-western wing. The less arid eastern portion of the Belt has a large cattle density and produces much beef. In the western wings pasture is easily overstocked, and as a fodder crop drought-resistant sorghums take the place of corn, especially in the south-west wing. In the Belt as a whole wheat is the most valuable crop, and often the only cash crop. As in the case of the Spring Wheat Belt, extension of the wheat area has depended upon a large-scale, machine-farming, technique. Climate makes diversification difficult, fallow must be frequent, and wind and sheet erosion is serious. Occupation has advanced westward in series of misleadingly wet seasons, and some recession is advisable and inevitable.

THE SPRING WHEAT BELT (see Fig. 42, p. 196)

This bears much the same relationship to the Hay and Dairying Belt, as does the Hard Winter Wheat Belt to the Corn and Winter Wheat Belt. Like the Hard Winter Wheat Belt, it lies almost wholly in regions sub-humid or semi-arid, and in regions of black or chestnut-coloured soils. Summer temperatures compared with the same latitudes in the Hay and Dairying Belt, are a little higher, sunshine considerably greater, the winters a little more intense.

Wheat ripens well in the short, sunny, growing season, but the moisture conditions for most of the Belt do not favour pasture, hay, or fodder crops generally. The eastern and northern boundaries were, and largely are, the margin of continuous close forest, and are pretty well defined. For much of the eastern boundary, this corresponds to the margin of the Laurentian Shield, which would set a limit to grain production whatever the climate. To the north and west, however, in Canada, the limit is the close forest, both because of the expense of clearing, and because of the relative poverty of the forest soils, rather than because of the shortness of the growing season. Everywhere in the prairie and grove areas this is more than 110 days, which is usually enough for the short growing season wheats now in use.

The lower temperature and evaporation, and the longer summer days, enable the growth of wheat with less precipitation than in the Winter Wheat Belt. Sixty to seventy per cent. of the small annual precipitation falls in the summer six months, and the winter snows are not usually heavy enough to protect a fall-sown wheat. Thus practically all the wheat is spring wheat, and practically all of it must be grown with summer fallow to preserve moisture, varying from one summer in three in the moister eastern portion of the Belt, to every other year in the drier portions. The western and south-western limits of the Belt are less definite. Here is not a boundary dividing one crop system from another, but a drought limit to any crops whatever.

As in the corresponding Hard Winter Wheat Belt, a cycle of wet years has led to an advance westwards, and south-westwards ; only to be followed by a retreat during a succeeding dry cycle ; and the dreadful droughts affecting most of the Belt in 1934, 1936 and 1937, have made it clear that much of the driest portions, with average annual precipitations of less than about 13 to 14 inches, should never have been ploughed.

The soils as a whole have excellent structure and moisture-retaining qualities, and are rich in humus and plant food generally. They are best in the sub-humid eastern and northern belts of black soil, and deteriorate with increasing aridity. Even with the best of them there is the danger of progressively rapid wind erosion consequent upon the use of summer fallow. Superior moisture conditions, and the deposits of glacial Lake Agassiz together favour the Red River plain in Canada and in the United States. Throughout the Belt, little but small grain is grown. Oats for the work animals is grown on almost every farm, besides the cash crop of wheat. Diversity is difficult because climatic conditions are not favourable for the provision of winter feed for mixed, or dairy farming ; nor is there at present much near-by urban market for other cash crops. Practically all the farms produce wheat, but it occupies a larger and larger proportion of such land as is cropped as aridity increases, though actually the yields per acre are greater in the more humid areas. Thus diversification has proceeded farthest in the northern and eastern grove belt of black or very dark soils, and least along the irregular western margin of the Belt.

In the Red River Valley, in the east particularly, barley tends to take the place of wheat, more fodder crops are grown, including corn for ensilage, more dairy cattle and swine are kept, and the influence of urban markets is greatest. Thus it is in the east that the area is approximating to the type of land utilization of the Hay and Dairying Belt.

Within the Belt as a whole, flat to rolling country favours the use of large-scale farming machinery. There are, however, some prominent and considerable areas of rough topography and poorer soils.

Such are certain tertiary outliers on the Missouri plateau, e.g. the Cypress Hills and Wood Mountains of southern Alberta and Saskatchewan, the bad land topography to the south of the Black Hills of Dakota, and the plateau summits of the Cretaceous cuesta, where this overlooks the Red River Valley in the Duck, Riding, Porcupine Hills of Manitoba, and the Pasquia Hills of Minnesota. Some of these areas are wooded and reserved as national parks.

The Spring Wheat Belt, like that of Hard Winter Wheat, represents the farthest wave of pioneer settlement in the interior. Some decades ago technique was chiefly concerned with making possible further and further inroads into the realm of aridity. Dry farming, the very essence of which is the preservation of a part of one season's moisture for the use of another by the institution of a weed-free summer fallow, became the prevailing usage. Extension northward was furthered by the breeding of quick-growing varieties, westward by the breeding of drought-resistant varieties.

The relatively small average yield per acre, inevitable in semi-arid conditions, received compensation from the large yield per man labour hour consequent upon the development of a large-scale labour-saving machinery. The dry weather usually prevailing at harvest time allows of immediate threshing without stacking, and the use of the combined harvester and thresher. The hard glutinous grains which do well in the steppe climates of either the Winter or the Spring Belts had to await the steel-rolling mill for their fullest use, and they are admirably suited to the modern bakery. Soft wheats do not make good bread in the modern bakery, though they may be admirable for biscuits and for poultry feed. They thus require strengthening by admixture with hard grain, and this is one factor in the large export of hard American grain to humid western European countries.

It has become quite clear that from the most arid portions of the Hard Wheat Belts there must be some withdrawal, and further, that steps must be taken to check soil deterioration in the other portions of the Belt. Thus at present the problem is rather one of conservation than of extension. Crops grown in belts of marginal climate are particularly dependent upon the season's weather, and the yields of wheat from these Hard Wheat Belts is very variable. As far the greater portion grown in the United States is required for the home market, export surplus is even more variable than production. A considerable portion of the Hard Winter Wheat Belt, if going for export, is shipped via Gulf ports. From the Spring Wheat Belt, if going for export, or if required in the Atlantic coast states, much of it will travel via the Great Lakes—often from Duluth and Chicago in the States—and from Fort William and Port Arthur in Canada.

The greatest flour-milling centre near the United States portion of the Spring Wheat Belt is at Minneapolis, while Buffalo, the eastern terminus of the United States lake movement, is the greatest milling centre in the east.

A more detailed account of that part of the Spring Wheat Belt' which lies in Canada, appears in the chapter on the Prairie Provinces, p. 514.

The conception of agricultural belts is fruitful if it helps us to gain a clearer view of the more important aspects of the geography of American agriculture. Not all the regional boundaries are of equal significance, however ; not all are stable, and still less so is the relation of main to subsidiary crops in each belt. The undermentioned recent changes merit attention.

(i) The tendency to diversification of crops in the more humid eastern portion of the spring wheat belt, both in Canada and the U.S.A., and in particular the increase of dairying.

(ii) The retirement from cultivation of much semi-arid land to the west of the Belts ; land which had only recently (1921–31) been broken to the plough. Some of this has now been seeded with crested wheat grass, a popular forage grass which does well under low moisture conditions.

(iii) Korean lespedeza has proved a valuable leguminous fodder crop in the rather acid humid soils of the eastern cotton belt, and dairying and mixed farming are increasing in this belt.

CHAPTER XVII

COAL [1]

IN the following chapters, the attempt is made to set out the principal natural factors affecting the production and distribution of coal in the United States, in relation to the chief industries based on coal as a source of power. Before proceeding to examine the actual conditions of production, let us endeavour to realize just what coal production in North America means as a part of the total world production. Prior to 1914, out of a world total of 1,400 million short tons, between 500 and 550 million short tons were produced in the United States, the Canadian production, a matter of about 11 million short tons, being almost negligible by comparison ; 200 to 300 million short tons were the contribution of Great Britain, while Germany accounted for about 170 million. In 1936, the situation was similar, except for general decreases, and the U.S.A. produced 42 per cent. of the world coal production. Under pressure of war conditions, in 1942, the U.S.A. output rose to 640 million short tons.

Fig. 57 shows that in the United States there are three large areas and a number of small ones which are indicated as being underlain by coal measures. In these areas the coal varies very much in character, and to some extent in accessibility, and largely because of these two factors only a relatively small portion of the total areas underlain by coal has been commercially developed. What we want to know then, is not where coal is known or is thought to exist, but where, and in what amounts, coal is being actually raised to the surface. To answer this question, what is needed is a map showing by counties the amount raised to the surface in a given year. Fig. 58 shows these facts for the northern part of the Appalachian Coalfield. An examination of this map will show that in the northern part of this field there are three main producing areas, while a similar map, not here reproduced, shows that in the southern part of the field there are three much smaller areas. Of the northern three, two are in Pennsylvania—one in the north-east of the state producing anthracite, the other in the south-west, and, as has already been pointed out, this latter area extends over the borders of the state into West

[1] Coal in Canada is discussed in the regional section of the book.

COAL, U.S.A., 1929, 1936 and 1942

	Million Short Tons.		
Appalachian :	1929.	1936.	1942.
Pennsylvania {Anthracite	73·8	54·7	59·9
{Bituminous	143·5	108·5	143·2
West Virginia	138·5	117·5	156·8
Ohio	23·7	23·0	34·0
Kentucky (Eastern)	46·0	39·1	46·0
Alabama	17·9	11·7	18·9
Virginia	12·7	11·6	19·9
Tennessee	5·4	5·0	7·4
Maryland	2·6	1·7	1·9
Michigan Field :			
Michigan	·8	·6	·3
Eastern Interior or Central :			
Illinois	60·7	50·5	63·7
Indiana	18·3	17·4	25·4
Kentucky (Western)	14·4	8·4	14·0
Western Interior or West Central :			
Iowa	4·2	3·5	2·9
Kansas	3·0	2·7 }	8·3
Missouri	4·0	3·6 }	
Southern Interior :			
Oklahoma	3·8	1·2 }	4·1
Arkansas	1·7	1·1 }	
Texas	1·1	·8	·3
Northern Great Plains and Rockies :			
Colorado	9·9	6·8	8·0
Wyoming	6·7	5·8	8·0
Utah	5·2	3·2	5·7
New Mexico	2·6	1·6	1·7
Montana	3·4	3·2	3·9
North Dakota	1·9	1·9	2·5
Pacific :			
Washington	2·5	1·7	2·0
All others	·1	·2	1·1
Totals	608·8	488·8	639·9

Virginia, Ohio, and Maryland. The third producing area in the northern part of the field lies in the south of West Virginia. As has already been noted, the Pennsylvanian area produces nearly half of all the coal raised in the United States, and is by far the greatest single bituminous coal-producing area in the world. As this latter area is also to a large extent typical of the conditions in the chief areas of the United States, it is considered in some detail in what follows.

The general relief and structure of the eastern half of the United States have been discussed already in another part of

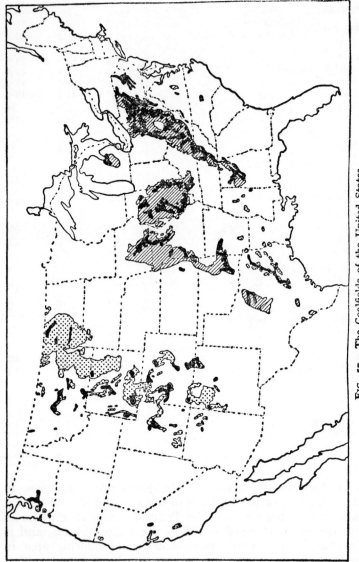

FIG. 57.—The Coalfields of the United States.
Areas in black represent mining regions.

this book, but it will help us to fix more clearly the actual location of the chief producing areas, and also the conditions underlying production, if we just briefly recall some of the more salient facts.

The eastern part of the United States is occupied by a series of parallel belts of country running from the north-east to the south-west. These belts are not only parallel to each other, but also to the Atlantic Seaboard. Close to the Atlantic lies the long, narrow strip of the Coastal Plain of which the western boundary is formed by the Fall Line. Beyond the Fall Line we come to the Piedmont Belt, which, formed as it is of old crystalline rocks that at one time made up the ancient continent now known to geologists as Appalachia, offers a marked contrast, well expressed in its somewhat uneven relief, to the young, undisturbed, and almost horizontal strata of the Coastal Plain. The western edge of the Piedmont is marked by a very definite ridge, to which the term Blue Ridge is rather loosely applied. Westward of this ridge lies the belt of country commonly spoken of as the Greater Appalachian Valley. It consists for the most part of a well-defined series of parallel ridges with intervening valleys, and is itself bounded to westward by a marked feature —the Allegheny Front, as it has been called. It consists of a great escarpment formed by the outcrop of the strata of which the country to westward is composed. This westward country is a great plateau sloping away south-west and west to the Mississippi Valley.

The structure of this plateau and of the rolling plains country which stretch away westward to the Mississippi consists of a series of low, broad anticlines and synclines running roughly parallel to the Allegheny Front. A principal anticline which forms a kind of backbone to the series, runs south-westward from the Toledo end of Lake Erie through the position of Cincinnati, and, crossing the Ohio, passes through the Nashville region. This upfold separates the Appalachian Coalfield from the Central Coalfield, which lies south-eastward of Lake Michigan. It is thought that in Carboniferous times, when the coal measures were being laid down, this south-westward-trending ridge formed dry land, separating two basins occupied by arms of the sea, in which were deposited over very long periods of time, and probably under conditions of progressive depression, the massive sandstones, limestones, and shales of the coal measures. The more easterly of these two basins which to-day carries the Appalachian Coalfield was limited in extent by the ancient continent of Appalachia, to which reference has been made above.

Towards the close of the Carboniferous epoch, the horizontal strata thus laid down in this basin were intensely folded and crushed by earth movements, acting at right angles to the present lie of this area against the old continent lying to the south-east. Erosion to a peneplain and subsequent uplift as described in Chapter V produced the ridges and furrows of the Greater Appalachian Valley. In this way, too, was the heavy faulting brought about, which, along the westward edge of this area of intense folding, has formed the escarpment—the Allegheny Front—separating the ridge and furrow structure of the Great Valley from the undulating structure of the plateau to the west (Fig. 17A, Chap. V). With the exception of the anthracite field of North-eastern Pennsylvania which lies in the rock structure of the Great Valley between the Susquehanna and Delaware Rivers, the chief coal-mining districts of Eastern U.S.A. lie wholly on this plateau of almost horizontal rocks, to be found westward of the ridge and furrow zone forming the Appalachian Valley. This is a fact, which, as will be seen later, has a very direct bearing on the methods of mining in vogue in each area, and therefore on the cost of production.

Let us now examine in a little more detail the plateau to which the name Allegheny Plateau is often given. Pittsburg is to-day situated in the river angle where two of those many streams draining eastward to the Mississippi unite to form the Ohio. Since its very genesis, these westward-draining streams or their forbears have been busy at the work of carving out the plateau surface. Subsequently uplifts rejuvenated the rivers. They began again the work of modelling the surface. They dug out those deep trenches which are such a conspicuous feature of the relief to-day. They entrenched themselves within their old beds. The more powerful captured their weaker fellows, and thus was brought about that concentration of stream-ways on Pittsburg which has played such a big rôle in determining the site of the great dominating centre of the iron and steel industry of the United States to-day. The shallow synclines and anticlines of the plateau structure close to the escarpment of the Allegheny Front have also played their part. The gentle downfolds have preserved the coal at no great depth below the surface. The low upfolds bring it still nearer to the surface, or where, as in the Connellsville District, their summits have been planed off, the coal outcrops on either flank.

If we glance at a map of the country between the Great Lakes and the sea, we shall notice that the Susquehanna sends long tentacles westward in the shape of its head-streams. The more southerly of these head-streams interlock with those of the Allegheny, which rise wholly on the plateau. A short distance south of the more southerly of these Susquehanna headstreams, the Potomac, draining into the flats to the east of Chesapeake Bay, reaches back almost to the head-waters of the Monongahela. Both of these stream-ways have been lines of movement from very early times in the history of westward movement in the States, and both centre on Pittsburg at the angle where the Allegheny from the north, and the Monongahela from the south, unite to form the Ohio. It was doubtless this nodality of Pitts-

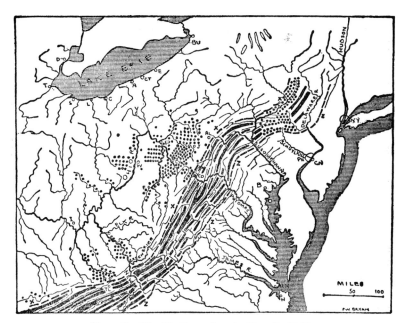

FIG. 58.—The Northern Appalachian Coalfield.

XXX equals position of Allegheny Front. **ZZZ** indicates position of Blue Ridge. Ridges between are diagrammatically shown.

The location of the dots showing production is based on county figures.

Key to Towns : **A,** Ashtabula ; **AL,** Altoona ; **B,** Baltimore ; **BU,** Buffalo ; **C,** Cleveland ; **CD,** Cumberland ; **CN,** Camden ; **CT,** Conneaut ; **CV,** Connellsville ; **D,** Detroit ; **E,** Erie ; **F,** Fairmont; **I,** Ironton ; **J,** Johnstown ; **L,** Lorain ; **N,** Norfolk ; **NN,** Newport News ; **NY,** New York ; **P,** Pittsburg ; **PH,** Philadelphia ; **PO,** Pocahontas ; **S,** Sandusky ; **T,** Toledo ; **TL,** Tazewell ; **W,** Wheeling ; **Y,** Youngstown.

To avoid confusing the picture the state and county boundaries have been omitted.

burg, combined with the fact that it lies just westward of the two passages through the ridges to the east, that led to the early development of the area as a coal-producing region, as it had already led to its settlement. This question of the eastward connection of the area with tide-water will be more fully dealt with later, when the question of coal movement is being discussed. For the moment it is useful to notice that 200 miles to the south-ward of these passage-ways, there occur through river action two

other routes through the ridges where the head-waters of the
James and the Roanoke have cut back into the Great Valley, and
that just to westward of these openings where the New and Big
Sandy Rivers have trenched deeply the horizontal rocks of the
plateau, we find the second largest of the bituminous coal-producing regions of the coalfield—the New River, Kanawha, and
Pocahontas Districts of West Virginia.   The main producing area
lies eastward and southward from Pittsburg.   It is not confined to
the state of Pennsylvania, but extends westward into Ohio and

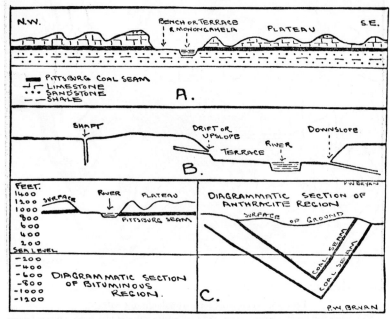

FIG. 59.—Diagrams to illustrate structure of Northern Appalachian Coalfield.
A, Sketch section to show position of Pittsburg Bed.
B, Diagram to show methods of Mining.
C, Positions of seams in Bituminous and Anthracite Regions compared.

southward into West Virginia and Maryland.   Considered very
broadly apart from that portion of the field which is in Ohio, it
is the country drained by the Middle and Lower Monongahela and
its tributaries, and by the Conemaugh, a left-bank tributary
of the Lower Allegheny.   All these river valleys focus on one
point, and that point is Pittsburg.   For this reason the coal-
carrying railroads have a down grade to Pittsburg and an up
grade out of Pittsburg.   Moving outward, the railways are for
the most part only carrying supplies and manufactured goods
to the mining areas, while the inward movement to Pittsburg

of the bulky fuel needed for a manufacturing centre is largely facilitated by the down-grade.

Let us see then what other natural conditions beyond nodality have placed Pittsburg in this dominating position in the coal and steel industries. From the name of the chief seam worked and the position of Pittsburg, this area lying south and east of the city has been sometimes called the Pittsburg District. The name has the merit of simplicity and also that of close relationship to the natural features of the region. The region contains a large number of seams, but by far the most productive of these is that known as the famous Pittsburg Bed. This seam lies at the base of a series of massive limestones, and is underlain by sandstones and shales. The overlying limestones and the coal seam itself are known as the Monongahela formation, from the name of the river valley where the formation is most fully developed (Fig. 59). This seam possesses many outstanding advantages, some of which mark it off sharply from its fellows, and have led to its greater exploitation. The seam lies almost horizontal over very large areas. It is of a fairly uniform thickness. Its depth below the surface varies to some extent with the relief, but it is seldom found below 400 feet. It lies mostly either at, or slightly below, or slightly above water-level, in the main valleys of the region. It is extensively mined where the seams are exposed at the surface. We will therefore expect to find the mines chiefly where the streams of the region have cut down to, or below, the level of the bed, or along the surface outcrops of the seam at the sides of downfolds. A glance at a detailed map of the area (Fig. 61) shows us that that is so, for we see the mines strung out in long lines along the streams and the outcrop. This detailed map, to which we shall have occasion to refer again in connection with the coking areas, shows us one of those very gentle downfolds near the edge of the coalfield, in which the coal has been preserved from erosion. They are separated from each other by regions from which the coal is absent, it having been removed during the erosion and disappearance of the intervening anticline.

This map is based on a series published by the United States Geological Survey on a scale of one inch to the mile, and may be taken as fairly typical of the coalfield as a whole, in so far as the position of the chief seam is concerned, though as one goes westward in the field one finds that the rocks are more horizontal, and that therefore the only outcrop of coal is that along the river valleys. The coal found in this bed is chiefly of a high-grade type, suitable for the manufacture of coke and gas. The most suitable coking coal is found in the extreme south-east of

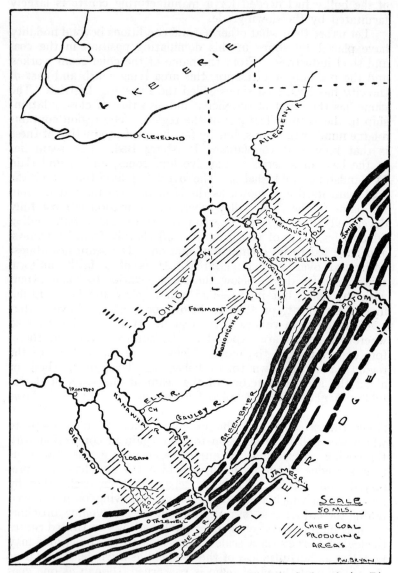

FIG. 60.—Sketch Map of the Pittsburg and West Virginia Coal-producing Districts. The Appalachian Ridges are only shown diagrammatically.

DC, Cumberland; CH, Charleston; F, Fayetteville; J, Johnstown; P, Pittsburg; PC, Pocahontas; W, Wheeling.

the district.   As one moves in a north-westerly direction towards
Pittsburg, the character of the coal changes, broadly speaking,
from a high-class steam fuel to a rich gas coal.   With the possible exception of the famous steam coals from the Pocahontas
region of West Virginia, the whole of this Pittsburg District
contains the very highest grade of bituminous coal found in the
United States.[1]

It will be helpful perhaps at this point to describe briefly
the area shown in the sketch-map of the Connellsville District,
as it will enable us to realize better the actual nature of much
of this coal-mining country.   We have seen that Pittsburg
stands at the junction of the Allegheny from the north, and the
Monongahela from the south.   Some 10 miles above the city,
the Monongahela is joined by its main tributary which flows
from the south-east, and is known by the name of the Youghiogheny.   Situated on the right bank of this stream, some 40 miles
from its mouth, is the town of Connellsville, the greatest coking
centre in the United States, and the natural centre of the region
shown in the sketch-map on page 252.   In the south-east of the
district we notice that there is a long narrow belt of country
shown by the shading as being underlain by the Pittsburg coal-
bed, and that parallel to this belt but in the north-western part
of the district there is a similar area, but one which covers a
very much greater extent of ground.   Separating these two
regions there lies a long narrow belt of country where no coal
is found.   These three areas correspond to the gentle hill and
furrow structure found at the edge of the Appalachian Plateau,
and to which reference has been already made above.   The belt
of coal country lying to the south-east is a shallow syncline in
which the coal has been preserved from erosion, while the district from which the coal has been removed is occupied by a
low anticline, beyond which in a north-westerly direction the
strata become almost horizontal, thus giving us the wide area
in this direction which is underlain by coal.   So much then for
the structure in general of this area, which is fairly typical of
the whole region, and which is very simple in type.   The rocks
consist for the most part of the massive sandstones, limestones,
and shales to which reference has already been made.   The surface rocks are limestones or limestones barely capped by sandstones.   At the base of these limestones lies the Pittsburg coal-
bed, resting on sandstones and shales (Fig. 59A).   These limestones

---

[1] Analysis shows that the Pittsburg Bed contains 57 to 65 per cent.
fixed carbon, 30 to 35 per cent. volatile matter, 4 to 14 per cent. ash,
and less than 1 per cent. sulphur.   See " Econ. Geog.," April, 1928,
p. 119.

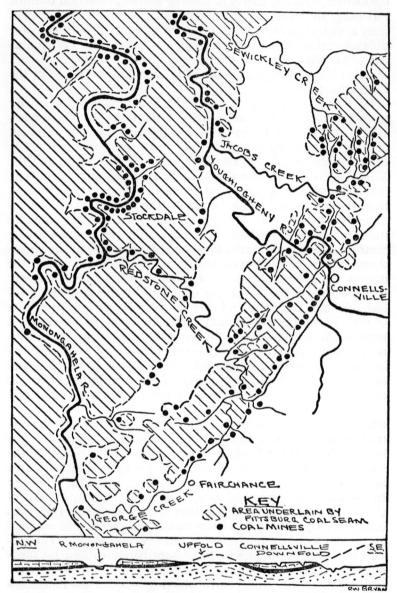

FIG. 61.—The Connellsville Coking Area.   Map and Section across the area.

have been deeply trenched by the numerous rivers of this well-watered area. The drainage originally was probably of a very simple type, flowing north-westward in accordance with the slope. Subsequently river capture, as in the case of the Pittsburg Region, has led to the present well-defined river basins, which have largely determined the main coal-producing areas. This trenching of the plateau surface has been usually carried sufficiently far to expose the coal-bed. This is more especially so in the case of the main rivers and their tributaries, while in the case of the smaller streams the coal-bed is only a short distance below the floor of the valleys, and can be easily reached either by slopes or by short shafts. In the actual district we have been considering, the eastern part of the area has been much dissected by the main stream of the Monongahela and some of its lesser tributaries, while the remainder of the area has been similarly treated by the Youghiogheny, the largest of the Monongahela tributaries. It will be seen that as a result of this arrangement of the streams, the shallow syncline to the south-east is bisected by the Youghiogheny, which has here cut below the level of the seam, as have also its north bank tributaries at this point. In contrast to this, those of the south bank have not quite reached the coal. Nevertheless, it will be noticed that in both cases the mines are shown located along the valleys. From this it is clear that mining operations are not confined to the actual coal exposures, but are carried on wherever the coal is fairly easily get-at-able. Where the coal is exposed, as along the two principal rivers and the outcrop, horizontal adits and upslopes are driven in from the river bank, the coal being run out by gravity planes to the waterside or to the railway track, which follows the stream. In the case of the canalized Monongahela, this coal is loaded into barges which are towed to the blast-furnaces and to the factories situated by the waterside in the vicinity of Pittsburg. One of the commonest sights on the river are these barges with their cargoes of fuel for the Pittsburg industrial region. To facilitate this traffic an elaborate system of locks, thirteen in all, has been constructed on the Monongahela. A dam has also been constructed on the Allegheny some 30 miles above Pittsburg to control the navigation, and coal now moves to Pittsburg by barge on this river as well as on the Monongahela. In this fashion two of the chief obstacles to navigation on these Pennsylvanian rivers are brought under control. These obstacles are low water during late summer and autumn, and floods in spring caused by the melting of the winter snows. These locks on the Monongahela make it easily navigable for barges as far as Morgantown in northern West Virginia, where the southern

extension of the Pittsburg coal area is found.　The advantages
of this navigation system are clearly shown in the fact that 14¼
million tons were shipped on the Monongahela River during
1935.

We have said that where the coal is exposed on the surface
it can be readily mined by adits and upslopes.　It helps us to
realize the extent to which this is done, when we observe that
over 50 per cent. of all the coal won in Pennsylvania is won by
drift, which is the local name for upslope ; 20 per cent. by down-
slope requiring some slight mechanical power to raise the coal
to the surface ; while rather more than 20 per cent. is won by
means of short shafts.　The deep shafts which are so common
in Great Britain and other mining areas, and which add so
greatly to the cost of the coal by reason of the expense of getting it to the surface, are unknown in this region.　Seldom is
the plateau surface more than 400 feet above the level of the
seam, and at these extreme heights for this area an examination
of the geologic folios of the region reveals no mines.　As has
been pointed out above, the mines are in the valleys and along
the outcrops, and even where they do not reach the seam the
valleys greatly reduce the depth to which the shafts must be sunk.

The seams of the coalfield are very persistent over great areas,
and they are also, over great areas, of a very uniform thickness.
This fact is emphasized in the numerous sections of the seams to
be found in the geologic folios published by the United States
Geological Survey, and is also clearly brought out by a table
published for the year 1917, showing the percentage of coal
mined from seams of certain thicknesses.　Thus for the year 1917,
63 per cent. of all the coal mined in Pennsylvania came from
seams of thickness between 4 and 7 feet, and it has been estimated
that a thickness of about 6 feet is a fair average for the famous
Pittsburg Bed.　That these conditions are by no means confined
to the Pittsburg Region, but are also the ruling conditions throughout the greater part of the Appalachian Coalfield, is shown by the
fact that of the coal mined in West Virginia 64 per cent., and of
the coal mined in Virginia 70 per cent., came from seams ranging
in thickness from 4 to 7 feet.　A seam 6 feet thick is one that is
very economical to work.　Where much thicker seams are found
they are expensive to roof, and where thinner seams are worked
the cost of raising the coal is proportionately higher, as practically
the same amount of work has to be put in as would be needed in
the case of a 6-foot seam, and a much smaller quantity of coal
would be won per unit of expenditure.

The uniformity and horizontality of these seams render possible the use of coal-cutting machinery on a large scale.　Again

we have a marked contrast with most British coalfields, where seams far from uniform in thickness, and frequently far out of the horizontal, are often met with. In 1935 the percentage of coal machine-mined in Pennsylvania in the bituminous fields was 75 per cent., while in Great Britain the percentage was 51 per cent. In Ohio the percentage was 96 per cent. (the highest in the U.S.A., except for Michigan). In the anthracite fields machines are little used, the seams being largely unsuitable for their use, as they are often narrow, frequently heavily faulted, and not merely out of the horizontal, but quite commonly nearly vertical. Here we have the contrast between the horizontal, though in parts slightly undulating structure of the Appalachian Plateau, and the crushed, folded, and heavily faulted structure of the Greater Appalachian Valley (Fig. 17A). The advantages accruing from the favourable geographic conditions on the plateau are clearly reflected in terms of cost of coal at the pit's-mouth.

In all coal-mining operations, there is a considerable amount of unproductive time spent by the miners in getting to their work, after they reach the surface opening of the mine. Although in many areas this time is not a very great amount, it mounts up to a very appreciable matter in many of the British fields, where the miner has not only to go deep, but has also to travel some distance, which may even be a matter of some miles underground, before getting to the working face of the seam. This latter situation more particularly arises in connection with mines such as those of Nova Scotia, where, owing to the fact that they run out directly under the sea, there is no opportunity of tapping the seam farther along by sinking a new shaft. In the Pennsylvanian fields which we are considering, this difficulty does not arise. As the seam lies near the surface, and is thus readily get-at-able from almost any point, the miner has rarely, if ever, to travel far to the working face from the mouth of the mine. Hence, other things being equal, he can either get out a larger quantity of coal in the same time as is worked in other areas, or he can afford to work shorter hours for the same output. Since April 1934, the average working day of the American miner at the coal face has been 7 hours, which is now slightly under that of the British miner. By reason, however, of the structural conditions and very high mechanization of American mining, the average individual output of the American miner was $4\frac{1}{2}$ tons per day in 1935 as against the $1\frac{1}{4}$ tons per day of his British competitor. This would seem to reflect two facts, the first being that conditions in Great Britain are becoming more difficult because of deeper shafts, etc., and the second being that the more favourable natural conditions in the United States have enabled her to avail herself more fully of the development of machine-cutting and other mechanical devices.[1]

It has been already pointed out that the rivers of the coal-field have dug out deep trenches in the horizontal rocks of the plateau, and we have already seen something of the importance of these trenches in the way in which they have laid bare the coal seam. There remain, however, accruing from these features of the relief, certain other advantages, which, although of minor importance in comparison with that to which we have referred, are nevertheless worthy of mention. The walls of these river trenches are frequently, in the case of the larger streams, as much as 100 to 200 feet in height, and may be almost vertical. In early days the development of this region was somewhat retarded, because these trenches, deeply sunk in the surface of the plateau, offered considerable obstacles to movement. These trenches are often as much as one mile in width, hence they would add greatly to the cost of railway construction on the plateau. The existence, however, of a bench or terrace alongside the water in these trenches, combined with the arrangement of these valleys all centring on Pittsburg, which is in consequence the natural focus of all movement, has obviated the construction of railways on the plateau surface at all. These terraces are usually found varying in width from a few feet up to half a mile or more, and from 10 to 20 feet above water-level (Fig. 59). The rivers are thus entrenched within their old beds. During the first uplift of the country after it had been reduced to a peneplain, the increased slope rejuvenated the rivers, which then cut out the present trenches as their beds. A subsequent uplift still further increased the slope and gave the rivers new cutting power. They then cut out their present beds within the old trenches, thus forming the bench or terrace to which we have referred, and which forms such a suitable site for the road-beds of the railways of the plateau. Between Connellsville and Pittsburg, the Baltimore and Ohio Railroad on the east bank, and the Pennsylvanian Railroad on the west bank of the Youghiogheny, make use of such terraces for their road-beds, while the Pennsylvanian Railroad, in carrying coke from Uniontown in the Connellsville District, makes use of a series of these terraces, first alongside Redstone Creek, a tributary of the Monongahela, and later alongside the Monongahela itself. Many other examples could be given from the large-scale maps of the region, but these will perhaps serve to illustrate the matter, as they are but typical of many others.

[1] Before the war there was one haulage worker in U.S.A. for each 50 tons of coal brought to the surface. In Great Britain there was one haulage worker for each 5 tons brought to the surface.

In summing up this aspect of the area, we may say that because of the facts discussed above as to the plateau structure of the country, and the nature of the material of which it is composed, many, if not all, of the railways of the coalfield in the plateau region tend to be confined to the river trenches, and that where terraces are absent in these trenches, heavy expenditure has to be incurred in carrying the road-bed alongside the water.

These terraces greatly facilitate the work of coal-getting in still another fashion. Located as they are alongside the water and on the same level in the majority of cases as the outcrop of the coal seam in the river bank, they form excellent sites for mining villages and other communities such as those connected with the coke ovens of the south-eastern part of the district. On such a bench on the east bank of the Youghiogheny, where the river as it enters the shallow syncline containing the famous coking coal has exposed the coal-bed, stands Connellsville, the centre of the coking industry. Stockdale and Bellevernon occupy somewhat similar positions, the one on a right-bank terrace and the other on a left-bank terrace of the Monongahela. These locations are no exceptions, as most of the smaller towns and mining communities of the coalfield are similarly situated. It is not necessary to elaborate here the many advantages flowing from this location in close proximity to the seam and on natural route-ways, as they will be readily appreciated from what has been said above as to the general effect of the dissected plateau structure of the whole area under consideration on coal-getting.

In summing up the natural factors at work in this region in relation to coal-getting, it may perhaps be suggested that, from what has been said above, it is clear that the dominating geographic factor at work is that of structure, if we include under that head all those geologic conditions and processes which have resulted in the rock structure of which the region is composed.

Before leaving the region to consider other areas, it may be well to point out that the Pittsburg mining district may be conveniently subdivided into three fairly distinct fields on a regional basis of river valley, types of coal produced, and distribution of coal raised. These districts are the Connellsville Coking District, the Allegheny-Washington District, and the Cambria District.

As the Connellsville District will have to be dealt with separately when the problem of the character and distribution of coke comes up for consideration, it will for the moment be left on one side. The Allegheny-Washington District may be connected in one's mind with the production of an excellent steam and rich gas coal, which is largely used in the vicinity where it is mined, that is, in close proximity to Pittsburg, while the Cambria District produces mainly steam and domestic fuels, a considerable proportion of which finds its way eastward through the Appalachian Ridges to the tide-water ports of New York, Baltimore, and Philadelphia on the Atlantic seaboard, chiefly for coastwise shipment to New England.

Leaving a consideration of this coastwise and tide-water movement until we can more conveniently consider it as a whole, we will pass on to examine in the order of their respective outputs of coal those other areas of large importance from the standpoint of bituminous coal output in the Appalachian Coalfield. These are two in number, namely, the region of Southern West Virginia and that of the Birmingham District of Alabama.

CHAPTER XVIII

COAL—*continued*

SOME 150 miles southward of the Pittsburg District we find the second largest producing area in the Appalachian Coalfield, and we find it located, as in the case of the Pittsburg District, where a series of large streams have deeply trenched the plateau surface, opposite to where a series of the Piedmont and Coastal Plain streams have cut their headstreams well back into the furrows of the Great Valley. The plateau is here identical in many respects with that portion of it which we have been considering further to the north. The general slope and therefore the drainage is still to the north-west; the rocks are still almost horizontal over great areas, and are composed of massive sandstones, limestones, and shales of Carboniferous Age. The altitude is, however, greater. We are here at the highest portion of the Appalachian system, and are just at the northern edge of that rather extraordinary area where the general tilt of the valley region changes from the south-east to the north-west, with the consequent result that the rivers of the Great Valley, instead of draining away eastward to the Atlantic, rise on the westward slopes of the Blue Ridge to the east of the Great Valley, and after cutting their way westward in great gorges through the north-east and south-west ridges of the valley, proceed to cut their way into the face of the escarpment forming the eastward boundary of the plateau. In this fashion they cut very deep trenches in the surface of the plateau itself on their way to join the Mississippi system. Of these westward-flowing rivers we are concerned here mainly with three, which drain the southern half of the state of West Virginia. These three are the New River and its tributaries, which occupy the south centre of the state; the Big Sandy, which forms the southern boundary of the state; and, lying between the two, the Guyandotte. Of these the New River is by far the largest system and the one which is most intimately related to the coal-mining area. It is the most northerly of those westward-flowing streams which rise in the Blue Ridge, and which have been referred to above. It has cut a great gorge across the valley ridges which has a significance in connection with coal distribution which will be discussed later. For the moment we are concerned with the allied fact, that on entering the plateau to eastward and in crossing the plateau it has carved out a trench which is in parts over 1,000 feet in depth. In the walls of this trench the coal seam is exposed (Fig. 62). The actual exposure of the seam lies some hundreds of feet above water-level, the exact elevation varying according to the locality. Towards the eastern edge of the field the seam lies about 1,000 feet above water-level, but as one follows the river westward across the plateau one finds this elevation decreasing fairly rapidly, until in the vicinity of Fayetteville, nearly half-way to the Ohio from the point at which the New River enters West Virginia, the main seam lies only some 500 feet above the river. Here, then, we have a rather striking contrast to the conditions existing in the Pittsburg District, and one which has

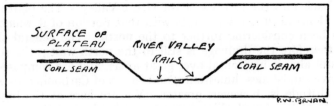

FIG. 62.—New River Coalfield. Section.

given rise to an important difference in the methods of handling the coal to those in vogue in the former district. In this field the coal when brought to the surface will be, as we have seen, some hundreds of feet above water, and therefore above railway level. To solve the problem of handling thus presented, gravity inclines are employed to run the coal by its own weight down to the route level, and the weight of these loaded trucks on the down journey haul up the empty trucks together with such supplies as are actually required in the mines. A study of the map (Fig. 63) of part of the New River field will make clear both this method of handling and also the nature of the gorge in which the river flows and which makes necessary the gravity planes. Here, as in the Pittsburg Region, the villages are found on the benches or terraces which lie alongside the water in the valleys. Movement over the plateau surface is much more difficult than in the Pittsburg District, hence we find that the railways are entirely determined as to location, and almost wholly as to direction, by the plateau trenches. The bulk of the coal movement is in directions parallel to the lie of the plateau trenches, being either north-westward to the Ohio and the Great Lakes, or south-eastward through the Appalachian Ridges to tide-water on Chesapeake Bay at Hampton Roads.

The conditions which we have been examining above apply

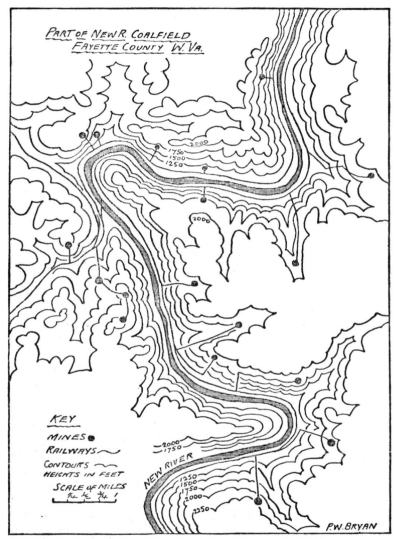

PART OF NEW R. COALFIELD
FAYETTE COUNTY W. VA.

1750
1500
1250

2000

2000

KEY

MINES ●
RAILWAYS ⌒
CONTOURS ⌒
HEIGHTS IN FEET
SCALE OF MILES
¼ ½ ¾ 1

2000
1750

NEW RIVER

1250
1500
1750
2000
1250

P.W.BRYAN

FIG. 63.—Typical part of the West Virginia Coalfield.

mainly to the New River Region of West Virginia, which produces about one-fifth of the total for West Virginia, or rather more than the coal output of the whole of Canada in a normal year. This region, which is found in the counties of Fayette and Raleigh, extends for some 25 miles or so up the New River above its junction with the Gauley.   An extension of the area lies to the south of the main area near the head-waters of the Coal River, a tributary of the New River.   To the south of the New River Region is the main producing area of West Virginia, that of Pocahontas and McDowell.   It consists of the counties of Mc-Dowell and Mercer in West Virginia, and that of Tazewell in Virginia.   It lies for the most part on the head-streams of the Tug Fork of the Big Sandy.   From the Davy seam in this field is obtained an exceptionally pure soft coal admirably suited for the manufacture of by-product coke.   The total output of this field is about two-fifths of the total for West Virginia.   The Pocahontas-McDowell Region is especially famous for the pro-duction of a very high-grade steam fuel which is said by the United States Geological Survey to be almost as good as the best Welsh.   In this connection it should be noted that the highest grade coal such as pure anthracite is too slow burning to make a good steam coal.   Such a coal needs to possess just sufficient volatile combustible matter to ensure rapid burning. It should also have a low ash and sulphur content and be free from tendency to clinker.   In this area the conditions as to mining are more nearly comparable with those of the Pittsburg District than those of the New River area, as here the Big Sandy rises on the plateau to westward of the escarpment.   For this reason we do not find those great gorges which leave the coal seam far above water-level.   The streams are smaller and younger, hence they have neither had the time nor the cutting power needed to etch out deep valleys.   It is easier, therefore, to handle the coal.   With this exception the geographical conditions in all this area are very similar to those of the New River area farther to the north.

In addition to the producing areas already described as lying high up on the New River and the Big Sandy, there are also some fairly large producing areas on the lower courses of both these rivers before they join the Ohio, as will be seen from a glance at the map on page 250.   The coal in these latter areas is not of such a high-grade type as the excellent steam and coking fuels which are found in the fields on the upper courses of these two rivers.   It is none the less extensively mined, and the total production of these scattered areas is about equivalent to that of the Pocahontas Region, which, as has already been pointed out, is the largest in the state.

In summing up the conditions in the region of the West Virginian fields, one may say that, with the exceptions noted above, they are very similar to those of the Pittsburg Region. We find all those advantages of horizontal seams of an economical thickness and fairly uniform character over great areas which we have already studied in the northern region. We have here also those deeply trenched and terraced river valleys which have exposed the coal on the surface and have thus made it easily worked, and which have also provided easy routes for movement and convenient sites for settlement. A marked contrast which we will have to consider later is the fact that there are here no manufacturing areas, hence all the coal produced is either converted into coke for shipment out of the area, or is shipped directly out either northward and westward to the shores of the Great Lakes, or eastward through the Appalachian Ridges to tide-water on the Atlantic Coast at Hampton Roads.

Alabama Field. Some 400 miles south of the Pocahontas area we come to the last coalfield of major importance in the Appalachian Region, if we except for the moment the anthracite area of the extreme north-east. This field is the Birmingham field of Alabama. In northern Alabama the coal measures have been largely eroded, but in the region round Birmingham they have been extensively preserved. We have already seen that towards the south-west the Appalachian Ridges begin to peter out and finally to vanish beneath the younger rocks of the Coastal Plain. In this south-western area, the streams which rise in the depressions of the Great Valley, instead of cutting their way eastward or westward through the ridges as is done by their fellows to the north, here follow the furrows between the great ridges, and thus flow out in a south-westerly direction to the Gulf of Mexico. This general direction is not only followed by the valley streams, but also by the streams rising on the southward continuation of the Cumberland Plateau, the portion of the plateau which we find in this area to the west of the Great Valley, and which corresponds to the Allegheny Plateau in the north. Here the plateau is composed of a series of detached blocks whose longer axes lie parallel to the ridge and furrow structure of the valley. So we find that in the valley we have among others the parallel streams of the Coosa and the more westerly Cahaba, while on the plateau flowing in a south-westerly direction is the Warrior, and its main tributary the Mulberry. The escarpment which, as we have seen elsewhere, forms such a prominent feature in the Appalachian country, is here found to eastward of, and parallel to, the Warrior River. At, or near to, its foot lies Birmingham, the centre of a steel industry. As in the Pittsburg country, there is here one seam which dominates the field to the almost complete neglect of any other for the time being. This seam runs away westward beneath the plateau, and is the chief seam of the Warrior Coalfield. The seam is known as the Pratt seam. On the average it is about 4 feet thick, but it is not quite so uniform throughout the area as is the Pittsburg seam in the more northerly part of the field. Close to this coal but further to the east, and therefore lying in the Great Valley Region, there are two other fields—the Cahaba and the Coosa, named respectively from the chief streams in their respective neighbourhoods. Neither of these areas has so far been worked to a great extent, and they thus serve as a useful reserve for future exploitation.

The Pratt seam provides an excellent coking coal. It is in fact to Alabama what Connellsville coal is to the Pittsburg district, for, close at hand are the iron ores upon which the iron and steel industry of Birmingham depends. It is stated that iron and steel are more cheaply produced there than anywhere else in the world. In close proximity to these two main raw materials there are to be found abundant supplies of limestone, while much timber for use as pit-props is available here, as indeed in all other parts of the Appalachian area, not far from the regions where it is needed for use. The coal can everywhere be easily mined by short shafts, its bed being readily accessible from the surface. In 1936, the state production was $11\frac{3}{4}$ million tons, of which nearly $4\frac{1}{2}$ million tons were converted into coke.

Although possessing all the advantages set out above, the Birmingham area, in common with all the other bituminous regions of the United States, labours under the very great drawback of lying a long way from tide-water. To the Gulf Coast in the vicinity of Mobile is a distance of about 200 miles, and there is no nearer sea. None of the rivers draining towards the Gulf are sufficiently large to be navigable in an unimproved condition. To overcome this difficulty a series of locks have been constructed on the Black Warrior and on the Tombigbee, the river into which the Warrior drains. The Tombigbee flows into the Gulf at Mobile Bay, a few miles eastward of the site of Mobile. A navigable waterway is thus available from the coalfield to the Gulf, and a government barge line using 2,000-ton barges has been established on the river, and this service has greatly reduced the cost of conveying coal and steel products to the Gulf.

In addition to the Pennsylvanian and Ohio, West Virginia, Virginia and Alabama regions, there are lesser regions of production in the Appalachian bituminous area. These are found in the eastern parts of the states of Kentucky and Tennessee and a very small field in Maryland. Their total production is some 45 million short tons annually. The conditions of production are very similar to those of the West Virginian fields.

Throughout the Appalachian bituminous field the higher grade coals as a rule lie towards the east, the higher pressures here having resulted in a marked increase in the carbon content and a decrease in the volatile elements. A good example of this is the George Creek field of Maryland in which one of the highest grade bituminous coals in the country is mined.

Anthracite Field. Let us turn now to a consideration of the anthracite coalfield of Eastern Pennsylvania, which, as we shall see, offers a marked contrast to the various bituminous fields which we have been examining heretofore. The eastern part of the state of Pennsylvania is occupied by three of the physiographic divisions into which Eastern North America is divided. These regions lie roughly north-east and south-west in three belts parallel to each other (Fig. 64). Beginning in the northern part of the state, they are, the Allegheny Plateau, which, with its deeply trenched valleys, we have already examined elsewhere ; the Great Appalachian Valley, consisting of the highly folded and contorted rock structure expressed in alternate ridges and furrows which is characteristic of this region wherever found ; and lastly, in the extreme south-east of the state, we find a small portion of the old crystalline area which forms the Appalachian foothill country throughout the eastern margin, but which here has almost the character of a low plain with gentle relief. Rising well back on the Plateau and crossing the other two divisions of the region on their way to the Atlantic, are two of the main rivers of the area, the Susquehanna, with its great network of head-streams and tributaries, and the lesser but still fairly large Delaware. The Great Valley is here separated from the lower Piedmont country by the sharply defined barrier of the Blue Ridge (Fig. 64). Immediately in rear of this ridge lies a valley between 5 and 10 miles in width, which is divided into two longitudinally by a lower ridge. Hence just in rear of the Blue Ridge we find two very clearly marked parallel valleys. The next subdivision of the Great Valley is an area of lesser ridges and basins which occupies the greater part of the region, and is bounded to the north by a more marked ridge of which the best defined part is called the Pocono Mountains. Beyond these mountains and lying between them and the edge of the Allegheny Plateau, we find a second large and clearly marked valley comparable to that already referred to as being just behind the Blue Ridge. On leaving the plateau country the Susquehanna enters this valley and receives a tributary from the north-east, the Lackawanna. It then turns sharply to the south-west and follows

the valley for a distance of about 70 miles, until it receives a
tributary coming this time from the plateau.   Thereupon it turns
southward and then south-eastward, cutting deep water-gaps
through the parallel ridges of the Great Valley before crossing
the Piedmont country beyond.   In this fashion the Susquehanna
forms a rough right angle, the longer limb of which lies parallel

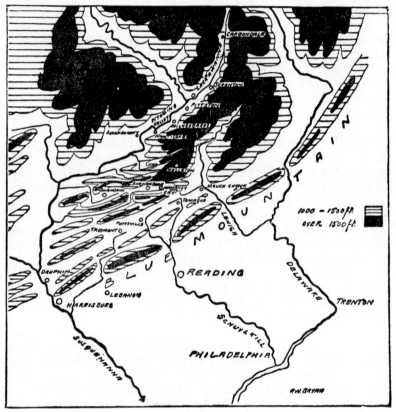

FIG. 64.—Sketch Map to show the relief of the Anthracite Coalfield of
Pennsylvania.

to the Blue Ridge but some 30 miles to the north-west, while the
short limb cuts directly across the ridges.   In the rough rectangle
thus formed the north-eastern end consists of the Delaware
River.   In contrast to the course followed by the Susquehanna,
this river cuts straight across the ridges and furrows of the valley
region, and does not turn south-east until forced to do so by the
Blue Ridge, the northern foot of which it follows for a distance

of some 40 miles, before turning sharply eastward through the great water-gap which it has cut in the Blue Ridge on its way seaward. It is within the limits of this rough rectangle, which lies, as we have seen, wholly within the region of highly contorted, faulted, and twisted strata lying between the Piedmont and the Plateau, that we find the great anthracite coalfield of the United States, a region which measures only some 120 miles in length by about one-third of that distance in breadth.

Before we proceed to examine the details of the conditions governing production and the various subdivisions of the area, let us try to form some concept of what this coalfield means to the economy of the States. In 1935, 54¾ million tons of anthracite were mined, against 434 million tons of bituminous coal, the anthracite production thus representing over 11 per cent. of the total coal production of the United States. Anthracite is mostly used to-day for heating purposes, particularly in large blocks of buildings where central heating is employed, such as offices and apartment houses. It is also possible for smelting purposes, and therefore it was used in the early blast-furnaces of the States, which, as we shall see more fully later, were established close to the anthracite coalfield in the thirties and forties of last century. Prior to this period the coal was floated down the Lehigh and Susquehanna Rivers in crude barges,[1] but so great was the inertia of the human mind to adopting anything new, that at first people refused to have anything to do with it, as they did not consider it possible that " black stones," as they called the anthracite, could be made to burn. This difficulty was accentuated by the imperfections of the early stoves. The new fuel, however, once the initial difficulties were overcome, steadily replaced charcoal as a blast-furnace fuel during the first half of the nineteenth century, and during the second half of the century it was itself steadily replaced by coke, mainly but not wholly, because coke is so much cheaper. Its higher price is partly due to the fact that the natural conditions render mining operations much more difficult here than in the bituminous fields, and partly because the organizations engaged in exploiting this natural resource have a monopoly. With such minor exceptions as to be negligible in any large view, there is no other anthracite-producing region in the United States.

We have seen that anthracite is found wholly within the Great Valley Region, and therefore within the region where great folding, faulting, and compression have taken place in past ages. We have, then, here a very remarkable contrast with the conditions in the bituminous fields. Here the seams are mostly

[1] About 1807. House Docs., 1926.

far out of the horizontal. They may also be very irregular, and may be as much as 2,000 feet below ground level (Fig. 59c). All these facts practically prohibit the use of machines, so that only some 3.5 per cent. of the coal mined is machine-mined. Hence, as we have already pointed out, the cost of anthracite is very much higher than that of bituminous coal, quite apart from any monopoly or semi-monopoly which may exist.

We have seen that the coalfield lies wholly within the rectangle between the Blue Ridge and the Susquehanna Valley, but within this general area there are a number of clearly marked sub-divisions which can be related to very definite relief features. The main producing area is that known as the Northern Basin, from which comes roughly half of the total output. This basin consists of the Lackawanna and Wyoming Valleys, the latter being part of the longitudinal Susquehanna Valley after the main river receives the Lackawanna as a tributary. It is shut in to the south by the Pocono Range—a fact of some importance in connection with the problem of distribution by rail. The basin is some 55 miles long by about 6 miles in breadth. The chief mining centres are Carbondale, Scranton, Moosic, Pittston, Wilkesbarre, and Nanticoke. In this basin the dip of the beds is less than in any of the others, nevertheless it ranges from 10 degrees to as much as 70 degrees. In addition to the difficulties already referred to in the way of general structure, this basin is still further handicapped by the fact, that from Pittston to Nanticoke there is a former valley of the Susquehanna now buried in sand. This gives much trouble in the mining, as it causes breaks in the shafts.

South of the main basin, as the sketch-map shows, are three others, each differing in minor details and accounting between them for the remainder of the output.

In the early days of the development of the area much coal was moved by water on both river and canal. To-day practically the whole movement takes place by rail. Relief control is clearly reflected in the concentration of rails on the water-gaps of the Blue Ridge, also in the north-east south-west movement along the valleys, and the use made of minor head-streams to facilitate approach to suitable tunnelling points. Thus we see from the map the double line of rail using the Lehigh Valley and its water-gap on the way to New Jersey and Philadelphia, and the similar concentration of lines on the Schuylkill water-gap to reach Reading and Philadelphia. The bulk of the anthracite is used in territory fairly close to the coalfields, certainly within the region of the north-eastern manufacturing area. Within this region, roughly one-third moves to the great centre of business administration represented by New York, New Jersey, and related areas. Nearly one-sixth goes to New England, while one-fourth is used in Pennsylvania. During the last decade or so the production of anthracite, always variable, has shown an unmistakable downward tendency. The difficulties of production, and the expense of processing are increasing, while at the same time other means of domestic, and building heating generally, are increasing in popularity. Oil, natural and coke-oven gas, by-product coke, and electric stoves, are prominent competitors. In recent years the production of anthracite has dropped to about 50–60 million tons.

Of the remaining coalfields of the United States, by far the most important is the Central Field, which is found in the states of Illinois, Indiana, and Western Kentucky. In general this provides a medium-grade bituminous coal, with a greater sulphur content, and lower heating value, than most of the coal of the Appalachian Field. For certain purposes, however, its close proximity to the rapidly growing great market centres of the Middle West, such as Chicago and St. Louis, give it a very definite advantage there over coal from the Eastern Field. As far as depth is concerned, the coal is readily accessible, and is usually mined at some 50 or 60 feet below the surface. The coal area forms a shallow basin with the coal outcropping along the edges, and for this reason the bulk of the mining is confined to the edges of the field. As in the Pittsburg District, the chief seam mined averages about 6 feet in thickness, and is therefore a very economical seam to work as far as thickness is concerned. Mining is mostly carried on by means of short shafts. As the whole of the area has been glaciated, the shafts have to be sunk through varying depths of glacial drift. This renders the sinking of the shafts more difficult, as it is always more difficult to sink a shaft through more or less unconsolidated material than it is through the solid. Trouble also arises because of the frequent presence of water in this looser matter. As has already been pointed out, the quality of the coal is inferior to that of the Pittsburg Region, and the large quantities of sulphur present make it very unsuitable for coking purposes ; hence, except for domestic consumption, it is unable to compete with that from the Appalachian Field except during the period when the Lakes are closed by ice and traffic becomes impossible. Were it of better quality, it would find a ready market in the great steel centres, which, as we shall see later, have sprung up in the vicinity of the head of Lake Michigan.

The remaining fields of the United States, including the

Western Interior, the South Western, the Northern Great Plains, the Rocky Mountains, and the Pacific Coast Fields of Washington, only produce, taken together, a total of some 50 millions. Development in the Western Interior and the South Western fields has been much hampered by the poor quality of the coal and the competition of fuel oil. The farther west one goes in the direction of the Rockies, the poorer the quality of the coal and the smaller the demand from a thinner population. Competition from fuel oil is also severely felt in these fields. In the Rocky Mountain area there are many detached fields which have been mainly developed either in connection with the transcontinental railways or in connection with the numerous mining camps. In these fields the coal varies much in quality and other characteristics from field to field, and a detailed examination of these differences would be quite out of the question in a study of this character.

On the Pacific Coast the Washington coal is mostly used either locally or moves southward along the coast to California. This movement is, however, very largely controlled by the price of fuel oil in Southern California. As it falls coal movement slacks off, while as it rises the movement increases. For the moment there does not appear to be much prospect of future development in competition with oil, as far from showing signs of decrease, the present prospects for oil development in California are steadily moving on the up-grade. In considering this question of competition it has also to be borne in mind that an apparatus suitable for oil-burning is not necessarily adapted for coal, hence the substitution of the one fuel for the other for industrial purposes cannot take place instantly. As the price of oil rises the increased coal export will tend to lag somewhat behind, as rather than incur the expense required to substitute coal-burners for oil, the tendency will be for certain firms, up to a point, to pay the higher price for oil.

Before we conclude our survey of the coal production of the United States, it may be helpful if we just examine briefly the possibilities of future production. The United States Fuel Administration, in a report published during the War, when reviewing the coal resources of the country, estimated that the United States possessed a coal reserve of some 1,400 billion short tons (1,446,000,000,000), or a sufficient quantity to keep the whole world going at the present rate of consumption for over 1,000 years, or about eleven times the estimated reserve of the British Isles down to a depth of 4,000 feet. This total applies only to coal within 3,000 feet of the surface, and excludes lignite and sub-bituminous coal, of each of which the United

States possesses about 1,000 billion tons. There is little doubt
that suitable methods of utilizing this coal for industrial purposes will result from the many experiments in this direction
which are being carried on both in the United States and in
Canada, a country which possesses an even larger reserve of the
lower-grade coals than does the United States. The lignite
region of the United States lies mostly in the Northern Great
Plains Region in the states of North and South Dakota and
Montana, all of which are in close relationship to the Canadian
frontier. As against the total U.S.A. reserve of some 1,400
billion tons, only some 16 billion tons in all have been raised
to the surface in the United States to date.

Fig. 65 indicates the uses to which coal is put in the United
States over a series of years.

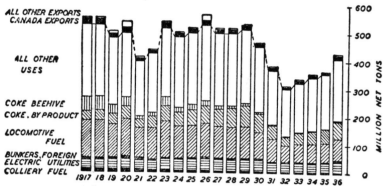

FIG. 65.—Output and Uses of Coal in U.S.A.

"Minerals Yearbook," 1937.   U.S. Dept. of the Interior.

It will be noticed that the making of metallurgical coke for
the iron and steel industry is one of the more considerable of
these, and one of which we shall have more to say in the next
chapter. The table indicates also a gradual change-over from
direct steam drive, in the production of mechanical energy, to
the steam-electric power station. With the development of
power generally in the United States we will deal in a later
chapter ; for the moment we would call attention to certain
characteristics of the American coal production.

Figs. 65 and 66 indicate the production of coal over a considerable period, and also the increase in the use of mechanical
aids to mining, and the resulting increase in the output per
man.

The coal industry is one in which the cost of labour represents a very high percentage of the cost of the product, and from this point of view the mechanization of the industry is important. Notice, too, that the annual production, though varying, shows little signs of a general long-term rise, though the capacity of developed mines is such that at any time the industry could respond to an increased demand with little additional capital expenditure.

The above diagrams indicate changes in many aspects of the United States coal industry.

In Mining Technology. The decline in number of mines working, and of men employed from 1923 to 1932 and their subsequent

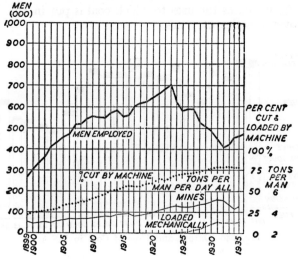

Fig. 66.—Number of Men employed and Output per Man, etc., in U.S.A. Coalfield.

increase, are in sympathy with general trade conditions. More interesting is the steady increase in the amount cut by machine. Coal-cutting machines were introduced in the eighties. The proportion of the national output of bituminous coal cut by machine was 84 per cent. in 1935, a proportion said to be near saturation point, though improvement in the speed and efficiency of the machines is expected to continue. The percentage of anthracite cut by machine was merely 3·5 per cent. Further, since 1923, mechanical loading has become important. In 1935, 13·5 per cent. of the underground production of bituminous coal and 21·2 per cent. of the anthracite was loaded with the aid of mechanical devices. These developments are reflected in increased amounts of coal won per man per day.

In Coal Use. Essential features are the consistently high percentages used for locomotive fuel—a reflection on the extent of the U.S.A., and the virtual disappearance of beehive coke. Electric utilities have increased their percentage, a commentary on the extensive use of electricity in American life.

CHAPTER XIX

IRON AND STEEL INDUSTRY

WE have seen (Fig. 65) that some 15 per cent. of the coal annually produced in the United States is required by the iron industry in blast-furnace practice. The amount used to smelt one ton of iron depends chiefly upon the constitution of the ore. The average for the United States gives one ton of coke (obtained from 1·42 tons of coal) required to smelt one ton of pig iron from nearly two tons of iron ore. All coals are not suitable for the production of a high-class coke. The coal for preference should be soft and friable, and of such a character generally, that when converted into coke it will form a coherent yet porous mass of a nature which will break into large blocks capable of bearing a fair weight in the blast-furnace, and pure enough to burn with little ash. Because of this fact and the enormous importance of an abundance of high-class coke for war purposes, and also to eliminate as far as possible all unnecessary transport, one of the first acts of the United States Fuel Administration was to prepare a table showing the value of the various fields from the standpoint of the possibilities of coke production. Judging from the table prepared by them, it would appear that in all parts of the Appalachian Field there is to be found coal of quality suitable for the production of commercial coke, but that the quality appears to vary very much within each locality. Thus of the coal used in Alabama in the year 1936, 40 per cent. was suitable for this purpose, while almost the whole of the New River and Pocahontas coals were suitable. Of the Pennsylvanian coals, over 50 per cent. were found to be of the right type, but the great bulk of this coal came from the Connellsville coking district. In 1935 nearly 30 per cent. of all coke produced in the United States was made in Pennsylvania, while nearly 25 per cent. of all by-product ovens were in that state. Much Pennsylvanian coal is used for coking at iron works in other states, e.g. in Ohio.

The Connellsville coking district, which occupies such a dominating position in the iron and steel trade of the United States, has already been described on pages 251–253. As we have seen, it is only some 60 miles long by 6 miles or so in breadth, and is really a detached outlier of the main Pittsburg Region, extending from Latrobe in the north-east to Fairchance in the south-west (Fig. 61). We have also seen that the central part of this outlier has been much cut up by the Youghiogheny and its tributaries, notably by Jacob's Creek and Sewickley Creek, lying north of the main river, and by the head-waters of Red-stone Creek and George Creek, tributaries of the Monongahela. The area dissected by these streams is the heart of the Connells-ville coking district, and Connellsville, situated on a river terrace where the Youghiogheny enters the coalfield, is the centre of the industry, and has given its name not only to the district, but to the coke produced.

Connellsville coke made in the old-fashioned " beehive " ovens on the coalfield was, in 1912, the standard blast-furnace fuel in the United States, and commanded the highest price. The process of manufacturing coke consists in heating suitable coal in an oven until all the volatile materials have been driven off. The " beehive " ovens employed in pre-war days in the Connells-ville district were most wasteful, as all the very valuable by-products dissipated into the air. In modern ovens the by-products are saved and converted into many useful products. Benzol derivatives, gas, ammonia, and coal-tar are the more valuable products thus obtained, and in the year 1936 the value of the by-products alone came to some 120 million dollars, while in the same year the coke produced at the same time was valued at 240 million dollars. Prior to the introduction of the by-product oven all these products were lost. It is true that by-product coke is much more expensive to produce than " beehive " coke because of the greater working and overhead expenses of the by-product oven. None the less, the rapid increase in num-bers of the latter indicates their more profitable nature. In this connection it is interesting to notice that while in the year 1900 only 1 million tons of coke, or 5 per cent. of the total, was manu-factured in by-product ovens, by 1918 some 26 million tons, or 46 per cent. of the total, was so made, and in 1936 96·3 per cent. " Beehive " ovens have now been practically eliminated, their place being taken by by-product ovens in which all the products of distillation are saved, only a sufficiency of the gas being burnt to heat the retorts. As a result of the rapid spread of the process, one finds a steady shift of the coking industry from the coalfield to large manufacturing centres, such as Pitts-burg and Youngstown, and to the lake shore smelting centres, as at Cleveland and Buffalo, where the by-products can be profitably used on the spot. Roughly one-half of the gas so produced is used in heating ovens, one-third in steel or related plants, and one-tenth for lighting and heating in adjacent cities. In this connection one should notice the great increase in the use of gas in the new Open Hearth method of steel making. In addition to the gas produced by retort ovens, gases are also produced and used for direct heating from blast-furnaces and Open Hearth furnaces. Many cities on the shores of the Great Lakes and in large manufacturing centres now get almost their whole supply of gas for heating, lighting, and power purposes from retort ovens. Indianapolis, Hamilton, South Chicago, Milwaukee, and Duluth may be cited as examples, which get their gas in this way much more cheaply than would otherwise be possible—a fact which has been brought clearly home to them during steel strikes, when they were forced to depend on the much more expensive water-gas. This shifting of the industry to the shores of the Great Lakes is clearly illustrated in the establishment of many steelworks in the Lake country of recent years, such as that of the United States Steel Corporation's great plant at Gary, at the southern end of Lake Michigan, where great batteries of retort ovens have been constructed, to which the coal is brought from the coalfield by rail. It is important, however, to remember that in spite of this change Pennsylvania still ranks first as a coke-producing state with Ohio second, Indiana third, New York fourth, and Alabama fifth.

The supply of the very best coal from the Connellsville District is limited, and other portions of the eastern part of the Appalachian Field have increasingly to be relied upon. Since the Pittsburg seam becomes less suitable for coking as we go westward, the change in the location of the ovens did not interfere with the great importance of the Connellsville District from the standpoint of the production of the finest coke. We have to notice that coke can be made in retort ovens from coal which would not produce a good quality " beehive " coke. The West Virginian coals are on the whole poorer in coking qualities than are those of the Pittsburg Region, but they are excellent from the standpoint of the production of retort-oven coke, hence they are being used to an increasing extent for this purpose more particularly in connection with the lake shore smelters, as there is a very small local demand and a down grade all the way on the whole from the West Virginian fields to the lake smelters. Thus we find these facts reflected in recent years in the steadily growing shipments of coal from the New River and Pocahontas Districts of West Virginia and from eastern Kentucky to the blast furnaces of Cleveland, Gary, South Chicago, and other smelting centres on the shores of the Great Lakes.

Since the eighties of last century the United States has led the world in the production of iron ore, and for many decades now 80 per cent. and more of this has come from a series of deposits in that part of the Laurentian Shield which extends into the United States about Lake Superior. Agriculturally a negative area, and distant from the most populous and important parts of the country, only the quality, ease of large-scale mining, and possibilities of large-scale shipments on the Great Lakes, brought it into a fundamental relationship with the industry of the country. How important is this area, and what are the other sources of iron ore in the States is shown in Fig. 68.

It will be noticed that the chief producing area is the Mesabi Range. Here we find the ore close to the surface, in vast masses which may be as much as 2,000 feet long by 1,500 feet broad and 500 feet in thickness (Fig. 67). These deposits in the case of the Mesabi Range, are covered only by a mantle of drift or boulder clay. Both the boulder clay and the underlying masses of ore are soft and friable, and this fact makes it possible to depart entirely from the normal methods of mining by means of tunnels and shafts. The cover of drift is first dug off by steam shovel, and in this fashion the underlying ore body is exposed. When this has been done, the ore is removed by cutting it away in a series of great terraces, which give the ore-fields, at a superficial glance, very much the appearance of those hillsides in the Far East which are terraced for rice cultivation in mountain regions. The great steam shovels used in the ore-fields dig 9 feet at a time and lift some $4\frac{1}{2}$ tons. Because of the exceptionally favourable geographical conditions described above with reference to the Mesabi Range, and which are present to a lesser degree in the other producing districts of the Lake Superior Region, ore can be obtained here much more cheaply than at any other centre in the United States. An interesting comment on the nature of the mining and its scale is found in the fact that one mine alone, that of Hull-Rust, near Hilling, produced in 1923 nearly 9 million tons of ore, or over three-quarters of the production of the United Kingdom for the same year. In the Cuyuna Range, which lies westward of the Mesabi, the conditions are identical, though this latter range has as yet only been developed to a limited extent. None of the ranges of the Lake Superior country are more than 100 miles from navigable water, the bulk of them are less than half that distance, while the Mesabi Range which we have been considering lies from 70 to 80 miles from the lake shore.

Of the six ranges of the Lake Superior country we have touched on two. There remain four to be located and considered. One of these is the Vermilion, which lies in echelon with the Mesabi about 10 miles farther inland towards the northwest, and therefore close to the Canadian frontier. It is entirely

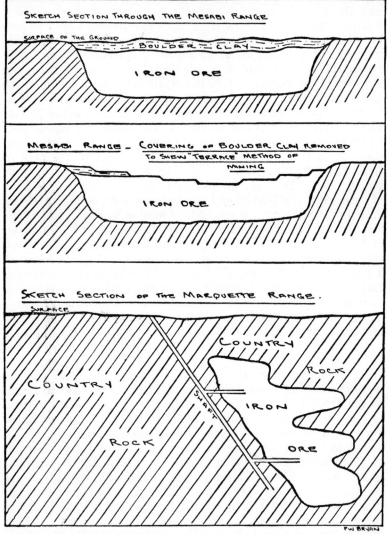

FIG. 67.—Diagrams to show Mining Conditions in the Lake Superior Country.

owned by the United States Steel Corporation, holds three-fourths of the total ore reserves in the state of Minnesota, in which are situated the Mesabi, the Cuyuna, and the Vermilion deposits.

Though the reserves are immense there is already a marked falling off in the iron content of the Lake Superior ores.[1]

The remaining three ranges all lie to the south of the lake in the northern part of the peninsula portion of Wisconsin. They lie, as can be best seen from the map, fairly close to the water, and are, in order from west to east, the Penokee-Gogebic, the Marquette, and the Menominee. As in the case of the regions already dealt with, the ore is present here in vast bodies, but the position of these bodies with reference to the surface and surrounding rock masses offers a marked contrast. The ore bodies being further underground, and being enclosed in hard rock strata, which are either steeply inclined or in some cases even vertical, have to be mined by shaft, and for this reason the cost of winning the ore is higher (Fig. 67). The quality of the metal and the percentage of metallic contents in the ore is just as high, and situated as they are much closer to navigable water, these districts are in a more favourable position for marketing their ore. The following figures for 1936 show that the Mesabi Range has far the largest output.[2]

							Million Long Tons.	
							1929.	1936.
The Mesabi .	.	.	.	.	.	.	42·4	30·2
Menominee .	.	.	.	.	.	.	5·4	1·6
Gogebic	.	.	.	.	.	.	7·0	4·0
Marquette	.	.	.	.	.	.	4·5	4·4
Vermilion	.	.	.	.	.	.	1·9	1·0
Cuyana	.	.	.	.	.	.	1·5	·4
			Totals	.	.		62·7	41·6

The Lake Superior ores were discovered in the mid-nineteenth century, and the desire to use these high-grade ores was a considerable economic motive for the building of the early " Soo " canals and for other improvements in the Great Lake channels.

In colonial days the bog ores of the coastal plain were used in small charcoal furnaces. Later came Piedmont ores, and then when coal was used, a much more important phase came with the use of Appalachian Valley ores and the anthracite coal of the East Pennsylvanian field.

Even in the Pittsburg area, the original furnaces worked with local ores in charcoal furnaces. Coke was used in the industry rather later than was the case in Great Britain, but the Pittsburg District was using the excellent coking coal of the district some decades before the first Lake Superior ores began to come in.

[1] When first mined the percentage of iron in the ore was 60 to 70 : to-day it is about 50.
[2] " Mineral Resources," 1930 and 1937. Total U.S.A. iron ore production in 1942 was 105·5 million tons.

It was long before there was any realization of the great part which these ores were to play in bringing about the dominating position now occupied by the United States in the iron and steel industry of the world. That this should be so is not surprising when one grasps the enormous distance lying between the coal country and these ore-fields. The modern industry demands coke as a blast-furnace fuel. Connellsville, the centre, as we have seen, of the coking industry, lies a distance of about 1,000 miles from the Lake Superior ore deposits. Had it not been for the fact that for the greater part of this distance a line of natural water communication, in the shape of the Great Lakes and their connecting streams, offers an easy route between the two areas, the double movement of iron to coal and coal to iron which takes place along this route to-day, and which forms such an outstanding feature of the industry, would have been impossible, and the American iron and steel industry would have been compelled to follow quite different lines in its development. As it was, although this great waterway existed, in its natural state it was of little use. The connecting streams between the lakes were interrupted by rapids and obstructions in the channels, which effectively prevented them from being used by anything but canoes. The most important of these obstructions existed where the St. Mary's River, through which Lake Superior drains into Lake Huron, falls a height of 20 feet in a series of rapids and cataracts in a distance of about one mile on its way to the lower lake. To overcome this obstruction, canals have been from time to time constructed and deepened to meet traffic demands. Of these canals, the first was constructed in the forties, and it was a 12-foot canal. After the Civil War this canal was deepened to 16 feet. To-day there are no less than five parallel locks, one of which is on the Canadian side and is 22 feet deep, while of the four remaining on the American side, two are 24 feet deep. The ruling depth of the route, however, is here 22 feet, as that is the depth of the approaches to the canals in the St. Mary's River. These canals constitute the famous " Soo " canals, which, as we shall see, have played and are playing a very big rôle in the American iron and steel industry.

Other barriers to free movement along the lakes were the obstructions in the channel linking Lake Huron with Lake Erie. This channel consists of the St. Clair River, Lake St. Clair, and the Detroit River, which empties Lake St. Clair into Lake Erie. A depth of 21 feet now exists at low water in this channel, and this is sufficient to take the large, specially constructed boats used in the Lake trade. The size of these boats has steadily increased, until to-day we have boats such as the " Grant Morden," which is no less than 625 feet in length, with a tonnage of 14,000 and is capable of carrying half a million bushels of wheat. The ore boats vary in size from 5,000 to 14,000 tons. With this channel made practical, a through waterway was provided from the head of Lake Superior to the southern shores of Lake Erie. Based mainly on this development and the introduction of coke as the standard blast-furnace fuel, by the early or middle seventies the centre of the iron industry had largely shifted to the district around the city of Pittsburg at the forks of the Ohio. To this point the coke moved from Connellsville, and met there the ore brought by water and rail from the head of the Great Lakes. We have not here the space available to consider the many other developments which were needed before the Lake Superior ores could move in this fashion and become the dominating factor in the industry which they are to-day. It must suffice for us to say that these improvements were related to the invention and application of machinery on a large scale to the efficient handling of the ore, so as to reduce to a minimum that most expensive item in the cost of modern transport—the transferring of commodities from one system of transport to another, and the putting of commodities on and off carriers.

This great movement of ore from the head of Lake Superior to the shores of Lake Erie has led to the growth of two groups of highly specialized ports on the lakes, the one group related primarily to the iron-fields engaged in despatching ore, and the other group related to the blast-furnace centres in or near the Lakes, and engaged in receiving and forwarding the ore to its final destination. Of the first group, we will expect that those having the largest traffic in ore will be those connected with the Mesabi Range at the extreme head of Lake Superior. These are Two Harbours, Duluth, and Superior. Of the rest, Ashland, towards the south-west end of the lake, is the port of the Penokee-Gogebic ; Marquette, on the south shore, handles the ore from the Marquette Range ; while Escanaba, on the north-west coast of Lake Michigan, serves as an outlet for the Menominee Range. All these ports have plenty of deep water for the large lake boats. The significance of this fact is rooted in the past. A slight depression of the region during late glacial times resulted in the drowning of the lower parts of the river valleys, which thus form excellent deep-water harbours. For this reason the depth available in Duluth and Superior for example, compares very favourably with that of many ports on the Atlantic Seaboard. Duluth handles the greatest quantity of ore, nearly one-third of the total, and is fairly closely followed by Superior and Two Harbours. These three ports are, of course, most intimately related to the great Mesabi Range. Of the three remaining shipment ports, each serves as the outlet for one of the smaller producing regions south of the lake, and handles, as we should expect, smaller quantities of ore.

Of the second group of ports engaged in this traffic, those on the south shore of Lake Erie are by far the most important from the standpoint of quantity of ore handled, the Lake Michigan ports being chiefly the two neighbouring ports of South Chicago and Gary, at the extreme head of the lake. Gary is wholly controlled by the United States Steel Corporation, and contains the Corporation's chief plant, which is said to be the largest steel manufacturing plant in the world. Of the Lake Erie ports, Cleveland, Ashtabula, Conneaut, Buffalo, and Lorain are the chief handlers of the ore. We may regard these Lake Erie ports as being of two distinct types. The first of these types is the port which merely receives the ore and forwards it inland by rail to the Pittsburg District, the Youngstown District, or some other steel district on or near to the coalfield. Of the ports of this type, the best examples are Ashtabula, Conneaut, and Fairport. These ports practically do nothing else but receive iron ore and ship coal. Thus, of Ashtabula's total receipts, over 99 per cent. consisted of iron ore, and of her water shipments over 90 per cent. was coal. The second type of port is the one which receives the ore both to forward it inland, and also to use it in the blast-furnaces set up in the port itself. This latter class of port, as we have already seen, has been increasing since the introduction of the by-product oven. Two of the best-known examples of this type of port are Cleveland, on the Cuyahoga River, in the middle of the south shore of Erie, Buffalo, on Buffalo Creek, at the eastern end of the lake, and the receiving ports on Lake Michigan.

Practically all U.S.A. exported ore goes to Canadian lakeside plants.

It will be seen that the really critical point in connection with this great traffic movement, regarded as a whole, is the St. Mary's River, with its system of canals, commonly spoken of as the " Soo." The fact that the lakes are closed from about December to late April, necessitates the accumulation of large quantities of ore at receiving ports and at works.

Iron now enters into use chiefly in the form of steel, of which it is by far the greatest constituent. Two or more of the elements carbon, silicon, manganese, chromium, tungsten, etc., are present in steel in proportions and physical states controlled according to the particular purposes for which the steel is being manufactured.

No dependable, economic, direct method has yet been invented of producing steel from the ore in one process. Actually pig iron is produced in the blast furnace, and is then removed, usually now in a molten condition, to steel works alongside. A considerable portion of pig-iron is distributed widely about the country to foundries in which it is converted into cast iron, but much the larger proportion goes molten to the steel works. In the States the Open Hearth process of making steel is chiefly used, one reason being, that in it, scrap steel may be used. Thus for many years now the country has produced considerably more steel than pig-iron, and the proportion of steel to pig-iron is obviously affected by the current price of scrap at the works. The raw materials assembled at the blast furnace are iron ore, coke (now usually made at the works, and not at the mines) and a quantity of limestone sufficient to combine with any siliceous matter in the ore, and so to form in the furnace a liquid self-separating slag, which floating on the molten pig-iron at the base of the furnace, can be tapped off separately. Some ores are so calcareous as to need no extra limestone, and in any case supplies of this mineral are so widespread that they seldom or never prove factors in the localization of the industry.

In modern plants economies accrue as a result of the juxtaposition of blast furnace, coke ovens, steel works, and rolling mills. When this exists full use can be made of the excess gases of the coke ovens and the blast furnaces, and indeed no further source of energy is then needed for the whole plant than that of the quantity of coal just necessary to make the coke required.

Apart from the scattered charcoal furnaces to which we have already referred, the beginnings of the industry were in the narrow Piedmont Belt lying between the anthracite coalfield and the Atlantic Seaboard. This industry depended largely on local iron-ore and supplies from the Adirondacks and on anthracite as fuel. The chief centres of the industry now in the Atlantic Seaboard Region are Chester, near Philadelphia, situated on tidewater on the north-east south-west stretch of the Delaware, where it forms the boundary of New Jersey before spreading out in the waters of Delaware Bay; Camden, in New Jersey, on the opposite shore of the Delaware facing Philadelphia; South Bethlehem and Allentown on the Lehigh just before it joins the Delaware; Reading, on the Schuylkill, located on the stretch of Piedmont between the Blue Ridge and Philadelphia, and the towns of Lebanon and Steelton (Harrisburg), which lie near the foot of the Blue Ridge not far from the great water-gap cut in the ridge by the Susquehanna on its way out of the valley region to cross the Piedmont to the sea. To this list must now be added the works at Sparrow Point, near Baltimore, at the head of Chesapeake Bay, which are excellently situated for importing foreign ore and despatching the finished products. With the opening up of the Pittsburg Coalfield and the application of coke to the smelting of the ore, a new centre sprang up beyond the mountains under such favourable conditions that the Atlantic Seaboard Region was forced to turn largely to coke from the Connellsville Region for fuel, and to abandon the much more expensive and no more effective anthracite. Close proximity to tide-water and to large centres of population are the chief advantages which this region possesses. It thus has, from the point of view of the world market, one of the great advantages possessed by Great Britain—the one which perhaps more than any other made her in the middle of the last century the workshop of the world. In view of this fact, it is interesting to notice in passing, that steel products are now being shipped from Pittsburg down the Ohio by water to the Mississippi country and to the Gulf ports of Texas and Mexico, in competition with the Atlantic Seaboard firms for the market offered in equipping the oilfields of the Gulf and Mid-Continental Regions. It should, however, be remembered that at present this route is interrupted by ice in the winter and by low water in late summer and autumn. To obviate the latter of these difficulties some 52 dams and locks have been constructed on the Ohio. Apart from this competition, firms on the eastern seaboard possess a distinct advantage, other things being equal, in tendering for oil or other equipment work in the Gulf Region—an advantage the measure of which is the difference between the all-water route to the Gulf ports, and the rail-and-water route from Pittsburg. The new route also facilitates the despatching of goods by way of the Panama Canal to the western seaboard at San Francisco. Since the opening of the Panama Canal the Atlantic Seaboard has possessed a marked advantage in connection with the canal, since it gave to it an all-water route to the west, the cost of transport by which was so much less than by rail across the continent as to render it impossible for rail-borne goods to compete with those carried by steamer through the Panama Canal. Although possessing this distinct advantage from the standpoint of foreign trade, the Atlantic Seaboard area is very far removed from the great markets of the middle and far west, and it is further handicapped by the distance which separates it from the main coking coal regions.

As we have already seen, what has been somewhat loosely termed the Pittsburg Region grew up based mostly on the coking coal of the Connellsville district. Its growth was rapid, and its chief centre became and is to-day for the steel industry, what Chicago is for the wheat industry, the great market and organization centre of the industry for the United States. Pittsburg at the forks of the Ohio dominates the whole region. Second to it stands Youngstown, in the famous Mahoning Valley, which, lying north-west of the position of Pittsburg, is about half-way to the south shore of Lake Erie. Close to these centres there is a great series of satellite towns, such as Allegheny, Warren, Akron, and Sharon (Fig. 68). In these towns almost all branches of the heavy steel trade is carried on, not to mention the vast number of subsidiary industries which such centres bring into being. These centres lie for the most part lower than the actual producing area of the coalfield, so that all coal moving to them follows the river valleys, and therefore has a down grade to the manufacturing centres, a fact which must have a very definite bearing on cost of transport as an item in total production cost.

One of the factors unfavourable to expansion in the immediate vicinity of Pittsburg to-day is the very limited area available. The trenching of the rivers as we have seen has produced a narrow strip alongside the water backed by a steep cliff. These conditions lead to the migration of the industry downstream. In the Chicago area, which bids fair to be Pittsburg's great rival in the future, the areas available for expansion are almost unlimited. The bulky raw materials, with the exception of coal, can also be more readily assembled at Chicago.

To the east of the main Pittsburg area, but forming really an eastern extension of it, lies the steel-producing district surrounding the town of Johnstown, on the Conemaugh, which, as we have already seen, is one of those left-bank tributaries of the Allegheny which have deeply trenched the plateau, and in doing so have exposed the coal. Lying to the south-west of the main district is the steel town of Wheeling, on the Ohio, and still farther to the south-west is the town of Ironton, not far from the junction of the Ohio with the Big Sandy, as this river comes out of the West Virginian Coal Region. All these districts may be regarded as minor extensions of the Pittsburg District and are quite distinct from the next, the most recent of the great steel areas which we have to consider, that is, the district which has grown up fringing the shores of the Great Lakes, and which is based largely on that very prominent feature of the modern development of the industry, the change over from " beehive " to retort ovens.

Turning then to discuss the rather scattered area which is somewhat loosely spoken of as the Lake Shore Region, we find that it falls naturally into two easily distinguishable districts, the region along the southern shore of Lake Erie, and the region on the south-western and southern coasts of Lake Michigan. The Lake Erie area is at the meeting-point, where, if one may so express it, the ore from the head of the lakes comes ashore and the coal from the Northern Appalachian Region goes afloat. The position here to-day is thus comparable in many respects with that of the industry in South Wales, where the coal coming from the hill-country beyond the Vale of Glamorgan meets the iron ore at ports such as Cardiff and Newport, coming from Spain by an all-water route. In both cases the coal is moving mainly downhill to the coast, while the iron ore is moving by an all-water route for the bulk of its journey. Here, too, the various satellite steel industries which depend on the smelter for their raw materials, are largely engaged in the different branches of the heavy steel industry, such as the manufacture of structural shapes, plates, and parts of large castings.

On the other hand, the steel industry of the Calumet District which we find located on the shores of Lake Michigan, mainly at South Chicago, Gary, Hammond and Indiana Harbour, was primarily developed at those points, not because of local deposits of coal and iron, as in the case of the Pittsburg or eastern areas, but because of the large western market available for steel products. Of these, perhaps the most important are all kinds of farm and other labour-saving machinery, ranging from the simplest of farm implements to the most elaborate combined thresher and harvester, and also steel products used in connection with transport in the vast regions of the west, ranging from automobiles to steel rails. Hence we find at Chicago such plants as that of the International Harvester Trust Corporation, which specializes in farming machinery ; and also to be connected in our minds with the vast prairie and plains environment of the city we find some of the greatest railway works in the world. Other products for which there is a great demand in this area are wire for fencing in the plains, tin-plate for canning, structural steel for building, wire mesh for highway foundation, and piping for gas, water, heating, sanitation and oil. In the Calumet District the production costs of steel are lower than in the Pittsburg area. This low cost is due to the excellent local conditions under which the industry is carried on. Land was available in large blocks at relatively low prices alongside of navigable water or water which can be made navigable at minimum cost. The necessary raw materials can be easily assembled. The large blocks of flat land have enabled each plant to develop on a large scale and to take full advantage of handling the molten metal without allowing it to cool between processes. The Illinois coalfield is near this district, but since this coal is unsuitable for making metallurgical coke, the coal actually used comes chiefly from the West Virginia and Pennsylvania portions of the Appalachian field. The greater portion is railed to Lake Erie and comes on by water, but some is railed the whole way, chiefly in winter. The recent development of the area has led to the employment of all the latest scientific methods in the layout of the plants, in the processes, and in the utilization to the utmost of the by-products.

Of the centres on Lake Erie, by far the most important, from the standpoint of production, are Cleveland, in the centre of the

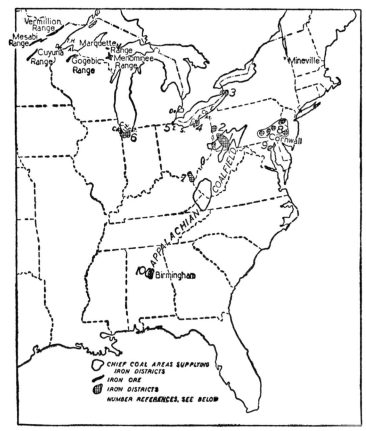

Fig. 68.—Chief Iron and Steel Regions of the U.S.A.

D, Duluth Superior. T.H, Two Harbours. M, Marquette. C, Chicago. Ca, Calumet. I.H, Indiana Harbour. Gar, Gary. De, Detroit. T, Toledo. S, Sandusky. L, Lorrain. C, Cleveland. F, Fairport. Co, Conneaut. As, Ashtabula. E, Erie.
Chief Iron and Steel Districts : 1. Pittsburg, Johnston, Wheeling, etc. 2. Youngstown. 3. Buffalo. 4. Cleveland. 5. Toledo and Detroit. 6. L. Michigan. 7. Huntingdon, Ironton. 8. Steelton, Allentown, etc. 9. Sparrows Point. 10. Birmingham.

south shore of the lake, on the Cuyahoga River ; Buffalo, or rather its northern suburb, Tonawanda, at the extreme end of the lake, at the mouth of the Erie Canal ; and Toledo, at the west end of the lake, on one of the old portage routes to the west by way of the Maumee River. It is unnecessary to dwell at greater

10

length on the development of this lake region as a steel-producing area, as the more outstanding facts have already been emphasized when considering the question of the relative advantages of retort ovens versus " beehive," and the allied question of the gradual change over from the one type of oven to the other. This change over, together with the convenience of the location as a meeting-point for the fundamental raw materials, plus the influence of the development of the west, and therefore of a new market rapidly extending, are the more important points to be borne in mind.

In passing, attention may be called to a minor development of the industry at the head of Lake Superior at Duluth, where coal can be obtained at a lower freight rate than at Chicago. This is based on the fact that coal moving to Duluth does so as a fill-up cargo on the return run of iron and wheat ships moving from the head of Lake Superior to the Erie ports, a position comparable in its effect on the price of coal, to that of the coal which moved in pre-war days to Italy in ships going to the Black Sea to load wheat from South Russia and Rumania. Coal moving from Lake Erie ports to Chicago may or may not get a profitable return cargo, there being no ore to move and much of the wheat from that centre moving east by rail. Hence the freight rate on coal must be high enough to safeguard the shipper against loss. The smelting industry at Duluth has therefore been built up partly on the basis of this return cargo coal, partly on the basis of the large local supplies of ore, and partly, and perhaps primarily, on the basis of the rapidly growing western demand for iron and steel goods, it being found cheaper, under the con-ditions explained above, to move coal to the iron, rather than to move the iron to the lower lake ports, and then move the manu-factured goods back over the same ground. Of a similar type to this last-named area are a number of minor areas on the Canadian shores of the lakes, which depend almost entirely for their raw materials on the ore from the head of the lakes, and coke made in retort ovens from Pittsburg coal.

FOREIGN ORE IMPORTED IN THE U.S.A.

In Million Tons

Origin.							1929.	1936.
Chile	.	.	.	.	.	.	1·70	1·26
Cuba	.	.	.	.	.	.	·64	·44
Algeria and Tunisia		.	.	.	.	·17	·01
Sweden	.	.	.	.	.	.	·31	·17
Canada	.	.	.	.	.	.	·003	·08
Others.	.	.	.	.	.	.	·316	·272
							3·139	2·232

These ores are brought chiefly to Baltimore, Philadelphia and New York, and mainly go to the few Atlantic coast sites of the industry.

PRODUCTION OF PIG-IRON BY STATES [1]
IN MILLION TONS

	1929.	1936.
Pennsylvania	14·0	9·4
Ohio	9·4	7·3
Illinois	4·3	3·0
Indiana	4·3	3·3
Michigan	·8	·9
New York	2·6	2·2
Alabama	2·7	2·1
Maryland	1·1	1·2
Kentucky	·2	·2
West Virginia	·6	·6
Minnesota	·4	·1
Others	·8	·4
	41·2	30·7

PRODUCTION OF PIG-IRON BY COUNTRIES
IN MILLION METRIC TONS

	1929.	1936.
United States	43·3	31·6
Canada	1·2	·8
United Kingdom	7·7	7·8
France	10·4	6·2
Belgium	4·0	3·2
Luxembourg	2·9	2·0
Italy	·7	·8
Spain	·7	·2
Sweden	·5	·6
Germany (exclusive of the Saar)	13·2	15·2
Saar	2·1	2·1
Austria	·5	·2
Czecho-Slovakia	1·6	1·1
Poland	·7	·6
U.S.S.R.	4·0	14·3
Japan	1·5	1·9
China	·3	·6
India	1·4	1·6
Australia	·3	·7
	97·0	91·5

Modern blast furnaces and steel works are very expensive to build, and the industry is one in which the charges on capital, the expense of the raw materials, and the cost of assembling them, are much greater than the labour charges. The industry is fundamental to manufacturing generally, and no industry feels

[1] Pig-iron production in 1942 was 54·3 million tons.

more the incidence of trade slumps. In the great depression of 1932, only about 13 per cent. of the steel capacity of the country was active.

It is of some interest to compare the major regions of blast-furnace practice in relation to the cost of the assemblage of raw material. Actual figures of course change from year to year, but they all illustrate the same principles. Thus on the Great Lakes, the chief cost is in port handling, and Lake Erie centres pay little more for iron ore than do Lake Michigan centres. On the other hand the rail freights are much higher than the water charges, and Pittsburg, and its satellite districts pay more than any other of the major districts for their ore, but less for their coal. On the other hand the Lake Michigan districts pay very little less for ore than the Lake Erie districts, but far more for coal, which comes chiefly from West Virginia, and has a long rail haul to Lake Erie in summer, and sometimes in winter, a very long all-rail haul.

Only the Birmingham district has all the raw materials within a few miles of each other, but neither ore nor coal are quite so suitable as is usual in the northern districts, and it is much less well situated in respect of general markets.

We emphasize the position of sources of raw material in the location of the industry, yet, in fact, all but one of the major producing districts have to go very great distances for either their coal or their iron ore.

This is not to-day exceptional. It is the case in most of the greatest iron industries of the world. Large-scale cheaply worked deposits of iron and of coal do not as a rule occur in proximity ; and since, in modern days, the efficiency of the blast-furnace has become such that seldom more than one ton of coke is required for one ton of metal, the coal-field no longer has a stronger pull on the industry than the ore. Actually the coal-field may have a bigger attraction in virtue of the fact that it so frequently has other industries for which the iron and steel is a raw material, in other words it supplies a market, and in the location of an iron and steel plant the question of the location of markets is often to-day the determining factor. Quite local factors are a large supply of water, and room for the layout of assembly yards, storage yards, etc.

The Birmingham area produces a much larger proportion of cast iron, and cast iron products, and a smaller proportion of steel, than do the northern areas.

Finally, though there are immense reserves of ore in the Lake Superior district, the reserves which without processing yield more than 50 per cent. iron are rapidly dwindling. Eventually this may lead to an increase in the relative importance of Atlantic districts, such as Sparrows Point, working on imported supplies of ore from Cuba, Chile and Brazil.

Fig. 68 gives a generalized picture of the chief iron and steel districts of the U.S.A. and the table of production by states will give some idea of their relative importance.   The Pennsylvanian and lakeside productions depend entirely upon Lake Superior ores, and the Alabama production upon the local ores and coal. Sparrows Point, near Baltimore, occasionally has taken a little Lake Superior ore, but is almost entirely dependent upon imported ores, chiefly from Cuba and from Chile.

The now small pig-iron production of, or near, the anthracite coal region has a more diversified supply, receiving some ore from Lake Superior, and also some from Mineville, N.Y., and Cornwall, Pa.   There are groups of blast furnaces also apart from the major districts, in the Appalachian Valley in Tennessee and in East Kentucky, near St. Louis, and in Colorado.   The total production from such scattered areas has never so far assumed any considerable proportion of that of the whole country.

Much steel is made from scrap in the open hearth process, and so the U.S.A. steel production (76·8 million tons in 1942) exceeds the pig-iron production (54·37 million tons in 1942) by a large amount.

The following table shows the expansion of steel production in the three leading countries and in the world as a whole in millions of long tons :—

	Aver. 1937–38	1948	1951	1952
U.S.A.	39·5	79·1	93·9	83·2
U.S.S.R. . . .	17·6	18·6	30·8	34·5
U.K.	11·7	14·9	15·6	16·4
World	121·0	153·3	207·4	208·3

Statistical Bulletin, Iron and Steel Federation.

CHAPTER XX

COAL TRANSPORT

IT now remains for us to discuss broadly the movement of coal as a whole from the two main coalfields—the Pittsburg District and the Coalfield of West Virginia. Regarded in the mass, the bulk of this movement will obviously be from the coalfields to the great centres of industrial activity in the north-eastern manufacturing zone which extends roughly from New England on the east to the Mississippi on the west, and from the Great Lakes on the north to a line joining the Ohio river and the head of Chesapeake Bay on the south. Thus we shall expect a large movement of Appalachian coal to the great steel centres of Pittsburg and Youngstown and their satellite towns; to the blast furnaces of Buffalo, Cleveland, Gary, South Chicago, and other places on the shores of the Great Lakes; to the populous industrial and commercial area which lies between New York and Baltimore; to the textile and metal-working regions of New England and to the textile areas of the Carolinas. In addition to this movement to industrial centres there is a movement to the ports for coastwise shipment and for bunkering ships.

From a study of a map (Fig. 69) it will be clear that of the four major regions to which coal will move, two, the Atlantic Seaboard Region and the New England Region, lie to the east of the Appalachian Ridges, while the other two, the Pittsburg-Youngstown Region and the Region of the Great Lakes, lie to the west. Of the minor regions, three are to the east and two to the west. The significance of these facts will appear when we examine the geographical factors conditioning the actual movement. Before doing so, let us get a clear idea of the movement of coal from the Pittsburg area of the coalfield. Between one-third and one-half of the amount raised is consumed in the district and of this about half is converted into coke. Of the amount not so retained for consumption in the region, about one-third is shipped for use as railroad fuel; another third moves northward and westward to the ports on the southern shores of Lake Erie, partly for shipment to the upper lakes and partly for use in the blast-furnaces of Cleveland, Buffalo, and other lower lake centres; while the remaining third moves eastward through or north of the Appalachian Ridges to the northern tide-water ports on the Atlantic Seaboard.

It will be clear, then, that the bulk of the coal moving from the Pittsburg Field may be divided into two main streams, one of which moves northward and westward of the Appalachian Ridges, while the other moves eastward through those ridges. We have then to consider how far geographic conditions assist or hamper these great movements. We have already seen that the coalfield is situated high up on the Allegheny Plateau. This fact, other things being equal, would give a down grade in every direction to sea-level. Between the coalfields and the Lakes the grade is mainly downhill, with a slight rise to cross the low water-parting which separates the Ohio system of drainage from that of the series of small streams which drain northward to the Lakes. As has already been explained, the dissected nature of the plateau surface offers some obstacle to movement, but this is offset by the fact that the river trenches, the chief cause of the obstruction, themselves provide lines of movement.

A marked contrast is presented when we analyse the factors conditioning eastward movement. Between the coalfields and the sea lies that great maze of ridges and valleys, which, from the point of view of movement east and west, bears the somewhat misleading title of the Greater Appalachian Valley. Looking eastward from the summit of the escarpment known as the Allegheny Front, one sees ridge after ridge and furrow after furrow lying between the point of observation and the Piedmont country adjoining the Atlantic Coastal Plain. This maze of hill and valley forms a very definite barrier to all eastward movement. Hence the critical points from the standpoint of coal movement will be found where nature assisted by man has provided relatively easy ways through. Of these, the largest, best known, and best defined is the famous Hudson-Mohawk Gap, which links the eastern part of the Lakes and the northern portion of the coal-bearing plateau with the Atlantic Seaboard at New York. In this gap are found the main lines of the New York Central Railroad, which, according to the U.S. Geological Survey, stands third in importance as a coal-carrying road, being only exceeded by the Pennsylvanian, and the Baltimore and Ohio. There is no doubt that a large amount of coal from the northern part of the coalfield moves by this route via the Hudson Valley to tide-water at New York.

South of this point the chief geographic control is exercised by the river valleys which cut across the ridges. The main valleys to notice are those of the Potomac, the Susquehanna, and the New River. A study of a detailed railway map will make the position clear. From the northern part of the producing districts a number of lines cross the Allegheny Front into the Great Valley,

and then concentrate on a point just south of the junction of
the two main branches of the Susquehanna, near the position
of Sunbury. Beyond this point the lines fan out to the northern
tide-water ports, New York, Philadelphia, and Baltimore (Fig. 69).
Some 80 miles to the south-west of this point another group of
lines concentrate near Altoona, on the Juniata branch of the
Susquehanna, and thence go eastward through the great water-
gap which the Susquehanna has here cut in the Blue Ridge at
Harrisburg, to Philadelphia and Baltimore. The principal rail-

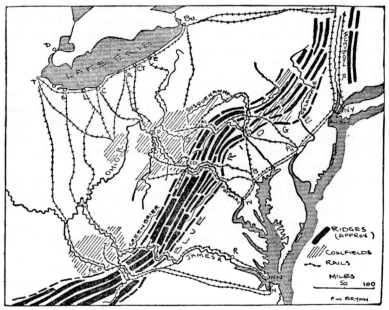

FIG. 69.—Sketch Map to show Railways related to ridges and rivers of the
Northern Appalachian Coalfield.

Main coal lines only are shown and are very incomplete in the coal areas.

road operating along this route is the Pennsylvanian, which is
the heaviest carrier of Pennsylvanian coal.

Some further 80 miles to the south-west we find a great network of lines from the Connellsville and Pittsburg country, all
concentrating, after crossing the Allegheny Front, on the position
of Cumberland at the great angle of the Potomac. From this
point two great main lines run eastward to tide-water, following
the north and south banks respectively of the Potomac, through
the deep water-gaps which this river has cut in the parallel ridges
of the Great Valley. By this route the Baltimore and Ohio

Railroad carries coal both from the southern part of the district within the state of Pennsylvania, and more particularly from that part of the district which extends southward into northern West Virginia.

South-west of the position of Cumberland on the Potomac, in a distance of 150 miles, no line crosses the sea of ridges, and it is not until a point is reached where the James River, by means of one of its head-streams, has cut back close to the Lower Greenbrier, a tributary of the New River, that a line is found crossing from the plateau to the Piedmont. This line, the Chesapeake and Ohio, uses for its road-bed the valleys of the Lower Greenbrier and the Upper James. It serves as an outlet to Newport News for the coal of the New River Field, and it stands second in importance as a carrier of West Virginian coal, being only surpassed in this respect by the Norfolk and Western.

Some 40 miles south of the route followed by the Chesapeake and Ohio Railroad, the New River, which has its source in rear of the Blue Ridge, and, as we have seen, cuts its way westward in a great trench through the ridges and into the plateau, forms a definite line of movement in conjunction with the more southerly of the head-streams of the James. Here the Norfolk and Western, and the Virginian Railroads make use of the great gorge of the New River for their road-beds, and carry through it the famous Pocahontas steam coals to tide-water at Norfolk on the south side of Hampton Roads opposite Newport News (Fig. 69). The distribution of coal from the West Virginian Fields forms a marked contrast to that from the Pittsburg Region, because of the scarcity of the industries found in the former area. Whereas nearly one-half of the coal raised in the northern field is used either at, or in close proximity to, the field, over 90 per cent. of the coal brought to the surface in West Virginia moves either northward and westward to the shores of the Great Lakes and their fringing states, or moves eastward through the ridges by way of the Greenbrier or the gorge of the New River to tide-water at Hampton Roads.

Two groups of ports handle the bulk of this tide-water shipment—a northern group, consisting of New York, Philadelphia, and Baltimore, related to the Pittsburg District ; and a southern group, made up of the Hampton Roads ports, which handle all the tide-water coal moving eastward from the New River and Kanawha Fields of West Virginia. According to the reports of the United States Geological Survey, the northern group handles some two-thirds of the total traffic coastwise, while the southern group handles the remainder. Of the northern group, New York is much the most important port, handling rather more than half the total for this group. To it Philadelphia is a rather bad second, with Baltimore a close third. The bulk of the coal traffic of the port of New York is handled at Jersey City and Amboy on the New Jersey shore. Traffic intended for New England is ferried across the harbour, and this traffic is very large. In addition to its large trade in bituminous coal, New York has a large cross-harbour trade in anthracite, based on its vast numbers of business offices and apartment houses, where central heating is so much in vogue. Philadelphia's trade is mostly anthracite for the local trade and bituminous for the coastwise trade, while Baltimore is mostly connected with the coastwise traffic in bituminous.

The two southern ports of Newport News and Norfolk form a highly specialized group connected with the West Virginian Field. Newport News forms the terminus of the Chesapeake and Ohio Railroad, and stands on the north bank of the estuary of the James River (Fig. 70). From the open roadstead leading to Chesapeake Bay, a 35-foot channel has been dredged to the coal-piers. Some 10 miles away to the south-east, on the opposite side of the roadstead, is situated Sewall Point, which is the shipping point for the Virginian Railroad, while some miles farther to the south lies Lambert Point, carrying the loading piers of the Norfolk and Western, which, as we have already seen, is the chief railroad handling West Virginian coal. Both of these latter sets of piers are served by a 40-foot channel from the roadstead. The terminal at Lambert Point, first constructed in 1885, marked the real beginning of the coastwise trade, though small shipments had been made during the preceding decade to New England. Granted a sufficient demand for export coal, the ability of these ports to ship it is only limited by the equipment available at present. These two shipping points on the south side of the estuary are usually referred to statistically as Norfolk, from the town of Norfolk, which lies just south of Lambert Point. The combined ports of Newport News and Norfolk are generally known as Hampton Roads, from the roadstead and small town of Hampton to the north of the estuary of the James.

We should in passing just notice that all the coal moving eastward through the ridges does not reach tide-water. Some of it is used in the Piedmont and Coastal Plain. Further, of the coal which does reach tide-water, some will remain for consumption in the tide-water ports. The bulk, however, is dumped at some tide-water port for shipment to some more distant point. Such coal totals some 30 million tons in round figures. Over one-third of this total is for coastwise shipment to other points in the United States—almost all of it being for the textile and metal-working centres of Southern New England, which, as we have already seen, obtains also large quantities of coal direct by rail from the northern part of the Pittsburg District. This water-borne coal moves along the coast chiefly from Hampton Roads ports, but also from the northern ports.

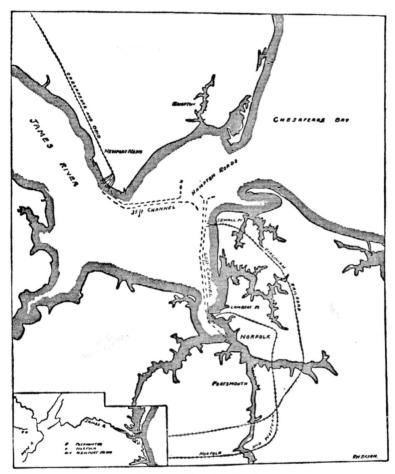

FIG. 70.—Hampton Roads.

In this total the export to Canada is not included, as it moves either by rail across the Canadian frontier, through Buffalo, or by water via the Great Lakes. The quantity so moving varies from year to year, but is approximately something of the order of 6 or 7 million tons, together with 2 or 3 million tons of

anthracite. Of the coal moving to Canada via the Lakes, the bulk
is despatched from Southern Lake Erie ports, though a small
quantity also moves via the south shore of Lake Ontario through
ports such as Oswego and the mouth of the Genesee River.
About three-fourths of the total export to Canada is handled
by Cleveland at the mouth of the Cuyahoga River, near the
centre of the south shore of Lake Erie, and by Buffalo at the
eastern end of the same lake. Canada, from the point of view
of population, consists of a long, narrow east and west strip lying
just north of the United States border. Canada has coalfields
of her own. What part, therefore, of this strip will be supplied
with United States coal? Roughly, a belt of country extending
from a point between Montreal and Ottawa, and a point west
of Winnipeg about one-third of the way across the prairies of
the Canadian west, is so supplied. On the eastern and western
margins of this belt, the United States export coal comes into
competition with coal moving inward from the Canadian Fields,
which, in the case of most of the chief producing districts, lie
at or near the Atlantic or Pacific seaboards. This territory
thus dominated by coal from Canada's great southern neighbour
has by no means fixed margins. These margins advance outward
towards the eastern and western seaboards or retreat inward
towards the Great Lakes in sympathy with the varying prices
of the coals of each of the countries concerned. Thus during
the year 1921, for example, the area supplied by the United States
was much restricted because of the adverse rate of exchange,
which made it profitable for coal from the Sydney (Nova Scotia)
Field to move up the St. Lawrence and Lake Ontario, and compete thus in a territory hitherto dominated by coal from the
Appalachian Field. In that year the rate of exchange added
about 15 per cent. to the cost of American goods in Canada.
There is, of course, never a hard-and-fast line between the areas
served by the two kinds of coal. Always on the margins there
is a belt where both coals sell freely in competition with each
other.

DISTRIBUTION OF BITUMINOUS COAL, 1936

(Tonnage Figures in Thousands of Net Tons)

1. *New England receipts :*

	Net Tons.	Percentage
Via rail across the Hudson	5,000	28·5
Via tide-water from northern ports . .	755	4·3
Via tide-water from southern ports . .	11,774	67·2
Total . .	17,529	100·0

2. *Tide-water loadings :*

	Net Tons.	Percentage.
(i) By ports :		
At New York and Philadelphia . .	9,203	29·7
At Baltimore, Hampton Roads, and Charleston	21,823	70·3
Total . .	31,026	100·0
(ii) By fields of origin :		
From Pennsylvania and northern West Virginia	11,344	36·6
From southern low-volatile . . .	15,021	48·4
From southern high-volatile . . .	4,661	15·0
Total . .	31,026	100·0
(iii) By destination :		
To New England	12,530	40·4
Foreign	837	2·7
Bunkers	1,648	5·3
Inside capes and other tonnage . .	16,011	51·6
Total .	31,026	100·0

3. *Lake Erie loadings (cargo and fuel) :*

	Net Tons.	Percentage.
Total Appalachian fields . . .	45,441	
By destinations (cargo only) :		
To American points	37,185	84·5
To Canadian points	6,835	15·5
Total . .	44,020	100·0

4. *West-bound rail to Mississippi Valley :*

	Net Tons.	Percentage.
Total from Appalachian fields . .	74,802	69·1
Total from Middle West fields . .	33,428	30·9
Total .	108,230	100·0

COAL IMPORTS, 1936

	Net Tons.
Anthracite (1935) :	
U.S.S.R.	395,413
United Kingdom	170,867
Canada	5,159
Total . .	571,439
Bituminous :	
Canada	194,596
United Kingdom	55,408
Total . .	250,004
Coke :	
Belgium	158,920
Germany	31,750
United Kingdom	54,429
Others	84,858
Total . .	329,957

COAL EXPORTS, 1936

	Net Tons.
Anthracite (1935) :	
Canada .	1,592,368
Others .	16,181
Total	1,608,549
Bituminous :	
Canada .	9,906,101
Cuba .	366,853
Others .	153,389
Total	10,426,343
Bunkers .	1,447,983
Coke :	
Canada .	650,036
Others .	20,276
Total	670,312

As a coal-exporting country the United States labours under two great natural disadvantages. The first of these is the distance of her coalfields from tide-water. Baltimore, at the head of Chesapeake Bay, is over 150 miles from Connellsville in the south-east of the Pittsburg District, while New York is nearly 300 miles from Johnstown, on the Conemaugh, in the north-east of the district, and Hampton Roads is nearly the same distance from the nearest point of the West Virginian Fields to tide-water. If we compare the position of the United States Coalfields with those of Great Britain, where the chief exporting fields are right on the coast, we have in part a measure of what this question of distance means from the standpoint of coal export. Those coalfields in Great Britain which are chiefly concerned with the foreign trade and the bunkering of ships, lie close to the water. Only a short, and therefore, relatively speaking, inexpensive rail-haul is needed to put the coal alongside ship. This fact, among others, is reflected in the cost of coal alongside ship, and therefore in the large export as compared with that of the United States. In this latter country, the expensive rail-haul made necessary both by distance and by heavier outlays for upkeep largely caused by the more difficult physical conditions, increases from two and a half to three times the cost of coal alongside ship.

In the second place, the United States is handicapped because she is, to a considerable extent, a self-contained country. She possesses within her own borders the bulk of the food and raw materials which her manufacturing districts require. She is also a heavy exporter of bulky raw materials, such as cotton and wheat. She does not therefore need, as does Great Britain, a bulky article such as coal to freight her ships on the outward run. Her outward-bound coal-ships must return empty or nearly empty, hence her freights for this reason alone would need to be heavier than those of Great Britain, whose outward laden colliers can fill up with raw materials or food on the homeward run, thus having paying cargoes both ways instead of one way only.

The fact that, for some decades now, the fuel electric power station has been obviating the individual works power unit, tends to simplify the final distribution of coal, and to concentrate it upon central stations built at suitable sites in the manufacturing areas to which we have alluded.

CHAPTER XXI

OIL

OIL exhibits many striking contrasts to coal. The more important of these contrasts group themselves under three heads—those relating to location of sources of supply, life of supplies in the ground, and mobility of the product.

Whatever the origin of mineral oil, and the matter is still in dispute, it is known to occur in the so-called oil shales in the form of minute drops, but such oil is not present, with some few noteworthy exceptions, on a sufficiently large scale to be commercially recoverable in competition with other more readily obtainable supplies. Future possibilities as to the availability of such sources of supply are considered later in relation to oil reserves and prices.

We have to ask ourselves, then, what are the conditions under which have been accumulated the great oil-pools, as underground reservoirs of oil are called, which are in process of exploitation to-day in many parts of the world. It will be readily realized that the necessary conditions will be such as will lead to the gathering together of these minute drops, which are present in some sedimentary rocks, into large reservoirs of oil from which the liquid can be transferred in quantity to the surface. For this gathering to take place, two essential conditions are needed. In the first place, there must exist above the shale or other rock in which the oil is present some porous rock, preferably a sandstone, or less often a limestone, capable of holding in the interstices between the grains of which it is composed, large quantities of oil. Secondly, there needs to be present overlying this porous rock an impermeable one such as a close-grained shale, to prevent the further upward migration of the drops of oil which have entered the sandstone. Such a rock is spoken of as a caprock, and is always the last rock pierced in tapping an oil-pool. Sedimentary rocks were originally deposited in horizontal layers, but in many cases these rocks have, subsequent to their deposition, been subjected to earth movements which have resulted in the production of folds or domes (Fig. 71). With oil in the original rocks there is usually present both gas and salt water. These three, migrating upwards along the slopes of the folds, generally arrange themselves in the order of their respective densities; hence we find that in the summits of the upfolds under the impermeable layer, or cap-rock, the gas is first met with in sinking a well. Beneath the gas and floating on the surface of the salt water lies the oil. It is because of the presence of the gas, which may vary very much in volume, that oil-wells are also commonly found to be distributed along the slopes of the anticlines, and in some cases may even be found near the bottom of an adjoining syncline.

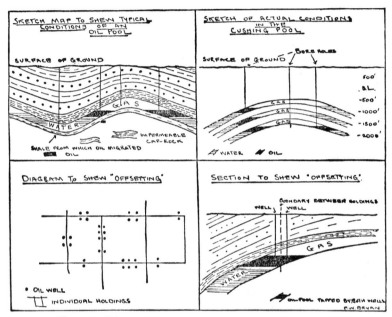

FIG. 71.—Diagrams to illustrate conditions in an Oil Pool.

Coal remains *in situ* in the place where it was originally formed. Oil, on the other hand, has migrated, and this migration only results in the formation of large supplies under certain rather special conditions of rock structure, which, while fairly abundant, are not always met with in combination with the other requisite factors.

It will also be readily seen that whereas coal seams may be, and usually are, continuous under great areas of country, and may be worked for many years, the amount of liquid available in an oil-pool will be of a much more limited character, since it is the result of the concentration in one small area of the minute drops of oil previously spread over a much larger region. Hence the life of an oil-pool, as each separate collection of oil underground is called, is usually very short, and is on the average in

Pennsylvania seven years.   In certain other areas, such as the
Salt Dome Region of the Texan coast, the average life is usually
much shorter even than this, two to three years being a common
life for such a well.   For this reason one finds that one of the
dominant facts about the oil industry regarded as a whole is
the constant search for new areas, whereas the bulk of the world's
coalfields have been worked for many years, and are likely to
continue to be worked in the future.   This fact may be regarded,
perhaps, as one of the minor reasons why manufacturing industrial centres are never likely to be based on the great oilfields
of the world, as they were on the coalfields.

The area which is indicated as an oilfield on most oilfield
maps only indicates in a very general way the area within which
oil-pools exist.   Hence in studying the map in Fig. 72, showing
the distribution of the oilfields of the United States, it should
be remembered that the areas indicated as oilfields are not in
any sense, as might be said in the case of coal, underlain
with oil, but only indicate regions within which oil-pools are
found.

Before we proceed to a discussion of the relative importance
from the point of view of production of these areas, it may be
well if we realize that oil, as found throughout the various producing areas, is by no means a uniform product.   It varies very
much from district to district, and even within the confines of
many districts.   This variation is chiefly related to the density
of the oil, and also to the base product left behind as a result of
distillation, both of which have an important bearing on the
percentage of the various products obtained through the process
of refining, and also on the relative degree of ease with which
the crude oil as it comes from the well can be handled by pipe-
line.   One method of grading oil, and consequently of price-
fixing, is to determine the gravity of the oil with the Baumé
hydrometer, and to grade it as to price and utility on the basis
of its grading on the Baumé scale.   The specific gravity of oil
ranges roughly from ·75 to ·99.   All oil, therefore, is lighter than
water, but some of the heavier oils approximate in weight to
that of water, and such oils—for example, the Californian crude
oils and also the Mexican crudes—are chiefly used as fuel oils
and run about 10 to 20 degrees on the Baumé scale.   On this
scale the density of water is 10 degrees.   These heavy oils usually
have an asphalt base, whereas the more valuable light oils, such
as those of Pennsylvania, have a paraffin base, and may run up
to as much as 40 degrees on the Baumé scale.   These lighter
oils are more valuable, chiefly because from them is obtained a
much higher percentage of gasoline or petrol, for which there is

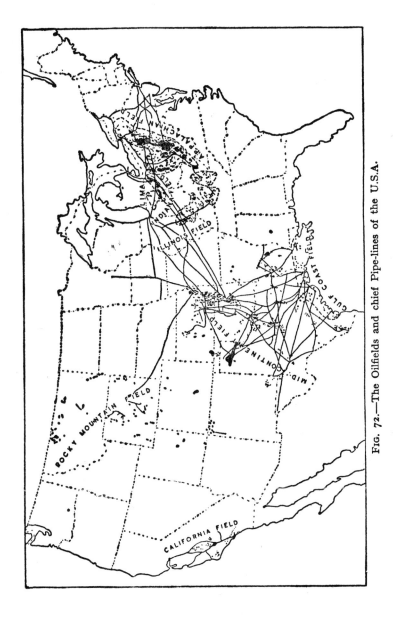

FIG. 72.—The Oilfields and chief Pipe-lines of the U.S.A.

such a heavy demand as the fuel used in internal combustion engines. The steady increase in this demand has greatly increased the value of these lighter oils, and has also led, as we shall see later, to great improvements in refinery practice in order to obtain the highest possible quantity of petrol from both heavy and light crude oils. The various other types of products obtained from crude oil are discussed later in connection with refinery practice, but it may be helpful at this point if we just glance briefly at some of the uses to which petroleum and its products can be applied. As these uses have been admirably summarized by the writer of the article on Petroleum in the " World Atlas of Commercial Geology," issued by the United States Geological Survey, the following quotation is submitted :

" Petroleum is used chiefly as a source of power, light, and lubricants, and these are the uses that every one knows. Crude petroleum is used in decreasing quantities from year to year ; more and more of it is prepared for higher utilization by breaking it up into refined products of greater value. The number of these refined products is almost countless, and their uses are as varied as the needs of mankind. The light-gravity ethereal products are employed as local anæsthetics. The gasolines are the universal fuels of internal combustion engines. The naphthas are extensively used as solvents and are blended with raw casing head gasoline to make commercial gasoline. The kerosenes, though used chiefly for illumination, are employed in increasing quantities as fuel for farm tractors. The lubricating oils and greases are indispensable to the operation of all kinds of machinery. The waxes derived from petroleum of paraffin base are utilized in many forms—as preservatives, as sources of illumination, and as constituents of surgical dressings made for the treatment of burns. Petroleum coke, an almost pure carbon, is used in metallurgy and in making battery carbons and arc-light pencils. Fuel oils obtained as by-products in refining petroleum are used for generating power by industrial plants, railroads, and ocean steamers.[1] Road oils are employed to lay the dust on streets and highways, and artificial asphalt, a product of petroleum, has in some places been used for paving."

The Tables following indicate the predominance of the United States as a world producer (62 per cent. of the total) and her production by areas.[2]

---

[1] In 1946, 75 per cent. of the world's merchant marine used fuel oil. In 1914, 3·4 per cent. ditto.

[2] Consumption of petroleum products is increasing so rapidly in the U.S.A. that it may in the near future exceed her production, hence her great interest in the Middle East.

TABLE OF WORLD OIL PRODUCTION, 1936 AND 1940

	Thousand Barrels of 42 gallons.	
United States	1,098,516	1,351,847
U.S.S.R.	189,941	215,659
Venezuela	155,229	186,780
Rumania	63,750	43,823
Iran	61,728	79,292
Netherland Indies . . .	49,360	60,830
Mexico	41,028	44,064
Iraq	29,406	25,725
Colombia	18,756	25,932
Peru	17,595	13,427
Argentina	15,455	20,266
Trinidad	13,237	20,169
All Others	36,270	66,367
	1,790,271	2,154,181

TABLE OF U.S.A. OIL PRODUCTION, 1936 [1]

Area.	States.	Million Barrels.	
Mid-Continent (including Gulf)	Oklahoma	206·8	
	Kansas	58·3	
	Arkansas	10·4	275·5
	Texas	427·3	
	Louisiana	79·8	507·1
California . .	California	204·7	204·7
Appalachian . .	Pennsylvania	17·1	
	New York	4·7	
	W. Virginia	3·8	
	Kentucky	5·6	31·2
Ohio . . .	Ohio	3·8	3·8
Rocky Mountain .	Wyoming	14·5	
	Montana	5·6	
	Colorado	1·7	
	New Mexico	27·2	49·0
Illinois and S.W. Indiana	Illinois	4·4	
	Indiana	·8	5·2
Michigan . . .	Michigan	11·8	11·8
	Total		1,088·3

A glance at the map (Fig. 72) and at this production table will show us that there are at least seven major areas or fields in the United States.

The fields lie more or less in echelon across the continent. They may be defined largely by the facts of geographical location,

[1] For later figures, see p. 333.

but are also differentiated to some extent by the considerations of structure and nature of the oil produced.

Oil is found in a long, narrow belt running from the south-west corner of the state of New York through Western Pennsylvania into West Virginia and the east of Kentucky. The output of oil comes from definite areas within this main belt. To-day the greatest pools from the point of view of production are those found in South-western Pennsylvania. In the early days of the exploitation of this area, after the incoming of the Drake well in 1859, the oil flowed to the surface, being driven upwards by the gas pressure underground, but to-day that pressure has been for the most part exhausted and with scarcely any exception the wells have to be pumped, while many of them are so near exhaustion that they can only be pumped once a week or so, the intervening period enabling the oil from the sands to gather in the well, and thus render it possible to recover with the pump what would otherwise be left in the sands. It has recently been shown that in the more porous parts of this field a system of controlled flooding results in a large increase in the amount of oil recovered and this method applied to other areas may produce important future results. The oil-pools in this area are usually long and narrow, and are situated on the flanks of anticlines running north-east south-west, that is to say, parallel to the general structure. Maximum production in this field was reached in 1900, in which year about 36 million barrels were raised.

The oil found in this field is the highest grade of oil found in the United States, and is known in the oil industry as " Pennsylvania " grade. It has a base of paraffin-wax, yields a very high percentage of gasoline, and grades 43 degrees on the Baumé scale. It is also easy to refine, as it is almost entirely free from sulphur or other impurities. Such impurities are frequently present in other oils—for example, in those of the Indiana Field, which, apart from this defect, would grade almost as high as the Appalachian.

It would appear that this field, which has played such a very large part in oil history in the United States, will have only a small share in future production. Were it not for the very high quality of the oil, many wells which are at present pumped at long intervals would not be paying propositions ; the daily average production for Pennsylvania was in 1918 only one-third of a gallon per well as compared with a daily average of 30 gallons in California. It should be remembered in this connection that any increase in price, other things being equal, would act as a stimulus to production in this old field.

In the rough triangle formed by the Ohio to the east, the Mississippi to the west, and the Great Lakes to the north, there lie two fields both of which have been important producers, but which have, as far as one can see at the moment, long passed their prime.   These are the Lima-Indiana Field and the Illinois Field.   The former lies south-westward from the extreme western corner of Lake Erie, and is partly in the state of Ohio and partly in the adjoining state of Indiana.   As its name indicates, the chief producing part of the field is in and around the town of Lima, in Ohio.   In some respects this field is very similar to the Appalachian ; in others, however, it offers a marked contrast to that field.   Taking the contrasts first, we notice that whereas the oil of the Appalachian comes from the well-known oil-sands of that region, in the Lima-Indiana Field we have one of those rather infrequent cases where the reservoir rock is composed of limestone.   Further, the harder layers of the limestone frequently act instead of shales as the cap-rock, while the oil gathers in porous lenses in the limestone itself. The oil also is very impure, although otherwise of excellent quality.   Sulphur is the chief impurity present.   This gives the oil such an offensive smell as to make it commercially useless until the sulphur is removed, hence the crude oil requires special treatment with the Frasch or some similar process to remove the sulphur before refining and breaking up into its useful constituents.   This process naturally adds to the cost of production, and, for this reason among others, this oil does not command so high a price as Pennsylvanian.   A further contrast between the two fields lies in the fact that the oil is often to be found in the terraces on the flanks of the great Cincinnati anticline, and not in definite fold structures, as is usually the case in the Appalachian Field.   This is an interesting example of the fact that even a slight change in the direction of dip of a stratum, such as that which gives rise to the formation known as a monoclinal flexure, is sufficient in many cases to arrest the upward migration of the oil to the surface, and in this fashion produce an oil-pool.   Like that of the Appalachian Field, the oil of this area has a paraffin base, and, besides yielding a high percentage of gasoline, is especially suitable for the production of a high grade of lamp-oil.

Lying south-westward from the above field, and between the south end of Lake Michigan and the Ohio River, is the Illinois Field, the only other field of any size to eastward of the Mississippi.   It consists of one long, narrow producing region running north and south in Illinois through Clark and Crawford counties, and thence southward into Lawrence county, the whole belt lying on the prairie country just to westward of the Wabash River. In addition to this main area there are a number of scattered areas in other parts of the state which lie chiefly to westward of the main area. As in the case of the Appalachian area, the oil here comes from massive Carboniferous sandstones, within which there are belts of shales which form the flooring in which were preserved the original organic remains, and which also serve as cap-rocks to-day for the oil-pools. The main pool lies along the flanks of the great La Salle anticline, which forms such a prominent feature of the structure of the state.

Whereas the oil in the two fields already discussed was of a fairly uniform character within the limits of each field, the oil in the Illinois Field is very far from being of such a uniform character, varying as it does from a light oil grading about 40 degrees Baumé to a comparatively heavy oil which is classed as 28 degrees Baumé.

These three fields with which we have dealt above may be classed generally as the Northern group, the bulk of the oil from which moves either eastward to tide-water on the Atlantic Coast, or northward to the big refineries in the vicinity of Chicago on Lake Michigan, or along the shores of Lake Erie. With these fields it is very improbable that much of the future lies. They have played their part in the development of the American oil industry, and now tend to give way more and more to younger fields beyond the Mississippi.

We now come to consider the Mid-Continental group, which consists of a belt of fields running north-south parallel to, but wholly westward of, the Mississippi. These fields lie within the boundaries of the four states of Kansas, Oklahoma, Texas, and Louisiana. Much of the oil raised here moves southward to the Gulf of Mexico.

The Mid-Continent Field may be divided for convenience of discussion into a number of minor fields, those of Oklahoma, Kansas, Southern Oklahoma, Northern Texas, the scattered fields of Central Texas, the Caddo, De Soto, and Red River Fields of North-western Louisiana, and, if we are using the term Mid-Continent in its very widest significance, we may include also the Gulf Field of Southern Texas and Southern Louisiana (Fig. 72). To west of the Mississippi and south of the Missouri lies a roughly quadrilateral area of which the western and southern boundaries are respectively the region of deficient rainfall and the shores of the Gulf of Mexico. Crossing this area from the western plains are a series of Mississippi tributaries, such as the Arkansas and Red Rivers. Centrally placed in the northern part of the quadrilateral is the Ozark massif, a mass of very ancient rock projecting through the surrounding layers of younger rocks forming the lower ground. Immediately to the west of these mountains, and distant about 300 miles from the Mississippi, lies the greatest of the Mid-Continental Fields, that of Oklahoma-Kansas, a long, narrow field running north and south through the eastern parts of Kansas and Oklahoma, terminating near the centre of the former state, and having a western edge which shows a tendency to expand. In this field there have been a great number of famous pools, such as the Cushing, the Glenn, the Bartlesville, the Jennings, the Shamrock, and many others, all of which are names to conjure with in the history of the oil development of this region. This area and that of Texas-Louisiana are by far the greatest oil-producing regions in the United States, and they alone produce about one-third of the world's production. Many predictions have been made that this field was on the point of exhaustion ; some of these were absurd ; some were based on the best available data ; all were wrong. One such prediction illustrates vividly the folly of them all.

In 1908 the " Day " estimate put the future production of Oklahoma at 283 million barrels. Since that date Oklahoma has produced about 2,000 million barrels, and is steadily increasing her annual output, which in 1936 was over 206 million barrels. In other words, she is now producing annually about the equivalent of the total estimated reserves in 1908.

That eventually this field will share the fate of all other fields there is no reason to doubt, but at present there are no signs of such exhaustion taking place, and there never has been a field which has produced on such a large scale.

As in the majority of the fields of the Northern group, the oil in this field comes from a Carboniferous sandstone which forms the reservoir rock. Pool formation depends upon a series of well-marked anticlinal structures closely connected, from the structural point of view, with the uplift of old crystalline rocks which form the Ozark region to eastward. These oil-bearing rocks were originally deposited horizontally, but the great earth movements which led to the production of the Ozark massif have wrinkled them into a series of north-south folds containing a number of distinctly marked domes in which the oil has been trapped. These domes vary much in size, the larger containing the oil, while the smaller usually only contain gas. It is thought that as the gas, oil, and water migrated upwards along the dip of the strata, the gas, moving first in order, filled the smaller domes, and in this fashion prevented the entrance of the oil, which was forced to move onwards to enter a larger dome capable of holding both gas and oil. This is probably one explanation of many of those wells in which gas alone is found, both in this and in many other fields.

The above conditions are clearly indicated in what was perhaps the most famous of all the pools of the Mid-Continent Field—that of Cushing. This famous pool, up to the year 1917, when it had just passed its maximum annual output, had produced some 170 million barrels in a period of five years from the sinking of the first well in 1912, or the equivalent of the annual output of what was then, next to the United States, the world's greatest oil-producer—Mexico. It lies along the slopes of a short anticline some 15 miles long, and from 2 to 4 miles broad, stretching southward from a point on the Cimarron River about 40 miles west of Tulsa, on the Arkansas. It thus marks the south-western edge of the Mid-Continent Field. The oil comes from three main sands, that nearest to the surface being reached by wells at a depth of 1,500 feet, while intervals of about 500 feet separate the others (Fig. 71). Within the limits of the main upfold, which is closely related to the formation of the Ozarks, there is a series of broad, pronounced domes, each of which constitutes a separate producing area within the main field.

We next come to consider the oilfields of Southern Oklahoma and Northern Texas. As the structural features of both these areas are very similar, they may be conveniently treated together. They lie the one to the north and the other to the south of the Red River, which here forms the boundary between the states of Oklahoma and Texas, and the producing areas in each case are found in connection with east-west upfolds which are in sympathy with the lie of the Red River in this district. The upfold to the north is known as the Wichita-Arbuckle anticline, while its fellow to the south is called the Red River uplift. The chief producing area in the Oklahoma part of the district lies to the south of the crest of the upfold, while in the Texas district the bulk of the output comes from the Burkburnett district lying not far from Wichita Falls, in the angle between the Wichita River and the Red River itself. A minor producing region lies just eastward of the main area, in the neighbourhood of Petrolia.

In the pan-handle district of north-west Texas much development has taken place and three pipe-lines have been constructed to oil markets. The heavy production from this pool, together with that from the Seminole pool in Oklahoma and the new districts of California and eastern Texas have been largely responsible for the recent world over-production and consequent drop in oil prices.

The cost of drilling in this field tends to be low, as the rock is more easily and more rapidly penetrated, and the oil is reached at a depth of about 1,000 feet. This also leads to a greater amount of speculative drilling, or " wild-catting," as it is called in the oil industry, because the capital required for each venture is less. For this reason the prospects of discovering oil in these regions of younger rocks are, other things being equal, rather better here than elsewhere.

It was with a well drilled at Corsicana in 1895, for water supply for the town, near a tributary of the Trinity River, that the oil industry of Texas started. Oil was struck in the well, and efforts were at first made to keep it out by casing the well, but the oil leaked to the surface. Other wells were rapidly drilled, and the Texas oil industry, afterwards to assume such gigantic proportions, was well on its way. The Corsicana pool really consists of two pools—that of Corsicana, lying to the west and producing an excellent light oil grading high on the Baumé scale ; and that of Powell, which lies about 8 miles to the east of the Corsicana, and produces a heavy oil of the fuel type. This area reached its maximum production in 1906, when it produced 1,000,000 barrels. At first the wells sunk in this field flowed, but because of the fineness of the sand in which the oil is held, and because of the absence, or rapid exhaustion of the gas pres- sure, they soon required pumping. This pumping is done by gas engines, using the natural gas of the field, and for this reason the low cost of the multiple system of pumping employed makes it possible to pump wells when they are yielding very much less than a barrel per day. While the Corsicana Field to-day is a small producer, about 30 miles to the south, on the water- parting between the Trinity and the Brazos Rivers, lies the town of Mexia, in the vicinity of which in the past great quantities of natural gas have been produced, and where to-day a large oilfield has developed. According to the Report of the Mineral Resources of the United States for the year 1917, issued by the Geological Survey, there were no prospects of oil being produced in this field on a commercial scale. In the last three months of 1921 and the first three months of 1922 over 10 million barrels of oil wer? produced, and the number of derricks in the field had increased from about 50 to over 600, with more going up. The development of this field offers an interesting example of the difficulty of foretelling what is going to happen in oil.

Another field in this region where rapid development has taken place is the Caddo-De Soto Field, on the Red River, in North- west Louisiana and North-east Texas. From here the oil moves by pipe-line to the Sabine Lake ports on the Texas border (Fig. 73).

Lying about 100 miles to the north-east of this region is the oil district of Arkansas, which in 1936 produced some 10 million barrels, in spite of the fact that an eminent geologist, who was rash enough to make predictions as to the future production of this region, offered to drink all the oil Arkansas would produce.

Development in the Gulf Field is a useful example also of how difficult it is to foresee future developments in oil. The Central Texas and Northern Louisiana Fields which we have been considering above, lie in a great curve rather more than 200 miles inland from, and parallel to, the Gulf coast. Also parallel to this line, but only some 50 miles away from the coast, there lies another belt of oil-pools which is known as the Gulf Field (Fig. 73). This field lies immediately in rear of the region of swamp and marsh and lagoon which here fringes the waters of the Gulf. It is marked off structurally from all the other oil-fields which we have considered, inasmuch as the oil is not found in connection with anticlines, but in connection with very definitely marked rounded salt domes due to local upthrusts. These domes dip away sharply from a central point. They therefore usually cover only a few hundred acres, and have a very definitely limited supply of oil under great gas pressure. Hence these domes produce gushers which are rapidly exhausted. Although they are found over an area extending from Matagorda in Texas to the Mississippi, a distance of some 400 miles, the chief producing pools at the time of writing lie in a comparatively small portion of this great area between Houston and the Sabine River (Fig. 73). Some of the more important of these producing pools have been the Spindletop, the Humble, the Goose Creek, and the Saratoga. Let us consider the production record of one of these pools. In 1916 the Goose Creek produced about 300,000 barrels. In the following year this production had become no less than 7,300,000 barrels, representing an increase of nearly 2,000 per cent. The oil in these domes is nearly always found in limestone with a cap-rock of clay. The first oil to be discovered in this field was the Spindletop pool near Beaumont in 1901, and it was followed by Sourlake and Jennings, all of which had in common with the more recently discovered pools in this area, a relatively short life of about three years. The discovery late in 1925 of a deeper productive sand has led to the reopening of the Spindletop, to a very heavy yield from it, and to extensive drilling in all the older coastal salt domes. The oils of this area form a marked contrast to those of the Mid-Continent region, as they are all very heavy oils forming good fuel oils, but not, of course, selling for anything like the price realized for the Mid-Continental oils. This drawback is in part

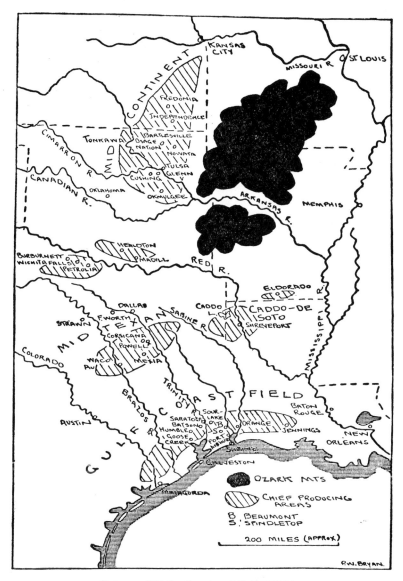

FIG. 73—Mid-Continent and Gulf Oilfields.

compensated for by the fact that all the fields are in close proximity to the coast, so that the oil can be readily and comparatively cheaply exported for steamer use, or can be refined at the numerous refineries which, as we shall see later, are situated on the Gulf coast. The main facts, then, which we should bear in mind in connection with the Gulf Field, are the position of the pools with reference to the coast, the heavy fuel oil in contrast with the lighter oils to the north, and the structural difference which in this field accentuates the normally short life of every pool.

There are known oil deposits off the shores of Texas, Louisiana, and California as yet undeveloped. Title to these has been recently granted by Congress (1953) to the first two states up to $10\frac{1}{2}$ miles from shore and to California up to 3 miles.

CHAPTER XXII

OIL—*continued*

LYING northward of the Gulf are the fields we have just been examining. Out of a total world production of over 1,790 million barrels in the year 1936, over 40 per cent. came from the Mid-Continent, the Gulf, and the Mexican fields. The output from the first two of these fields comes in part to the shores of the Gulf either at Baton Rouge, near New Orleans, or at some one or other of the Sabine Lake ports on the Texas-Louisiana border, or at Galveston, the great cotton port (Fig. 73). In, or in close proximity to, all these ports are numbers of refineries, where the crude oil is broken up by distillation into the many useful commodities, such as gasoline, kerosene, etc., which enter into commerce. From these ports the oil is exported in the crude state both for use either as fuel oil or for distillation elsewhere, and also in the form of refined products. The bulk of the oil moving from these ports is in the crude state, partly because of the greater ease with which the crude can be handled in bulk, and partly because of the greater facility with which the oil can be refined, and the refined products distributed from large centres of population, such as New York, Baltimore, Philadelphia, Providence, etc. It is usually found more convenient to handle the refined products in smaller quantities by rail, whereas the crude is most economically handled in bulk by pipe-line or in tank steamers. Nevertheless there has recently been a development of pipe-lines for petrol—the chief of the refined products.

Refineries are of three main types. The first of these is what is known as the " topping " plant. It removes by simple distillation the lighter products, mainly gasoline and kerosene, but the removal is incomplete in the case of these plants. They are mostly to be found to the west of the Mississippi, either on the oilfields at such centres as Tulsa in Oklahoma, where there are a number of large refineries, and at Fort Worth in Texas, or on or near the Gulf coast, as at Port Arthur, Beaumont, and Houston in Texas, and at Baton Rouge and New Orleans at the head of the Mississippi Delta. Many other centres both on the

coast and on the various fields have refineries of various types
and capacities. The main refining centres of the Gulf ports
may be grouped under three heads, namely, those of the
Mississippi, those of the Sabine Lake ports, and those of the
Mexican coast, which will be referred to separately.

The second type of refinery is that which is usually known
as the " straight run " plant, which by a process of simple distillation removes a full range of products from gasoline through
kerosene and lubricating oils to heavy fuel oils. It may be
useful at this point to examine for a few moments the following
table, which gives the principal refined products obtained from
a very similar oil to the heavy Gulf and Mexican oils :

Refined Products.	Degrees Baumé.
Gasoline	72–48
Kerosene	48–35
Fuel Oils including Lubricating Oils	35–10
Asphalt	Semi-solid
Coke	Solid

In this process of distillation there is no way of increasing
the yield of any product from any given oil. For this reason the
heavier oils, which yield a very low percentage of gasoline, are
not nearly so valuable as the lighter oils. It is this fact that has
led to the development of the third type of refinery, that which
employs what has been called the " cracking " process. This
process does not deal with the crude petroleum, but takes some
of the heavier products, such as fuel oil, subjects it to great heat
and great pressure, which break up the molecules of the oil and
force a re-arrangement. In this fashion the production of gasoline
from the heavy fuel oils can be very greatly increased. The
importance of this process to the industry to-day can hardly
be exaggerated, more especially in view of the fact already
referred to above, that the Gulf Fields and also the Mexican,
not to mention those of California, produce almost entirely the
heavier types of oil, which, until the development of the " cracking " process, yielded a very low percentage of the more highly
prized products. The majority of the plants of the first type
referred to above, are to be found on the shores of the Gulf or on
the fields themselves, whereas those of the second and third
types are chiefly to be found on or near the Atlantic Seaboard.
Of these latter the more important ones are those of Bayonne
and Jersey City across the Hudson opposite New York, those
of Philadelphia on the Delaware, and those of Baltimore at
the head of Chesapeake Bay. In addition to these are the
more recently developed refineries in New England, of which
perhaps the more important are those of East Providence and

Fall River on the shores of Narragansett Bay, in Rhode Island and Massachusetts respectively. The main factors at work in locating this type of refinery appear to be adequate rail and water facilities for the assembling of the crude oil, and for the distributing of the finished products in relation to the main producing centres on the one hand, and the chief areas of consumption on the other. The main governing factor in the location of a refinery would thus appear to be the relation between the respective costs of transporting crude and refined products.

From the various oilfields, oil moves to the Atlantic and Gulf ports by means of pipe-lines. These are small on the fields and serve to convey the oil from the wells to field storage tanks. From these the oil is conveyed to the coast by main pipe-lines of about 8 inches diameter. These are made of iron plate and are usually below the ground. Along these pipe-lines, at intervals of 15 to 40 miles or so, are situated pumping stations, which keep the oil moving on its journey seaward. Some crude oils are much more sluggish than others. Where this is so the pumping stations need to be much closer together, and it may even be necessary to provide apparatus at each station to heat the oil, and thus increase its fluidity. The movement of oil from the northern fields mostly takes place to the Atlantic centres mentioned above. To that movement may be added the oil coming from Kansas. Oil from Oklahoma may move either to the great refining and shipping point of Baton Rouge on the Mississippi, or it may move southward to the Sabine Lake group of ports—Beaumont, Port Arthur, and Sabine. Texas and Louisiana oil may move either to Sabine Lake or to Galveston, the bulk probably going to the former, because of its more central position in relation to these fields. From the Gulf ports the crude or semi-refined products move by tank steamer to the Atlantic coast ports,[1] or abroad to such centres as the great refinery at Skewen, near Swansea, in South Wales, or the refineries on the shores of Southampton Water.

Returning, then, from our digression on the subject of refining to the position on the shores of the Gulf of Mexico and the Caribbean Sea, we find that to the north of this great area of island-studded water between North and South America there are the flourishing Mid-Continent and Gulf Fields, to the west the Mexican Fields, to the south the fields of Venezuela and Columbia, with at the extreme south-east corner the partly developed but very promising fields of the island of Trinidad.

Let us now turn to a consideration of the Mexican Fields, which we shall examine in some detail, partly because of their importance from the standpoint of production, and partly

---

[1] During the last war, to avoid losses due to sinking of tankers, two pipe lines were constructed from Texas to Bayonne, New Jersey.

11

because of the many interesting contrasts which conditions here exhibit to those which we have already studied in the United States.

Mexico is a fascinating example of the entirely unpredictable things which happen in connection with the development of the world's oilfields. In the year 1910 Mexico was producing rather less than 4 million barrels. By 1921 she was producing close on 200 million barrels, or over one-fourth of the total world production, which in that period had very greatly increased. She now stands sixth to the United States as an oil-producer, but whereas the production of the U.S.A. increases, that of Mexico has very much declined. The great bulk of this oil comes from that long, narrow field which lies back of and north-west of Tuxpan.

Mexico, as has been explained in another part of this book, consists essentially of a great plateau with a mountain rim which slopes steeply in every direction to a narrow coastal plain. Along the west coast of the Gulf of Mexico this plain runs north and south, and situated roughly midway in its length between the Rio Grande del Norte and the Isthmus of Tehuantepec on the south, are the chief producing fields of Mexico. These are two in number (Fig. 74). The first lies inland from Tampico near the joint estuaries of the Panuco and Tamesi Rivers. From the eastern slope of the plateau of Mexico, the Tamesi flows south-eastward across the coastal plain to the sea ; while also coming from the eastward-facing escarpment of the plateau, the Panuco, rising about 100 miles to the south, flows north-eastward to the sea across the plain. Some 20 miles inland in the triangular area between the two rivers is the most northerly of the Mexican oilfields. The two chief developed areas of this field lie respectively in the vicinity of Ebano, about 40 miles to westward of Tampico and close to Panuco on the river of that name lying about 30 miles south-west of Tampico. Both in this region and in that farther to the south, early development was very much hampered, as in other tropical and sub-tropical oilfields, by the dense jungle which here covers the greater part of the coastal plain.

Tampico is the port for all this northern region, and to it the oil moves partly by river down the Panuco, partly by pipe-line, and partly by rail. Only a small proportion of the oil raised in this area is handled by pipe-line, as being a heavy fuel oil it tends to clog up the pipes unless special methods are adopted to keep it very liquid, all of which methods increase the cost of production. From Tampico the oil moves, either in the form of crude or partly refined, chiefly to the United States. The great bulk of the Mexican oil is a low-grade heavy fuel oil, and is largely sold on the American seaboard for fuel purposes.

The gasoline content of this oil is low, being commonly from

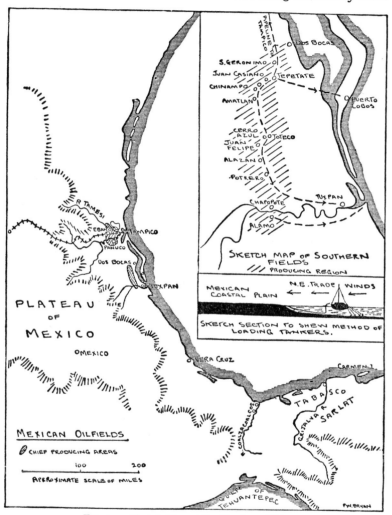

FIG. 74.—Sketch Map of the Mexican Oilfields.
Insets : Southern Fields and method of loading Tankers.

5 to 15 per cent., whereas the gasoline content of most of the American oils usually ranges from 20 to 40 per cent. The kerosene yielded is also much less than that yielded by the American oils. For this reason the process of " cracking "

petroleum is likely to prove of special utility in connection with these oils.

Mexican oil comes from a massive limestone of Cretaceous Age. This limestone, the Tamasapo limestone, lies in folds about 2,000 feet below the surface sympathetic to the direction of the coast-line. These folds have been much cut up by dykes, and are particularly well marked in the case of the Southern Fields, as they have been called, although the true southern fields are those largely undeveloped fields situated on the Isthmus of Tehuantepec, and now being chiefly developed by the Mexican Eagle Company. The former came to be called the Southern Fields because of their position with reference to the Tampico Fields, which were the first to be developed. These Southern Fields consist essentially of a long, narrow strip about 40 miles in length by 1 mile in breadth. They start about 60 miles south of Tampico and are continuous as far south as Tuxpan on the coast. The oil comes from what has been called the " knife-edge " fold, which is in essence of the same character and structure as the area to the north. Oil seeps come to the surface where the underlying folds are fractured by the basaltic dykes, and these seeps serve as guides for the drilling of the wells. The area consists of a very great number of distinct pools, each of which usually produces about 100 million barrels of oil before exhaustion takes place through the inroads of salt water. All the wells in this area produce oil under great hydrostatic pressure, hence they are what the oil world refers to as " gushers," and do not require pumping unless in the very last stages of the lives of some of the wells.

It was in this region that the oil industry of Mexico may be said to have started on a large scale with the bringing in, in 1907, of the great Dos Bocas well at the northern edge of the field. It caught fire and burned for three months, after which salt water was found flowing from the well, showing that that particular pocket of oil had been exhausted. It was not followed on a large scale until 1910, when the Juan Casiano well was brought in, which gave a daily production for some time of over 100,000 barrels and was not exhausted till 1920. It was in 1910 that the Southern Fields began their heavy production. Since that date many famous wells have been brought in successfully, among which some of the more noteworthy are the great Cerro Azul " gusher " which had an initial daily capacity of about 300,000 barrels, the Amatlan pool, the Potrero del Llano, the Toteco, the Alazan, and the Alamo, which lies to the south of the Tuxpan River (Fig. 74), and forms the extreme south point so far developed of the Southern Fields.

Although Porto Lobos, on a sandspit lying off the coast near the central part of the area, has been opened up as an outlet for this field, the chief outlet is Tuxpan. This port lies some 5 miles up the Tuxpan River on the north bank, and is therefore very conveniently situated for pipe-lines coming from the main part of the field lying to the north-west. The mouth of this river has a bar which is closely related to the prevailing north-east Trade winds of this coast. Tankers cannot negotiate this bar. Hence they have to lie out in the open roadstead off the coast, and load from floating pipe-lines which are moored in the bay. In this position they require no less than four anchors to prevent them going ashore in face of the north-east Trade wind from the Gulf (Fig. 74). Needless to say, this condition of affairs considerably hampers loading operations and adds to the cost of handling the oil, but the only alternative—a very expensive one—is pumping all the way to Tampico. Conditions at Porto Lobos are similar.

Many pools in this area have been exhausted much sooner than was desirable both from the standpoint of the money return obtainable from the oil, and also from that of the continued producing power of the particular well concerned, through the unrestricted operation of competition among the owners of parts of the same pool, for rather than let the other fellow get an excessive amount of oil from the pool, they exploited their section of it to its full capacity, thus bringing about a condition of over-production which lowered the price, and also led to the trapping off of quantities of oil through the uprising of salt water. This would not have occurred if the pool had been operated by one company with a view to the most economical results in the long run (Fig. 71). As will be seen from the diagram, the ground over an oil-pool may be in the hands of a number of different holders. A single well driven by one of these holders would in time take the bulk of the oil from the pool and thus leave nothing for the other holders interested in the pool. For this reason, as soon as one holder sinks a well, the owner of the adjoining area will also sink a well to avoid losing his share of the spoil. As many as four or five wells may thus be drilled into the one pool where one would have been sufficient and the capital outlay would have been much less. This practice of " offsetting," as it is called, is very uneconomical, and should be avoided where possible by arrangement between the owners of adjoining sections. It is a useful example, perhaps, of the advantages of large-scale production or even of monopoly conditions, as compared with unrestricted competition.

A marked contrast between the oil industry of Mexico and

that of the United States is furnished by a comparison of the output per well in each country. In Mexico, in the year 1920, there were about 300 producing wells, the average production of each well being about 1,800 barrels ; in the United States there were no less than 260,000 wells, and the average output per well was of the order of 5 barrels. Here we see not merely the contrast between an area, many of the wells in which are reaching the end of their lives, and one where, as is the case in Mexico, the wells were on the whole much younger, but the much more marked contrast which exists between the size of the pools in the two areas. This great size in the case of Mexico rests on the fact that the limestone formation in which the Mexican oil is contained must, to explain the rapid and enormous production of each pool, have great caverns and other open spaces in which the oil has accumulated under very great hydrostatic pressure, conditions which are related partly to the nature of the limestone itself, and probably also to the great earth movements giving rise to the Caribbean Islands and the adjoining marine abysses.

The great Southern Fields from which the bulk of the Mexican output of recent years has been drawn, have passed their maximum production. Salt water has invaded most of the great pools. The future of Mexican production would appear to lie in the third of her producing areas, that of the Isthmus of Tehuantepec. Although we have referred to it as a producing area, its production is infinitesimal as compared with the other areas. Its development, which began in 1902, was largely hampered by the swampy nature of the ground in the isthmus, and also by the dense covering of vegetation. With the discovery of the "gushers" of the Tampico district, operations in the isthmus were largely neglected, and with the decline of that district, interest is again being taken in this region. This isthmian area consists of two quite distinct fields, the one of which lies on the Coatzacoalcos River behind the port of Puerto Mexico, while the other, that of Sarlat, lies inland from the port of Frontera in the province of Tabasco on the Grijalva River. These fields offer a strong contrast to those already considered, inasmuch as they produce a light oil with a paraffin base, and therefore one which is much more valuable than the heavier northern oils.

Tampico, Tuxpan, Minatitlan on the Coatzacoalcos River, and Progresso in Yucatan, all have oil refineries. One of the chief drawbacks to Mexican oil from the view-point of the refiner, is the presence of a large quantity of sulphur which is difficult to remove.

In other parts of Mexico a certain amount of exploratory

work has been carried on without much result as far as development is concerned. It has been ascertained that there is oil in the Peninsula of Lower California and also in the Carmen Islands. It is not within the province of this book to consider the oilfields of the other areas surrounding the Gulf and the Caribbean, hence we will pass on to a consideration of the only other area of large production in North America, namely, the fields of Southern California.

There are five principal oil-producing areas in California, each of which consists of a number of distinct districts, but for simplicity we need only consider these very briefly. The five main areas are the San Joaquin Valley Fields, the remainder coming mostly from the Orange County, Los Angeles, Ventura, and Santa Maria Fields. The San Joaquin Valley Fields are confined to the southern end of the valley and mainly to the south-west corner. This valley is here shut off from the coastal country by a series of ranges, of which the Temblor and the San Emigdio are the best known in the vicinity of the oilfields. These ranges lie south-west of Lake Buena Vista, and between them and the lake lie the Midway and Sunset Valleys, in which are located the chief producing wells of this field. From this point the producing area extends north-westward along the eastern foot of the ranges in the plain of the San Joaquin Valley (Fig. 75), under the names of the McKittrick, Lost Hills, and Coalinga Fields, and finally peters out about 150 miles from the Buena Vista Lake. On the north-east side of the valley there is only one field of any size, namely, that of the Kern River, a river which comes down from the Sierra Nevada but never reaches the sea. This field is located where the Kern River leaves the foothills of the Sierra, and is some 50 miles away from the Midway Field.

Unlike any of the other oilfields of the United States, it has been definitely ascertained that the oil of this San Joaquin Valley was produced by the distillation of minute animal remains (foraminifera or diatoms), which were preserved in the Maricopa shale, a fine-grained shale deposited in Eocene times, and which is itself very largely made up of the remains of these minute sea animals, although a certain amount of vegetable matter is also present. The gathering-ground or reservoir for the oil is occasionally the sandy beds which are found interbedded in the shale, but more usually the oil has migrated into the younger sandstone beds which overlie the shales, and has been caught in the anticlinal formations which are here found running sympathetically to the lie of the valley and bordering ranges (Fig. 71). The cap-rock is usually a close-grained clay.

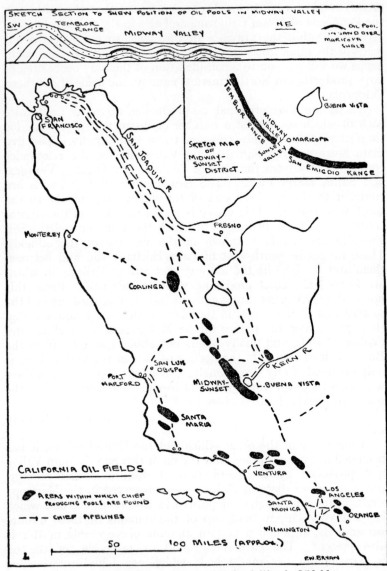

FIG 75—Sketch Map and section of the California Oilfields.
Inset Midway-Sunset District.

Whereas in the year 1919 the Appalachian and Mid-Continent oils yielded about 28 per cent. of gasoline, those of California only yielded about 13 per cent. It will be seen, then, that the bulk of the oil from the Californian Fields is comparable in many respects to that of Mexico. It is for the most part a heavy fuel oil grading less than 20 degrees Baumé, and apart from use in the refineries employing the " cracking " process, it is chiefly employed for direct burning. In this connection it has to be remembered that apart from oil California produces no fuel if we except timber. Coal it has none, and has to import what coal it needs from Washington and Vancouver Island. Oil is used on its steamers, in its factories, and in its homes. The railways to Portland, El Paso, and into the Great Basin are operated with Californian fuel oil. Even the Alaskan fishing fleet depends largely on this oil. Oil is therefore one of the fundamental facts in the prosperity of California, and for that reason this grade of oil is of more value here than it would be elsewhere in the United States, although such excess in value is strictly limited by the cost of transport from the Mexican and Eastern Fields.

From the San Joaquin Valley Fields the oil moves by pipeline northward along the valley to the shores of San Paulo Bay opposite San Francisco (Fig. 75), where many of the larger refineries are situated. It also moves westward and southward to the Pacific side at such centres as Los Angeles and Monterey. Because of the viscosity of the oil the pumping stations in California are much closer together than in the Eastern Fields. Thus the average distance apart of the pumping stations in the Mid-Continent Field is about 40 miles, while in the Kern River Field, which produces the heaviest grade of Californian oil, it is only 15 miles. This fact means that the Californian Fields require a heavier capital expenditure for a less return, in addition to which it should be remembered that the oil fetches less than the higher grade eastern oils.

Of the remaining Californian Fields, that of Los Angeles is by far the most important from the standpoint of production, and, as far as we can see at the moment, from the point of view of future development also. This region has a number of subdivisions. Of these, three have been outstanding : the Signal Hill District overlooking Long Beach, a seaside resort near Los Angeles ; the Huntingdon Beach Field, which is close to the seaside resort of that name ; and the Santa Fé Springs Field, not far from the other two. During the years 1922 and 1923 the development of these three fields proceeded with great rapidity. The oil is mostly of a high grade, ranging from 25 to 31 degrees Baumé, it is under heavy gas pressure, and is found in a number of distinct sands one below the other.

There has been much wasted effort in these new fields through " offsetting," as the land is held in small parcels by individuals and small companies, and all the evils described in the case of the Mexican fields from this cause have been evident here.

Of the other Californian fields it is not necessary to say much. They all lie outside the coastal ranges on the Pacific slope in fairly close proximity to the sea, and are clearly indicated on the accompanying map (Fig. 75). Their outputs are small compared with that of the area with which we have been dealing. As a result of their nearness to the coast, they each have a separate little port to which the oil moves by pipe-line, and from which it is shipped either as crude or partly refined. Thus Port Harford, Ventura, Wilmington, and San Pedro are ports of this description, and the bulk of the outer traffic is oil.

Although oil was being recovered in California in the seventies, she did not begin to be a large producer until the year 1900, in which year her output of over 4 million barrels nearly doubled her production of the preceding year. By 1902 her output was nearly 14 millions, and by 1910 it had reached the total of 50 millions, while her present production is in the neighbourhood of 300 millions.

To complete our survey of the North American oilfields it is necessary to draw attention to the Rocky Mountain Field, to the fields of Canada, and to those of Alaska. The Rocky Mountain Field is chiefly found in the states of Wyoming, Colorado, and Montana, but by far the most important part of the field is in the first named. In Wyoming development has chiefly taken place in the Salt River Field, which is located in Natrona county on the head-waters of the Powder River, which is itself a tributary of the Yellowstone. The oil is found in an anticline in a coarse sandstone formation which offers very favourable conditions for operating, as a fine sandstone tends to clog up the well, a difficulty often met with in the Trinidad Fields. In quality the oil resembles that from the Mid-Continent Field, being a high-grade light oil with a paraffin base. This field may be taken as typical of the other Wyoming Fields, such as that of Lander. Much of the oil from the state is refined at Casper, on the Platte River, where the chief refineries are situated, and also at Greybull and Laramie, but a pipe-line 700 miles long has recently been constructed from this field eastward to the Mississippi. In the neighbouring state of Colorado the two chief centres are at Boulder in the Rocky Mountain foothills north-west of Denver, and at Florence in the Arkansas Valley south-west of Colorado Springs, while in Montana one of the chief centres is Cat Creek.

In Canada, the annual output of oil is about 8 million barrels,[1] and almost all of it comes from the recently developed Turner Valley field of Western Alberta. There is still a small output of about a quarter of a million barrels from the much older district of Oil Springs and Petrolia in Lambton County (Ontario Peninsula).

As we have already seen in the case of the Oklahoma Fields, the Mexia Field of Texas, and the Mexican Fields, the attempt to estimate the future of a field is largely futile. Also the attempt to limit oil production to certain formations or certain known conditions falls very much within the same category. In the early days of oil development it was regarded as useless to look for oil except in areas where the Trenton rock was found, as it was then thought to be the only possible source of oil. At a very much later date in oil history, it was held by many authorities that oil would never be developed on a commercial scale in, of all places, California, because the rocks were too young and too much faulted in what have since become the great San Joaquin Valley Fields. Many other examples could be given : the " Mississippi lime " was said to be too thick ; the " red beds " of Oklahoma were said not to be stratified. Much oil has since been found in both formations. Hence not only is it impossible to predict the future of known fields, but it is still more impossible to limit future developments to certain areas, as oil may be found in the future under conditions that are not even suspected at the moment.[2] Should the demand in the future increase at a greater rate than the supply, this will result in a rise in price which will stimulate prospecting. It will also encourage better methods of refining, which will help to relieve the situation by producing greater quantities of the more valuable lighter oils. At present it is estimated that only from 10 to 30 per cent. of the petroleum in the ground ever reaches the pipe-line. Much of this oil could be recovered with better methods. Many wells which are not worked at present, and many wells which have never been sunk in certain fields, could be made producers. Stimulus would be given to the invention of internal combustion engines which use coarser types of oil, and thus tend to eliminate the present very wasteful use of oil for direct burning. The increase in the use of the Diesel engine has had this effect, because of its more economical consumption of oil. Gasoline is being increasingly produced in the United States from the gas which escapes from the casing-head of a well. It is thus known as " casing-head " gasoline, and, together with

[1] 1944. In 1950, 29 million barrels. See also p. 536 and tables p. 564.
[2] It is unlikely that oil will be found in igneous rocks, though oil may exist in sedimentary rocks underlying basalts.

gasoline produced by the "cracking" process, forms about one-fifth of the total gasoline output of the United States. The new Californian producing districts are said to be very rich in this "casing-head" gasoline. Hence it is quite clear that a rise in price will directly stimulate production in many ways. But quite apart from this expansion, a rise in price will have the immediate result of bringing in a competitor on a large scale —a competitor which may come in, in the near future, without any rise in price at all, if invention takes a definite step forward in the discovery of more effective ways of utilizing the practically limitless shale-oil resources both of North America and of many other parts of the world. Many of the large oil companies have secured holdings in the shale-oil districts and are experimenting with the problems of distillation.

To-day this industry is awaiting the invention of an improved retort in order to compete with oil from wells, but a slight increase in price, and a reasonable prospect of such increase being maintained, would make it a successful competitor. Much capital would be required, and much preliminary development work, but there is no doubt that these would be forthcoming, granted the conditions necessary for success. In this connection it should be remembered that the distillation of shale results in many valuable by-products, such as ammonia and paraffin-wax, which have enabled the Scottish companies to prosper.

While there are many parts of North America where oil-shales are found, there are three areas of major importance. These are the region comprising the Rocky Mountain states of Colorado, Wyoming, and Utah, the district of Pictou in Nova Scotia, and the Athabaska region of Alberta. According to the estimates of the United States Geological Survey, the Rocky Mountain shales are richer in both recoverable oil and ammonia by-products than the Scottish shales, which are, however, much more favourably situated. These American shales are also much thicker and more easily worked. The oil yields grades about 20 to 33 degrees Baumé, that is, it is of a fairly light type yielding a high percentage of gasoline. One ton of the Utah shale yields about one barrel of crude, and at this rate the shales along the southern margin of the Uinta Basin in Utah would alone yield some 40 to 50 thousand million barrels of crude, while it is estimated that those of Colorado and Utah combined would yield some 200 to 300 thousand million barrels. It should be remembered that these figures only refer to a very small part of the future oil-shale areas of North America.

For the rest of North America, as has already been indicated, oil-shales are found in many areas, chief among which may perhaps be mentioned the Nova Scotian and New Brunswick shales, the latter of which were worked before the discovery of well-oil in Pennsylvania wiped out the industry, while in the vicinity of McMurray in the Athabaska and Slave River regions of Alberta, there exist vast deposits of oil-sands which are estimated to produce, at the rate of a minimum of 10 gallons per ton, no less than 300 thousand million barrels of oil. In connection with the utilization of this vast resource, the chief difficulty is that of getting a process of extracting the oil cheap enough to make it at the moment a commercial proposition.

Finally, we summarize some of the characteristics of petroleum as a resource, which will have emerged in the foregoing chapters.

(1) Petroleum is a limited resource. Wells, pools, and even fields, may be, and often have been, short-lived. This fact led to many pessimistic prognostications as to reserves. In recent decades, however, improvements in the technique of exploration (e.g. geo-physical methods)[1] and of drilling have enlarged our estimate of reserves. Conservation technique, too, is adding to the life of the present resources. It is becoming quite clear that only by controlled and scientific exploitation can the fullest percentage of the oil present be brought to the surface. Such control would avoid off-setting, would direct the exact location of wells, would conserve gas pressure, and would use certain modern technical methods of obtaining more oil from disused pools.

(2) Petroleum is a mixture, essentially consisting of hydrocarbons ; and different fractions of the distillate have different values at different times. Hence the importance of " cracking " and of the more recent process of hydrogenation. Elaborate refineries engaged in these processes are very expensive, and through obsolescence are apt to be short-lived.

(3) As " cracking " and " hydrogenation " add to the cost, the heavier constituents still cost less than petrol, and improved design has enlarged the field of the Diesel engine, so that it is now used not only in marine engines but in road vehicles, and even for aeroplanes.

(4) As a fuel for steam raising, fuel oil has the following advantages over coal—(a) greater energy per unit volume and weight ; (b) quickness and less labour cost in re-fuelling ; (c) ease and exactness of control ; (d) cleanliness.

(5) Because of their use in internal combustion engines, petroleum products are pre-eminently the fuels for transportation agents—automobiles, lorries, and aeroplanes—and this is their greatest field of service. Nevertheless, increasing quantities are used in industry. Thus in 1944, cut off largely from natural supplies, the U.S.A. produced nearly one million tons of synthetic rubber (i.e. more than her 1938 import of natural rubber), and

[1] Experiments are now being made with radar.

all made from petroleum gas and oil products. Large fractions, too, are used as lubricating oils, for domestic heating, and in many minor industries.

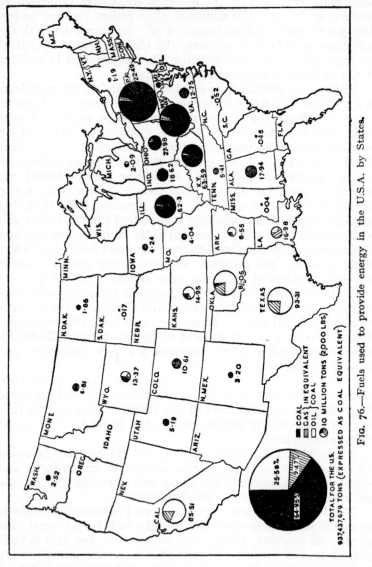

FIG. 76.—Fuels used to provide energy in the U.S.A. by States.

(6) Most petroleum wells yield gas as well as oil, and although still much is wasted, and much should be retained to conserve pressure, yet an enormous amount is used. In addition, from

petroliferous districts generally, thousands of wells yield gas only. From the " wet " gas of oil wells an additional amount of gasolene can be condensed, and modern technique allows, too, of treatment of the lighter *gas* molecules to form *liquid* hydrocarbons. Most of the natural gas, however, is piped for direct use in industry, for power, or for heating.
Appended are production statistics.

	1938	1939	1940	1941	1942	1943	1944	In million barrels
Arkansas. .	18·4	21·4	26·1	26·3	27·6	27·6	29·1	included in total
California .	249·9	225·5	223·1	230·3	247·1	284·3	311·8	3,000
Colerado .	1·3	1·4	1·4	1·7	2·3	2·4	3·0	included in total
Illinois . .	22·8	92·2	146·5	128·5	106·6	77·6	77·0	370
Kansas . .	58·1	61·0	64·8	81·9	96·9	105·7	99·8	750
Kentucky .	5·8	5·6	5·2	4·8	4·2	7·9	9·6	included in total
Louisiana .	94·9	94·2	103·4	117·6	129·2	125·8	135·4	1,150
Michigan. .	19·1	23·6	19·7	16·3	21·7	20·5	18·2	included in total
Mississippi .	0·0	0·1	4·4	16·3	27·5	18·8	16·5	,,
Montana .	4·8	5·8	6·5	7·3	8·0	7·6	8·7	,,
Nebraska .	0·0	0·0	0·3	1·7	1·3	0·8	0·5	,,
New Mexico.	36·0	37·9	39·5	39·6	31·9	38·9	39·8	500
New York .	5·0	5·1	5·0	5·1	5·0	4·3	4·7	included in total
Ohio . . .	3·3	3·2	3·2	3·2	3·7	3·2	3·0	,,
Oklahoma .	169·3	152·4	149·6	153·2	137·8	120·6	123·4	1,150
Pennsylvania	17·4	17·8	17·4	16·5	17·8	16·7	15·6	included in total
Texas. . .	470·8	382·3	489·2	501·3	477·8	589·1	747·2	11,650
W. Virginia .	3·7	3·8	3·4	3·4	3·5	3·1	3·3	included in total
Wyoming .	19·0	21·2	26·2	30·0	32·7	34·8	33·5	580
Others . .	0·06	0·09	0·07	0·06	0·06	0·06	0·06	—
Total . .	1,199·7	1,254·6	1,335·0	1,385·1	1,382·7	1,487·8	1,680·2	20,150

PETROLEUM PRODUCTION IN U.S.A., 1938-44, IN MILLION BARRELS

Estimated reserves in *known* areas of leading states.

NATURAL GAS
(IN THOUSAND MILLION CUBIC FEET)

	From Oil Wells	From Gas Wells	Total	Marketed
California	419	13	432	315
Louisiana	101	260	361	284
Oklahoma	254	76	330	263
Texas	435	715	1,150	882
W. Virginia	14	136	150	134
Others	258	367	625	417
In 1938	1,481	1,567	3,048	2,295

In the war year of 1944 no less than 3,750 thousand million cu. ft. were *marketed*.

CHAPTER XXIII

NON-FERROUS METALS OF THE
UNITED STATES

ONE of the most striking and significant facts of recent years in the mining and metallurgical worlds has been the great increase in the demand for the non-ferrous metals. This increase has been partly due to the natural development of demand in response to industrial expansion, but in the cases of certain of the metals, such as copper, lead, zinc, silver, and aluminium among others, it has been due in addition to the rapid development of special types of industry. Let us examine for a moment the case of copper. In 1903 a production of just over 1,000 million pounds of copper satisfied the world demand. By the year 1912 it took no less than 2,240 million pounds to do so. Five years later, in 1917, it took some 3,000 million pounds to meet the world's requirements, while in 1936 the world consumption was 1·5 million metric tons. After a war the industry suffers from the large accumulations of stocks which are released by the various Disposal Boards of the belligerent countries, and also through the masses of old material which are converted from war uses to the arts of peace, for, copper being almost indestructible, a large percentage of the amount marketed in any one year is old copper remelted. Probably about one-half of all the copper produced in any one year is consumed in some branch or other of the electrical industry— the spread of which is one of the most interesting developments of modern times. This expansion has been greatly accentuated by the rapid development of hydro-electrical plants in many parts of the world. In addition to this demand, there is also a large demand for copper for use in the manufacture of various alloys, of which the more important are bronze and brass. The development of the electrical industry has also increased greatly the demand for zinc for use in battery parts. Zinc is also extensively used for brass-making, for the manufacture of galvanized sheets, and also for the manufacture of paints and type metal. The electrical industry has also expanded the demand for lead for use with tin in solder and in storage batteries. Lead is also used for paints and in the manufacture of pipes and cable covers among other things. When we go to the " pictures " we seldom realize that it is an industry of recent growth and that its phenomenal expansion has been of great benefit to the world's silver producers, since silver is the main raw material used in the manufacture of the sensitive film on which the pictorial record is taken and printed. Aluminium is a metal, the lightness coupled with the strength of which were recognized in connection with the manufacture of many articles in pre-war days, but these qualities were not fully appreciated until the automobile and aeroplane industries attained their present stages of development, and until alloys of aluminium were forthcoming to meet these demands. It is thus not merely to the expansion of old industries that these non-ferrous metals owe their importance, but also to the building up of new industries many of which are capable of very great future expansion.

We have now to see how the United States stands as a supplier to the world of these very essential commodities. An examination of the statistics will show the dominating position which she occupies with reference to the greater part of these metals. She supplies about one-fourth of the world's copper, lead, zinc and silver. Of recent years she has also been the world's largest producer of each of these metals. It has further to be remembered that she has reached this commanding position in spite of the fact that as a producer of these metals she suffers from certain very definite disadvantages. Her labour compared with that of most other areas is highly paid, and because her producing areas lie far inland and away from her industrial areas, her transport costs are very high. With three noteworthy exceptions, to be considered in greater detail later, almost the whole of the mining districts of non-ferrous metals lie in the western area of mountain and plateau which occupies roughly one-half of the country. These districts are some six in number. They are the region of the Northern Rockies in Montana and Idaho, that of the Central Rockies in Colorado, that of the Salt Lake country in the Western Rockies, that of Southern Arizona, and that of Nevada in the plateau country, and lastly, that of the Northern and Central Sierras of California. There are also certain minor areas which are, however, of slight importance in comparison with the six named above. All these districts are in regions of, or in close proximity to regions of, igneous rock.

The various metals enter largely into the composition of the igneous rocks. From these igneous rocks the metals have been gathered and concentrated in the form of ores—that is, in the form of rock material which contains a sufficiently high percentage of one or more of the metals to make the working of the deposit a paying commercial enterprise. In what fashion or fashions has this concentration taken place? It has taken place in three main ways. As the igneous masses cooled, certain minerals crystallized out of the mass and formed certain bodies in close relationship to the general body of rock. Gases and solutions under certain conditions of heat and pressure dissolved the minerals from the rocks and frequently redeposited them in cracks either in igneous rocks or in adjacent sedimentary rocks, or in some cases carried them into seas or lakes. Lastly, through the ordinary processes of weathering, the metals were carried down by running water and redeposited to form detrital accumulations at lower levels, the concentration in this case being due to the varying weights of the materials in relation to the carrying power of the running water. It is because of these facts that the chief mining areas for these metals are found in regions of, or in close proximity to regions of, igneous rock. They are further likely to be found where volcanic activity has given rise to metal-bearing solutions, and where much folding and faulting have produced suitable fissures where deposition could readily take place.

Bearing in mind these facts, it remains for us to locate the main areas in the United States from which each of these minerals comes. Arizona is the most important copper producer in the United States. In Central and Southern Arizona there are at least six mining areas, but the Jerome, Bisbee and Globe-Miami are outstanding. In Arizona camps the copper is found mostly in connection with porphyry. At Bisbee the metal has been carried by solutions from the porphyry to adjacent limestones. At Globe and Miami to north of the Gila River, the metal is found in conjunction with other minerals in a schist. Butte, Montana, situated on one of the head-streams of the Missouri in the Northern Rockies, is now the leading copper producing district in the United States. In this district about one-fifth of the total output of the United States is obtained. Here the copper is found in definite veins in a granite in connection with other minerals of which the more important are silver, zinc, and lead. The silver raised here is the largest single supply of silver raised in the United States, and represents about one-fifth of the total. These Butte mines are considered to be among the richest copper mines in the world. The ore was originally worked for silver, and silver-mining as a separate industry was discontinued when silver fell in price in the nineties. To-day it is worked as a by-product of the copper production. It is only possible to work such deposits on a commercial basis under conditions of the most efficient organization and on a large scale. There are a number of other minor areas· of which perhaps the most important is the district of Santa Rita near the Rio Grande in New Mexico.

The Bingham area of Utah has greatly increased its importance in recent years, and is on the point of surpassing the Butte area. Indeed, in 1936 Utah was second to Arizona. It lies between the Great American Desert and the western slopes of the Wasatch Range. The metal is found in conjunction with lead, zinc and silver, the minerals being fairly evenly disseminated throughout a porphyry.

The Nevada production has also increased, but is much less than Montana. The mines are in the Ely district, among the basin ranges.

Finally, there is the Keeweenaw Peninsula on the south shore of Lake Superior. Here copper is found without other metals in a basaltic lava in which it has been concentrated by mineralized solutions. As in the previous cases, the ore is very low-grade, and almost all U.S.A. copper ores contain less than 2 per cent. of copper.

Because of the fact that the bulk of the copper mined to-day is a low-grade ore, the average copper in ore for the United States being about $1\frac{1}{2}$ per cent., the greater part of the ore mined to-day is concentrated on the spot. Were this not so, it would often be necessary to shift 100 tons of ore in order to obtain half a ton of metal, and the cost of transport in such cases would be prohibitive. Copper goes through three main processes or groups of processes as a rule in refining. As a result of the first, the ore is converted into concentrates, which contain some 15 to 30 per cent. of metal. The result of the second process is what is termed " copper matte," which has a metallic content of from about 40 to 50 per cent. of copper. As a result of a still further process of refining, blister copper is obtained, containing, as a rule, over 95 per cent. of the pure metal, and a further electrical refining yields the pure metal.

Lead and zinc, which are very commonly found in the same ore, may be conveniently referred to together. Missouri leads in the production of lead, and it comes from the south-east of the state. The Joplin region, Cœur d'Alene and Bingham are the most important producers of lead after South-east Missouri. For zinc, the Joplin region of Kansas, Missouri and Oklahoma is supreme. Of remaining zinc areas the New Jersey production is interesting and important. It is mined at Franklin and Ogdensburg, the ore being found in white crystalline limestone. Butte is the Montana producer, while the Idaho production comes from Cœur d'Alene in the Northern Rockies. Finally, the Appalachian Valley in Eastern Tennessee, and the Bingham district of Utah, should be noted.

About one-fourth of the world's silver and about one-ninth of the world's gold come from the United States. Gold and silver are usually found in close association, and this is the case with practically all the producing areas of these metals in the States. While this is so, however, it by no means follows that a district which has a heavy production of silver will also have a heavy gold output. The most important silver-mining area, that of the Northern Rockies at Butte and at Cœur d'Alene, has only a small output of gold. This region produces nearly one-half of all the silver raised in the U.S.A., but only about one-twentieth of the gold. We have already seen its great importance as a copper-producing region. Standing second as a silver-producer is the Utah region to south of the Great Salt Lake, a region also of great importance as a copper-producer. Other large silver-producing districts are the scattered camps of the basin ranges in Nevada, the main range of the Rockies in Colorado, and Central and South Arizona. Of gold-producing camps, the most important are in the Californian Sierras. South Dakota, though much less important in total production—has the largest individual mine, this being in the Black Hills. The Alaskan production comes from Fairbanks, Juneau and Nome. For Colorado, Cripple Creek is the leading district. The Nevada production is from scattered camps. Other gold-producing regions are found in the Northern Rockies, in the Salt Lake country, and in Arizona.

In connection with the production of silver in the States, it is interesting to note that the extension of the cyanide process on a large scale has led to the working of camps where low-grade ore is found which had been previously abandoned. As an example of this fact, perhaps reference may be made to the erection on the famous Comstock lode at Virginia City, Nevada, of a great cyanide mill. This lode, the scene of one of the greatest " rushes " in the history of mining in the west, has been almost derelict for years, but with the application of large-scale methods of operation on thoroughly economical lines, for the handling of low-grade ores, it looks as if this old camp, together with many others, may be restored to something of their former glory.

The war-time increase in the use of non-ferrous metals has been most marked in the case of aluminium and of magnesium, both required for the light alloys essential for the aeroplane industries.

One of the commonest constituents of the surface minerals

of the earth, aluminium has so far been produced economically only from bauxite, a naturally occurring impure hydrated oxide of aluminium. Drying and concentration usually takes place at or near the mines, for about half the weight of the ore is usually water and impurities. On the other hand, the separation of the alumina (almost pure aluminium oxide) from impurities is often carried on far from the mines, while the final electrolytic process by which the metal itself is deposited from alumina fused with chryolite, a process requiring some 25,000 kwh. per ton of metal, is inevitably situated in areas of cheap sources of electrical energy. The chief source of bauxite in North America is the village of that name, 14 miles south-west of Little Rock (Ark.). This provides about 95 per cent. of the *native* production, the remainder coming from scattered deposits in the south-east Piedmont.

However, Canada wholly, and the U.S.A. as to much of its requirements, are dependent upon imports. These come, at present, from Dutch and British Guiana, where they are mined on the verge of the coastal lowland and near to navigable water.

Alumina is produced at East St. Louis, Mobile, Lister (Ala.), Hurricane Creek (Ark.), Baton Rouge and at Arvida (L. St. John area, Quebec) ; and we may note the position of these in relation to home and imported supplies of bauxite and to navigable water.

For the electrolytic extraction of the metal the alumina is sent to Massena, Niagara Falls and Morpeth in New York, to Burlington (N.Y.), Badin (N.C.), Aleva (Tenn.), Lister (Ala.), Jones Mills (Ark.), Long View (Vancouver, B.C.), Mead (Wa.), Troutdale (Or.), Los Angeles (Cal.), and Arvida (Quebec).[1]

These are all situated where cheap and plentiful electricity is at hand, the Washington and Oregon centres using the great supplies recently available from the Grand Couleé and Bonneville developments on the Colombia river.[1]

[1] "Aluminium Industry," by W. Harris. "Economic Geography," Vol. 20, No. 4, 1944.

PRODUCTION OF NON-FERROUS METALS BY CHIEF
PRODUCING STATES, 1936

	Copper. Thousand Metric Tons	Lead. Thousand Short Tons	Zinc. Thousand Metric Tons	Silver. Million Fine Ozs.	Gold. Million Fine Ozs.	Bauxite. Thousand Long Tons
Alaska . . .					0·5	
Arizona. . .	204	10		8	0·3	
Arkansas . .						355
California . .				2	1·1	
Colorado . .				6	0·4	
S. Dakota . .					0·6	
Idaho . . .		91	50	15		
Kansas . . .		11	80			
Michigan . .	48					
Missouri . .		110				
Montana . .	109	19	50	12	0·2	
Nevada . . .	68	12		5	0·3	
New Jersey .						
Oklahoma . .		25	129			
Tennessee . .			45			
Utah . . .	126	70	36	10	0·2	
Others . . .	45	24	100	4	0·2	17
Total U.S.A. .	601	363	580	62	3·8	372
U.S.A., 1942 .	966	492	630	56	5·9	900
World, 1936 .	1,495	1,500	1,349	250	35·2	2,600

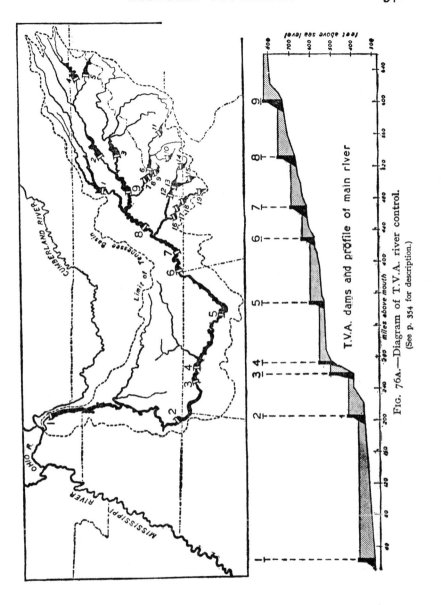

Fig. 76A.—Diagram of T.V.A. river control.

(See p. 354 for description.)

CHAPTER XXIV

POWER RESOURCES OF THE U.S.A.

IN the preceding chapters we have been dealing with some of the major sources of power, and with one of its most significant applications as instanced in the iron and steel industry ; that is to say, with activities somewhat controlled by geographical circumstance. For this very reason there is a danger that in a geographical handbook they receive undue attention. Coal mining is the classic example of an industry in which a large proportion of the costs of production are in wages, and there are 400,000 to 500,000 coal miners in the U.S.A. The heavy iron and steel industry is at the other extreme. Here the chief costs are in raw materials and plant.

Over 60 per cent. of the industrial workers of the U.S.A. are living in New England, the Middle Atlantic states, and the East North-Central States, and obviously most of these are neither engaged in coal mining nor in primary iron and steel production. As we have seen, Trans-Appalachia was largely settled via the Ohio and, later, via the Hudson-Mohawk gap ; that is to say, by routes in the same latitudes as the largest coastal centres, and at a period when coal was becoming the world requisite for industry. Thus it happened that much movement westward took place across the area of the largest deposits of easily accessible high-grade coal in the world ; an area sandwiched between the great commercial capitals of the Atlantic Seaboard and that great agricultural area, which from its predominant activities, has become known as the Corn Belt. And all this in a period in which steam became the prime mover, and during which the efficiency of the steam-engine was, by modern standards, very low. That is to say industry was attracted to this, the first U.S.A. coalfield to be worked on a huge scale, to an extent which would not be so, were a fresh start being made to-day. The heavy industries, of necessity at first on the coalfield, attracted more complicated industries making consumers' goods but using producers' goods, and themselves deriving some benefit from nearness to a power resource. But new industries brought new population, and as the presence of markets and of labour supply are almost the only general localizing factors in much industry to-day, we can thus account for the disproportionate growth of industrial activity in the north-eastern district generally.

The absence of customs frontiers over so huge an area as the United States has retarded the evolution of that great number of producing centres in respect of some particular product, which distinguishes the continent of Europe. On the other hand, the vast area of general and continuous farm settlement, punctuated with widespread nodally-placed commercial centres, has necessitated *some* reduplication of industrial areas, and a general region of markets and of industry has spread from its concentration on the Pennsylvanian coalfield, westward, between and about the Ohio and Great Lake systems.

Population and industry are inseparable, the growth of the former implies the market for the latter, and in most modern countries the initial momentum came from the coalfield.

But in the present century, less importance attaches to the source of power as a localizing factor. This for two reasons. Increasing efficiency of the steam-engine or turbine, either as a prime mover or as a source of electrical energy, means a less amount of coal used for the same amount of energy. Secondly, the greater efficiency of transport means that more coal can be carried for the same cost. That a greater and greater amount of the energy used in industry is derived from coal-fed electric power stations has a similar liberating effect. With the occurrence of coal and of petroleum we have already dealt. It will be convenient at this stage to deal with the development of water power in the U.S.A. and then to add a few notes on the competitive characteristics of these to some extent rival sources of power.

The Water-Power of the U.S.A. In its descent from a mountain valley to sea-level, a quantity of water produces an amount of energy which is measured by the product of the weight of the water and the distance of its fall. It is only practicable to utilize this energy if nature concentrates a considerable part of the descent at a point, as in an actual waterfall, or in a short stretch of rapids. Even so the actual head of water used is in part dependent upon some barrier engineered across the stream, the very possibility of which, as also its effects, depend on the detailed topography of the site. It may be convenient to lead a part of the flow from the stream by a canal to a point farther downstream where a considerable head is available. This is done at Niagara, notable in the Queenston plant, where water is led from well above the falls, to discharge through penstocks over the side of the gorge at a power station 12 miles below the falls. The actual layout of the plant will vary with every site, but in all there must be topographic possibilities of using a head of water. Such constitutes the first physiographic factor in water-power development.

Then comes the question as to the capacity for power development of the plant actually to be installed. If this corresponds to the maximum flow of the stream, then most of the installed horse-power will be inactive for most of the time in the case of most streams. Very few streams have at all a regular flow. Even in the case of a stream the basin of which has an almost

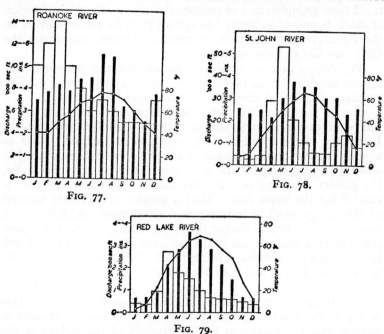

FIG. 77.

FIG. 78.

FIG. 79.

constant mean monthly precipitation, the flow may be very irregular, for the actual monthly flow may not at all correspond to the mean, and in any case, rainfall is not in the least likely to be at all regularly distributed throughout the month. Furthermore, evaporation in the warm months, directly, and through vegetation transpiration, takes more of the run-off in the summer months than in the winter season. Obviously, intense and prolonged winter frost will hold back run-off till the spring thaws, and rivers under such climatic conditions will normally have the greatest flow in the spring. High mountains will have the same effect, and alpine streams usually have their greatest flow in May

and June, even when, as in the Sierra
Nevada of California, the actual precipitation is greatest or even confined to the
winter months. A few graphs illustrat-
ing these principles are shown in Figs.
77, 78 and 79.

In these, discharge is indicated by the
open columns, mean monthly precipitation over the basin, by the vertical lines,
and mean monthly temperatures, by the
continuous graph. In the case of the
Roanoke we have the ordinary régime of
a river with well-distributed precipitation, in a region having considerable
range of temperature, but no extreme
and prolonged winter frost.

Although there is more rain in
summer than in winter, the run-off is
noticeably greater in the winter six
months, especially in the late winter,
and the minimum occurs in the autumn.
This is due to evaporation and transpiration in the summer months, while
with lower evaporation in the winter
months, a larger proportion of each
successive rainfall goes to run-off as the
ground becomes more and more waterlogged.

The St. John's River is in northern
New England, and as the temperature
graph indicates, is completely frozen up
in mid-winter. The greatest discharge
comes with the break-up of the frost in
spring, and the minimum is in the early
autumn. Similarly with the Red River
in northern Minnesota we have a spring
maximum flow, though in this case the
precipitation is predominantly a summer
one.

It must be emphasized, however,
that these are graphs of monthly mean
flow, and that actual day-to-day flow is
apt to be very much more irregular.
Thus in Fig. 80, which shows the daily
discharge of the Roanoke for a particular

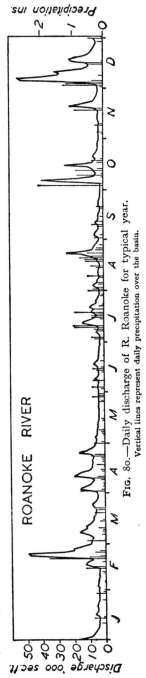

FIG. 80.—Daily discharge of R. Roanoke for typical year.
Vertical lines represent daily precipitation over the basin.

year, the actual and quite usual irregularities are discernible. In detail one may notice the greater effect (for the same amount of rain) in winter than in summer, and the cumulative effect of consecutive daily rain.

It follows then that in the case of most streams, hydro-electric installation can only deal continuously with a very small part of the total energy unless the stream flow is regulated in some way. Lakes in the stream basin tend to regularize the flow, and the extraordinary regularity of the flow at Niagara is due to this unexampled natural storage. Usually even if the stream basin is studded with lakes, artificial storage has to be added if a considerable portion of the natural energy available is to be used. Much of the cost of hydro-electric development is due to the expense of regulating works, and this expense, per horse-power developed, is apt to increase as more and more of the possible power of a basin is harnessed. Thus, in addition to the cost of the power-house itself, there is often the much greater expense of stream regulation works, which may be far up-stream, at sites naturally convenient for storage.

The cost per horse-power installed is thus apt to be much greater for hydro-electric than for fuel-electric plants. The running expenses of the latter, of course, are higher. In cases of very marked seasonal variation of flow, it may very well be more economic to use auxiliary steam plants during the season of low flow, rather than incur extra expense on a more complete system of storage reservoirs.

Geographical Distribution of Potential Water Power. Water-power development in North America is greater than in any other continent, and potential water power is only exceeded in the continent of Africa, mainly there because of the prodigious potential of the Congo as it crosses the Crystal Mountains not far from its mouth. We cannot here detail for North America the innumerable power sites which have been examined, nor even the sites of actual development. Water-power developments and possibilities can, however, be grouped according to the general characteristics of geographical regions, and this we will attempt, reserving any reference of specific sites to the regional portion of this work.

Laurentian Shield Basins. Here the unevenly graded streams, rocky basins, innumerable lakes, low evaporation, and prolonged and severe winter frost are important factors generally applicable. In spite of the natural storage of the lakes, flow is usually at a very marked minimum in the winter ; storage dams are usually necessary. The greatest developments have taken place where large streams cross the Laurentides to reach the St. Lawrence

Valley (e.g. Ottawa and St. Maurice), partly because of the great powers here available, but also because of the near-by market. Far in the interior of the Shield are scattered developments connected with the mining and pulp and paper activities. The very largest of these are to be found on the Saguenay between Lake St. John and the gorge. Large streams such as the Churchill and Nelson Rivers have enormous possibilities where they cross from the Shield to the belt of Palæozoics which border the south and west of Hudson's Bay. These, however, are too remote from markets for present development. All the Shield developments have the quality of at least considerable distance from coal-mining areas.

The St. Lawrence itself shows the greatest development and the greatest possibility of any river of the continent. This is concentrated in Niagara Falls and rapids and in the stretch of rapids between Prescott and Montreal. Though situated in a climate usually resulting in marked winter minimum flow, the unexampled natural storage of the Great Lakes gives an equally unexampled regularity of flow. The possibilities are characterized then, by no necessity for storage, by enormous volume per second, and, apart from Niagara itself, by low heads. The region is fairly accessible to American, but not to Canadian, coal competition. If the St. Lawrence Deep Waterway is actually constructed the power development (some 5 million h.p.) between Prescott and Montreal will be an essential part of the scheme, and we will deal with the question at greater length in the chapter (Chapter XXXII) on Eastern Canada.

The Mississippi Basin. In the following table the mean monthly gauge heights at some points on the Mississippi are shown.

	J.	F.	M.	A.	M.	J.	J.	A.	S.	O.	N.	D.
Ohio at Cincinnati	26·1	25·1	32·5	27·2	19·6	15·7	13·6	10·5	9·5	9·6	10·8	16·8
Missouri at Kansas City	5·8	7·5	10·8	12·6	12·0	16·9	15·6	10·9	8·6	8·0	7·5	5·8
Mississippi at St. Louis	6·7	8·7	13·8	18·7	18·9	20·1	19·5	11·4	8·9	8·1	8·0	8·0
Mississippi at Vicksburg	22·1	29·9	35·5	39·9	37·6	30·9	26·4	16·7	11·5	9·7	10·1	14·7

The Ohio shows the spring maximum and late summer minimum characteristic of the eastern rivers of the country. The Missouri at Kansas City responds both to the prevailing summer maximum of precipitation in the west centre of the continent, and even more to the main June maximum of its snow-fed mountain tributaries. This régime is little altered by the coming in of the Upper Mississippi and the Illinois, but at Vicksburg the effect of the junction of the Ohio with its March maximum is felt and the maximum is shifted back to April.

Fifty-eight per cent. of the average annual flow of the river comes from the Ohio, and 22·7 per cent. from the Upper Mississippi, and these relatively flat basins yield, with one or two exceptions, such as the Keokuk site on the Upper Mississippi, few very great developments. The Ohio and Illinois basins, moreover, are amply supplied with developed coalfields and with some of the largest thermal power stations in the world.

The Tennessee River has very considerable possibilities, and these are being developed at very considerable expense (because of the irregular flow and necessity for many reservoirs) in the Tennessee Valley Authority schemes.[1] The head-waters of the Missouri, and other right-bank tributaries, yield Rocky Mountain power sites characterized by relatively small flow, high heads, early summer snow-melt maxima, the necessity of great storage dams, great distance from general industrial markets, and connection with irrigation development.

New England. Here, as in the Shield, the irregular grading of glacially deranged streams, the incidence of hard volcanic rock across some of the streams, the heavy precipitation, winter minimum flow, snow-melt spring flooding, and considerable natural lake storage, are all characteristics. The early industrial development of the area has much to do with the fact that we have here, not the greatest powers, but the greatest proportionate development in the U.S.A.

The Piedmont Plateau. Here the irregular surface and varying hardness of the old crystallines provide a number of possibilities. The stream basins have good rainfall, and frost and snow incidence too irregular to give a winter minimum. Flow is normally at a minimum in the late summer, because of evaporation, and the area as a whole is some distance from coal, but near industrial and port centres in the north, and supplies much of the southern textile industry in the south.

The Pacific Cordillera. Here the greatest development and possibilities are for the most part concerned with the high heads, winter precipitation and early summer snow-melt maxima, of the main Pacific water parting.

If the basin concerned is mainly of high altitude, maxima run-off will be in May and June, and flow will be very little in the autumn and winter. In the lower basins of the Sierra, and in

MEAN MONTHLY PERCENTAGE DISCHARGE

	Map No.	J.	F.	M.	A.	M.	J.	J.	A.	S.	O.	N.	D.
Mc. Cloud R.	1	11·4	13·3	12·4	12·2	10·5	6·6	5·5	5·0	4·7	5·0	6·2	7·2
American R.	2	12·3	11·6	15·8	17·0	19·1	12·8	3·7	0·9	0·6	0·8	1·8	3·6
Fresno R.	3	7·1	18·4	24·4	17·4	14·2	7·9	2·3	0·5	0·3	1·6	2·1	3·8
Kings R.	4	4·5	3·9	7·2	12·4	24·7	26·2	11·5	3·5	1·4	1·6	1·4	1·7
Kern R.	5	5·1	5·4	9·1	14·0	20·6	20·4	10·9	4·5	2·3	2·5	2·4	2·8
Mad R.	6	26·0	15·1	12·2	12·3	10·2	2·1	0·8	0·4	0·5	0·3	8·7	11·4
San Diego R.	10	38·6	18·1	16·7	10·2	7·5	2·4	0·9	0·5	0·4	0·7	1·1	2·9
Salinas R.	7	24·5	23·1	26·8	9·9	4·7	2·1	0·8	0·3	0·3	0·6	1·2	5·7
San Gabriel R.	9	15·6	17·1	27·6	13·6	8·4	4·7	2·8	1·8	1·4	1·8	2·0	3·2
Santa Ynez R.	8	20·7	34·0	27·1	6·6	4·0	1·8	1·1	0·7	0·6	0·8	0·9	1·7
E. Fork Carson R.	11	3·4	3·5	5·6	12·9	26·5	26·1	10·1	3·5	1·9	1·8	2·2	2·4

[1] See pp. 353–4.

the coast ranges of Washington, Oregon and southern California, precipitation is not to any extent as snow, and the flow is confined

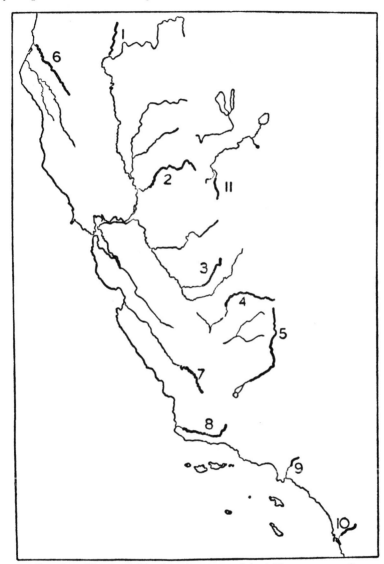

FIG. 81.—Key to Californian rivers named in table on page 348.
The part of the main stream above the gauge concerned is represented by a thick line.

to the winter and spring months. In both cases much storage is necessary. The table and the accompanying key map (Fig. 81) make this clear.   Thus the Mc. Cloud and American River basins have considerable winter rain and snow at relatively low levels, all of which increases the discharge in the early months of the year. Kings and Kern Rivers are much farther south, and get most of their precipitation at high levels in the form of snow which remains unmelted till the early summer.   In part too they are glacier-fed.   Thus they have their maximum in early summer. The Mad, San Diego, Salinas, San Gabriel and Santa Ynez Rivers have low-level coastal basins, getting nearly all their precipitation in the form of late winter rainfall.   The régimes reflect this incidence of precipitation quite clearly.   The East Fork Carson River rises in high snow-covered mountains to the east of the Sierra Nevada, and has the May–June maxima which we should expect. The region is far from coal, and power supply is chiefly to the great cities of the Pacific coast, and to mining activities.   The gigantic developments, completed and in progress, of the Colorado at Boulder Dam, and of the Columbia River at Grand Couleé Dam, are mentioned in the regional chapters.

Quite normally in the arid west, irrigation lands fringe the mountain systems whence come their supplies of water.   The storage works in the mountain valleys which are necessary for the development of hydro-electric power often serve also to regulate the supply of water to the irrigated lands, which are situated generally where the mountains join the plains, and below the power stations.   Not that the two requirements are usually coterminous.   The water for irrigation is required in the warmer portion of the year, while the power demands may be about the same for each month of the year.   On the whole, however, the double demand does help to pay for the storage works.

Fig. 82 indicates the position in the United States of all but the smaller fuel and hydro-electric power stations.   The relative absence of hydro-electric plants in the north-eastern interior is noticeable, and the great coalfields and consequent fuel-power stations makes the area relatively independent of the great hydro stations of the St. Lawrence and of New York State.

Some of the largest of the fuel stations in this north-eastern interior area are situated on lake-side.   Hydro stations become important, but not predominant, in the north-eastern coastal states, though great fuel-power stations occur at New York and other coastal cities using tide-water coal.   Hydro-electric stations are important in the Piedmont textile area, and on the Tennessee River.   They are, of course, predominant in the Pacific cordillera.

The steam-engine in the factory is become obsolescent.   To an increasing extent industry either buys its power or distributes it from its own power-houses.   In either case it is electric energy,

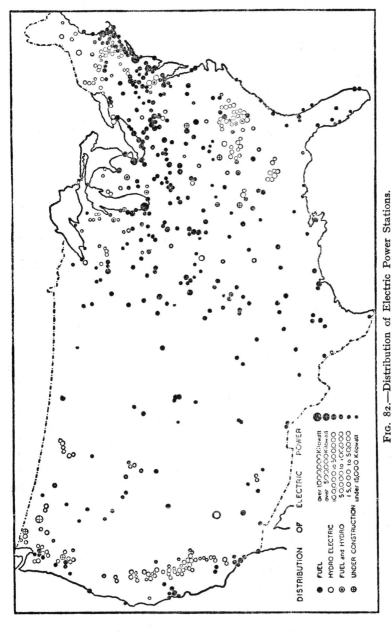

FIG. 82.—Distribution of Electric Power Stations.

Many of these stations are inter-connected, and in particular many of the hydro-electric stations are inter-connected with fuel stations. Many of the fuel stations on the Pacific coast use oil fuel, otherwise coal is used.

whether hydro-electric or fuel electric.   Perhaps the most noticeable recent feature has been the increased efficiency of the fuel-
power station.   In the more recent large-scale plants a unit of
energy is usually produced from less than 1 lb. avoirdupois of
average bituminous coal.   This efficiency combined with the
very serious cost of long distribution lines will tend to limit
the range of the hydro-electric station in competition with the
fuel-power station.

The position of the hydro-electric station is very definitely
limited by physical circumstance.   The siting of fuel stations
increasingly depends on position of markets and of fuel sources
in general, and upon the supply of large quantities of condensing
water, in detail.   Such is the modern efficiency of transport and
of power stations, that in the case of a newer industrial area situated some distance from a coalfield, it *may* be more economic to
place the fuel-power station in close proximity to the new markets,
rather than supply power by long lead from a power station on
the coalfield.

Electrical energy cannot at present be economically stored.
The continuous working of a plant implies both a uniform demand,
and the possibility of its continuous supply.   As far as supply is
concerned, we have already noticed that stand-by fuel-power
plants may be necessary in connection with hydro-electric stations
using an incompletely regulated water source.   As far as demand
is concerned, industries fully occupied and working day and night
shifts are infrequent, and traction services and municipal power
and light requirements have demands which vary enormously in
the twenty-four hours.   Thus expensive machinery is inactive
for a large part of the twenty-four hours.   Some saving of capital
expenditure may be effected if a number of power stations, fuel,
hydro, or both, can be linked together in a regional system, and
this is now frequently done.   The current frequencies should be
the same.   Besides smoothing the load somewhat, such combinations tend to minimize the effects of a breakdown in any
particular power station.

Some industries (notably the wood-pulp industry) are in a
position to take large amounts of power at off-load periods of the
day, and are at such times quoted very low rates, but these
requirements are unusual.

The development of electrical energy in the United States is
well shown in Fig. 83, which indicates the various sources of
energy employed.

The increasing use of hydro-electric energy, and of petroleum
products, has sometimes led to the statement that coal production
is suffering from the competition of rival sources of power.   This

is only partly true. Indeed these other sources make big demands on the coal industry in the provision of material, etc. What certainly is very effective in reducing the demand for coal is the greatly increased economy in its use, notably in the power station itself, and in the iron and steel industry.

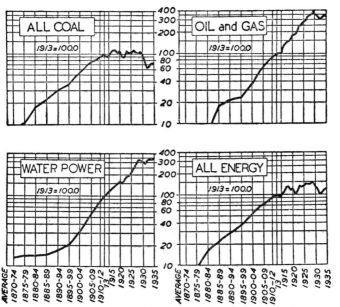

FIG. 83.—Energy Graphs for U.S.A. Coal, Water Power, and Oil and Gas.

A fundamental advantage of water power, but one perhaps which will appeal more to our successors than to ourselves, lies in the fact that it is an unexpendable resource. The continent of North America has the greatest coal and oil resources of the world, but it is usually the most accessible fuels and those of highest quality which are first used, and these are but a fraction of the total resources, and cannot be regarded economically as practically unlimited.

Between the cities of Decatur and Florence (Alabama) the Tennessee river falls 134 feet in 37 miles, and 100 feet of this is in the 16 miles stretch of mussel shoals. Here was built the Wilson Dam to provide power for synthetic nitrogen production. Planned in the last war, it was yet completed only in 1925. So irregular was the flow of the river—in spite of the heavy and fairly well distributed rainfall of the basin generally—that additional upstream storage was necessary before the power at the Wilson dam could be continuously available.

To-day the T.V.A. has no fewer than eight large dams operating on the main river, and another eight on the Appalachian mountain tributaries.

Over 2 million horse-power has been developed, and no river in the world has been so completely regulated.

But what makes the work of the T.V.A. so interesting and important is that it was not planned merely as a power scheme, but as a multiple purpose plan involving a great regional and social experiment.

The Tennessee river drains an area of 40,910 square miles—roughly that of England—and had a population of but 2½ million (25 per cent. only urban). Nearly one-half of this area was cut-over land, and much of the cultivated land had suffered intense erosion—the result of continuous cultivation of the inter-tilled crops of maize and cotton, on sloping lands subject frequently to intense showers.

The multiple purpose of the T.V.A. may be summarized :—
(a) The provision of a 9-ft. channel up to Knoxville at any time.
(b) Prevention of flood in the basin, and the lessening of the danger of flood in the Lower Mississippi.
(c) The provision of power for industry, farm, and home.
(d) In particular, the fixing of nitrogen, and the manufacture of phosphatic fertiliser from rock phosphate.
(e) The restoration of worn-out soils by the application of phosphates and the growth of legumes.
(f) The reforestation of denuded hill-side land.
(g) The checking of erosion by contour strip farming and the use of scientific rotations.
(h) The provision of holiday amenities on the reservoirs.

The following table gives some details in respect of the chief completed power sites on the main streams. See also table on p. 571.

DAMS ON THE TENNESSEE RIVER
(Dam numbers refer to diagram on p. 341.)

	Height	Location	Completed	Power
1. Kentucky . . .	160 ft.	22·4 mls.	1944	160,000 k.w.
2. Pickwick . . .	113 ft.	206·7 mls.	1938	216,000 k.w.
3. Wilson	137 ft.	259·4 mls.	1926	444,000 k.w.
4. Wheeler . . .	72 ft.	274·9 mls.	1937	259,000 k.w.
5. Guntresville . .	94 ft.	349·0 mls.	1935	97,000 k.w.
6. Hales Bar . . .	83 ft.	431·1 mls.	1913	50,483 k.w.
7. Chickamauga . .	129 ft.	471·0 mls.	1941	108,000 k.w.
8. Watts Bar . .	97 ft.	529·9 mls.	1942	150,000 k.w.
9. Fort Loudoun . .	135 ft.	602·3 mls.	1944?	96,000 k.w.
				1,680,483 k.w.

PART III

REGIONAL GEOGRAPHY

CHAPTER XXV

NEW ENGLAND

THE states of Massachusetts, Connecticut, Rhode Island, Maine, Vermont, and New Hampshire are included in the designation, New England. Structurally, they have much in common with the Canadian Atlantic provinces, and the exact boundary dividing them therefrom is in no sense a natural one. Yet the *zone* traversed by it is rather high, rugged, forested, and little populated. On the west a natural barrier exists in the Berkshire and the Taconic Mountains, which yielded late, meagre, and difficult connections with the Hudson-Mohawk route-way. On the south, lower land and a short sea passage have helped to make much of the territory tributary to New York.

Yet, in spite of its external relations, structural as an Appalachian province, economic in its relation to New York, the territory of New England as a whole has more the character of a major geographical region than has any other considerable Atlantic area. This is emphasized in its history, for that very history records a momentum which still gives to the economic activities of the area a continued importance not to be explained by purely geographical factors as these affect *modern* requirements. Without coal, iron, or oil, Southern New England has remained eminent among the manufacturing areas of the continent ; sending her textiles, leather goods, paper, copper and other metal manufactures to every state in the Union, as well as to every country in the world. Such a position would be impossible were the country a new one.

It is a vestige of the colonial and pre-steam period when there was no mid-western manufacturing area to compete, and when among Atlantic settlements those of New England were most favourably situated for maritime, commercial, and manufacturing development. The factors which then applied—and they have received some consideration in Chapter IV—are no longer of the same importance, but their incidence in former days has resulted in a legacy of skill and custom, and of capital expenditure in buildings, plant, and transport. We must seek in these the causes of the continued industrial importance of the region.

Let us attempt to summarize here the essentials of the general geographical environment. The geological map shows us that we have in New England exposures mainly of the older Palæozoic rocks—Cambrian to Devonian—and that the strike of these rocks is roughly north and south. It shows also that there have been very great areas of intrusion of igneous material of many periods. Structural sections show that the present relief is to be ascribed to the differential erosion of an already folded, fractured, and peneplained surface. The region differs from the Piedmont province in having large exposures of Palæozoic sedimentary (though often metamorphosed) material. It differs from the Great Appalachian Valley in that these sedimentaries are mostly older and have suffered more metamorphism and volcanism. The result was a less regular distribution of hard and soft material than was to be found in the Great Valley province. Uplift and erosion have thus established a less regular relief. The several (Cretaceous and Tertiary) uplifts to which the region has been subjected have not been evenly applied, but have resulted in a broad warping with a general slope of the peneplain from north-west to south-east. The latest effective movement has been a coastal depression, for the islands and submerged channels, as well as the branching inlets, betray a drowned topography. The peneplanation of Triassic and Cretaceous times was not at all complete, and residual heights abound, especially in the west and north.

We are dealing, then, with a country high in the west and north, low towards the east and south, yet with no real coast plain unless the Tertiary and Quaternary sediments of Long Island and Cape Cod Peninsula are thus described. The main river valleys are north and south in sympathy with the strike of the rocks, and communication is therefore relatively difficult east and west. There is much irregularly distributed igneous rock and much metamorphosed rock. Hard old crystalline rocks abound, but where soft material outcrops—as in the case of the limestones of the Housatonic Valley, or the sedimentaries (Triassic) of the Connecticut Valley—wide, open valley plains have been eroded.

The generally accordant summit slope seawards is illustrated in Fig. 84. The section there drawn has been reduced from the 1-inch map contoured every 100 feet, and clearly illustrates the generally regular slope to the east ; the marked Berkshire and Connecticut Valleys ; the Boston Lowlands ; and the intervening plateau-like blocks of the Taconic Mountains, the West and East Highlands, and the eastern plateau.

A most important factor has been the glaciation of the country. There has been no continuous till, as in the case of the glaciated middle-west, but a great distribution of locally derived rock waste, so that much of the soils of New England are boulder-strewn. Stream diversion, new ungraded rock channels, and moraine-dammed lakes, are of frequent occurrence. In spite of an unusually well-distributed precipitation, the rivers of New England experience a somewhat irregular régime because so much of the winter precipitation is apt to be in the form of snow. Spring floods are not infrequent. They would be more noticeable but for the natural storage of the many glacial lakes.

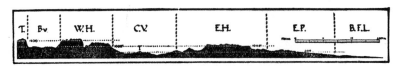

FIG. 84.—East-West Section through Massachusetts.

T., Taconic Mts. ; **Bv.**, Berkshire Valley ; **W.H.**, Western Highlands ; **C.V.**, Connecticut Valley ; **T.**, Trap Ridge ; **E.H.**, Eastern Highlands ; **E.P.**, E. & S.E. Plateau ; **B.F.L.**, Boston and Framlingham Lowland.

As we saw in Chapter IV, in the period between the invention of machinery requiring mechanical power for its movement and the introduction of steam-power, the frequent falls in the New England rivers were of assistance in the development of industry. Although in coal-less New England, coal now provides the larger power source, yet the region has about 7 per cent. of the developed hydro-electric power of the U.S.A., and the largest ratio of *developed* to *total* water-powers in the country. The presence of such powers is dependent upon the heavy regular precipitation, the possibility of storage, and on the falls provided by the new drainage consequent on glaciation, or on the rapids produced by the intrusion of hard igneous material across the stream-bed, as in the trap-rocks of the Connecticut River.

We must think of New England, then, as a country of irregular relief, becoming positively rugged only in the north and west ; a country having difficult routes east and west and easy ones north and south ; a country of unnavigable fall-obstructed rivers with many lakelets, of boulder-strewn soils, sandy wastes, moraines and eskers ; a country with a bold, rocky, indented, islet-fringed eastern coast.

Figs. 85 and 86 indicate the main features of relief, and we should notice the broad, populous valleys of the Housatonic and Connecticut Rivers, the intermediate uplands, the low but irregular topography of the coast lands, and the drowned bays

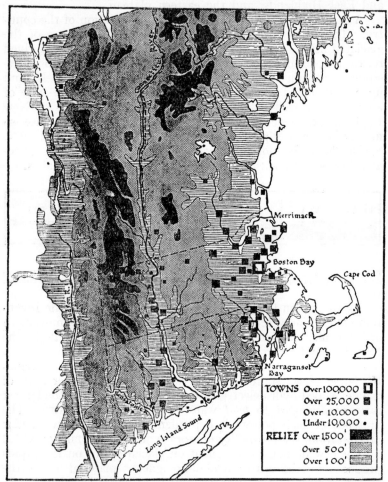

FIG. 85.—Relief and Town Population of New England.

of Narragansett Sound and of Boston. Partial passage valleys east and west across the barriers of the East and West Highlands are provided by four tributaries of the Connecticut River. Thus the Deerfield River and the Miller's River combine to give a northern east-to-west route, now followed by the Boston and Maine Railway, and similarly the Westfield and Chicopee streams are followed by the Boston and Albany Railway. The third and most southerly route follows the southern coast. Beyond the east coast are the shallows of Quereau, Western Georgia, and Brown's Banks—important fishing-grounds, which, with the shore fisheries, helped to give a maritime bias to the colonial population of New England, and provide an important fishing industry to-day.

In the early history of New England and in its present development, the comparatively mild relief of the Connecticut Valley

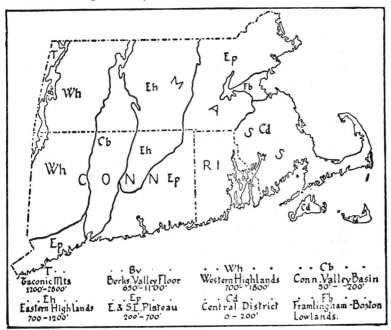

FIG. 86.—Relief Regions of Southern New England.

has given to it quite special significance. This valley lowland is some 90 miles long and from 15 to 18 miles wide at its broadest. It is developed upon sandstones and shales of Triassic period derived from the waste of the older and higher rock material to east and west. The Triassic rocks were deposited in their narrow strips horizontally—as in the narrow Triassic belts of the Piedmont to the south—and, as in their case too, deposition was interrupted by lava-flows which in turn became further covered by beds of sandstone and shale. These beds and the intervening basaltic layers were then block-faulted by a series of faults which lowered much of the Triassic rocks between older rocks to the east and west, and which tilted the blocks so that they dipped mainly to the south-east. The subsequent erosion reduced the whole to a peneplain, and final uplift resulted in differential erosion, which

(i) resulted in a broad lowland area between the eastern and western uplands of hard and older rock material ;

(ii) left a succession of basalt ridges where the trap was exposed at the surface.

The course of the lower river is curious. Instead of maintaining its direction due south to the coast and remaining upon the softer Triassic material, it deviates in a narrow valley to the south-east across older crystalline rocks. This is explained by the fact that a Cretaceous cover such as now forms a part of the coastal plain in the Southern Atlantic states at one time overlapped Southern New England also, and continued into Long Island, where Cretaceous rocks still underlie Quaternary material. Across this plain the course of the river may have been turned eastward by local irregularity, and with the gradual removal of the shallow Cretaceous cover the river would be let down bit by bit upon the older rocks and would maintain its channel, but with a narrow incised valley.

In respect of climate there is little to add to what was stated in Chapter X. New England has a remarkably even average distribution of precipitation, but, like all the north-eastern states, suffers low winter temperatures, when much of the precipitation is in the form of snow.[1] The Housatonic and Connecticut Valleys have, of course, a markedly lower rainfall than their bordering uplands, but are as little subject to real drought as any agricultural lowlands in the continent.

The period free from killing frosts in the southern valleys of New England varies from 180 days on the coast to 150 days in the interior. North temperate fruits (apples, pears, plums) do well, but peaches and apricots are grown only to a small extent in specially favourable areas. Maize is grown for fodder, ensilage, and early grain rather than for ripened grain. Apples are chiefly grown on the South-eastern Plateau and Upper Connecticut Valley ; peaches in the Southern Connecticut Valley.

As in the case of the Canadian Atlantic provinces—though to a less degree—the considerable upland areas, the patchy distribution of fertile soil, the boulders, and the forests, all tended to make New England farming difficult as compared with that of the mid-west. The cultivated land area has actually decreased in the last half-century. Derelict farms are scattered over the

---

[1] The heavy snowfall, together with the relief and relative proximity to large centres of population, are geographical factors affecting the growing winter sports region of northern New England.

country-side and many small holdings are merged in big country estates taken up by wealthy townsfolk.

In extensive farming the New Englander finds himself under-cut by the products of the middle-west. It is in intensive farm-ing with specialized products—milk, fruit, and vegetables for the great manufacturing cities—that success is most general.[1] Only Washington, New York, and Virginia have an individual output of apples greater than the joint production of Massachusetts and Maine.

The small size of New England farms and the patchiness of good lands, the relative difficulties of communication, together with the emigration to the west of much of the best farming personnel, have led to a somewhat backward condition of farm practice. The great manufacturing district of Southern New England receives from the west agricultural products, standard-ized and in good condition, at prices which undercut those for the same articles produced nearer home. Much grass-land in particular is impoverished by continuous overgrazing, and much agricultural land is exhausted for lack of fertilizers.

Fig. 85 shows the position of the centres of population of New England, and we may notice that any considerable agglom-eration is confined to the southern states (Connecticut, Massa-chusetts, and Rhode Island), and in these to certain coastal basins and river valleys, viz. Boston Lowland, Narragansett Sound, the Connecticut Valley, the Housatonic Valley. Thus considering Massachusetts alone, 38 per cent. of the population is in the Boston Lowland, mostly in almost contiguous cities with localized occu-pations, e.g. Lynn (shoes), Somerville (abattoirs), Chelsea (rubber goods), Cambridge (printing).

Further than these, we have only those inland water-power centres which were originated after 1750 but before 1825, i.e. after the invention of power textile machinery, but before the use of steam-power. Such are the great "fall" towns of the Merrimac River. In addition there are a number of lumber and pulp centres sited on falls amid the forest lands of Northern New England. The later developed and greatest textile centres, e.g. Fall River and New Bedford, are, like the earliest settle-ments, on the coast.

The ports and coastal industries now work on coal, shipped either at New Jersey or at the mouth of the Chesapeake. The most noteworthy cotton centres are (i) in the south-eastern bays, e.g. Fall River, New Bedford, Providence, and

[1] There is some local large-scale specialization, e.g. the tobacco area of the Connecticut Valley, the cranberry area of C. Cod Peninsula, and the huge potato production of the Aroostok Valley in N.E. of Maine.

Pawtucket; and (ii) in the Merrimac Valley, e.g. Lowell and Lawrence.

Big woollen centres occur at Lawrence on the Merrimac and at Providence, Lowell and Holyoke. A large proportion of the boot and shoe manufactures of the U.S.A. are made in the Boston Lowland, especially at Lynn, Brockton, Haverhill and Boston. The Naugatuck and parts of the Connecticut Valley form the Birmingham district of the U.S.A., a great hardware and machinery and brass-ware district. New Britain, Newhaven, Hartford and Springfield (Mass.) are among the chief centres. The amount of wood cut for pulp—chiefly spruce and poplar—in Maine and New Hampshire exceeds that in any single state. There is a tendency for paper-making to concentrate at pulp-mill centres, and also to rely to an increasing extent upon Canadian pulp. Timber, pulp, and paper are the chief manufactures of Northern New England. Holyoke is an important paper centre in the Connecticut Valley, and the Androscoggin Valley (e.g. at Gorham) produces much pulp and paper.

Three distinct influences have been at work in the localization of industry in New England. Firstly, in colonial days local domestic industries were a side product of the coast town populations. Then with the use of water-power came a partial shifting of industry to innumerable small inland valley powers. Then these scattered small units, capable only of very small and very irregular power development, were abandoned in favour of the really big power sites, such as Lawrence and Lowell on the Merrimac, and Holyoke on the Connecticut. Finally, *after* the adoption of steam-power, increasing manufacturing developed once more at coastal sites and with imported coal.

A further interrelation of geography and localization is to be found in the specialization of certain valley regions in certain branches of manufacture. Here the comparative isolation of the separate valley regions is the factor, rather than the fact that any one valley was found particularly favourable to any one industry. New Bedford, the largest of the New England cotton towns, was relatively unimportant in the industry until its whaling interests petered out in the seventies. Capital was then diverted to cotton factories, and the town was well situated for the receipt of coal and cotton by water. More than 50 per cent. of the cotton consumed in New Bedford is of relatively long staple, and it is thus the chief big centre of fine spinning. Fall River combines a coastal situation with considerable water-powers, and thus was prominent in the industry before New Bedford. The old water-mills were, of course, all below the falls, but the modern mills have a wider choice of location.

Probably more than 50 per cent. of the cotton used in New England uses water transport on some part of the journey from the south, especially if it comes from the south-western cotton areas. Certainly much comes wholly by rail.

Until after the close of the Civil War there was no considerable cotton industry except in New England. Then was developed the southern industry to which reference will be made in Chapter XXX. This has rapidly developed in importance and in recent years has been taking from two-thirds to three-quarters of the raw cotton used in the United States cotton textile industry.

The Southern States have nearly three times as many active cotton-spindles as New England, but New England spins finer yarns, and uses therefore a greater portion of long-staple cotton, including most of that imported from Egypt.

In the early stages of the industry, the urban nature of early New England settlement, the engagement in commerce, and the capital available therefrom, the water-power and moist coastal situation, were all factors of real importance. Steam began to be used in the industry by 1830, but the engines were, of course, most uneconomic and a real advantage remained with water-power for some decades. Then coal was used more economically and there was a shift of the industry to the actual coast. To-day most of the power is applied in the form of electrical energy, and rather the larger part of this is derived from fuel plants.

The percentage of cotton which is mercerized has been increasing in recent years, as has also the production of wool, silk, and rayon admixtures.

Finally, we have to notice that New England manufactures are increased absolutely with the expansion of population and its movement westward, but not relatively. The southern states of South Carolina and Georgia now use much more raw cotton in their factories but are engaged for the most part in lower-count yarns. The woollen industries have to compete with those of Pennsylvania and New York. The copper industry has to compete with those of New York and Michigan, and the boots and shoes with those of New York and Missouri; the paper industry with those of New York and Wisconsin, and so on.

In New England, as a whole, a larger proportion of the population is engaged in industry, and is living in urban centres, than in any other province of the U.S.A.

To a very considerable extent, also, the products are shipped to, and the raw materials of industry received from, other states and other countries. This condition of affairs in a coastal province should lead to the development of major ports. There is only one—Boston—and only to a very limited extent is it the port of New England. Boston Bay is a drowned river basin. A number of small creeks enter the crescent of the bay radially and their channels may be traced under the waters of the bay and between the islands now formed by the highest portions of their divides. A number of early settlements were situated around the bay, e.g. Gloucester, Salem, Lynn, Braintree, Weymouth, etc., but the greatest growth took place where the two longest and deepest valleys reached the shore, those of the Charles and Mystic. Here the port of Boston has its wharves about the common mouth of these two rivers and around the peninsula lying between them.

There were great natural advantages. Immediately north and south of Boston Bay there is some development of the sandspit and swamp coast that from here southwards characterizes the whole Atlantic coast. The good rock harbours of Maine were obviously too far north. The Boston and Framlingham coast plain, though by no means flat, is one of the few lowland areas of New England.

In its Atlantic relationship the port is :

(a) Open all the year round.
(b) 110 nautical miles nearer Liverpool than Montreal.
(c) 194 ,, ,, ,, ,, ,, New York.
(d) 337 ,, ,, ,, ,, ,, Philadelphia.
(e) 493 ,, ,, ,, ,, ,, Baltimore.

It is the nearest port to Europe which has a dense population and a manufacturing hinterland. Its natural deep-water approaches had to be less improved than is the case with most modern harbours, and will now take vessels of 35-feet draught. Railways now radiate from Boston like the spokes of a wheel—to Portland, to New Brunswick and Montreal, to Albany and the Mohawk Valley, to Hartford and Springfield in the Connecticut Valley, to Newhaven and New York, and to Rhode Islands centres. Yet with it all, Boston deals with less of the traffic of New England than does New York.

The development of transport facilities and the localization of industry are obviously mutually dependent, and it would seem that in these days the most localized of all industries are those pertaining to a port. About 60 per cent. by value of the port traffic of the British Isles is handled through London and Liverpool. More astonishing is the case of New York, which handles one-half of the overseas traffic of the States, and a very large proportion of its coastwise traffic also. Apart from any signal increase in U.S.A. trade, Boston, Philadelphia, and Baltimore can only handle more traffic by taking some from New York, and in this they have so far been unsuccessful. A host of economic factors not directly concerned with the *natural* advantages of a port affect its power of attracting freight, yet it can quite safely be said that the pre-eminence of New York was due to its early canal and railway connections, and those relatively easy and early connections depended entirely on the physical setting of the port. We will discuss further in another chapter the pre-eminence of New York, but, as a fact, it must be constantly in mind in considering the position of any other of the Atlantic ports. The whole relief of New England is against east and west traffic, the worst obstacles coming precisely where such lines should join up with the Mohawk passage to the Great Lakes. Here the Hoosac tunnel through the Taconic Mountains took many years to complete, and indeed was not opened till after the opening of the Erie Canal and the completion of railway connection between Albany and Buffalo. Boston has never made up, and to-day all New England to some extent, and Western and South-Western New England almost entirely, are tributary to New York. Only the Boston and Framlingham Lowland is predominantly within the hinterland of the Massachusetts capital.[1]

The immediate topography of the port has presented some disadvantages as well as some advantages. The city is built on the three peninsulas, which enclose the dual entrance of the Mystic and Charles Rivers, and separate railway companies have led their tracks to what are virtually separate ports. Extra expense is therefore incurred in switching tonnage originating on one of these lines, which is destined to be shipped from the wharves of another. This little difficulty has its geographical origin, but there are a number which are purely economic ; e.g. railway rates which in fact, at any rate, favour New York, Philadelphia, and Baltimore ; and a manufacturing hinterland, having no bulky return freight to offer, though there is a large import of bulky raw materials, e.g. coal, cotton, wool and hides, to feed the typical industries. Boston's future development depends upon its obtaining such bulky goods from the mid-west or from Canada (in winter), and upon the possibility of attracting shipping connections with the southern ports, so that more freight might avoid the congested lines through Baltimore, Philadelphia, and New York.

It would be interesting, if space permitted, to elaborate an

[1] For a careful analysis of the non-geographical factors which have adversely affected the development of Boston (e.g. port switch-lines and differential rail rates), as well as for proposals for attracting freight to the port, see Clapp's " The Port of Boston."

analogy between New England and Old England, as exemplars of the incidence of geographical momentum. Each in its continent achieved an early pre-eminence in industry—Old England on a basis of coastal coal and iron, and an already developed oversea trade and dominion ; New England on water-power and a particular commercial relationship with the West Indies and the other Atlantic States. Both have had periods specially favourable to development : Old England because of the requirements for development of distant lands in the later middle nineteenth century, and New England as an arsenal for the North in the Civil War. And now both have had to compete for some decades with newer producing areas which have stimuli, variously ; of more accessible raw materials, of more economic and modern industrial equipment, of nearer markets, and sometimes, as in the Southern Cotton Industry, of longer hours and lower wages.

And both, also, have to some extent adapted themselves to these conditions by a growing specialization in quality and variety, as opposed merely to large-scale production. Yet with some analogous characteristics there are many points of contrast. New England has no coal and much water-power. Within Europe are many tariff boundaries. The U.S.A. is the largest area of internal free trade in the world. Finally, from 1860 to the date of the quota system, New England has received a great population from southern and eastern Europe and from French Canada, which has little counterpart in the United Kingdom.

CHAPTER XXVI

GEOGRAPHICAL FACTORS CONCERNED IN THE GROWTH OF CITIES IN THE CENTRAL LOWLANDS

THE environmental factors concerned in the siting and development of both cities and industries form the subject-matter of a special province of geography from the study of which two principles immediately emerge.

(i) The importance of any particular factor is subject to variation; indeed, has proved often to be definitely limited in time. It is not too much to say that the factors concerned in the early exact siting of either town or industry are quite commonly of little or no influence to-day.

(ii) The environmental factors themselves admit usually of a twofold classification according as to whether they are (a) purely local influences, or (b) those of the larger environment. Generally, local factors may help to explain why, within a certain general and considerable area, a city or an industry is precisely where it is. The larger environment suggests reasons for its existence and growth within the area at all.

These principles apply in all countries and at all times. The incidence of any particular factor, on the other hand, is limited regionally and in time. The social needs of which an agglomeration of population is the outcome, themselves define the nature of the environmental factors. Protection against the enemy required not merely that people should live together, but that they should do so at or within a few yards of a defensive site. To this was sometimes added the general factor of a natural route concentration. Division of labour makes for community life, but it makes also for specialization, in the village, in the country, and now, in the world. Specialization depends on the very possibility of trade, and the trade routes are subject to some physical control. A nodality with regard to natural routes is the most usual controlling fact in the siting of cities. Or, again, the need for a water supply is exemplified in stream sites, spring sites, or sites providing the possibility of shallow wells. The towns and villages of Europe illustrate such factors with extraor-

dinary precision.   We may instance the lines of spring-fed villages
along the scarps of S.E. England, with the old-world town at
a water-gap in the scarp, nestling under the shadow of a castle
on a shoulder of one of the flanking hills, with town ana main
road a little above the flood plain of the river.

Now in this chapter we are to ask ourselves whether such
factors could have been operative in determining the location of
the larger cities of the interior plain of the United States, most of
which as sites of any considerable population are less than one
hundred years old.   But that period happens to be just long
enough to admit of the incidence of all these factors.   Sites
chosen for protection against the Indians are exemplified, though
they are in the nature of the case not important, but 100 years
saw the evolution of river routes, canal, road and railway ; and
Nature had a hand in the distribution of all of them.   Railways in
the United States, as in Europe, though not quite in the same
degree, were originally connecting links between already existing
centres, rather than through routes.   The already considerable
river or lake towns attracted the early railways, and each new line
was a dominant factor in continued growth.   In one way the
development of the interior cities of the U.S.A. is without parallel
in Europe, for it formed part of a definite migration of population
westward.   Of the larger cities we may say that each was in turn
(i) a pioneering outpost—perhaps a fortified fur-trading post,
(ii) an outfitting and refitting centre for pioneers passing westward, (iii) a commercial nucleus of a settled and considerable
population.   As much may be said of Pittsburg, Cincinnati,
St. Louis and Kansas City, each of which has been in turn a gate
to the west.

Let us consider briefly some of the local and general environments concerned in the growth of these and some other great
American cities, premising, however, that for the detailed local
factors the student should study detailed topographic maps when
these are available.

Pittsburg.   This city has received some attention in the historical and economic sections and we will add little here.   The
outspread arms of the Allegheny and Monongahela gathered up
the line of trans-Appalachian movement to the navigable Ohio
at this, their meeting point.   It is of interest to notice that even
around Pittsburg the iron and steel industry showed for a brief
period its early phase of charcoal furnace and water mill.   When
a great industry becomes localized in any considerable area, one,
or sometimes more than one site becomes identified not merely
with the common industry, but more particularly with the commercial rather than with the producing side of the industry.   The

industrial area, in fact, requires a commercial capital which may or may not be itself a producing unit of the industry. It will, however, house the organization of the industry, and the facilities for that collecting, re-assortment and distribution necessary to a densely populated area. The commercial capital of an industrial area is a city of office and warehouse, of wholesale house and assembly yards, of stores and of places of amusement. Quite frequently within its limits are typical large city industries, e.g. clothiers, printing, preparation of food-stuffs, etc., which are not characteristic of the industrial region as a whole. So much is true of all very large commercial cities, and is true of Pittsburg, though the characteristic iron and steel industries of the area are represented on the very outskirts of the city itself. The Pittsburg area was an important producer of iron and steel goods from local materials before the improvement of the Soo canal made the Lake Superior area tributary to Pennsylvania on a large scale. This industry and its later lakeside phase are sufficiently dealt with in Chapter XIX.

Let us now consider the cities west of Pittsburg and its Alleghany Plateau, lying on or between the Ohio and the Great Lakes. In pioneer days this area was crossed by three main routes. *First* and earliest, the river Ohio ; *second*, the Wheeling (Ohio R.), Zanesville (Muskingum R.), Columbus (Scioto R.), Indianapolis (West Fork of White River) to St. Louis (Mississippi R.) pioneer road (itself, of course, directed to and increasing the importance of these stream settlements) ; and *third*, the Great Lakes. The earliest pioneers were bound for the Lexington Blue Grass country with its fine phosphatic limestone soils. For reasons already given, the Great Lakes route was used little till after the thirties, but after settlement around Lexington, development proceeded from the Ohio northward along the Muskingum, Scioto, and Miami rivers, and importance accrued to settlements on these streams at the crossing-place of the main road. Later the connection of the Ohio country with the Great Lakes was to provide the requisite nodality for city growth. *Louisville* and *Cincinnati* were the river cities dominating the Blue Grass and Miami settlements. At Louisville, rapids meant transhipment. Hence storage and trade, boat-building, and the shipment of typical Blue Grass farm products—particularly tobacco. A considerable city attracted the railways. Even to-day no line crosses the Ohio between Cincinnati and Evansville except at Louisville.

Cincinnati shows no such definite local physical factor in its siting as the Louisville rapids—yet local factors are not wanting. The Mississippi system as a whole, once the head-waters of its tributary streams are clear of topographically difficult country, has its streams flowing in wide, definitely-marked flood plains. These on the main river, and on its tributaries, were not suitable for settlement. The swing of the river to one or other of the enclosing line of bluffs, and the existence at or near such a point of river terraces, clear of the flood-plain indeed, yet not usually at the full general level of the surrounding plains, together formed favourable circumstances. Thus Cincinnati, on the Ohio, is built about the terraces of a number of tributary valley creeks concentrating at this point. One of these—Mill Creek—was the site of flour mills in the early days of settlement. The site also is at an essential northern bend of the Ohio ; that is to say, at a point favourable for a connecting line with the Great Lakes, within easy river communication of the Allegheny coalfield, yet with better agricultural land immediately surrounding than is to be found in the plateau area of the upper Ohio. Cincinnati grew as the river port and commercial centre of a very valuable agricultural district, with grain mills, a hardwood timber industry, boat-building and carriage-making industries. From the thirties when lake traffic was beginning to be important, but before railway competition was serious, both lake ports and Ohio ports derived advantage from a series of canals connecting the two systems. Some of these are derelict, none of them are of importance to-day, yet they were effective influences in their time. Thus in this case a canal system began in 1824 and finished in 1842, connected Cincinnati via Mill Creek with the great Miami valley and thence by the Maumee Valley to Lake Erie at Toledo. Cincinnati was the most easterly, and the first of the great Corn Belt meat-packing stations.

The city then became the focus of railways, a railway crossing site of the Ohio. It has not ceased to grow, but the more recent rate of growth of this great city, which owed so much of its early importance to water traffic, has not been equal to most of the other great American centres. Meat-packing, milling and agricultural machinery remain important industries. In *Indianapolis* we have a city which owes much to the artificial traffic routes attracted to it as the state capital of Indiana, a state originally forested with hardwood, and apart from the sand-dunes about Lake Michigan, an excellent farming country set again between the Great Lakes and Ohio traffic routes. Indianapolis was selected as State capital in 1820, and it is curious to notice that even the meagre navigability of the Whitewater River was then considered an advantage. The Cumberland Road reached it in 1835. Early railways concentrated upon it, and indeed it is in an almost direct line between either Pittsburg or Detroit and St. Louis, or between Chicago and Chattanooga. Railway works, foundries, automobile works and meat-packing are important industries.

Fort Wayne has a typical portage site between the headwaters of the Wabash and Maumee, on one of those channels used by an outlet to the Mississippi in the time of the Glacial Lakes. A military post in 1794, it then became a fur-trading station, and grew rapidly when in 1832 a canal was built connecting the two streams, and therefore the Ohio with the lakes at Toledo. It is now an important railway junction with large electrical and engineering works.

The Niagara Falls have been effective in determining that the great Canadian cities of Toronto and Hamilton should be on the northern shores of Lake Ontario, the southern shores of which have no big cities ; as also that the great cities of Lake Erie should be on the U.S.A. side of that lake. Niagara plus the Mohawk gateway made *Buffalo*, and helped to make New York, whose development again had repercussive influences on Buffalo. That was Niagara in its character of obstacle, making Buffalo the main eastern terminus of the upper four lakes ; but as a source of power it has also aided in the industrial development of Buffalo, a city of grain and lumber mills, iron and steel works, foundries, electrical engineering and a host of minor industries.

If detailed maps are examined it will be seen that Lake shore settlements are usually—as we might expect—to be associated with a coastal configuration affording shelter and a ready graded access to the land, for the lake shore of Lake Erie, e.g., is frequently a bold though not a high cliff. This is certainly so in the case of the larger and older cities of *Erie, Cleveland* and *Toledo.*

Of these, Toledo, at the head of Maumee River Bay, is on the river rather than on the lake, a natural point to leave the lakes for the Maumee-Wabash route to the Ohio and one which derived considerable advantage at one time from the canal connection with Evansville (Ohio) and Cincinnati. It had not, however, the Canadian connection of Detroit, nor the coalfield connection of Cleveland. In the case of the last-named city the Cuyahoga river valley gives a well-graded approach from the lake, and with the Tuscarawa valley, the best graded route to the Muskingum and the Ohio.

Cleveland and Buffalo are the most important centres of the Lake Erie iron and steel industry, and the former has also an important woollen industry. Erie was the terminus of an historic connection between Lake Erie at Presque Isle and the Upper Allegheny. It is the most considerable lake port of Pennsylvania and engages *inter alia* in marine engineering and shipbuilding. It and indeed all the considerable towns between

Lake Erie and the Pittsburg area, if not engaged in the actual production of iron and steel, are engineering centres, some of them with local specialization for which it would be idle to look for any geographical grounds. Thus *Dayton*, a city on a Cumberland Road crossing of the river, now makes accounting and shop machinery for the world. The narrowing, and possible crossings, of the Lake system at the St. Clair River gives *Detroit* a nodality sufficiently obvious on any map. The site of an old French fort and fur station, it became also a point of departure from the lakes for emigrants bound for southern Michigan. It came to have a considerable lumber industry, having the white pine of the Michigan peninsula to the north of it and being itself within the hardwood belt. Among other interests it manufactured road vehicles ; something more than a presage perhaps of its enormous present interest in the automobile industry, an interest spread to surrounding cities and towns since Henry Ford provided a new technique in large-scale production.

Grand Rapids, the second city of Michigan, has a geographically interesting site. The rapids provided there a power site on a lumber stream at the junction of hardwood and softwood forests. Here has developed a gigantic furniture industry. Southern Michigan received from and was tributary to Lake Erie, and has no big commercial settlements on the fruit-growing, holiday-making eastern shores of Lake Michigan. The latest development of the lakeside iron and steel industry at *Gary* and *Hammond* in Indiana, and adjacent to the similar industries of South Chicago over the border in Illinois—these have received attention in Chapter XIX.

Chicago. The Great Lakes are bordered by lake plains which represent their greater extension in glacial times. These are covered by smooth, fine lacustrine deposits, and that of Michigan is separated from the Mississippi drainage by the Valparaiso moraine. The lake border plain of the state of Illinois is 80 miles long and varies from 4 to 20 miles in width, and, with an area of 722 square miles, represents 1·3 per cent. of that of the state. It contains, however, 41 per cent. of the population of the state, and 95 per cent. of this lakeside population belongs to the city of Chicago.[1]

Here with a population of nearly 3 millions and covering more than 200 square miles, with 26 miles of lake front, it is the fourth largest city of the world. Its population has increased a hundredfold since 1850, and it is now the greatest receiving.

[1] See " The Geography of Illinois," by Ridgely, p. 254 (University of Chicago Press).

distributing, and manufacturing centre of the middle-west. The chief geographical factors in its early development are abundantly clear. The Great Lakes, considered as a waterway system, send two great arms to the west and south-west. That of Lake Superior stretches towards, but does not reach, the wheat lands, and the development of its immediate hinterland is confined to mineral and lumber-work. That of Michigan, on the contrary, thrusts deep into the most extensive and continuous of fertile areas on the face of the earth. With navigation to New York (by the Erie canal after 1825), to Montreal, or to Lake Superior, before any very considerable development of railways, some big port was certain to develop at or near the head of Michigan. The actual site—as always—was at the sheltered entrance of some tributary creek—in this case the Chicago River, an essential bend of which is separated by a short and low portage from the Des Plaines River, a tributary of the Illinois River.

The marked channel, a notch in the Valparaiso moraine, over 100 feet deep and several miles wide, between Summit and Lockport, was formed by the overflow of the ice-dammed glacial Lake Chicago. It is followed by several railway lines, by the Chicago drainage canal, and by the Michigan and Illinois canal. The canals which connect the Great Lakes and the Mississippi tributaries are themselves a comment upon the importance of both water systems in the initial development of the middle-west. The little harbour of the Chicago River, backed by the low water-parting, attracted canals to this point on the lakes.

As the Illinois River was considered navigable from La Salle to the Mississippi, the Michigan and Illinois canals began at La Salle, followed the Des Plaines River to Joliet and the South Chicago creek to Chicago. It was opened in 1858, when there were still only a few miles of railways in Illinois. Another canal, the Hennepin, was designed to connect Chicago more directly with the Mississippi, and runs from the great bend of the Illinois to Rock Island on the Mississippi. It was opened in 1907. The Chicago drainage canal was opened in 1900. It is a deep waterway paralleling the Illinois and Michigan as far as Lockport on the Des Plaines River. Here is a hydro-electric station supplying Chicago. The canal was planned in the first case as a sanitary canal for Chicago, and it fulfils this function and incidentally makes Lake Michigan partly tributary to the Gulf, thus reviving a habit of glacial times. The canal was also meant as the first stage in a deep waterway scheme from Michigan to New Orleans, to which a second stage is being provided by a deepening of the Des Plaines River from Lockport to La Salle. But these last are modern works. Only the Michigan and Illinois is of the canal *era,* and it only has been of importance in the growth of the city. None of these canals, not even the recent ones, carry any appreciable traffic to-day.

It is often stated that Chicago owes much to the fact that railways from the north-west become tangential to the extremity of Lake Michigan in following the shortest route to the east. That is so, but the passage of goods *through* a locality does not make of it a population centre. Chicago to-day is pre-eminently a railway *terminal* centre, and a manufacturing centre. In earlier railway days and in pre-rail days it was pre-eminently a port—a place of transhipment between lake and land (or canal) transport.

Chicago as the lake port was the *focus* for lines from the prairie, and each new line was an additional factor making for further development. And these were not through lines to the east, but terminal lines to a great port. There was a rapid increase in population, and with a surplus urban population the step from the transhipment and handling of raw materials to their manufacture is a short one, and Chicago rapidly became the chief industrial centre in the middle-west. Now 40 per cent. of the railway mileage of the U.S.A. terminates at Chicago. Its huge population, of itself, provides a great market and a ready labour supply. Chicago as a great railway and manufacturing centre could continue its importance if the lakes were dried up, except that it depends on them for its water supply. This is not to say that the present lake traffic at Chicago is unimportant. It has not, however, in recent years increased *pari passu* with the size of the city, and it has, moreover, changed its character. General commodities are no longer carried by lake ; even bulky raw materials and manufactured articles use the rail, and lake traffic is almost confined at Chicago, as at other lake ports, to iron ore, coal, grain, and timber.

The two modern harbours are at the mouths of the Chicago River and of the Calumet River. The latter has fewer ships but a larger total tonnage, and deals entirely with bulk cargoes of iron ore, coal, and grain. Chicago River receives hard coal only, ships a smaller amount of wheat, corn, and oats than the Calumet, and handles more general cargoes.[1]

Just over the state border in Indiana, yet almost contiguous with Chicago, is the modern town of Gary, with huge iron and steel plants (see Chapter XIX). The site of the town, which in 1920 had a population of 55,000, and of 100,000 in 1930, was covered with sand-dunes in 1906. Chicago's situation at the Lake gateway to the Prairies, yet with its water contact with northern lumber and iron ore, was enough to explain its com-

[1] For additional material on the city of Chicago see " Man's Adaptation of Nature," by P. W. Bryan, pp. 237-72.

mercial position, but it has become one of the greatest manufacturing centres of the world. In particular its meat-packing, railroad material, and agricultural machinery productions are literally unrivalled. Primary iron and steel works adjoin it, and it has the multitude of lesser industries associated with all very great cities.

If we compare the two land-masses—the generally anticlinal area of Wisconsin and Northern Illinois, and the basin area of Michigan—in respect of the influence of the lakes on their respective development of population, some interesting results emerge. We have already noticed the climatic differences which have made fruit-farming a feature of the Michigan shores of Lake Michigan in contrast to the lake shores of Wisconsin. We have seen, too, that a large proportion of the population of Illinois, Wisconsin, and Indiana are at lakeside. Yet the Michigan shore of Lake Michigan has no big towns. The reason is largely to be found in the early development of the two areas. Wisconsin and Illinois were—in pre-railway days—largely peopled by emigrants from the east via the Great Lakes. The lake towns became the chief commercial and supply centres, and as such were the *starting-points* of railways to the south and west. The rail plexus and waterway terminals were then the chief factors in growth.

In Michigan, too, entrance was from the east, but the corresponding lake centres were developed on Southern Lake Huron and Western Lake Erie, where a corresponding plexus of railway was developed. Thus Western Michigan was more lately settled and has few big rail centres. " In short, Lake Michigan has been only a minor factor in the industrial life of Michigan, but it has been *in the past* a very large influence in that of Wisconsin. However, when the present is considered, water transportation seems to have very little to do with the great industrial development which is taking place in the Wisconsin cities on Lake Michigan. Even the receipts of coal by lake are declining, while the great quantities of heavy raw materials passing between Gary, Chicago, Milwaukee, Racine, and Kenosha are practically all carried by rail, and this in spite of the fact that many of the largest manufacturing plants that ship or receive these heavy commodities are themselves on the water front. The cause seems to lie in the fact that railway service is usually more dependable and more convenient, operates twelve months in the year, and costs little, if any more, except in the case of cargo shipments of bulk commodities carried long distances, as is the case with iron ore, coal, and grain." [1]

[1] R. H. Whitbeck, " The Influence of Lake Michigan upon its Opposite Shores, with Comments on the Declining Use of the Lake as a Waterway," in "Annals of the Association of American Geographers," vol. x, 1920, p. 55.

Milwaukee, at the mouth of the river of that name, was once a fur station of some importance. It owes its importance to some extent as being the lake port for the State of Wisconsin, and the port of entry of the immigrants (among whom were very many Germans) of that state. It lacked Chicago's early connection with the Mississippi, and is a place of altogether more local hinterland. To its typical and expected industries of milling, leather work, and brewing, it adds the making of electrical apparatus, and a minor iron and steel industry. It receives coal and timber by water, and ships grain.

Minneapolis and *St. Paul*. Here we have a break in navigation as the earliest factor, and the use of water-power at the Falls of St. Anthony, which for long have made the centre the nearest limit of navigation to the Red River plains, and at the same time one of the greatest milling sites of the United States. With the intensification of western population it has become a centre of general manufacture, with large iron foundries and engineering works and boot and shoe factories. The break in navigation was the first factor, then the bridging of the Mississippi and consequent concentration of routes, road and railway, confirmed the position.

Duluth is at the head of navigation on the Great Lakes. Here a considerable port must have grown up, though there is a much less concentration of population and industry than obtains, e.g., at the head of Lake Michigan, for Superior, unlike the other lakes, is surrounded by a wide zone of the thinly peopled Laurentian Shield. To the west of this lie the wheat prairies of the Red River Valley. Canadian grain, however, moves chiefly to the Canadian ports of Fort William and Port Arthur, and only a small stream comes to Duluth. The U.S.A. Red River grain goes to Minneapolis and Lake Michigan, because of more favourable rail rates. Duluth and its attendant ports are left then to the local products of the Laurentian zone, and these are considerable. The zone is timbered, and lumbering and timber-work are the chief industries of Duluth. Even more important is the iron traffic from the surrounding iron ranges (see Chapter XIX), for which Duluth is the biggest single shipping point.

The exact site of the city is—as almost always on the Great Lakes—at the mouth of a river which formed the original shelter. A sand-spit across the mouth of this St. Louis river gave complete shelter to the harbour, but a rather roundabout entrance. This last difficulty has been avoided by the cutting of a canal across the spit, giving more easy and direct access to a completely sheltered harbour.[1]

[1] See " A Geographical Study of Duluth," by Eugene van Cleef, in " Bulletin of the American Geographical Society," vol. xliv, 1912, p. 401.

St. Louis is the greatest of the Mississippi confluence cities. The actual junction of the Missouri, the near junction of the Ohio, and the crossing, therefore, of the great east-west route formed by these two streams in pre-railway days, were the major factors in the city's early history. The site was originally a fur-trading station chosen deliberately on the west (i.e. French) bank of the river by a French fur-trader, Laclede Largeist. It received its supplies from the Upper Mississippi and the Upper Missouri. The river flood plain narrows here because of an island mass now partly attached to the east bank. The town was placed on a terrace well above flood reach. The junction of the Missouri gives deeper water on the Mississippi below St. Louis, and as bigger boats could be used below the city, it tended to become a point of transhipment and a centre of river-craft production. The heaviest traffic was down-stream either from the Ohio or the Upper Mississippi, though after the introduction of steamers on the river, the up-stream traffic grew rapidly. The east and west traffic, however, was considerable, and in this connection we must remember the importance of the eastward-flowing tributaries of the Mississippi, which, though shallow and of very irregular regime, were followed by the trails across the arid high plains and led up to the Rocky Mountain passes.

Thus the *Oregon trail* started from Westport at the junction of the Kansas and Missouri Rivers, proceeded overland to the Platte, crossed the Rockies to the head-water of the Snake, and thence by the Columbia to Fort Vancouver near the present Portland. A branch of this route, the Californian trail, left it at the Upper Snake, and crossed to the Humboldt River of the Great Basin, and thence by the Truckee and Bear Rivers to the Great Valley of California. Or, again, a trail left Westport and struck across to the northern bend of the Arkansas and thence to the Upper Rio Grande and Sante Fé.

We see, then, that these routes from the west concentrated on the Missouri near the present site of Kansas City, and from there led eastwards by the Lower Missouri to St. Louis. Emigrants travelling west by these routes concentrated at St. Louis, which for a time formed a kind of gateway to the far west just as Pittsburg had provided the main entrance to the near west. Traffic in the lead and timber of the Ozarks, river boat-building, forges and foundries depending on Ozark ores—all added to the importance of the city.

To-day, because of the low rates charged on the government's barge lines, a revival of river traffic is beginning, yet it is difficult to realize that in 1844 some 450 steamboats were employed in navigating the Mississippi. Indeed, at that date the internal navigation *steam* tonnage of the U.S.A. was greater than that of the sea *steam* tonnage.[1] The early character of St. Louis as

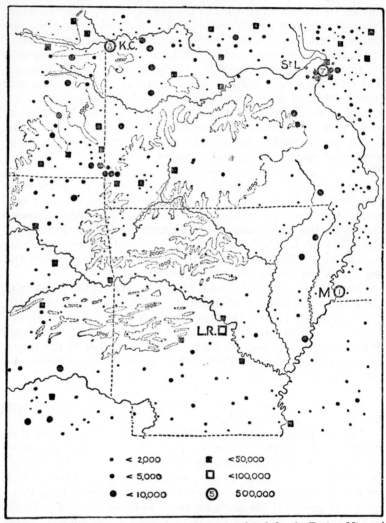

FIG. 87.—Map showing the relatively thinly populated Ozark, Boston Mt. and Ouachita areas surrounded by areas of denser town population.

St.L., St. Louis; K.C., Kansas City; M., Memphis; L.R., Little Rock.

an outfitting station for the west and south-west is still maintained in the trade connection in these directions of its great

[1] Hulbert, " Historic Highways," vol. 9, p. 142.

wholesale stores. Its importance achieved as a river port attracted early rail connection which terminated on either side of the river. Later the river itself was bridged. East St. Louis on the right bank provides the site for the more modern industrialization. It has the advantage of proximity to the best part of the Illinois coalfield and to a St. Louis labour supply. Among other activities on this side are a great coal electric power station, and one of the largest aluminium plants in the world.

We should notice the importance of meat-packing here, but this industry forms an even greater proportion of the activities of *Kansas City, Omaha*, and *Fort Worth*—all towns on the western tributaries at or about the junction of the grazing high plains and the agricultural prairies, and all equipped with great stockyards, fattening farms, and elaborate packing factories, and good railway connections.

Nashville grew up as the capital of the southern Blue Grass area at an essential southern bend at about the head of navigation of the Cumberland River. *Chattanooga*, long known as the " landing," or " gate " city, is on the Tennessee, which is navigable upstream in the fertile Appalachian valley, but broken by rapids down-stream. It is at a marked gap in the Cumberland Plateau edge. This nodality has been emphasized by railways. Important industries (iron and steel among others) are based on the local coal and iron, and the water-power development of the Tennessee River.

Cairo, at the mouth of the Ohio, is a river junction city. *Memphis* and *Vicksburg* are river bluff towns at the eastern edge of the flood plain. At Memphis is the only bridge between Cairo and New Orleans. Cotton is shipped down-stream from both these river ports.

New Orleans on the Mississippi is 110 miles from the Gulf of Mexico, on a narrow neck of land between the river and the shallow lake Pontchartrain. Below New Orleans the main channel of the river threads the longest of the delta fingers for some 90 miles in a south-easterly direction to the Head of the Passes, before breaking up into distributing channels each enclosed by a narrow finger of land. These are the south-west, south and south-east *passes*. The first provides a 23 feet channel (to be improved to 35 feet), the second 31 feet and the third 6 feet only. Above New Orleans there is over 30 feet of water to Baton Rouge (a great petroleum port). The Mississippi and its distributaries are protected by levées. There is almost no tide, but a mean river range of 14 feet.

New Orleans grew to importance in the early days of French River settlement—first as an outlet for the fur trade. With the general occupation of the Mississippi basin in the first half of the nineteenth century, the whole basin was tributary to it till railway lines from the Atlantic across the Appalachians cut into its northern hinterland. Recent rail freight rates have been as favourable for the north central interior to the Gulf as to the Atlantic, and New Orleans exports great quantities of grain from Missouri and Kansas. New Orleans is a great cotton port and exports this product, refined petroleum, and wheat, to north-west Europe. Its import connections are particularly with Mexico, the West Indies, Central and South America. Thus it receives great quantities of crude petroleum, of sugar from Cuba, of coffee from Brazil, of sisal from Yucatan, nitrate from Chile, etc.

In Texas, *Dallas*, *Waco*, and *Austin* lie on a narrow exposure of the Austin Chalk on the verge of the Black Prairie. They and *Fort Worth* in the same fertile belt are at river crossings and have become railway junctions. Their activities reflect the agricultural interests of the region. Fort Worth and Dallas in particular have large cotton oil-seed mills, meat-packing factories, and grain mills, and Dallas makes ginning machinery and harness and saddlery as well. At the extreme south-west end of this belt, at a river cañon opening in the Balcones scarp, is the old Spanish city of *San Antonio*.

Houston and *Galveston* are the chief ports for the south-west interior states; Houston made so by the 30-feet ship canal which connects it with Buffalo Bayou and the Gulf at Galveston.

The wharves at Galveston are situated on the inner sheltered side of a sand-spit island which is protected from the Gulf storms by a concrete sea wall 17 feet high, and connected with the mainland by a concrete and earth causeway carrying four railways and a roadway. Almost entirely artificial, it has become one of the great ports of the continent with exports of cotton, petroleum, and wheat, and imports of petroleum, sugar, sisal, etc. Thus it has a large bulk movement to north-west Europe and from Mexico, Central and South America.

Its connection with the south-west mining states is shown by a considerable coastwise movement of ore concentrates, and it ships also the Texas sulphur from the sulphur domes of the East Texas Coast Region. The chief bulk imports of Houston are petroleum, and the chief exports are cotton, grain (wheat and rice), petroleum products, sulphur and lumber. It should be noticed that all these gulf ports have large traffic in petroleum, in and out, foreign and domestic. This is because of the large imports of crude oil and the shipment of refined oils.

It will have been noticed that most of the towns of the interior of the continent derived their original importance because of their situation in relation to some major navigable waterway. It is not merely that so many are situated at waterside, but that waterborne traffic was the chief feature of their early commerce. It is right, then, that we should conclude this chapter with a fuller account of the Mississippi system itself.

Above Cairo the major affluents have incised courses with flood plains sometimes a few miles in width and sharply contained by well-marked bluffs. Below Cairo, however, the river meanders over an exceedingly extensive flood plain, usually over 70 miles in width, and developed on the much younger material of what is essentially a great embayment of the Gulf coast plain. Detailed topographic maps reveal the present stream flowing in great meanders over this plain, and retained, except in high floods, by natural and by artificial levees. Such maps also reveal an extraordinarily complex system of abandoned meanders and of ox-bow lakes. Much of this flood plain below Cairo is of exceptional fertility. Early settlers reclaimed portions piecemeal ; but eventually State and Federal authorities have made themselves responsible for an elaborate system of levees, which, while affording protection in most years, is yet not proof against the exceptionally high floods which inevitably recur at intervals.

The Ohio, at Cincinnati, shows the normal late-winter and early-spring maximum of a river in temperate latitudes and well-distributed precipitation. Lower evaporation in the cool season leads to saturated land and a big run-off.

Heavy snowfall and cool weather followed by warm winds with heavy rain, leads to very rapid snow-melt and the occurrence of floods, and these conditions are most likely at the end of the winter season. Under such conditions the Ohio may rise on occasion as much as forty or more feet. These occasional floods are, of course, masked in the use of average figures.

The Missouri, on the other hand, receives most of its run-off from the mountainous upper basin. In crossing the great plains, it and its tributaries receive little addition from the light summer rains which characterize this region of great evaporation. The high mountain tributaries have their maximum with the early summer snow-melt, and these conditions are all reflected in the marked summer maximum of the Missouri itself at Kansas City.

The Upper Mississippi lies in higher latitudes than most of the Ohio basin, the precipitation is less and tends to a summer maximum. The winters are cold enough for run-off to be continuously restricted in the winter months, and the day-to-day flow is somewhat evened by the number of lakes in the basin. These facts are illustrated in the marked summer maximum of the river. Now the Ohio provides 58 per cent., the Upper

Mississippi 19 per cent., and the Missouri 22 per cent., of the flow below Cairo. Thus the régime of the main stream at St. Louis reflects, in a smoother form, the summer maxima of the Upper river and of the Missouri, but after the junction of the Ohio, the influence of this master affluent is seen in the shift of the maximum to the spring months. Really serious flooding in the Lower Mississippi is always the result of floods in the Ohio coinciding, or nearly coinciding, with heavy rain in the Lower Mississippi itself. This may be disastrous. Estimates for the great flood of 1937 are not to hand, but the previous heavy flood of 1927 did damage to the extent of about £50 million, and caused some loss of life.

Levees deal moderately well with average conditions. They cannot conceivably prevent, and indeed tend to accentuate, the high floods which will certainly recur from time to time. Two main lines of amelioration are being pursued. The floods can be mitigated by the construction of gigantic reservoirs in the upper basin, to be filled in flood time. If such are used for other purposes however, such as power, then they will be unavailable for that purpose during periods when floods are likely. Secondly, the most extensive region of flooding, the lowest areas, may be definitely and of set plan sacrificed to the higher floods, the waters being guided by levees into great slipways to be carried off as rapidly as possible to the sea.

We have already referred to the importance of this great navigable system in the early settlement and commerce of the Interior.

Up to the time of the Civil War tonnage on it steadily increased, and some of the earlier railways were designed as feeders rather than as competitors. The subsequent railway building was definitely competitive, and no effort was made—quite the reverse—to provide any combination of the two systems. Exchange facilities between the modes of transport were lacking, and the speed, ease of branching, and general terminal elasticity of the newer form of transport caused a virtual extinction of waterborne traffic.

Congestion during the Great War, however, led to the government taking a hand. Vast sums have been expended on the improvement of the main streams. At low water the Ohio had only one or two feet of water in places ; similar conditions obtained on the Upper Mississippi, and the Missouri could only be used at high water. On the main river just below Cairo there was at low water only about 5 feet of water. Of course for much of the year depths were much greater than these, and for all the year were so over considerable stretches. Now a whole series of locks and weirs maintain a minimum of 9 feet of water on the Ohio, and of 12 feet of water from St. Louis to New Orleans.

In addition to these improvements, projected and completed, the government have improved exchange terminals, and have forced the institution of combined rail-and-water freight rates. Further, they have provided a fleet of up-to-date steel barges, some of 3,000 tons capacity, and of powerful Diesel-engined tugs, to provide service on the Mississippi between St. Louis and New Orleans, and between this port, and Port Birmingham, making use of the Warrior River system, and connecting up the Warrior coalfield, with the Mississippi, and with the Gulf. They provide smaller carriers on the Upper Mississippi, and the Missouri. Such are the Federal Barge Lines initiated in 1918. Some resuscitation of traffic has certainly resulted, but as the expense has been out of all proportion to the results achieved, and, as the money is found out of public funds, it may well be argued that a greater public good would have accrued had the money been devoted to other forms of transport. Some coal is brought from the Appalachian coalfield by the Ohio, but the heaviest traffic here, is, as it always has been, on the canalized Monongahela. Little actually is taken beyond Cincinnati by water. Iron and steel manufactured articles from the upper Ohio industrial areas are using the waterway to some extent. Considerable quantities of wheat are shipped from St. Louis to New Orleans, and of sugar in the opposite direction. Cotton is shipped down-stream from such centres as Vicksburg and Memphis, and bauxite from Arkansas to the alumina works at East St. Louis.

So great a stream, with so considerable a flood plain, must always have been a barrier to east and west traffic. There are now railway bridges at St. Louis, Cairo, Memphis, and Vicksburg, and a number of train ferries connect up railway terminals on either side, as well as at other places.

We have seen that most of the more considerable urban centres of the Mississippi basin (as of that of the St. Lawrence) arose in relation to inland water routes, and then attracted road and rail communications. Later, at most of them, manufacture has supervened and has employed the labour of an expanding population in increasingly diversified industry.

In the early and middle nineteenth century the very existence of the richest coal-field in the world set between the Great Lakes and the Ohio routeways, at the very threshold of western movement, tended to concentrate industry in what has become known as the north-eastern industrial belt. Improved transport and the electrical distribution of energy now make for a wider distribution of industry. The colossal petroleum production of Texas and the increasing use of petroleum products in industry (e.g. synthetic rubber) have helped to augment industry in the South.

13

CHAPTER XXVII

WASHINGTON AND OREGON AND THE COLUMBIA AND SNAKE BASIN IN THE U.S.A.

WE have noted elsewhere that everywhere between the highest mountain masses to the east of the Pacific Cordillera, and those to the west, are extensive interior plateaux—the British Columbia Plateaux, the Columbia and Snake Basin, and the Great Basin of Utah and Nevada. Each of these possesses a certain structural unity.

In the present instance the unit forms the larger portion of the basin of one mighty river, which rises, it is true, outside the physiographic region now considered, and flows from the great mountain trenches of British Columbia. It flows, too, into another well-defined region after crossing the Cascades, where its two tributaries, the Cowlitz and Willamette, occupy the northern section of the Great Pacific Valley. We shall deal in this chapter with that part of the river basin which lies within the U.S.A. We are concerned, then, with two major physiographic regions, viz. :

(i) The Columbia and Idaho lava plains with their mountain fringes ;

(ii) The Willamette-Cowlitz Valley, and Puget Sound Region ;

and with two subsidiary regions, viz. :

(iii) The Cascade Mountains of Washington and Oregon ;

(iv) The Coast Ranges of Washington and Oregon.

Such divisions are obvious and fairly satisfactory, even if the elementary relief only be considered. Climates, structure, and soils still further emphasize the distinctions.

THE LAVA PLAINS OF THE COLUMBIA AND SNAKE BASIN

The dominant feature giving unity to this region is the huge extension of lava flows which occupy all the lower ground, burying an older relief and bounded by the higher ground towards the International boundary on the north, by the Bitter Root Mountains and by the irregular mountain masses of Idaho on the east, by an extension of the fault block ranges from Nevada on the south, and by the Cascades on the west. Rising like a great

384

island mass from the midst of this sea of lava are the Blue Mountains of Oregon.

The flows must have been characterized by unusual fluidity and have taken place from a multitude of widely distributed vents and cones. About the fringe of the Blue Mountains and Cascades where the lava beds are shallower, the deeper valleys sometimes expose great feeding dykes. The general character and relief of the whole region received its present set in Tertiary

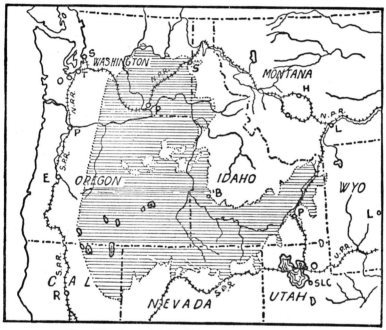

FIG. 88.—Area of Columbia and Snake Lava Flows.

S, Seattle ; T, Tacoma ; O, Olympia ; P, Portland ; E, Eugene ; R, Redding ; Pa, Paseo; Sp, Spokane ; H, Helena ; L, Livingston ; B, Boise ; Po, Pocatello ; La, Lander; Og, Ogden ; SLC, Salt Lake City.

times. At the beginning of this period there were no Cascade ranges, but a great lowland country over which the rivers wound a way to great estuaries and freshwater lakes, in which were built up a series of early Tertiary deposits. Then from innumerable vents poured flow after flow of lava, eventually covering the whole area. The outpourings were not continuous, but were interrupted often by time periods sufficient for a soil and vegetation covering to be developed, the remnants of which are interbedded between successive flows. In places, this immense lava mantle reaches a thickness of 4,000 feet. It shallows to its eastern and southern mountain boundaries, and through these marginal shallows emerge rock masses of much earlier date.

To the south-east, and occupied by the Snake River, is a great east-west extension of the lava sheets, though here probably of more recent dates than those of the Columbia Basin proper. But the surface soils of this vast region are not wholly derived from the decay of basalt. In the west of the region, and before the completed uplift of the Cascades, a great inland lake existed which received deposits from natural drainage and from volcanic ash. Also over great areas, and particularly in the west, the lava flows have been covered by a mantle of loess. Thus were laid down the light, porous Ellersburg beds. They probably occupied at one time a much greater area, but from their very nature have been easily removed by denudation. In post-glacial times, and with increasing aridity, these light soils have been removed too, by æolian action, and spread over much of the land of the Columbia Basin, giving on some of the good wheat lands of the east a soil of very fine texture, and one which is not derived from basaltic weathering.

After the extensive lava flows, which, we should note, covered much of the region occupied now by the Cascade Mountains, as well as the basin to the east, came the gradual uplift of these mountains, giving the most significant and effective relief system of the whole area, and providing a gradually rising barrier against the course of the Columbia River. The river is interrupted by rapids, and narrows to a gorge in its passage through the Cascades.

The great volcanic cones, which rise to double the general height of the raised lava block of the Cascades, are of a much later date. The Cascade uplift of a portion of the lava plains was the most important deformation of these beds, but it was not the only one. There have been noticeable warpings of them in both an east and west direction and a north and south one. The first set were the more important in the north-western part of the basin. These occurred after the Columbia River and its tributary, the Yakima, had developed their present north and south line of flow, a flow which has been maintained across the grain of these warped ridges with certain economic results, to which reference will be made presently.

If we compare the geological map of this region with a relief map, we see that from about the junction of the Okanagan with the main stream, to the town of Wenatchee, the Columbia River flows in a cañon, which marks the junction of older crystalline rocks to the north-west, with the relatively undisturbed lava plateau to the south-east. From Wenatchee southwards the main stream is crossing the lava beds, but they have here been warped into an east-west series of sharp monoclinal folds through which the river has cut deeply. So also with the parallel tributary stream, the Yakima. They both cut through the folds in gorges or cañons, and to the east of each the crossing spur dies out in the plain. These east and west ridges are the largest of a number of spurs originating in the Cascades, some dying out before the Yakima and Columbia are reached, and some, as we have just described, crossing these streams. The Columbia itself is generally too deeply entrenched to be of much use for irrigation purposes, but the succession of flat, roughly triangular basins into which these barrier ridges have thrown the Yakima system, offers much land for actual and potential irrigation.

Another important series of phenomena affecting the district occurred in Pleistocene times, and they depend on

(i) the greater precipitation attending this period ;
(ii) the shifting by ice of some of the river courses ;
(iii) the lacustrine deposits of temporary glacial lakes.

Great glaciers descended into the Columbia Basin from the mountains in the north and east, by the Okanagan Valley and by the Spokane Valley. The Okanagan ice-flow seems to have crossed the 200-foot cañon of the Columbia River, detaching blocks of basalt from the south-east cañon wall in its course. Advancing on a wide front, it must have displaced the course of the Columbia waters to a great convex line, leaving the old course and flowing by the route since marked by the Grand Coulée, Moses Lake, and Crab Creek, to join the old course again just north of the Saddle Mountain escarpment at Sentinel Bluffs.

" Opening from the cañon of the Columbia near the south-west corner of Lincoln County, the Grand Coulée extends in a south-westerly direction for over 30 miles. Throughout the greater portion of this distance it is a wide, flat-bottomed cañon walled by cliffs. But a little south of its middle point its western wall subsides, and it is joined by a broad valley with gently sloping sides. Opposite the mouth of this valley a plateau rises nearly a thousand feet above the bottom of the Coulée, but the ascent of this upland is made on a moderate slope unbroken by cliffs. This break in the wall of the chasm, constituting the only point where the Grand Coulée proper can be crossed by a wagon, has determined the location of the small town known as Coulée City. Above this middle pass the Coulée bottom, partly covered by alkaline lakes and flanges, is about $1\frac{1}{2}$ miles wide, with basalt cliffs which rise on either side to a height of about 400 feet. Two miles below the town the bottom of the cañon abruptly drops, and two amphitheatres, separated by a narrow point and walled by vertical cliffs 400 feet in height, mark the place where the Columbia once poured in a mighty cataract." [1]

The gorge extends 15 miles to the south, and is probably

FIG. 89.—Relief Map of Washington and Oregon.

Old Course of Columbia River ....
PR, Priest Rapids ; A, Astoria ; P, Portland ; S, Seattle ; T, Tacoma ; Y, Yakima ; Sp, Spokane;
Pa, Paseo ; Sa, Salem ; CdA, Cœur d'Alene ; W, Wallace.

continued beneath a mantle of surface material in the depressions marked by Moses Lake and Crab Creek. Many other and

[1] "Geology and Water Resources of a Portion of East-Central Washington," by F. C. Calkin. Water Supply and Irrigation Paper, No. 118, U.S.G.S., p. 18.

shallower stream gorges bear witness to a former greater precipitation. The shallow lakes occupying the old glacial Columbia track are higher in the north than in the south, and occasionally the northern lakes overflow to the south. Thus in the north they are fresh, and in the south (e.g. Soap Lake) progressively saline.

Considering broadly for a moment the relief of the Columbia and Snake lava plain as a whole, we should notice that the Blue Mountains and the raised lava plains, which continue their line to the south-west in Oregon, cut off the relatively low plain of the Middle Columbia, both from the barren basins of inland drainage of Central Oregon, and from the east and west basin of the Upper Snake River in Idaho. The Snake enters the Columbia Lowland through the great cañon south of Lewiston.

Now, how have these structural and topographical phenomena affected human activities? The most significant results are those determined by the climates. Precipitation in this region is almost wholly derived from Pacific cyclones. As we noticed in Chapter X, the area dominated by the Aleutian Low and its attendant cyclones extends to the south in winter, so as to yield the characteristic winter rains of California ; and contracts in summer, leaving that state almost without summer rainfall. On the Coast Ranges and Pacific valley of Washington and Oregon, of course the precipitation is much heavier than in corresponding situations in California, and the summer minimum, though sharply marked, does not result in the complete drought characteristic of the last-named state. At least this is so west of the Cascades. But this long, compact barrier effectively screens the Columbia Lava Basin from precipitation (see Figs. 29 and 30, and Chapter X).

The prevailing characteristic of the Columbia Lava Basin climate, then, is firstly aridity and secondly a seasonal distribution showing a winter and spring maximum. It is important to notice, however, the effect of the gradually rising ground towards the mountain plexus of Idaho in the east, for the rainfall here increases to more than 17 inches while still in fairly open undulating country. About the mountain border of the basin, as well as around the interior mass of the Blue Mountains, there is much heavier precipitation, giving summer pasture lands, and the possibilities of stream irrigation.

We may divide the Columbia Basin, then, into a central and western portion, where precipitation is insufficient for agriculture, and an eastern half, where rainfall is sufficient for the growth of wheat and barley if suitable grain and methods are used. The northern and eastern mountain boundaries of the Columbia Plateau have a much heavier precipitation, which gives rise to

forest-covered hills, to much grass land, and to considerable
orchard cultivation in the valleys of the foothills.

The district around Spokane and the Palouse River, approximating to the eastern third of the basin proper, has very extensive wheat lands, which give way to orchards, alfalfa grass, and
timber as one approaches the mountains of Idaho.　Wheat cultivation has now been pushed farther and farther west, almost
to the Columbia River, with, however, poorer and more uncertain yields, and encroaching more and more on what at one
time was sage-bush grazing country.　The possibility of growing wheat on the arid Columbia Plateau is dependent upon the
following considerations :

(i) The precipitation, though small, is much of it in the form
of winter and spring snow, and is subject to but slight
loss from evaporation.

(ii) The soil of the wheat lands are " fine loams, very light,
open, and friable."　This, together with the open nature
of the country, makes for ease of cultivation.　The soil
is sufficiently porous to prevent a too rapid run-off,
yet is fine enough to be moisture-retaining.

(iii) The relative cheapness of these semi-arid lands in a
" new " area.

(iv) The use of summer fallow and general dry-farming
methods in the drier regions.

(v) The use of selected seeds, giving varieties of wheat in
which the grain is not too easily loosened when ripe.
This, in the very dry summer months characteristic of
the area, allows the farmer to delay his harvest in any
particular plot without waste, till labour and machinery are available.　Another consequence of the dependable dry summer weather is the possibility of using
combined headers and threshers.

Some parts of the wheat area are far from flat, being diversified
by a rolling whale-back topography, smooth but at times of
considerable gradient.　These hillocks, which are generally aligned
in a north-east–south-west direction, are steepest usually on the
north-east slopes.

The natural vegetation of this eastern third of the Columbian
lava plains region was grass, and a moisture-retentive black soil
rich in organic matters has resulted, but since crop production
has necessitated summer fallow in a region of so low a precipitation, sheet erosion is making itself felt on the slopes.　Up to the
present the wheat yields in this area have been surprisingly high
for a region of small precipitation.　Spring and winter wheat are
both grown, and in about equal proportions, but with more spring

to the north, and winter to the south. The fertile soils of this Palouse country are interrupted in the north by what are known as the *scablands* ; a series of roughly north-east–south-west stretches of almost bare lava. These areas were laid bare by the erosion of streams originating from an ice-sheet lying immediately to the north.

The Palouse country is the only large-scale area of farm land in the whole of the Cordilleran states, and it normally has about 10 per cent. of the total wheat production of the country. Most of the wheat moves westward, and much of it is exported, either as wheat or as flour, from Portland, and to a lesser extent from Seattle.

The Spokane Area and the Cœur d'Alene District. The Spokane Valley, and that of its tributary, the St. Joseph River, above the Cœur d'Alene lake, are the two routes by which transcontinental lines enter the Columbia Basin after crossing passes in the Bitter Root mountain system of Idaho.

The summit level of the crossing on the former is much lower than on the latter. Pend d'Oreille lake is 50 miles long and very deep. At the entrance of the Spokane Valley, the Spokane River runs due east and west from Cœur d'Alene lake. It has twice been interrupted in its course—once by lava flows which fill the floor of the valley and through which the older rocks sometimes protrude ; and after grading a way through these obstructions, by the great glacier, which in Pleistocene times filled the valley. After the recession of the ice the valley was left filled with glacial material, into which the river is cutting its way back.

The gorge has thus been extended up-stream to the Falls of Spokane. These are used in a 30,000-h.p. development for light and power in the city, and in the Cœur d'Alene mining district, which is on the hillside above Wallace, in Idaho. The district provides 85 per cent. of the value of the mineral output of Idaho and one-third of the lead production of the U.S.A.

Orchards and meadows occur in the better watered valley above Spokane, but at this place the river enters the open dry plain, and the growing of wheat (and some barley) occupies most of the cultivated land from Spokane to the northern end of the Blue Mountains, and westward through the Palouse country, to the longitude of the Grand Coulée.

The Yakima Valley. This gives a route for the rail from Paseo to Seattle and Tacoma, and contains a number of partly irrigated plains separated by low lava ridges through which the stream runs in gorges. North Yakima, at the junction of the Nachez River, is situated in one of these plains, in this case between the Rattlesnake Ridge and the Yakima Ridge. It is the centre of one of the most important irrigated areas in Washington. Apples, prunes, plums, cherries, and hops are grown in very large quantities, though the valley rainfall is only about 8 inches. Ellensburg is the corresponding centre of the next enclosed plain higher up, and produces dairy produce, alfalfa, and forage crops.

Prunes and peaches grow in the irrigated plateau valleys, but there is a greater danger from frost, and actually more considerable damage has been done by this agency here than in the Great Pacific Valley. Apples are the most important crop of the Yakima.

The Wenatchee and Okanagan Valleys. The Wenatchee also drains the arid slopes westward from the Cascades and lies a little to the north of the Yakima. There is plenty of water for irrigation during the early summer season when it is most wanted, and the valley is almost entirely given up to apple orchards. The Okanagan Valley is a continuation of that occupied by Lake Okanagan in Canada, and again is a centre of orchard irrigation. The products of these irrigated valleys, with their warm summers, sunshine, and, for the latitude, long growing seasons, place Washington first among the states with commercial apple production.

In this arid region of the Columbia lava plateau is now being engineered a combined irrigation and power plant even more remarkable than that of Boulder Dam. The Columbia River carries a much larger amount of water per annum than the Colorado, rather more, indeed, than the St. Lawrence, but not of course with so regular a régime as that of the latter. It receives its greatest affluents from high mountain regions, and so the months of maximum flow are from May to June inclusive.

The present scheme uses a substantial part of this flow for the irrigation of the western, flatter and drier part of the lava plain basin. A gigantic dam has been built immediately below the junction of the Grand Coulée and Columbia River. This creates in the well-defined valley of the river a reservoir running for 150 miles to the Canadian border. The present development is for a dam 300 feet in height, but the ultimate plan is to raise this to 500 feet. Over this dam and on either side of a spillway capable of taking 1·2 million cubic feet each second, are the power houses which, in the present scheme, are of 700,000 h.p., and in the extension, are to be of 2·88 million h.p. Besides providing these unexampled powers, the dam will regularize the supply of water for a tremendous irrigation scheme. Water will be led (in part pumped) from the Columbia above the dam into a great reservoir to be formed by placing another dam at the southern end of the Grand Coulée. From here water will be led by irrigation canals to a vast area lying to the east, or left bank of the Columbia between Pasco and Wenatchee. Here some 1·2 million acres are to be irrigated. The completed dam 500 feet above bed rock, and 4,000 feet long, will develop three times the power of Mussel Shoals, 50 per cent. more than Boulder Dam, and will equal the total installed capacity of Niagara. 65,000 h.p. of this is required for lifting water into the Grand Coulée irrigation reservoir at the rate of about 600 tons a second.

The completed works increase the efficiency of up-stream projects, and the regulation of flow will benefit navigation on the Columbia. Only the 300-foot dam is at present in view, and it is not expected that the whole scheme would be completed for another forty years or so. The first part of the development was commenced in 1935 and is now completed. The whole cost at present estimates may well be of the order of £60 million. If it is to be a success, markets must be found for the power, and for the irrigation produce grown in an area with only about 140 to 170 frost free days.

The Cascades. The Cascades in Washington and Oregon can be subdivided into two regions. The Northern Cascades, extending southwards as far as Mount Rainier, are an uplifted mass of peneplained metamorphosed Palæozoics. The uplift was contemporary with that of the western portion of the lava plateau, which resulted in the Cascades south of Mount Rainier. In both cases deformation accompanied uplift.

The northern end, at the International boundary, is formed by a branching of the range into the Okanagan, Hoyomeer, and Skagit Mountains. Uplift here was accompanied by north and south warpings, giving the three ranges and two intermediate valleys. In relief the Cascades consist of a 75-mile-wide, dissected, rather flat-topped range, with somewhat accordant altitudes which suggest earlier peneplanation. Running north and south in a straight line rather towards the eastern side of this mountain mass are a number of volcanic cones, many of them snow-covered and glaciated. These rise from 3,000 to 4,000 feet above the general level of the range. Its geographical position gives to the whole system the function of a most effective climatic and communication barrier. The climatic factor we have considered. With regard to railways, only three cross from the Columbia Plateau to the Pacific Valley.

The eastern slopes of the Cascades—as we have noticed in the case of the Yakima Valley—are characterized by a number of long, radiating ridges gradually descending to the plateau and carrying rather a heavier precipitation and more abundant grasses than the arid aggraded flat valleys between them.

The Cascades have robbed much interior land of its water

supply, but the account is balanced perhaps by the wonderful richness of forest timber which clothes the whole of the western slopes, and, save where the volcanic cones reach above about 9,000 feet, the top of the range. The trees, gradually changing in character, cover also the eastern slopes down to a dry line of about 4,000 feet. Douglas fir predominates in the west, and yellow fir on the drier eastern slopes.

Between the Cascades and the Coast Ranges four drainage basins with low divides occupy the down warp of the Pacific Valley. The irregular drowned basin of Puget Sound, with its 1,750 miles of coast-line, is fed by a number of short streams from the south, which are separated by a low divide from the Chenalis River basin. This latter river rises in the Cascades, and is exceptional in cutting right across the Coast Ranges and communicating direct with the Pacific. A low divide (450 feet) separates its basin from that of the Cowlitz, which continues the Pacific Valley to the Columbia River. A more considerable stream, the Willamette, occupies the Valley to the south as far as Springfield. South of this basin the river Umpqua, like the Chenalis in the north, rises in the Cascades and cuts right across the Valley and through the Coast Ranges to the Pacific. South of this again the Pacific Valley is less well marked, and the ground becomes progressively irregular until the east and west striking Klamath ranges form a broad barrier between the Pacific Valley of Oregon and its analogue in California.

The Coast Ranges in Washington and Oregon are formed of folded, peneplained, and uplifted rocks of Tertiary age, and often of easily eroded material. They are lower and less continuous than their prototypes in California, save only in their final development in the Olympic Mountains (8,000 feet). As we have noted, they are crossed successively by the Chenalis, Columbia, and Umpqua Rivers. The whole area—Coast Ranges, Pacific Valley, and Cascades—was found forested, and most of it remains in timber.

The influence of the Coast Ranges in limiting the precipitation of the Pacific Valley is sufficiently indicated in Fig. 30, Chap. X. We must emphasize once more, however, the marked midsummer minimum. This becomes more marked with decreasing annual precipitation to the south. In the Middle and Upper Willamette Valley irrigation is increasingly used. As in the case of California, wheat was a predominant crop some decades ago, and its continual growth without rotation has impoverished much soil, which, though originally fertile enough, had not the lasting qualities of the Palouse district soils or of those of the prairie states.

The growing season is longer, the winter milder, the summers less hot, than in the Columbia Basin to the east. Dairy-farming, hay production, and the cultivation of orchard fruits are now the chief agricultural pursuits. The valley has an increasing market for these, and for vegetables, in the growing terminal ports of Seattle, Tacoma, and Portland. Much fruit and milk are sent eastwards also. There is some local specialization in the small fruit production : witness the strawberries of Centralis, the cherries of Salem, and the loganberries of Brooks. Prunes and peaches are important in the Upper Willamette Valley, with its rather greater summer temperature.

In the Pacific Valley north of the Columbia River much less land is cultivated. It was, and largely is, a forest land of big trees and heavy precipitation. Stumping is expensive, and the soils are leached and low in lime, potash and humus. Here and about Puget Sound present activities are concerned with a few big rather specialized ports, with the greatest forest industry of the U.S.A., and with a considerable fishing industry.

There is little cultivated land on the Pacific Coast Ranges, where an extremely heavy rainfall, dense forests, considerably lower summer temperature, and relatively difficult communication have hindered developments in competition with the more promising and more accessible valley lands.

PUGET SOUND. THE LOWER COLUMBIA AND THE PACIFIC PORTS OF SEATTLE, TACOMA AND PORTLAND

Washington and Oregon together have a population of just over two million, and one-third [1] of it is accounted for in the three great ports of the region. For their present size and rapid growth we must seek some other explanation than is to be found in their immediate environment. It lies, of course, in the transcontinental railways and in the rapid development of Far Eastern trade.

All three ports are of recent growth. Only Portland with its direct exit to the sea, with its low gap through the Cascades, with its Columbia River water connections inland, had any considerable pre-railway existence. The Oregon trail, which led the earliest considerable bodies of settlers to these lands in the mid-nineteenth century, followed the Columbia River, and so emerged at Portland. In the first half of the century it had been the scene of conflict between rival members of the Hudson Bay Company and of the America Fur Company, both inimical to real settlement. To these few hunters and traders we may add small groups of missionaries and settlers from the Atlantic states. But by the mid-century a number of settlers from Missouri and the mid-west, chafed perhaps by the slump in mid-west farm produce, sought more favourable conditions on the Pacific coast.

[1] 1920 Census.

The Oregon trail, the usual mode of ingress into the Columbia Basin, approached by the North Platte, crossed the Rockies via the Sweetwater and Green River valleys, and so to the Upper Snake, which was followed to its junction with the Columbia. Thence the trail followed the river to the Pacific Valley, and thence to the Willamette and so to California.

In spite of its frequent rapids, much of the course of the Columbia is navigable. Portland stands at the mouth of the Willamette River, at the head of ocean-going navigation on the lowest of the trans-Cascade routes. It is at the connecting gap between two very different regions, viz. the Columbia Basin and the Pacific Valley. It was the most nodal point in all the new north-west, and the obvious site for the regional capital in pre-railway days. This character it has maintained to some degree. There are 29 feet of water at Portland and a mean tide of 1 foot. A river flood may add as much as 20 feet of water. Above the confluence of the Willamette the Columbia shallows rapidly. In crossing the Cascades the river is interrupted by rapids and falls, viz. the Cascades, Dalles Rapids, and Celilo Falls. In the Cascade gorge, with its basaltic cliffs and numerous hanging valleys and tributary waterfalls, the rapids are avoided by canals which are however only 8 feet deep. Above this, river communication for 3-feet draught can usually be carried to Priest Rapids. The Snake River is navigable (3 feet) from its mouth to Asotin,[1] but it is not of very much importance to-day. The Cowlitz is navigable to Toledo for river steamers, and carries much timber in rafts.

The Willamette has regular lines of river steamers to Oregon City, where a great 40-foot fall has led to a 50,000-h.p. hydro-electric station. These falls are avoided by a canal, and the river steamers now continue to Dayton and Cornwallis. The Lower Columbia itself is the most noted of the Pacific salmon rivers. The fish are caught in nets and salmon wheels, and Astoria is a great canning station. With the coming of the railways and the development of Pacific trade with the Far East, Portland has rapidly increased in importance. The Cascades are crossed on easier gradients from Portland than from Seattle, yet till the channel through the bar at the mouth of the Columbia was deepened the port was seriously handicapped. It will probably ship an increasing quantity of Washington and Oregon wheat. Yet it remains the most conservative of the three north-western cities, and the most definitely regional in character.

Puget Sound—Seattle and Tacoma. The irregular, long open-

[1] In each case for light-draught river steamers only, and many rapids have to be run.

ing of Puget Sound has nearly 2,000 miles of coast-line, and in its very outline suggests a drowned river system. Actually there are evidences of several changes of level, and that in recent geological times and while the general topography was much as at present. The considerable depth of the Sound—often right up to the shore-line—suggests the depression of a deeply eroded but quite ungraded river system. On the other hand, high terraces, some 200 feet above the present water-line, bespeak an even greater depression in quite recent times. The shore-line frequently consists of low but sharp cliffs of unconsolidated glacial drift material, with frequent water seepage and land-slides where this rests on a clay bed. The coast railway lines have frequently suffered from this cause. The valleys leading down to the Sound, whether from the Olympic Mountains, the Cascades, or from the south, are filled up with glacial material, with stretches of fertile alluvium on the present flood plain. In fact, it is definitely ascertained that the present Puget Sound depression was the site where three great glaciers met—a tongue of the Northern Cordillera glacier extending from the north, and more local glaciers from the Olympic Mountains and from the Cascades. There is evidence also that here, as elsewhere, there were several periods of ice extension. The present condition is the result of ice erosion, and of varying levels of the land relative to the sea, with a consequent varying erosion in the drift-filled valleys.

From the point of view of human geography, we have to emphasize the following points :

(i) A general position in the extreme north-west of the U.S.A. coast, such that its ports are many miles nearer Yokohama (say) on a great circle route than is San Francisco.

(ii) The presence of a great sheltered inlet giving easy access many miles into the Pacific Valley region, and deep enough for the very biggest vessels.

(iii) Two relative weaknesses of the Cascades between Mt. Rainier and Mt. Stuart, giving transcontinental railway access to Seattle and Tacoma.

(iv) The nearest U.S.A. inlet to Alaskan territory.

(v) A mountainous environment with heavy precipitation, enormous timber, and undeveloped water-power resources, and great salmon fisheries.

Until the railways reached Puget Sound, Portland remained the chief port of the two states, but with their advent here however the more permanent deep water, and other factors above indicated, began to give the Puget Sound ports some advantages.

Seattle occupies a series of terraces in the drift covering

between the Sound and the fresh waters of Lake Washington, which lies just to the east of the port, and with which it is connected by a ship canal. This gives a completely sheltered fresh water [1] harbour, and additional wharf-space. The unconsolidated materials of the shore have been bevelled down by waterjets—a method adopted, no doubt, from the similar treatment of gold-bearing foothills in California. Where fifty years ago a few log huts on a clearing represented all there was of settlement, there is now a great city of over 300,000 inhabitants, and with many regular steamer lines to the Far East. The railway from Seattle to Tacoma traverses much land along the shore-line and receives feeders from the Tertiary coal areas about Newcastle to the north-east of Seattle, and from the Wilkeson Carbonado group in the south-east. The coal varies from subbituminous to anthracitic. Some coking coal is obtained. These fields and that of Clealum together give Washington state an annual output of three million tons.

Tacoma is rather overshadowed by Seattle, but it has a similar traffic and development. Its lead refineries are to be related to the Cœur d'Alene lead district in Idaho and it, too, has a growing trade with the Far East.

Since the gold-rush to Klondyke, Seattle has been the natural collecting centre for Alaskan products and for supplies for Alaska. Regular steamers now run from Alaska to Seattle twice a week. Alaskan gold-dust, copper-ore, even vegetables (a comment this, surely, on the climate of Alaska as well as on the regular service) and salmon, are sent to Seattle ; while stores, mining machinery, and other manufactured articles make the return journey. Puget Sound has many smaller ports, for which Tacoma and Seattle are the collecting centres. They are mostly lumber and fishing stations.

One event has been of paramount importance in the recent development of these harbours. They, and with them the great ports of Vancouver and San Francisco, have derived quite special advantages from the growing use of the Panama Canal. The most striking and obvious saving in distance which this route provides is in the case of traffic between the Eastern and Western coasts of the Americas themselves, and it is such tonnage which forms the bulk of the traffic using the canal. Hawaian sugar, Chilean iron-ore and nitrates, and Californian oil use the canal eastwards ; Central and South American oil and timber from the Southern States move westwards, but for the north-western ports of North America the canal has specially stimulated the shipment of timber (largely Douglas fir) and of wheat. Increas-

[1] Ships are able to lose their barnacles, therefore.

ing quantities of Canadian and Washington wheat are using the canal, and Washington and Oregon now rank first in the timber production of the States.

Washington and Oregon are said to contain about one-third of the standing timber of the whole U.S.A.[1] The forests of the Coast Ranges (precipitation over 80 inches) and of the western Cascades (precipitation over 80 inches) are the most extensive and densest in the United States. Yet even they are becoming all too rapidly depleted. Forest fires and the burners of the lumber factories cause a haze which hides, as at Vancouver, magnificent mountain scenery for weeks at a time.

" West of the Cascades the country is mainly occupied by four species—red fir, cedar, hemlock, and spruce. East of the Cascades the climate becomes rapidly drier, and the timber consists almost entirely of lodgepole and yellow pine." The eastern lower slopes are bare.

In Oregon the timber consists of about the same species as in Washington, with the addition of sugar pine, noble fir, and yellow pine in the south-western part of the state. The red fir constitutes by far the larger part of all the timber in the state. Cedar, hemlock, and spruce are comparatively unimportant except along the coast. The Douglas Fir occupies the entire timbered portion of the western slope of the Cascades, the eastern slope of the Coast Ranges, and the depression between these mountains, where it forms more than three-quarters of the forest.[2]

The timber line in the Cascades is at about 6,000 feet, which means that only isolated hill-peaks are unforested. The best growth is at about 4,000 feet. In the higher portions of these ranges the snowfall is exceptionally heavy, and glaciers flank Mt. Hood, Mt. Rainier, and other high peaks.

In 10⁶ feet. B.M.	Total Timber Cut	Douglas Fir		Western Yellow Pine		Hemlock		Spruce	
			Per cent.		Per cent.		Per cent.		Per cent.
Washington	4,603	3,578	61	220	13	275	16	275	28
Oregon . .	2,710	1,898	33	437	26	68	4	215	22
U.S.A. . .	31,890	5,819	100	1,707	100	1,696	100	980	100

The table above shows both the pre-eminent place of these two states in the U.S.A. timber production, and also the fact

[1] Department of Commerce and Labour. " The Lumber Industry," Part I, p. 79.
[2] Bowman, " Forest Physiography," p. 163.

that a few types represent almost the whole production. Note particularly the enormous proportions of the Douglas fir cut.

Another economic effect of the heavy precipitation, steep gradients, and partial snow-covers, is the enormous water-power resources of these north-western states. Washington, Oregon, and California probably have about one-third of the possible water-powers of the U.S.A. The actual developed power in Washington and Oregon is less than in California, but in any estimate of the future of these states we must keep the potential power in view. Hydro-electric power is at present used for lighting, lumber mills, and much transport, but it is easily available for general manufacturing.

During the second world war the Grand Coulee dam has been largely completed, and by 1944 about one million horse-power had been installed. Ultimately 2·88 million horse-power will be here developed. Further down-stream at Bonneville, where the river begins to cut through the Cascade mountains, a further 0·69 million horse-power has been developed.

From the Canadian border the Columbia river falls 1,300 feet in 600 miles and often in a bed so deeply cut that dams produce great elongated reservoirs upstream. The chief dams remaining to be built are to be at Umatilla, Rock Island and Foster Creek. Ultimately the basin should yield over 6 million horse-power.

The already considerable development of power has found a ready market in the war-time metallurgical (especially aluminium) and ship-building industries of the Puget Sound area.

CHAPTER XXVIII

CALIFORNIA

CALIFORNIA is not included in any single natural region. The second largest of the states, it rivals any in the variety of its topography, climates, and resources. Yet, even as a state, its boundaries are to some degree natural. On the north the irregular mountain massif of the Klamath breaks the continuity of coast range and valley provinces, and interposes a region of different age and structure between these units as they appear in Oregon and in California. In the east and south the exact boundary-line is somewhat arbitrary, but here broad belts of complete aridity form, at any rate, very effective boundary zones. California as the scene of any extensive occupation lies west of the Sierra Nevada and of the San Gabriel and San Bernardino ranges.

Perhaps in no other so considerable area in the world is the influence of relief so clearly expressed in climatic conditions and in routeways. The high Sierra and its foothills, the coast ranges, the coast range valleys, the Great Valley of California itself, have all different resources and different climates, yet they should not be considered quite separately, for from the point of view of human geography, they are parts of one great Pacific province, and are often interdependent in the matter of outlet routes and of water supply.

Let us examine the general relief (Fig. 90). The most striking feature, of course, is the Great Valley, almost entirely surrounded by mountains and extending some 400 miles from Red Bluff on the Sacramento in the north, to Kern in the south. Its greatest width is about 50 miles. Here is a larger and more completely even plain than that of the Willamette and Cowlitz ; contained on the west, too, by a less broken coast range system, and with a shorter and less intense rainy season. To the north of this and partly in Oregon, the Klamath ranges strike east and west against the general north and south grain of the country, and provide the water-parting between the Rogue and Klamath River systems. The core of these hills consists of granitic masses intruded into Devonian, Carboniferous, and later rocks. Somewhat extensive intermont plains exist. Thus, near the boundary, we have the Rogue River valley about Medford (Oregon), a flat-floored, completely enclosed lowland at about 1,400 feet

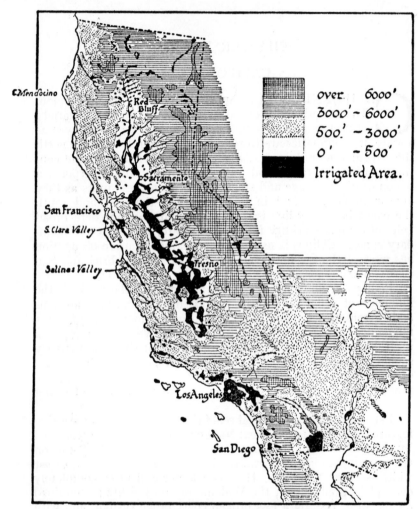

FIG. 90.—Relief and Irrigation Areas of California.

above sea-level, and some 20 miles in length and 5 to 10 miles in width. Here are many orchards of apple and pear. Then, again, just over the California border, on the Upper Klamath, we have the higher (2,800 feet), slightly more extensive intermont plain of the Shasta Valley (just north-west of Mount Shasta), largely devoted to stock-raising. Apart from these and smaller valley settlements, the land of the Klamath hills is too high for agriculture and is given up to timber and mining. After leaving the Shasta Valley the railway crosses to the Sacramento Valley at a height of nearly 4,000 feet. The Sacramento River rises in the Shasta range, just south-west of the volcanic cone itself, and flows in a difficult gorge (followed by the railway), some 60 miles to Redding. About Redding is irregular open country, but the real flood plain is not reached till just above Red Bluff, the old limit of effective navigation.

To the west of the Great Valley lie the coast ranges. These expose Cretaceous and more recent rocks and some igneous intrusives, the whole broadly deformed and dissected ; but the most effective agent in their present general relief (as in all the mountain systems of California) has been the block faulting. The western edge of the dissected block upon which the coast ranges are developed, should be considered the submarine line at about 600 feet depth. West of this the surface falls sharply to 8,000 feet and more in the Pacific abyss. The eastern edge overlooks the Great Valley, and between these major scarps are a number of longitudinal valleys outlined by parallel faults, and set somewhat obliquely to the coast-line ; so that the extremities of the ridges reach the coast in bold promontories and the ends of the valleys in low bays. Since the main relief of the whole state was outlined, there have been many fluctuations in level relative to the sea. Raised beaches are a feature of the coast, but, on the other hand, San Francisco Bay and Monterey Bay are the results of local subsidence. San Francisco Bay is obviously a drowned river system which had its outlet through a narrow gorge in the outer coast range, where even to-day the waterway has a minimum width of 1 mile in the Golden Gate. A similar constriction—the Carquinez Channel—marks the crossing of a second hill-spur, so separating the drowned river valleys of San Francisco Bay from the shallower waters of Sui Sun Bay.

We shall be concerned with San Francisco as a port presently ; for the moment let us emphasize its site at the only complete gap in the coast ranges. For the rest, we need to note that, though these coast ridges are seldom more than 3,000 feet high, yet they are remarkably continuous, and are high enough to afford a very real rain barrier for both the Great Valley and the long, narrow valleys between the ranges themselves ; notably the Salina, Santa Clara, and Sonona Valleys, each of which is important both agriculturally and for the routeway it affords. Apart from the line between Stockton and Alvarado just south

of the Berkeley hills, no line crosses the coast ranges from the
Great Valley to the Pacific, south of San Francisco.

East of the Great Valley, the Sierra Nevada ranges correspond
in relief (not in structure) and climatic function to the Cascades
of Oregon and Washington.   Rocks of many geological ages have
been close-folded, metamorphosed, subject to repeated volcanism,
and peneplained, representing, in fact, an extremely complicated
geological history.   They were folded at the close of the Palæozoic age, and suffered igneous intrusion and some erosion. At
the close of the Jurassic there was further compression, folding,
and uplift, with batholithic intrusion and much metamorphism.
Then followed peneplanation—less complete in the south, the
major massifs of which are residual—and then the great tilting
and faulting of the whole peneplained block.   To the east, overlooking the arid plateau of Nevada, is a belt of foothills representing a 20-mile-wide series of north to south parallel faults,
and in the depression between the edges of the multiple scarps,
are Owens, Mono, and Tahoe Lakes.   In general, the more precipitous edges face east.   The main peneplained block slopes
more gently to the Great Valley than towards Nevada.   But
on the western slopes the uplift has resulted in heavier precipitation, and where the rejuvenated streams have cut through the
harder rock-bands, deep, intricate cañons result, some of which
are from $\frac{1}{2}$ to 1 mile in depth.   The snow lies late in summer
in the Sierra at about 5,000 feet, but in Pleistocene times these
mountains were glaciated down to about 5,000 feet, and now the
upper valleys are U-shaped and the lower V-shaped.   Numerous
cirques and hanging valleys are discernible above this line.

Of the influence of this, the greatest range of the continent,
on climate, we shall deal presently.   Let us notice at once that
it is crossed by only one great railway, that which enters the
Sierra from the east by the Truckee River valley and uses the
Donner Pass with a summit level of 7,000 feet.   This is the only
transcontinental line between the Tehachapi Gap in the south
and that emerging at Portland, Oregon.

On the south, mountain masses completely close the Great
Valley, from which the railway emerges by the high Tehachapi
Pass.

The general north-west to south-east fault lines of the coast
range are continued in the tilted block mountains of the San
Gabriel and San Bernardino ranges.   Here, again, the steepest
slopes are to the east, and, in spite of the deep dissection of
rejuvenated streams, there is evidence of former peneplanation.
These ranges are 6,000 to 9,000 feet in height, and present a
formidable barrier to communication.   We should notice the gaps

by which the transcontinental lines reached the coastal plain. West of this faulted ridge the coastal lowlands are divided into two strips by the similar but lower Santa Ana range. East of the Gabriel-Bernardino massifs, yet still in California, lie the Mohave and Colorado desert lowlands.

Completely surrounded by mountain ranges, then, is the Great Valley itself—its whole economy based on their influence. Climate, possibilities of irrigation, power, lumber, and mineral resources, are all dependent upon its mountain margins.

Before proceeding further, we should examine the essential features of the climate of California as influenced by this clear-cut relief. California stretches through some 10 degrees of latitude—the same latitudes which compass the coast land of Algeria and Morocco and the southern two-thirds of Spain. Apart from special factors, then, we have an insolation which should result in hot summers and warm winters, and these conditions obtain in the Great Valley and in the lowlands of Southern California. The prevailing northerly winds, however, are accompanied by a coastal belt of cool water, and there is a rapid decrease in summer temperature as one approaches the actual coast lands.

This cold belt is *not* due to the fact that the water has come from high latitudes, but to the normal deflection to the right of bodies moving in the Northern Hemisphere. Thus, continued deflection to the west of water bodies moving in a general southerly direction along the coast of California causes upwellings of cold water.[1]

Then the position of the state in relation to the Pacific wind zones is such that with the winter increase of the influence of the Aleutian Low, a succession of cyclones brings rain to the whole country, which in summer is within the régime of the normal Pacific HIGH. We have, in fact, the general winter maximum precipitation experienced in Oregon, Washington, and even in British Columbia, but with the vital difference that in California the progressive diminution in total precipitation noticeable in all the Northern States as we go from north to south, reaches a critical point in its relation to agriculture, and is combined, too (apart from the actual coastal strip), with much higher temperatures. Besides the general decrease from north to south, there is the major influence of relief. Precipitation is much heavier on the western side of the coast ranges and of the Sierra Nevada than in the coast range valleys (e.g. Salinas, Santa Clara, etc.) or in the Great Valley itself. This variation with altitude is brought out in Fig. 91. Notice, however that the Sierra Nevada are sufficiently high to show an actual decrease

[1] See "Peculiarities of the Californian Climate," "M.W.R.," vol. 42, p. 14

of precipitation with height in their highest levels. This begins
to appear at about 5,000 feet, and is discernible in the precipitation of all months.[1] Much of this high-level precipitation
takes place in the form of snow. The transcontinental line
along the Truckee River route is elaborately protected from
snowfalls, and it was in this same high valley that one of the
first expedition parties to California—the Donner party—were
overtaken by winter snows in 1848. Destitute of supplies and
weakened by the journey across arid Nevada, many of the party
succumbed. Below 1,500 feet snow seldom falls, and never lies
long. Above 4,000 feet the winter fall is very heavy.

Very marked aridity to the east does not occur until the

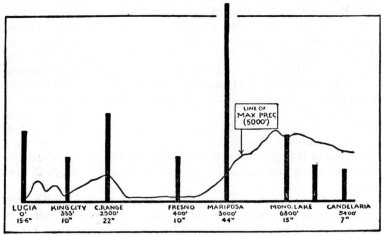

FIG. 91.—Correlation of Precipitation and Relief along a section through
California.

summit levels are well passed. Truckee and the fault scarp region
about Tahoe Lake have a precipitation of 27 inches. On this side
of the Sierra, the hills are still forested, though with different
species in a narrower belt, and less densely than on the western
slopes. The characteristic aridity of the Great Basin is not met
with on this route till Reno (8·65 inches) is reached.

In any consideration of the climate of California, the low
summer maximum temperature and small temperature range of
the coastal fringe should be emphasized.

Port Orford (Oregon).		San Francisco.		San Diego.
58·5 (Aug.)	··	59·1 (Sept.)	··	68·7 (Aug.)
45·8 (Jan.)	··	49·2 (Jan.)	··	54·0 (Jan.)

[1] See " M.W.R.," November, 1920, p. 648.

This is most noticeable about the latitude of San Francisco. It is a characteristic wholly confined to the coast lands, save at the break in the coast ranges at San Francisco, where the cooling effect is extended a few miles inland. " The traveller coming across the Sacramento Valley in the day during midsummer, is likely to find the trip warm, but on reaching this gap in the coast range, he almost invariably notices a change. The cool breezes sweeping in from the west and carrying the smell of the salt marshes becomes fresher as the train proceeds, and it is a reasonable precaution to have wraps handy from this point on." [1]

This low summer temperature is to be related to the northerly winds, the coast cold current belt, and the lack of insolation resulting from the prevalence of summer fogs. These last are a feature of the whole coast and we have referred to them already in Chapter II. It should be noticed that the fog does not extend into the Great Valley and hardly into the coastal range valleys. But on the coast proper it helps to lower the summer temperatures. As on the coast of Central Chile, a high relative humidity is associated with a rainless period. The low summer evaporation and the relatively high winter rainfall give both forests and pasture land on the coast ranges, but the Great Valley is without wood and is dried up in summer. The coast ranges are forested to a short distance south of San Francisco, and have good pasture land south of that again. Peculiar to the coast climate and its fogs is the great Redwood timber belt of California (Fig. 92).

The Redwood is a magnificent tree, second only in size to the Sequoia of the Sierra, and giving a very valuable timber.

The depression and break in the coast ranges at San Francisco allow some of the cooling influence of the coastal winds to reach the Lower Santa Clara and Sonona valleys about San Francisco Bay. It also actually causes a very slightly lower summer temperature in the very centre of the Great Valley than occurs either to the south or to the north, e.g. :

	Red Bluff (North).	Stockton (opposite Gap).	Bakersfield (South).
Av. July temperature in F.° . .	82·1	72·6	85·3

At San Francisco itself the monthly mean temperature determined from hourly readings shows an extraordinary equability, and also a very low average temperature for a place of such latitude. Thus :

	J.	F.	M.	A.	M.	J.	J.	A.	S.	O.	N.	D.
Temp. in F.°	49·2	51·3	52·1	53·8	55·7	56·3	56·4	57·0	59·1	58·5	55·2	50·2

[1] G.S. Bull., 614, p. 78.

Note the maximum temperature in September, when there is less fog than in midsummer and a greater movement of air from heated land to sea. This is a characteristic of the coast-line—not of the Great Valley, which has the usual July maxima. These conditions indicated by the San Francisco figures are

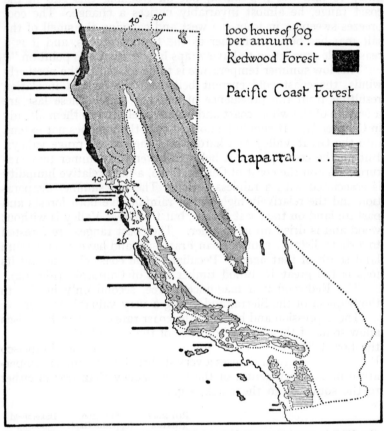

1000 hours of fog per annum ..
Redwood Forest .

Pacific Coast Forest

Chaparral. ..

FIG. 92.—Showing duration of Coast Fog and the Forest Areas of California.
..... 20° and 40° isohyets.

confined to the coast. In the Salinas and Santa Clara valleys (though still in the coast ranges) we have a variation from July 67·2 to January 46·2. We have also a noticeable decrease in rainfall. The higher summer temperature makes it possible to produce prunes, peaches, and small fruits. The Santa Clara Valley has for its area the greatest prune production in the world.

We next come to the Great Valley. Here the annual precipi-- tation varies from 25·03 inches at Red Bluff through 14·63 inches at Stockton to 5·92 inches at Bakersfield, most of it, of course, in the winter five months (December–April).

Irrigation is now much used in the Santa Clara and Salinas valleys, and in the centre and southern Great Valley it is essential, though cereals are grown without irrigation in the centre and north. A feature of the Great Valley, too, is that the high summer temperature varies little with latitude. Citrous fruits (not in very great quantities) and rice are grown in the Sacramento Valley, and cotton is now cultivated. There is, however, greater liability to frost in the north than in the south, and the rainfall steadily diminishes from north to south. As the winters are not cold—frosts are occasional only, and snow almost unknown—winter wheat will grow through the winter rains and is ready for harvest in the spring, for the winter rainfall tends to the spring side of mid-winter. At one time it was the chief crop of California. There has been some absolute, and an enormous relative, decrease in its production. The open even plains and dry weather make large-scale methods of harvesting possible. A good deal of wheat land has passed out of cultivation through impoverishment of the soil, and to an increasing extent irrigated orchards occupy the agricultural land.

The dependable dry, bright weather makes it possible to sun-dry much preserved fruit, and the Valley ships enormous quantities of dried raisins, prunes, figs, peaches, and apricots. Now, all this fruit-farming requires irrigation, save in the very north, and even here irrigation is an advantage and is being rapidly developed. This fact brings us to the water supply of the valley. This is derived mainly from the heavy precipitation of the Sierra and the melting of the winter mountain snows. The coast ranges contribute little. They are lower and present their drier eastern edge to the Great Valley. No tributaries regularly reach the San Joaquin from the west, but from the better watered northern coast ranges, Stoney, Cache, and Putah Creeks reach the Sacramento, and could be used for irrigation purposes. It is quite otherwise on the eastern side. Here at least sixteen considerable streams flow to the Great Valley.

The San Joaquin tributaries come from the highest parts of the Sierra, which are less forested here in the south. They are torrential and bring down great quantities of detritus, which spread out in intersecting deltaic fans over the Great Valley, and have gradually shifted the main stream to the western limits of the valley.[1] Much of the combined Sacramento and San Joaquin

[1] For the régime of the Californian rivers, see p. 348.

delta is subjected to inundation. It is becoming increasingly controlled by dykes and levées, and these are the more necessary as the silt brought down in flood season is raising the river-bed above the surrounding levels. This detritus in some cases, notably just south of the volcanic butte of Marysville, has been increased in the operations of hydraulic gold-mining among the auriferous gravels of the foothills. At present large tule-covered marsh areas adjoin the main river levées, and the chief irrigation areas of the Great Valley tap the Sierra tributaries before these reach the main streams. In the south, one of the deltaic fans has grown sufficiently to form a water-parting between Lake Tulare and its natural outlet, the San Joaquin. In flood-time some water reaches the San Joaquin, but for the most of the time Lake Tulare is the focus of a basin of inland drainage, losing so much water by evaporation and seepage as to have no regular visible outlet. With increasing use of its tributaries (Kings, Kaweah, and Tula Rivers) for irrigation, the lake is getting smaller, and much of it is now actually reclaimed farm land, though subject to inundation in a very wet season. Similarly, the Kern River is normally now cut off from its connection with Lake Tulare and loses itself in the Buena Vista Lake. In nearly all of the San Joaquin Valley irrigation has always been necessary to settlement, and most of the waters of the Sierra tributaries are now used up in irrigation lands. The water is used carefully.

In the Sacramento Valley the change has been from one-crop dry farming (wheat and barley) with impoverished soil, to crop rotation, with a big production of alfalfa and consequent dairying, on irrigated lands. Cattle, too, can be pastured in the lowlands in the wet winter season and moved to the moister foothill uplands in the summer drought. Though not absolutely necessary for the prune and peach orchards in the north, such good results are obtained that irrigation is being increasingly used. Nearly 1,000,000 acres of the rich bottom lands of the Sacramento are subject to annual inundation—much of them is covered by unhealthy and useless tule-marsh. A comprehensive scheme of levées and drainage channels will reclaim this land and yet render it accessible to a regulated supply of water.

An interesting irrigation crop in the Sacramento Valley (Butte and Colusa Counties) is the production of rice, which was begun here experimentally in 1909. In 1919 nearly 8 million bushels were harvested, all on irrigated land (about 150,000 acres), in the middle Sacramento Valley.[1] A short-growing, short-grained variety is grown on clayey soils which can be

[1] Farmers' Bulletin, 1141.

inundated and yet drained for harvesting. In California one-fifth of the rice grown in the U.S.A. is raised. Louisiana, Arkansas, and Texas produce the remainder. Similarly a large area near the junction of the Sacramento and San Joaquin has been drained and used for truck farming on a gigantic scale.

Within the valley itself, besides large areas of extensive barley and wheat production, and an increasing amount of dairy farming depending upon irrigated alfalfa, there is some localization in the typical productions of the irrigated deltaic fans. Thus prunes and apricots are typical of the northern valley, while in the southern is the enormous production of the raisin grape of the Fresno irrigation district, and the citrous fruit of Kern County in the extreme south.

Set between the scorching summers of the Great Valley and the cool coast-line, are valleys of the Coast Ranges, such as the Santa Clara and Salinas. The rainfall is more considerable (15–18 inches) than in the Great Valley, but irrigation (pumped from ground water) is used and the water-table is becoming lowered.

In the still cooler coastal lowlands about Monterey Bay artichokes and apples are specialized productions.

In the extreme south of California, surrounded by really desert conditions, is an important agricultural area which is dependent upon supplies of water from the Colorado River. In this case, California is borrowing its water from the Rocky Mountain region. The river is dammed up at Laguna and irrigation channels lead water to the Imperial Valley district, excess of water and seepage water draining to the Salton depression. This lake depression has become separated from the Gulf of Colorado by the delta of the Colorado. In 1905 the flood-waters of the Lower Colorado temporarily regained the Salton depression via the Imperial irrigation canal, but now the lake is diminishing in size, and will diminish still further as evaporation removes the balance of the seepage from the irrigated district. In this district the rainfall is less than 4 inches ; the mean summer temperature is over 89° F. The irrigation area is continued over into Mexico. Fruits, vegetables, and cotton are the chief crops. The chief centres are Calexico and El Centro.

The great Boulder Dam on the Colorado River[1] just outside the border of the state will ensure a regular supply for irrigation, the protection of the area from floods, and the possibility of increasing the irrigation acreage. The main canal passes into Mexican territory on its way to the Imperial Valley, but an all-American canal is being engineered by which this detour is avoided (Fig. 93).

[1] See also p. 428.

Besides the Great Valley, the Imperial Valley, and the Coast Range Valleys, California boasts a fourth major producing area, lying between the San Bernardino, St. Gabriel, San Jacinto

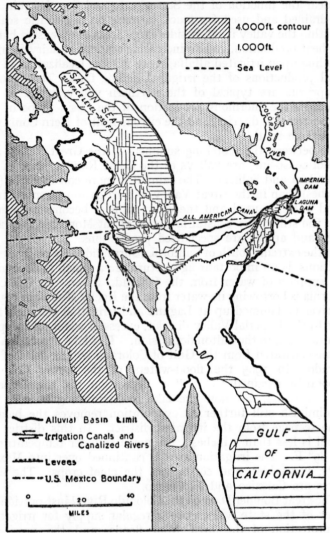

FIG. 93.—Irrigation Areas of the Colorado Delta.
Y, Yuma. C, Calexico. M, Mexicali.

ranges and the sea. These ranges here continue the function of the Sierra Nevada farther north, in causing condensation from the winter westerlies, and thus give rise to streams which

¹ See map of S. California, p. 435.

saturate the detritus at their mountain bases and provide (by pumping mainly) irrigation water for a great fruit industry.

The lowland between these ranges and sea is divided into two by the low hills of the Santa Ana range which runs parallel to the coast and which are breached by the St. Ana River. The inner lowland (about Los Angeles, Pasadena and Riverside) differ from coastal areas further to the west in having temperatures high enough for citrous fruits, and from the Great Valley in having almost complete immunity from frost. E.g. :

Los Angeles .	.	. July, 71·1° F.	Jan., 54·6° F.
Riverside	.	. " 75·5° F.	" 51·6° F.
Bakersfield .	. . " 84° F.	" 47·5° F.
(S. Great Valley) (note the greater extremes).			

Or again in January, 1927, the *average* January *minimum* temperature for Bakersfield was 38·6° F. (with three frosts). That for Los Angeles was 49·4° F. with no actual minimum below 46° F. On the outer lowland and coast-line the winter temperature is higher, but the summer averages are distinctly lower, e.g., San Diego, January, 54·3 ; July, 67·2.

Near the coast barley, beans, beet and truck crops are important, but on the inner lowland just as the land begins to rise to the San Bernardino and Jacinta Mountains, are the chief Californian orchards of citrous fruit. Nearly all the water is obtained from wells and large-scale development here again has meant a serious fall in the water-table.

The same qualities of luminous, equable warmth, which have attracted the specialist farmer, have attracted also the tourist. Many of these, having reared a family and raised at least a modest competence in climates of harsher extremes, are glad to settle down permanently ; perhaps adding to their income by small fruit orchards, poultry farms, or clerical work.

One industry only, that of the films, is of outstanding importance. Varied scenery—a short motor run takes one from the gardens of Los Angeles to the Mohave desert ; to the sea coast, or to the high mountain forests—and the bright dry dependable weather, made this an ideal spot for the early industry, though in the present organization of studio work such circumstances are of small importance.

Some emphasis has been put on the question of irrigation because it is intimately bound up with the whole question of agricultural production in this state. In the south one can hardly look for much further development apart from new storage works as the water is economically used. In the north, where for certain products irrigation is advisable and supplementary rather than absolutely necessary, there is a bigger water supply, and at present a much less economical use.

California contains the enormous total of 4·2 million acres of irrigated land, which amounts to 21·9 per cent. of the total area irrigated in the United States.[1] The height of the Sierra which determines a supply of water for irrigation provides also the possibility of hydro-electric development. Washington, Oregon, and California have the greatest undeveloped powers of the U.S.A., and these are based on the heavy rain and snow-falls of the Cascades and Sierra. In California, the greatest powers are in the Sierra tributaries to the Sacramento, all available in the Great Valley and its great outlet city, San Francisco. California leads all the states in its developed water-power, and has enormous reserves. Much of the power is used in traction, light, lumber, and milling, but the great resources available for general manufactures should not be overlooked.

Related both to the climate and to the water supply possibilities of the state are its forests. The Great Valley was, and is, almost unforested, though much eucalyptus has been introduced. Apart from fire and cutting clearings, the northern coast ranges and the Sierra are forested, the forest type and the depth of the timber belt varying with the amount of precipitation and the temperature.

It will be noticed in Fig. 92 that the forests extend much further South in the Sierra than in the coast ranges—a comment on the greater height and precipitation of the Sierra. Yet, in the Southern Sierra, the forest belt is much narrower and less dense than in the north, and tends to be extinguished between the too cold areas of the greatest heights and the too dry areas of the lower slopes, i.e. the upper and lower timber lines tend to coincide.

On the coast ranges the forests begin at sea-level and the hills are not high enough to reach a marked treeless zone. A well-defined, important and interesting species confined absolutely to a part of the coast country is that of the Redwood. This is of the same genus as the Big Tree, which occupies scattered groups on the Sierra Nevada. It grows to an even greater height, but has a smaller girth. It may reach a height of 350 feet and a diameter of 20 feet. It is a coniferous tree of straight, slightly tapering stem bearing a crown of almost horizontal branches in the upper one-half to one-third of its length. The wood is easily worked, takes a fine polish, and is extraordinarily durable. It is, however, difficult to season and expensive in lumbering. The wood grows on the coast ranges where the total

[1] 1920 Census, vol. vii.

precipitation is from 30 to 60 inches, and where the location is accessible to the summer fogs. These last appear to exercise a pretty complete control over the distribution. Beginning at Chetco River in Oregon, the tree occupies a zone from 6 to 30 miles in width, as far as the southern limit of Mendocino County in California [1] (Fig. 92). South of San Francisco on the coast ranges and occupying much of the hill country of Southern California is a " sclerophyllous " forest of Chaparral (Fig. 92). " The term ' sclerophyllous ' is employed by Schimper in connection with xerophytic bushland and bush forest in sub-tropical regions, where the rain falls in winter. It refers to small, thick coriaceous entire leaves which are so extremely common in these regions. . . . The prolonged summer drought is hostile to vegetation. Hence the rarity of larger trees. The trees are small, with gnarled trunks and boughs ; and most of them may occur in the guise of dwarf trees and shrubs. The leaves of the trees and shrubs are as a rule evergreen and protected from desiccation in various ways, yet their structure is not so extreme as that of desert plants.

" Winter and spring form the true vegetative season of sclerophyllous vegetation, even though brief cold periods sometimes cause a lull." [2]

From an economic point of view, the chief value of this Chaparral cover is in the conservation and partial regulation of the all too meagre rainfall. This is a country where crops are absolutely dependent upon rainfall, and where reservoirs are difficult to engineer and to keep free from silt. Already the water is being over-used. The water-plane as shown in wells is being lowered. A big city like Los Angeles has had to go 200 miles to the Owens Lake watershed for its supply.

The fact is that the water resources of California south of San Francisco are now taxed to the utmost. Further development for city, industry, or agriculture, must go outside the area for further supplies as Los Angeles has already done. A notable scheme for achieving this is put forward by Mr. Marshall. It depends upon the fact that the streams running from the Sierra Nevada decrease in volume as one proceeds to the drier south. Those in the north have a surplus, those on the south a deficit. By the scheme—which would entail the construction of gigantic canals beheading the Sierra streams in echelon—the northern part of the San Joaquin valley would be watered from the Sacramento watershed, the southern part of the San Joaquin would

---

[1] U.S. Dept. of Agriculture. Bureau of Forestry Bulletin 38.
[2] Warming, " Œcology of Plants," Oxford, 1909, p. 303 ; quoted in U.S. Dept. of Agriculture Forest Service Bulletin 85.

14

receive water from the northern part, while the head-water of the Kern River would be led by tunnels and canals from the Great Valley to the Los Angeles area. A truly gigantic scheme, but within the bounds of practicability. In the meantime the completion of the great Boulder Dam on the Colorado is destined to provide both power, and an increased water supply to Southern California. The wonderful transport services and the great free trade area of States helps the development of highly localized special farming areas within their territory. Yet with a highly developed interior market and a considerable export trade there is constant risk of over-production of the typical Californian orchard and truck farming. The difficulties have been alleviated but not entirely met by a notable development of co-operative marketing organizations, yet in general, the market may have reached its saturation-point, and it may be unwise to undertake colossal schemes for the development of similar producing areas.

The Sierra Nevada are rich in minerals—particularly in gold. Detritus from these mountains contains auriferous gravels which have been worked in many areas since 1848. The present production is about 1,000,000 fine ounces, one-third of the total U.S.A. gold production. The mining centres are now chiefly in the Klamath mountains and in the foothills of the Sierra Nevada of the northern Great Valley.

The chief geographical factors in the development of San Francisco are obvious from a mere glance at the map. The population of California, for a number of geographical reasons already referred to, is concentrated in the Sacramento Valley and foothills and in the foothill area of the San Joaquin Valley ; also in the Sonona, Santa Clara, and Salinas valleys. For all these there is only one natural outlet, the Golden Gate. In pre-railway days the early settlers used the Sacramento River to Red Bluff and the San Joaquin to Stockton, and both these rivers had their outlet via the Golden Gate. The river focus has been followed by a rail focus, and the city has grown with the growth of the state. San Francisco Bay is completely sheltered and almost tideless. San Francisco is on the hilly peninsula to the south of the Golden Gate, and is connected with Oakland (virtually the same port) by train ferries, and by a railway bridge. An even greater work is the huge suspension bridge which (opened in 1937) now spans the Golden Gate itself. The biggest vessel can reach the innumerable jetties of both towns. Handling of lumber, grain, oil and fruits is considerable. There are large imports of Asiatic origin—tea, silk, sugar, etc. There is some barge traffic to Sacramento (7-foot channel) and Stockton (6-foot channel).

The only other good natural harbour of California is San Diego, but it is too far to the arid south. Los Angeles is really 20 miles from its great artificial harbour of San Pedro. The city may be regarded as the capital of the great irrigation areas south of the Great Valley. It has an enormously important industry in its film activities. Manufactured articles, lumber, and oil are the chief concern of its port. The extraordinarily valuable oilfields of California are dealt with in Chapter XXII. The importance of this great source of power on the Pacific coast must be emphasized in any consideration of the region.

A much modified version of the Marshall scheme (see above, p. 415) is now under construction. The Upper Sacramento is being regulated by a great dam (Shasta dam, Fig. 94A, p. 434), 560 feet high, which will ultimately develop 500,000 h.p. This regulation will improve navigation and prevent, on the one hand, flooding of the lower Sacramento, and on the other, that infiltration of salt sea water into the delta irrigation area which occurred in the times of very low river water.

A great delta canal will carry excess water from the Sacramento over into the lower San Joachin valley to maintain the supply there by pumping, and to make up for a diversion of the Upper San Joachin to Kings river for the use of the area around and to the south of Lake Tulare. This supply will be regulated and the possibility of irrigation much extended by another great new reservoir on the upper San Joachin—the Friant reservoir.

No attempt will be made (as was envisaged in the Marshall plan) to carry water southward to the Los Angeles area, where the position has been relieved by a supply from the Colorado below Boulder dam brought by a great aqueduct.

CHAPTER XXIX

WESTERN INTERIOR OF THE U.S.A.

BETWEEN the agricultural areas of the Central Lowlands and the most significant western element of the Pacific Cordillera (i.e. the Coast Range of British Columbia, the Cascades and Sierra Nevada of the States) lies a vast area of mountain, plateau, and inland basin, exhibiting every variety of geological history, structure, topographic form, and economic importance, and alike only in its general aridity. This aridity increases from north to south—that is to say, precipitation is most lacking where, because of evaporation, it is most needed. Of the physiographic areas which lie within these gigantic limits, those of British Columbia and of the Columbia River Lava Basin are considered separately (Chapters XXXIV and XXVII).

The remaining area is divided into the following major physiographic provinces : (*a*) the Great Plains ; (*b*) the Rocky Mountains ; (*c*) the Colorado Plateau ; (*d*) the Basin and Range Provinces (see Fig. 1).

Now, if we except the Great Plains for the moment, then, in spite of the most diverse physical features, we may yet enumerate certain major geographical factors which characterize the whole area.

(*a*) As in all semi-arid mountainous regions, the actual mountain ranges receive the greater part of the precipitation. Forest land is confined to them, and the dry line rises to the south.

(*b*) The mountain building forces in the Pacific Cordillera were favourable to concentration of metal ores, and in a region generally too arid for agriculture the mining of the more valuable metals led to the original settlement, and determined that such settlement should be of a scattered and impermanent nature. The metals obtained, gold, silver, lead, and copper, were such as would pay for the enormous transport charges consequent upon great distances, and the value of the finds encouraged railway development.

(*c*) In the northern intermont and plateau areas, there is sufficient continuous grass to support great herds of cattle and sheep (e.g. in Montana and Wyoming). Further south, in Utah, Arizona, Colorado, etc., much of the plain and plateau area is covered with sage-bush, but even so, there is much grass in the shade of the bush, and vast herds are kept on these ranges, though, of course, a continually larger area per animal is required with increasing aridity to the south. There is a summer movement to the higher ranges.

(d) There is some dry farming in Idaho and Montana, but for the rest agriculture is dependent upon irrigation, and close settlement (apart from some outlying mining centres) is confined to irrigable valleys, and to the fringes of some of the great ranges (e.g. of the Wasatch). From the rudimentary systems at first used to supply the mining settlements, the increase of large-scale engineering works on the one hand, and of transport facilities on the other, has led to large, closely settled and intensively farmed irrigated districts, which ship the products to great distances. Alfalfa, sugar beet, potatoes, and fruits are the most important products. The fact that the mining and metallurgical centres require power, and the irrigation areas storage dams, provides a double economic factor for the engineering works necessary for the storage and use of the mountain streams. All the streams have an irregular régime, some flooding with the melting mountain snows, and the smaller streams after occasional heavy rains. Storage, then, is necessary for the continuous use of the water either for power or for irrigation, and in some cases the water is led to the irrigation ditch after passing through the power turbines.

The Great Plains (Fig. 35). This province in Canada will be considered in Chapter XXXIII. In the U.S.A. it is usually distinct from the prairie plains :

(i) *Geologically*, in being *chiefly* developed on little disturbed Cretaceous and Tertiary sediments. In the Dakotas and in Kansas a resistant Cretaceous formation presents an east-facing escarpment which may be taken as the boundary of the province. As in the case of the prairie provinces of Canada, some of the Palæozoic rocks of the Interior Lowlands reappear in the Rocky Mountain foothills and lie, little disturbed, underneath the younger rocks of the Great Plains. Upon these a great Cretaceous sea stretching from the Arctic to the Gulf gave marine deposits which have been consolidated into persistent beds which remain little disturbed. The raising of the land which took place at the formation of the Rocky Mountains resulted in the detritus from these mountains being distributed somewhat irregularly over the Cretaceous surface in great stretches of rather unconsolidated Tertiary material. Base-levelling of this raised belt is incomplete. The great rivers rising in the Rockies and crossing to the Mississippi do so in wide flood plains set between well-defined bluffs.

(ii) *Climatically*, the Great Plains contain all the land east of the Rockies where rainfall is insufficient for agriculture, and the variable zone separating lands sufficiently watered and semi-arid is never far from their eastern boundary (see Chapter X, Fig. 30). It is not, however, a hard-and-fast line, and dry-farmed wheat has spread into the Great Plains area of the Dakotas and of Montana, while drought-resistant grains and sorghums invade the plains of Western Kansas.

Woodlands are confined to the watercourses. Sand barrens cover large areas, and are particularly in evidence in Western Nebraska between the North Platte and the White River tributaries of the Missouri, and again in South-western Kansas between the Arkansas and Cimarron Rivers. The great semi-arid interstream areas will support large herds of cattle, but agriculture and town settlement are confined to the stream-courses. These rivers are of very irregular régime; e.g., now that so much irrigation water is taken from the Platte River in its upper courses, there is almost no water running in the river-bed west of long. 97° 30′ in the dry season. Or again, in the pre-rail days, when the navigation of the Missouri was of some importance, it was only of some six to seven weeks' duration, Fort Benton being then the upper limit reached by river steamers. On the North Platte River there are big irrigation districts about Gothenburg and North Platte. A ribbon-like belt of agriculture, then, extends westward along the flood plains of the rivers from the vast agricultural area of the Central Lowlands, invading the semi-arid territory of the Great Plains. The head-waters of the rivers as they issue from the Rockies, too, are utilized for irrigation, and supply the line of settlement just east of these mountains.

Besides the river bluffs, and the 5 to 10-mile-wide flood plains, the relief is diversified by the very irregular distribution and dissection of the Tertiary cover. There are areas of sand-dunes, of flat gravel-capped mesa, of fantastically shaped wind-eroded rocks, and Bad Lands. These last are most extensive south-east of the Black Hills, and between the White and Cheyenne Rivers. The pillars, gulches, and alluvial fans of this difficult terrain are due to the weathering of " slightly consolidated, fine-grained material lying at a considerable altitude above the sea in a region of low rainfall and sparse vegetation." [1] The varying resistance to erosion both horizontally and vertically accounts for the

[1] " Forest Physiography," by I. Bowman, p. 415.

extreme complexity of topographic detail of the Bad Lands. Erosion is the result of infrequent but torrential showers on a clay which expands on wetting, and still further on freezing, and which therefore tends to flake with alternating wet and dry, and cold and warm, conditions.

The tributaries of the Great Plains rivers which rise on the plain, and not actually in the mountains, are usually intermittent, so irrigation is limited to the main stream and to Rocky Mountain head-waters. In the Northern Great Plain vast areas are underlain by lignite coal in thick, undisturbed seams at little depth. These continue over the border into Canada (see Chapter XXXIII) and represent the heaviest reserves of the continent. They are apt to contain 40 per cent. of moisture when mined, and only about 40 per cent. of fixed carbon when dried. They are thus of very low calorific value, and are little used at present.

A complete structural and topographic break in the Great Plains is afforded by the Black Hills of Dakota, an oval hill group about 100 miles long in the north and south direction and about 50 miles broad. They owe their existence to local earth movements which, occurring in late Cretaceous times, domed up both Palæozoic and Cretaceous cover, so that subsequent erosion has exposed a central core of crystalline schists and granites surrounded by oval outcrops of Palæozoic and Cretaceous sedimentaries exposed in ridge or valley according to their relative resistance. The streams have maintained their direction against the strike of the rocks and cut through the concentric ridges in narrow valleys. The hills have a higher precipitation than the surrounding plains, and are forested. South of the Black Hills of Dakota, and extending into Texas, the western part of the Great Plains are usually termed the High Plains. The whole of the Great Plains slopes from about 4,000 feet at the foothills to 1,200 feet at their junction with the Central Lowlands, and there is little general significance in a further subdivision. Physiographically, large areas in the Western Plains are relatively little dissected, and are formed of material deposited by aggrading streams of moderate gradient largely in Oligocene times from the denudation of the Rockies. These High Plains are best developed and least dissected in the arid Llano Estacado of the Texas Panhandle. Dissection of this vast plain area is active only at the edges, and is evident in the irregular but well-marked scarps which overlook the Pecos Valley in the west, and in the east, at the " Break of the Plains," the eroded plains of Central Texas.

The Edwards Plateau forms a topographic continuation of the Llano Estacado, for the Pecos escarpment and the " Break of the Plains" form, too, its marginal escarpments. On the south it is bounded by the dissected Balcones fault. Though topographically and climatically continuous with the High Plains, the Edwards Plateau differs from them in being developed on a resistant Cretaceous limestone.

The Rocky Mountains. The vast territory included in this physiographic division (see Fig. 1) comprises gigantic mountain ranges, intermont valleys, plains, and "parks." It is in no sense uniform in structure or history, and owes its classification in one division to the fact that it is on the whole higher than the surrounding areas, and is almost entirely surrounded by plateau or plain forms. There is usually a distinct topographic break at the junction of the Great Plains and the Rockies, though this is least apparent in the region of the Laramie Plateau, an area of rolling desert plain continued westward from the High Plains as far as the Colorado Plateau, and dividing the Rockies into northern and southern groups.

The eastern face of the Rockies is along a lie of disturbance where earth-forces in early Tertiary times caused an uplift which bent and broke both Palæozoic and Cretaceous rock cover, and where subsequent denudation has frequently exposed pre-Cambrian crystalline rocks. Thus several of the main ranges (e.g. the Uinta, the Colorado Front Range, the Wind River Range, the Big Horn Mountains) now expose an uplifted core of schists and granites surrounded by progressively younger sedimentary formations.

At the junction of the Great Plains and the Rockies the horizontal rocks of the plains were frequently bent up so that after differential erosion, a hog's-back topography developed on steeply dipping strata of varying resistance. This ridge country is typical of the foothills in Alberta, in Montana, and in Colorado. In some areas it is lacking because obscured by a Tertiary cover of detritus from the mountains themselves ; in others the junction is a great fault line, and the strata of the Great Plains have not been seriously deformed.

The mountain building forces engaged in this mighty upheaval were accompanied by volcanic activity and igneous intrusion, by faulting and mineralization. Nearly all the considerable centres of population have grown up either in, or in connection with, mining districts. Indeed, from the point of view of human geography, the scattered mines, the irrigated rail-threaded valleys, and the relatively heavy precipitation of the forested uplands which renders power and irrigation possible, are the essential factors in the development of the whole region. A great deal of railway mileage is used up in branch lines to mining camps, but transcontinental main lines cross the Rockies from east to west. These should be followed on a good relief map. Nothing is gained here by a mere enumeration of the river valley routes followed. The importance of the Rockies as supplying summer pasture must be borne in mind.

There are many mining centres and irrigated valleys. We will enumerate only some of quite outstanding importance. Thus in Western Montana, Helena grew up as a gold centre in the sixties, and communicated by wagon with Fort Benton, the head of a brief seasonal navigation of the Missouri. Helena is no longer important for gold production, but it has become the capital and route centre of a great mining district; it is on a transcontinental line, and is situated in the famous irrigated Gallatin Valley, the most intensively farmed area of Montana. It is connected by rail with Butte, at present one of the most important copper-mining centres on the globe. The smelting is now carried on at Anaconda. Silver, gold, and zinc are obtained in the same area. There are big power developments on the Madison River.

The Union Pacific Railway, which crosses the High Plains by the Platte Valley to Cheyenne, crosses the Rockies at their lowest, and then traverses a great arid basin (the Red Desert) between the Laramie Mountains and the Wasatch. This is the most direct route to San Francisco, but the journey across the Rockies is one of the least interesting and one of the least productive of local traffic. The route connecting Cheyenne-Denver-Pueblo and Trinidad along the Rocky Mountain front should be noted. These towns are so many gateways to mining areas in the Rockies. The eastward flowing mountain streams provide an irrigated fringe, upon which have developed a number of important cities.

Denver has a population of a quarter of a million. Near by, the Upper South Platte irrigates 100,000 acres. Originally a mining centre, the city owes its present importance to its railway connections.

Colorado Springs—a well-known health resort. It is near the Cripple Creek gold area, and near, also, one of the most interesting of national parks.

Pueblo is the chief of the Colorado mining smelting towns. It uses a good coking coal from the Trinidad field, and has important glass furnaces also.

Cañon City marks the entrance to the Cañon of the Arkansas, through which a difficult railway route joins a line from Colorado Springs, near the great mountain mining centre of Leadville (zinc, silver, lead, and gold).

One of the largest of the irrigation schemes in the Rockies is that whereby the North Platte is held up in a reservoir in the Seminole Mountains, which supplies 130,000 acres in the Wyoming and Nebraska plains with water.

In spite of the intricate mountain plexus of Colorado, the mineral wealth has led to a considerable development of railway lines, and the valley irrigated plots cover so much space in the aggregate that Colorado ranks next after California in the area under the ditch. Alfalfa, potatoes, and beet are the chief irrigated crops. Colorado has a bigger production of potatoes than any other western state.

But besides the intricate system of valleys, the region of the Rockies contains a number of high intermontane plains. Chief among these are the North, Middle, South, and San Luis Parks, of Colorado. These are all structural basins; areas of present aggradation with relatively flat floors (especially North and San Luis) and high, rugged, frequently snow-covered, mountain borders. North Park is drained by the North Platte; South Park by the South Platte; Middle Park is the most easterly Pacific drainage basin, for in it flows the Upper Grand River, a tributary of the Colorado. San Luis Park is occupied by the Upper Rio Grande. All four are unforested, and provide summer grazing. The height of these great intermont basins varies from 7,500 to 9,000 feet.

Colorado Plateau (see Fig. 1). This division is bounded on the north by the east-west range of the Uinta Mountains, a member of the Rocky Mountain system; on the east by the Rocky Mountain ranges of Colorado; by its own escarpment in the Grand Wash Cliffs on the west, and by the Arizona Highlands in the south.

The structural characteristics serving to delimit this great unit, which occupies large areas of Colorado, Utah, Arizona, and New Mexico, are the general horizontality of sedimentary strata on the one hand, and a great north and south series of faults, by which huge blocks of these still roughly horizontal rocks have been at various periods elevated or depressed. Topographically, the area consists of a great number of individual plateaux of varying elevation, fault scarps, and erosion cliffs, and threaded by deep cañons.

Erosion is everywhere most active on the vertical surfaces, and the great and characteristic cliffs of Central Utah (e.g. pink, white, and vermilion cliffs) are the receding scarps of slightly north-dipping strata which are being stripped from the plateau surfaces.

The San Francisco Plateau, which occupies the country to

the south of the Colorado River, is little dissected, though its evenness is interrupted by the lava-capped hills and volcanic cones of the San Francisco Mountains. These mountains support a fine forest growth, though surrounded by the treeless and arid plateau. North of the Colorado the plateau units are of smaller extent and greater dissection. Only the high plateaux are forested ; e.g. the Kaibab Plateau, which borders the Grand Cañon about long. 112°, is over 8,000 feet, and is forested with an open forest of yellow pine. At these great altitudes much of the precipitation is in the form of snow, and even the summer nights are cold. The lower plateaux are covered with bunch-grass, and desert species occur in the lower terraces of the great cañons.

The river Colorado crosses the plateau region diagonally on its course from the Rocky Mountains to the Colorado desert. The main stream and its tributaries have cut deep cañons in the upraised strata of the plateau. The most noted of these, and without a doubt the most impressive in the world, is the Grand Cañon itself. From about long. 111° to 114° the river is flowing in deep gorges : first the Marble Cañon for 65 miles, and then the still more gigantic Grand Cañon for 125 miles. Here the aridity of the climate, the general horizontality of the strata, and their varying resistance, have led to the typical arid cañon form of cliff and bench. Within the Colorado Plateau region there is in general less mineral wealth and fewer possibilities of irrigation than in the valleys of the Rocky Mountain province.

The Basin and Range Provinces. This region (Fig. 1) covers the whole of Nevada, much of Utah, and much, too, of Arizona and New Mexico. The most general physiographic characteristics are the great number of isolated north and south trending ranges, most of which are tilted and block-faulted masses of previously folded and peneplained sedimentaries. The area includes some real deserts, and in general is the most arid in the continent. Precipitation decreases from north to south. Under these circumstances many of the intermittent streams are unable to find outlets to the sea. They are unable also to carry off the weathered rock waste, so that the sharp scarp edges of the faulted ranges jut through broad, smooth plains of aggradation.

The greatest continuous area without natural outlet is usually referred to as the Great Basin of Utah and Nevada. It is bounded on the north by the lower plateau of the Columbia Basin. On the west and east are the Sierra Nevada and Wasatch ranges respectively, which are alike in that they are both great tilted fault blocks (of complicated structure and geological history), and that they both present their steepest slopes inward to the Great Basin.

Structurally, these great boundary ranges might perhaps be considered as a part of the Basin and Range region, but the whole human geography of California is bound up with the climatic characteristics of the Sierra Nevada, while the Wasatch, being much higher than any of the intervening basin ranges, receive sufficient precipitation to be forested, and to supply the irrigation which supports the fringe of thriving settlements along their western border. The Great Basin, between these two ranges, is not, of course, a single basin of relief. It consists of a great number of independent basins of inland drainage, existing between the roughly parallel hill ranges. The intermittent streams from these hills lose themselves in the sands or in shallow playas, which are frequently dried up. The lowest parts of the Great Basin occur in the east at the foot of the Wasatch, and in the west at the base of the Sierra Nevada, and in each are permanent bodies of salt water, e.g. Salt Lake and Lakes Carson and Humboldt, etc. These are remnants of the great water bodies which existed under the heavy precipitation conditions of Pleistocene times. To the east was Lake Bonneville, which covered a great area, rose to more than 1,000 feet above the present level of Salt Lake, and for a period was a great freshwater lake discharging to the Snake River in the neighbourhood of Pocatello. As the climate gradually became drier, the great water body had its level reduced below that of its notch to the Snake Basin, and was gradually diminished to its present area of less than 2,000 square miles. Evidence of its great extent and former level is obvious to all in the straight, level shore-lines high up on the Wasatch hillsides. The present remnant, Salt Lake, has varied much in the last century. It increases in size with a run of wet years and decreases in abnormally dry years. It has suffered some decrease, too, through the deviation for irrigation of tributary streams from the Wasatch. Its waters are very salt, and in them a man may float upright with head and shoulders above water. It is nowhere more than 18 feet deep, and contains possibly half a million tons of saline matter—chiefly sodium chloride and sulphate. Its shores are often white with the incrustation of these salts. Similarly in the west, the great glacial Lake Lahontan is now represented only by a scattered series of saline lakes.

The most considerable watercourse of the region is the Humboldt River, which flows westward through the northern basin and discharges through Lake Humboldt to the salt Carson Lake. It is followed closely by the transcontinental line.

The Great Basin is about 800 miles north to south, and 500 miles wide, and is about the size of France. The precipitation in the north (Oregon) is 10 to 12 inches, and in the south dwindles to 3 to 4 inches. Sage-bush is the typical vegetation, but there are large areas of drifting sands, and of bare forbidding playa mud plains which are inundated after any heavy rain. The whole forms a range ground for sparsely herded cattle. Cottonwood and willow line the watercourses. Apart from the mining centres, the chief close settlement is found in irrigated districts at the foot of the Wasatch. This great tilted block has been deeply dissected and is crossed in narrow valleys by two railways: one from Cheyenne, emerging from the mountains at Ogden ; the other from Denver, striking the plains at Utah Lake, a freshwater body fed from the mountains and draining to Salt Lake.

From this latter a mountain line branches to Park City mineral district, where lead, silver, gold, and copper are mined. Bingham has a big copper production, the smelting being done at Garfield. At the base of the mountains and about the deltas of a former Lake Bonneville are the irrigated lands which stretch like a line of gardens between the deserts to the west and the great mountain flank to the east.

Of special interest is the belt of land extending to the north to where the Bear River breaks through " the gates " of the Wasatch, and limited to the south by east and west hills just south of Lake Utah—a stretch of about 130 miles almost continuously irrigated and varying in width from 2 to 18 miles. Water is pumped from the Bear River for the strip in the north, but for the rest, the water is obtained from the Wasatch cañon streams which here break into the Salt Lake Basin, e.g. the Box Elder, Ogden Canyon, Weber Canyon (followed by the Union Pacific), and the stream coming down to Lake Utah. The middle level delta lands provide the best irrigable soils—neither so gravelly as the upper delta, nor so clayey, and saline, or waterlogged as the lower. Precipitation increases from 11 inches on the plain, about 4 inches for each 1,000 feet up the Wasatch slopes. It occurs mostly in winter and spring. Thus on the lower slope winter wheat is dry-farmed without irrigation, or the slope is used for pasture. The irrigated land supports an intensive production of beet (the chief cash crop), alfalfa, and wheat, which crops occupy about three-quarters of the irrigated land, the remainder being devoted to fruit and vegetables. There are many beet and canning factories, and large flour mills at Ogden, and meat-packing plants at Salt Lake City. Salt Lake City and Ogden are the chief towns. Most of the farmers live in villages—a heritage of the Indian days when concentration for protection was necessary.

As in all the Cordilleran irrigated valley and mountain-fringe settlements, alfalfa growing supplements the range pastures for the livestock industry. It may be noted that the most recent and most direct east to west route is now built right across Salt Lake itself, avoiding both the detour and the gradients of the lines north and south of the lake.

That part of the Basin and Range region which lies to the south of the Great Basin proper has a similar structure and an even greater aridity, yet it is not entirely a basin of inland drainage, being traversed by the Lower Colorado and its great tributary Rio Gila, streams which take their rise in the higher and wetter country to the east. Apart from its mining centres, and from one or two major irrigation works, the whole region is economically unimportant. But these are considerable exceptions. Arizona and New Mexico rank high in the production of gold, silver, lead, and copper (see Chapter XXIII), and the Phœnix and Yuma irrigation areas are among the most important in the States. The Phœnix scheme depends upon the Roosevelt dam, which has turned a valley in the Upper Salt River into a great reservoir, and so supplies perennial water to a large area about the city of Phœnix. This has become one of the chief areas for irrigated cotton in the States (see Chapter XIV). Finally, we must emphasize the importance of irrigation in all the Western United States. Including California, Oregon, and Washington (not treated in this chapter) over 18 million acres of the western states are under the ditch ; i.e. an area equal to about half the area of England. In spite of the enormous value of the minerals of the west, its irrigated farm produce has a much higher total value.

In the chapter on California we mentioned the need in Southern California of an increased water supply, both for the domestic use of a rapidly growing population, and for intensive and long season irrigation. We saw how already water had been brought by aqueduct from Owens Lake, and we mentioned that the Boulder Dam reservoir had yielded another source.

The Colorado River, upon which the Boulder Dam is the greatest work, has one of the most extensive basins of the continent, and all but the high mountainous part of this basin is semi-arid and thus many smaller rivers yield more water. In its middle course the Colorado receives little addition, and that usually in streams of excessively irregular régime. As nearly all its water comes from high mountains the maximum run-off is in the early summer, is regular as to date, but very irregular in amount. After passing through the hot arid gorge of the Grand Cañon it emerges silt laden to continue its building up of a delta extending into the Gulf of California.

Raised on its own silt bed, it has cut off the tectonic depression of Salton sink which lies 250 feet below sea-level. Water from the Colorado is taken by canals to irrigate lands in the Imperial Valley, which, however, was always in danger of being flooded if the Colorado should break through her lévees. This indeed happened in 1905, destroying thousands of acres of crops, and the track of the Southern Pacific Railway. It was more than a year before the lévees were restored, and the danger remained. The great Boulder Dam [1] project so recently completed is situated on the boundary between Utah and Nevada, at a point where the great stream turns southwards on its way to the Gulf. A point was chosen where the river narrowed into a cañon—Black Cañon —and where a narrow but very high dam would hold up an immense lake in a hilly but more open stretch just above. There was an enormous difference between the maximum and minimum run-off on the Colorado, but the dam will hold up no less than two years' total flow, and is therefore capable of entirely regulating the flow below. The dam will, at a maximum, raise the water-level 584 feet and is itself 726 feet above rock level. During its construction the river had to be diverted through four great tunnels.

The dam is to fulfil a number of functions. In the first place the Imperial Valley will be protected from flood because of the more even flow of the water below the dam. Secondly the irrigated land there can be much increased now that the supply of water is evened out through the year. Before the dam was completed there were about 600,000 acres under irrigation in the Imperial Valley and over the border in Mexico. The dam will allow of an increase to over a million acres.

By an aqueduct 250 miles long the Metropolitan Water district of Southern California with a population of nearly three millions will have access to 1,500 second feet from the reservoir. Power available will vary with the height of water above the dam, but this will average about 530 feet with 590 feet as a maximum and 420 feet as minimum. The installed horse-power is about 1·7 million, i.e. one of the largest single installations in the world. Finally, though the reservoir if left to itself must gradually silt up, for the Colorado is one of the most silt-laden of streams, bringing down it is estimated about 170 million tons of sediment to the delta each year, yet it would take 300 years to completely silt up the artificial lake impounded behind the dam, and in

---

[1] Now called the Hoover Dam.

the meantime, the absence of excessive silt obviates expensive and laborious work on the irrigation channels lower down.

IRRIGATION

In the United States about 20 million acres are irrigated, and most of this great aggregate lies in the arid western half of the continent, where the heavier precipitation of high mountain ranges, often stored till the early summer in the form of snow, provides the necessary water. Fig. 94 indicates the general distribution of the irrigated areas. They fall naturally into a number of drainage groups.

(i) On the High Plains to the east of the Rockies, where parts of the upper valleys of the main streams of the Missouri, Platte, and Arkansas are irrigated in long strips which depend upon regulating reservoirs in the mountains.

(ii) The fringe of the Rocky Mountain front where the head-waters of these same streams form alluvial fans which are irrigated.

(iii) Within the Rocky Mountain regions, where in high valleys the numerous tributaries eventually contributing to the Colorado and the Snake provide irrigation water.

(iv) The irrigated fan fringe of the west front of the Wasatch Range in Utah.

(v) The irrigated valleys tributary to the Columbia river in Washington (e.g. Wenatchee, Okanagan, Yakima, etc.).

(vi) The irrigated fan fringe at the western base of the Sierra Nevada in the Great Valley of California.

(vii) The irrigation fringe at the base of the San Bernandino, San Jacinto, and San Gabriel ranges in Southern California.

(viii) The Imperial Valley, for which water is abstracted from the lower Colorado near the head of the Gulf of California.

All except the first and the last of these groups are irrigated areas of the mountain fringe type. Factors which are involved in irrigation development may be classed as physical and economic.

Of the physical, the amount of water, and the period for which it is available, are the most important. Further, it must be topographically possible to lead the water to some plain but gently sloping area for actual use. In most of the western states the streams require regulation if a supply is to include any considerable proportion of the total flow, and is to be available throughout the growing season. We have already (p. 350) touched upon the fact that to some extent regulation for power purposes may obviate further regulation for irrigation. It must be emphasized, however, that the two requirements are by no means usually coterminous, irrigation water being required, for the most part, for a period approximating to that of the growing season, while the power requirement is apt to be more evenly distributed throughout the year.

In all except the Coast Range areas of irrigation the stream régime tends to the early summer mountain snow-melt type. Thus the high mountain snow proves a valuable source of storage,

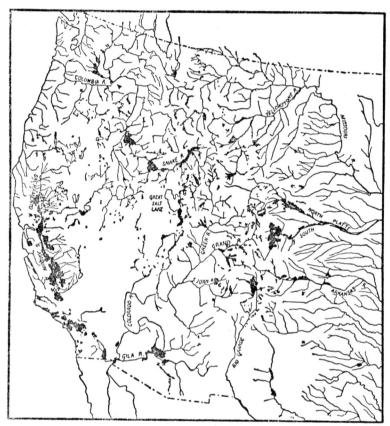

FIG. 94.—Generalized Drainage Map of Western States, showing chief Irrigated Areas.

and of regulation, for although there may be, and usually is, an enormous difference between the flow in the high water *months* (say May to July) and the low water *months* (say Sept. to Feb.), the day to day variation is apt to be much less than in the case of streams dependent upon rainfall alone.

This latter is the condition of the streams which rise in the coast ranges, and to a large extent, too, of those rising in the mountains (San Bernandino, etc.) of Southern California. Such are quite useless without regulation works. Fortunately a form of natural storage is often present, and can be used to supplement the supply obtained by distribution canals from the river. The higher portions of mountain-fringing detrital fans are usually of course material, and into this much of the river water may find its way, thus becoming available by pumping from the ground water lower down. In some cases—as in southern California—the underground structure is such as to permit of the storage of a vast quantity, but as has long been appreciated, a by no means inexhaustible supply. Now ground water can be pumped at periods irrespective of the stream régime. The two disadvantages are expense of pumping (both hydro-electric and petrol pumps are used) and the possibility, realized in too many instances, of using up the ground water more quickly than it is naturally replenished, and so of depressing the water-table.

On the other hand good drainage of irrigation land is essential, to prevent accumulation of salts.

On the physical side, too, production must conform to conditions imposed by the type of climate concerned.

On the economic side, problems arise in connection with priority of water rights, the settlement of an irrigation colony sometimes in rather isolated surroundings and often of people unacquainted with irrigation farming; and above all in the finding of satisfactory markets for the produce.

The getting of water to the land, however it is done, involves expense; and if an irrigation project is to pay, it must do so in virtue of some advantages not shared by competitive humid areas.

In general if water, soil, and topography are suitable, the actual limiting physical factors affecting the kind of production, are the temperature conditions, and the cost of transport to market.

Bearing these factors in mind we can essay a classification of irrigation areas on a functional basis.

(i) Areas almost frost free, and with high or very high summer temperatures. Thus in the Imperial valley the date palm can be grown, truck crops like lettuce and tomatoes can be ripened in the winter months, and frost sensitive perennials and tree crops (e.g. the citrous fruits) can be produced. Much the same may be said of the great citrous areas of Southern California, though here the summer maxima are considerably lower.

(ii) In the north and south (but not opposite the Golden gate) of the great valley of California, we have areas where frost incidence makes citrous production hazardous, though actually the summer temperatures are higher than in Southern California.

The vine, and stone fruit—fresh, canned, or sun dried—become important.

(iii) At the junction of the Sacramento, and the San Joaquin Rivers, and again in the Coast Range valleys we have a long growing season, but the summer temperatures become less. Vines and citrous production cease, orchard fruit and truck production remains. Apart from the Californian regions, most of the western irrigation areas have a relatively limited growing season, in virtue of inland position combined with the effect of, either latitude, as in the inland irrigation areas of British Columbia and Washington, or with the effect of altitude, as in the case of the Great Basin and Rocky mountain areas, which often lie at altitudes between 4,800 feet and 6,000 feet.

In the Washington, Oregon and British Columbian irrigation districts, apples become the chief fruit crop ; though in the less extreme of them, peaches may still be grown, as they are also in the Salt Lake Oases ; but in the higher districts of the mountains, and in some of the great plains areas, no fruit is grown, and spring grains, alfalfa, sugar beet and potatoes become the typical crops. It should be noted at once, that alfalfa is grown in almost all the irrigated districts—whatever the climate. If the growing season is long, as in the south-west low-altitude districts, more cuttings can be obtained. In populous areas, as in Southern California, much of it will be fed to dairy herds ; in the sparsely peopled mountain margins, it will supplement the poor winter grazing to which the cattle come down in the winter months. In many of the interior districts, having little population, and poor communications, the production of alfalfa for winter feed may be the only function of irrigation.

Sugar beet requires neither very high summer temperatures, nor a very long growing season. It is also tolerant of alkali. Where there are good communications, and a sugar factory has been installed, it becomes an important irrigation crop. Apart from the considerable production of Michigan, it is chiefly grown, in the United States, by irrigation in the western states ; the leading producers being Colorado and Nebraska, where it is produced on the High Plains in districts watered by the South and North Platte Rivers respectively. There is a considerable production, too, in the Salt Lake Oasis of Utah.

Of the 21 million acres of irrigated land in the U.S.A. in 1942, 21 per cent. were in the Missouri Basin, 18·2 per cent. in the Colombia Basin, 16·2 per cent. in the Great Valley of California, 12·6 per cent. in the Colorado Basin, 9·9 per cent. in the Great Basin, and 7·2 per cent. in the basin of the Rio Grande.

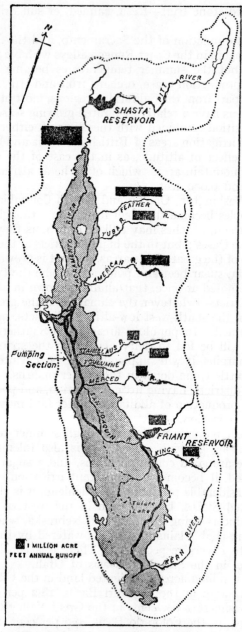

FIG. 94A.—Great Valley Water Scheme.

(Alluvial area stippled)

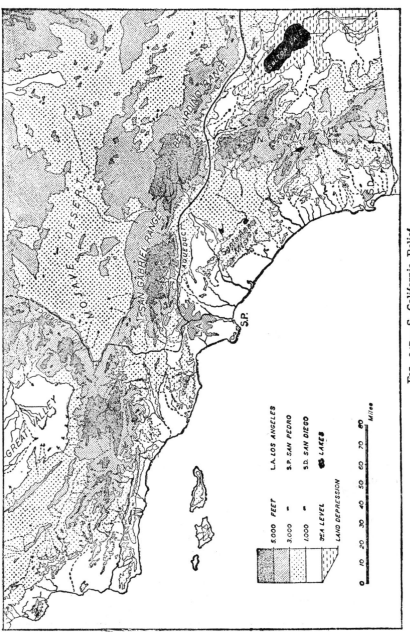

Fig. 94B.—S. California Relief

CHAPTER XXX

THE MIDDLE AND SOUTHERN ATLANTIC COASTAL REGIONS

IN this chapter we shall deal with the geography of those parts of the Atlantic States south of the Hudson and between the Appalachian Plateau and the Sea. In Chapters IV and V we divided, on a physiographical basis, this region into (*a*) *Coastal Plain*, (*b*) *Piedmont Plateau*, (*c*) *The Great Appalachian Valley*. We there noticed, furthermore, how the characteristics of each of these regions affected early settlement and lines of movement. We will treat first of all that portion of this great area which lies to the north of the Chesapeake entrance, for here was a zone of relatively easy ingress, whether to the Great Lakes, the Ohio, or south-westwards, following the trend of the Great Valley. Thus its major coastal ports come to have vast hinterlands, while Charleston and Savannah, and even Boston, functioned within a much more restricted range.

Again, the Appalachian coalfield with its anthracite detachments, here approaches most nearly to the coast, and early canals and railways emphasized that connection, giving thereby a static character to the considerable industries of the coastal cities.

We see then that superimposed upon a distribution of activities which would naturally be based upon the various characteristics of the physiographic units concerned, we have a distribution consequent upon the position of great industries, and of great cities, and this influence is implicit in the following brief treatment of the agricultural production.

Climatically the area has a fairly heavy, extremely well-distributed rainfall, rather cooler winters than the latitude suggests, and heavy snowfalls. January shows temperatures varying from about 31° F. to 37° F. along the coast, and July temperatures from 72° F. to 78° F. There is a slight tendency to lower winter temperatures inland. The growing season is over 150 days and corn is grown for grain as well as forage. The influence of the coast and bay waters in moderating frost incidence is important in coastal truck farming, as is also the similar effect of air drainage caused by the hilly topography of the orchard areas of the western Piedmont.

The coast plain elements here consist of the two major peninsulas which enclose the Delaware and Chesapeake Bays respectively, and the tide water peninsulas projecting into Chesapeake Bay from the west shore. They have much in common. On the ocean side is the sand-spit, lagoon and marine marsh formation which follows the whole Atlantic coast, but proximity to great cities here accounts for a number of seaside resorts on the sand-spits, particularly on the New Jersey Coast Beaches, e.g. Atlantic City.

Much of the western shore of the two peninsulas is bordered also by marsh country. Both peninsulas have considerable areas of infertile sandy soils occupied by pine or cut-over land. Some of this is used for cranberry cultivation. Proximity to Baltimore, Philadelphia and New York has resulted in the warm, sandy soils of the western margin of these peninsulas being largely farmed for truck. Local specialization [1] on large holdings permits of large-scale production, transport, and marketing. The canning of vegetables is an important industry (e.g., at Baltimore and Camden), and the ramifications of Delaware and Chesapeake Bay are followed by a considerable movement of vegetable products by boat. The Western Peninsulas of the Chesapeake, the sites of the original tide-water plantations of Virginia and Maryland, also show a lot of truck farming, and much corn and tobacco are grown. Mineral fertilizer (one of the big imports at Baltimore) is largely used for the truck production. But all the light soils of the coast plain cannot be used for truck farming. There is apt to be over-production as it is. Yet by introducing legumes into the rotation, by keeping some beef cattle, by using some potash and lime fertilizer, and by growing corn, a paying system of farming may be introduced again on the coast plain in view of the low price of land not especially favourably situated for truck production.

West of the narrow Cretaceous zone of heavier soils on the belt Baltimore-Philadelphia-New York, and crossing the Fall Line at these cities, we come to the Piedmont, a rolling country of residual soils which becomes positively hilly to the west. Relief is slightly smoother and agricultural production rather more intense within the area covered by the Triassic outliers of Newark Rocks with their trap ridges. Truck farming now ceases to be of importance and we have an extension northward— to Jersey City, in fact—of the corn and winter wheat belt, with mixed farming, with considerable dairy farming, too ;

[1] E.g. cranberry swamp areas of the N.J. peninsula, the sweet corn of the same peninsula and the great tomato and potato areas of the E. shore of Chesapeake Bay.

particularly in the northern part of the Piedmont, because of the large city population.   There are, however, some specialized productions.   The Piedmont of North Carolina, Virginia and Maryland has an extremely large tobacco crop, though on any particular farm this very exhausting crop usually occupies only a small fraction of the total land at one time.   Tobacco factories are important at Richmond, Lynchburg and Durham Salem. On the hillier western Piedmont, particularly between the James and the Rappahannock, there is great concentration of apple orchards.

Further west again, between the Blue Ridge and the Alleghany Front, comes the Great Valley Province.   Here we must distinguish between the broad, continuous, limestone-floored, productive eastern valley, which lies immediately beyond the Blue Ridge, and the narrow, crowded, ridge and valley elements to the west.   The former, known in succession from north to south as the Lehigh, Lebanon, Cumberland and Shenandoah valley, was from its earliest occupation a valuable farming belt threaded by an important route-way.   It is a mixed-farming area with corn and wheat as important crops.   The limestone soils are good, but sometimes thin, and every now and again a limestone pavement appears at the surface.   Proximity to limestone and coal has given rise to a number of large cement factories, e.g., at Easton, Hagerston and Roanoke.

In contrast with this great fruitful valley with its historic communications, its good roads and well-kept farms, we have the jumble of ridges and valleys to the west where the more difficult topography, the absence of communication, the greater distance to centres of population, have led to poorer farming and more waste and woodland.   Fruit farming (peaches especially) has some local development, however.

It remains to analyse the position of the great centres of population in the middle Atlantic Region.

About the mainland at the mouth of the Hudson, and upon a few adjacent islands, are distributed some eight millions of people.   We may ignore for the moment state and administrative divisions.   The essential fact is the prodigious concentration, unequalled in the world, save perhaps in the case of London. The very greatest cities present facts not to be explained easily by what have become the routine formulæ of modern geography. The more general geographical factors are seen to be of importance in the initial stages of these vast growths.   They are so in this case.   They have already received some attention in this work.

It would seem almost that in recent times the most powerful

factor at any stage of growth may well be the very size of the population already attained at that stage ; and we may find reasons for this. A great urban centre cannot, of course, be self-supporting, but it forms the ideal market for foodstuffs and for the raw materials of manufacture—ideal in the very concentration of its zone of final distribution. It provides also a ready and varied labour supply, and the possibilities of the economic reassortment of such labour.

The ramifications of any great modern industrial organization are intricate and widespread, but such must have its nerve ganglion, its directing centre, where reports are received and decisions taken, and whence impulses are propelled to the very limits of the system. And each directing centre is best placed when in proximity to other directing centres. The very possibility of personal communication is important. Thus the banking, industrial, transport, and newspaper concerns, aspiring or already great, must have their central offices in cities such as London, New York, Paris, and Berlin. Every additional quota to provincial population, whether industrial or agricultural, has its counterpart in metropolitan expansion. And the whole thing implies and is dependent upon the great modern transport facilities which enable millions to live in a restricted area, drawing their supplies from enormous distances, and distributing their products as far. Each urban centre of certain size was a point of attraction to the earliest transport links, and with each connecting link a city added a material and somewhat permanent factor for its continued expansion, while the very wealth and political pressure potential in a great city are sufficient to secure that constant development of terminal facilities which alone can overcome the congestion incident upon rapid growth.

The whole process of metropolitan growth seems sufficiently natural. It might reasonably be made the subject of judicious control. But the city must have its origin. With the site of this, as with the factors concerned in a development more sturdy than that of less favoured localities, geography has everything to do.

West of the Hudson Valley we come to the massive beds of the Alleghany Plateau, here represented by rocks of Devonian Age. It is the escarpment of some of the more resistant of these rocks which forms the western barrier boundary of the Hudson, and the southern limit of the Mohawk Valley. The rocks, like those of the lake plain which underlie them, form part of a Palæozoic series lapping about the Archæan mass of the Adirondacks, and dipping away from that mass to the south. The Lockport dolomite and Onondaga limestone form the minor

escarpments facing north, but the much greater portage escarpment (a massive sandstone over shale) forms the real boundary
to the great route-way.

On the north the formidable forested mass of the Adirondacks
divides the Mohawk from the Champlain route. East of this
last, the Taconic and Green Mountains of the New England
province close in the route on that side. The route so defined
is forced to a right-angular shape by the great shoulder of the
Catskills, which so occur as to forbid an easy direct route to the
lakes. The route is circuitous then, but nowhere from Nova
Scotia to Alabama is there an Appalachian crossing with easier
gradients (Fig. 18, Chapter VIII). To the importance of this
great breach in the early American wars, we have referred again
and again. We are concerned now only with its function as a
factor in the growth of New York. We have already shown
that for many reasons it was ineffective in this respect until
after the 1812 war.

The upper Hudson itself, and its tributary the Mohawk, flow
in rather narrow lowlands where there was little room for agricultural expansion, and both were interrupted by falls. Below
Albany, too, the river provides only a narrow belt for agricultural
settlement, with no easy east and west routes. On the other
hand, the river itself below Albany is wide and deep—a veritable
arm of the sea. If America were an old country in the European
sense, with an interior already populous and developed before
the era of big ships, then Albany might have become the port
of the Hudson—something corresponding to the *head of the estuary*
type in Europe. It remained, however, almost a frontier town
till the Erie canal period. The Hudson and Mohawk valleys
then formed just a narrow zone of occupation. The first considerable lowland agricultural area is that of the Erie and Ontario
plains—the lowland about the Genesee River. Here were good
soils and a climate moderated by the lake water bodies. We
have seen how the Genesee road made this area tributary to New
York.

The disposition of the major physiographic elements about the
Hudson-Mohawk Gap are indicated in Fig. 95A.

The River Hudson itself rises in the Adirondacks, that is to
say in an extension into the United States of the pre-Cambrian
Shield. From them it flows down into a narrow lowland which,
geomorphologically, is the northward-trending continuation of the
Great Appalachian Valley ; and, in it, the Hudson flows, as
a subsequent stream, between the massive escarpments of the
Catskills which here represent the edge of the Appalachian Plateau, and the rugged heights of the Taconic Mountains of New

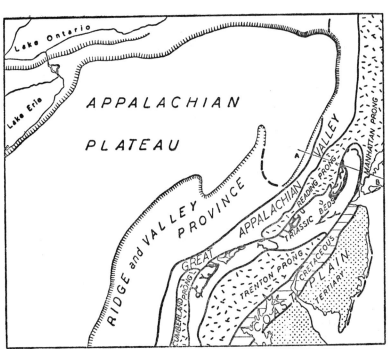

FIG. 95A.—Physiographic Regions of the Middle Atlantic States.
The black markings in the Triassic Beds indicate the outcrop of trap rock ridges.

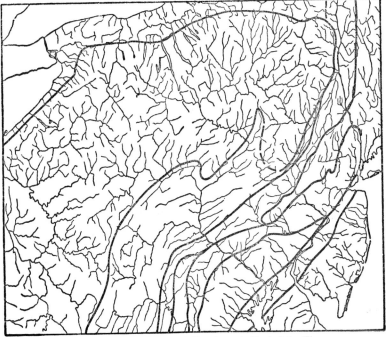

FIG. 95B.—Main Drainage of the Area indicated in Fig. 95A.

England, which are structurally a continuation of the Blue Ridge.

Farther down-stream, however, the river leaves the physiographical province of the Appalachian Valley, and cuts diagonally across the Blue Ridge—here called the Hudson highlands—the Piedmont, and the Coast Plain. For essentially southern New England is of the Piedmont province—a coastward-sloping peneplain of metamorphic crystalline rocks, with igneous intrusions, and with some areas of infaulted or infolded Palæozoic and Mesozoic sediments of lesser resistance which now form relative lowlands. Immediately west of the lower Hudson this crystalline Piedmont is covered by an infaulted cover of Triassic sandstones and sandy shales which constitute the Newark beds.

As in the similar occurrences, in the Annapolis Valley of Nova Scotia, and in the lower Connecticut Valley of New England, these are here of clastic material of continental origin, and are interspersed with dikes and sills of basic igneous rock. In general the Triassic lowland is of smoother relief than the surrounding crystallines, but the resistant trap rocks just mentioned stand out the more abruptly. In the neighbourhood of New York they form that precipitous wall of basalt overlooking the Hudson which is known, because of its columnar appearance, as the Palisades ; and some miles west of these, and separate by some hundreds of feet of Triassic shales, are three more closely spaced trap ridges. These form the Watchung Mountains—curved, parallel, abrupt, east-facing scarps, rising some hundreds of feet above the general lowland, and of even sky-line.

In general the Newark beds dip north-westwards to terminate against the fault scarp of the Blue Ridge. Apart from these ridges the Triassic lowland is markedly smoother than the Piedmont, which surrounds it.

The surround is not quite complete, however, for the coast plain sediments overlap the Triassic lowland between Trenton and New York, and the Triassic sediments abut the Great Valley where the Blue Ridge peters out between Reading and Carlisle. Thus the Piedmont nearly surrounds the Triassic lowland in wedgelike areas of rougher topography, each of which narrows to a terminal " prong "—the so-called Manhattan, Trenton, Reading and Carlisle " prongs " (see Fig. 95A).

To the south-east the gneisses and schists of the Piedmont are covered by the sands and clays of the young coast plain. In this region this is represented by Long Island, by all but the northern portion of Staten Island, and by the large sandy peninsulas of New Jersey, and of the East Shore Chesapeake. Between the cuesta of the New Jersey peninsula and the Piedmont lies a corridor of Cretaceous clays and marls which runs just below the fall line from Baltimore to New York itself. Here where the great estuaries met the fall line, were the relatively fertile soils, the early settlements, the early roads, canals, and later railways and industries, which have constituted this the greatest route-way in America, a route-way which in some sense makes tributary to New York every activity through which it passes.

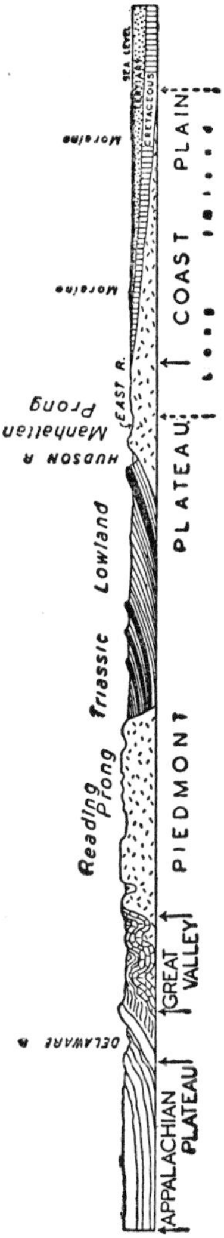

The incidence of glaciation, and subsequent readjustments of land level relative to the sea, have each set further effective imprints upon the physical environment of the great city. Terminal moraines form the main axes of relief throughout Long Island, the southern half of which is a smooth outwash plain. The moraine, cut by the Narrows, then curves south-westward through Staten Island. The channel of the Hudson was itself deepened when the land stood higher than at present and the deep rock valley has been partly filled up with detritus, but even so the recently drowned nature of this coast makes of the Hudson below Troy a veritable arm of the sea, and has separated Long Island, Staten Island, and Manhattan Island itself from the mainland.

New York is the only Fall Line city having no coincident interruption of navigation. Not till the passing of the Indian buffer state between French and English, not indeed until after the various wars of Independence, and of 1812, was the Genesee country occupied on any scale, and not till the opening in 1825 of the old Erie Canal did New York begin to rapidly outstrip her rival state ports. Then, for the first time, did the Hudson-Mohawk Gap become an effective factor, adding one more, and the most important one, to the great pioneer routes instrumental in filling up the Middle West. It was by this route that much of the country immediately to the south of the Great Lakes became occupied and so joined up with that portion of the land between the Ohio and the Great Lakes which had previously been occupied via the Ohio route.

FIG. 96.—Section along line A—B indicated in Fig. 95A.

A graph of the population of New York City as compared with Philadelphia and Baltimore shows a steep rise beginning shortly after 1825 and still in evidence. This indicates the real beginning of New York supremacy, and is to be associated quite definitely with three interrelated facts:

(i) The building of the Erie canal from Buffalo to Albany (1825).

(ii) The great obstacle of Niagara, which diverted traffic to this route.

(iii) The occupation of the interior lowlands north of the Ohio, an occupation begun via the Ohio tributaries Scioto, Muskingum, and Maumee, but enormously facilitated by the Erie canal itself and by the later canals connecting Lake Erie and the Ohio.

Neither the St. Lawrence nor the Mississippi, neither the Pennsylvanian nor the Maryland routes, could compete with this route either for the further peopling of the mid-west or for the freight traffic which resulted. The coming of the railways —at first, at any rate—only served to emphasize the advantage, for what the other trans-Appalachian lines gained in distance to the Atlantic, they lost in gradient, curves, and expense of construction. So effective was the natural deep water from New York to Albany that these towns were not linked by the New York Central till 1852. Even so, without the deep natural harbour and the comparatively direct access to the sea (contrast Baltimore and Philadelphia) the supremacy of New York would not have been so decisive. Let us look, then, at the immediate environment of the harbour itself before returning to a consideration of important subsidiary districts within the state.

The Hudson River below Hudson is really a narrow arm of the sea, owing much of its form to glacial scouring, to the later glacial outlet of the lake waters (see Chapter III), and, finally, to a coast submergence. It is often over a mile in width, so, until very recently, the lowest bridge was at a narrowing, some 55 miles up, at Poughkeepsie. The river has now been bridged at New York itself. There are 24 feet of water all the way to Hudson, and 11 feet on to Albany and Troy, so from Albany southward the river itself forms a natural link with the Erie and Champlain canal system, though to meet the requirements of the deep modern barge canal, the shoally stretch between Hudson and Albany has had to be improved somewhat. The real barrier hills (over 1,000 feet—i.e. Catskill, Green, and Taconic Mountains) stand well back from the river, which nevertheless runs in a narrow but not deep gorge, in which the railway tracks are confined almost to the water's edge. Fig. 97 shows the waterways about New York itself. South of Long Island and of Staten Island we have the marine marsh and sand-spit coast so typical of the Middle and Southern Atlantic coast-line. The

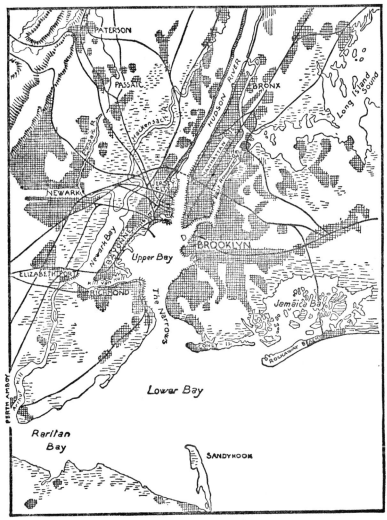

FIG. 97.—New York.

drowning of a deeply trenched river system, however, has provided a submarine cañon opposite the Hudson mouth and has turned tributary streams, such as East River and the Lower Raritan, into tidal arms of the sea. The configuration of the coast-line is such as to divide the Hudson mouth into upper and lower bays separated by the Narrows.

The Hudson is not a great river in proportion to the size of its channel, and such detritus as it brings down is deposited in what is actually the head of its estuary about Albany and Troy. More serious are the coastal current washings, which tend to extend the enclosing arms of Sandy Hook and Rockaway Beach and provide material for the formation of shoals at the entrance to the lower bay. There is a tide here of 4 to 5 feet, and it is here only that extensive dredging operations (on the Ambrose and Gedney Channels) have been necessary to keep the port open for the very greatest vessels. There is now 40 feet of water through this bar, and on to the wharves of New Jersey and Manhattan.

The original port was, of course, Manhattan Island. Now a continuous line of wharves extends from the Battery some 9 miles up the river on the New Jersey and Manhattan shores, and for 6 or 7 miles on the East River between New York and Brooklyn, while New Jersey, Brooklyn, Newark, Paterson, and a number of smaller places form virtually one great centre of population. The main entrance to the harbour is through the Narrows, but in a port where lighter traffic is of immense significance, connecting bays and channels, e.g. Raritan Bay, Arthur Kill, Kill van Kull, Jamaica Bay, and, of course, East River itself, are of great value, and have their share in development schemes. Thus at the head of Raritan Bay vessels of 19 feet draught can reach the coal port of South Amboy. Arthur Kill and Kill van Kull [1] cut off Staten Island. The latter has a least depth of 25 feet, and vessels of 18 to 19 feet draught can make the whole round from the upper bay to Raritan Bay. It is proposed to deepen the whole to 25 feet. Considerable traffic uses this channel to Perth Amboy, Elizabethport, New Brighton, and Port Richmond, and to a number of waterside factories, shipyards, and coal depots. There is over 30 feet of water at the great oil shipment points of Bayonne.

Newark Bay is largely shoal, but a channel has been dredged to the junction of the Hackensack and Passaic Rivers at the head of the bay. The tide is 5 feet at Newark, and it is proposed to deepen the channel through this great manufacturing centre to 20 feet, and to 6 feet as far as Passaic.

Vessels of 30 feet draught have been taken to some of the East River piers, but 20 feet is about the deepest draught of vessels regularly using the through route to Long Island Sound,

[1] Kill van Kull is a breach in the Palisades trap, which ceases to present a barrier escarpment at about the middle of Jersey City.

though great barges drawing 23 feet are towed through. East River is a drowned valley developed on old metamorphic rock. It has a rocky channel and swift tidal currents. Important blasting operations have been necessary to provide the modern channel and to prevent damage from rock shoals. It bears a very heavy traffic, especially in barge coal to New England points.

All these navigable waterways, with their enormous aggregate of water front, and possibilities of further development, give character to the port, but the main harbour, the densest traffic, the biggest vessels, are concentrated in the 4 to 5 miles of river above the Battery.

There never yet was a port which had not its natural obstacle to expansion, as well as its natural advantages of situation. And New York is no exception. Population, industry, and terminal points have long extended beyond the old Manhattan site. In particular a vast amount of freight entering by rail and motor on the New Jersey side is wanted for shipment or distribution on the New York side. So, too, liners regularly berthed in Manhattan Island, have often cargoes which must be distributed from New Jersey rail terminals. The necessity of the redistribution of cargoes as between wharves and rail terminals is common to all ports, and is usually accomplished by belt lines.

The great extent of New York waterways, the expense of bridging the gorge-like Hudson just above New York, make belt lines almost impossible. To a large extent the transference is done by car ferries (between New York and New Jersey) and by an extensive lighter traffic. There is thus an enormously heavy ferry traffic from New Jersey to all parts of the waterways, but more especially to Manhattan terminal, and it is so dense that it somewhat obstructs the Lower Hudson for through traffic. The foreshore on the New Jersey side is owned by the railway companies, who have been more concerned with providing rail terminals and sidings than ship accommodation. The whole matter is complicated by rival New York and New Jersey interests. It would appear that Newark Bay might serve as a relief if provided with deep-water channels and terminal facilities. The only through traffic across the river is provided by the passenger tunnels. A vehicular tunnel is now constructed under the Hudson, and relieves much motor congestion.[1] Jamaica Bay also is deemed by some experts to be a feasible site for the lay-out of a great relief out-port on modern lines. The channel would be entirely artificial as the bay is shallow.

One may notice finally how the rapid urban growth west of the Hudson is confined between the trap ridge of the Palisades and the much higher trap ridge of the first Watchung Mountain

[1] There are now two vehicular terminals: Holland (1927) and Lincoln (1938).

15

(Fig. 98). In crossing this latter the Passaic River forms valuable power falls in the great silk manufacturing city of Paterson. South of this water-gap and in the same ridge are a number of wind-gaps, evidence of former river capture.

For its great manufacturing and urban population, for shipment to New England industrial points, for the bunkering of its huge foreign and domestic tonnage, the whole area requires a great deal of coal.[1] It is a hundred miles from the anthracite fields, and much more from the bituminous—but so are all the Atlantic ports. Its great requirements in this respect have led to rail siding and shipping facilities on the New Jersey side.

With regard to the total traffic handled, New York is supreme in America. London shares much the larger portion of the shipping of the British Isles with Liverpool. In the whole continent of America there is nothing to compare with New York.

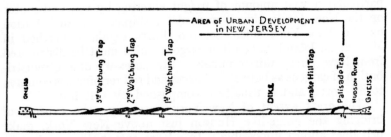

FIG. 98.—Section showing Trap Ridges and Area of Urban Development west of the Hudson.

It deals with more than one-half of the whole foreign commerce of the U.S.A., and has by far the heaviest coastwise traffic as well. Besides being beyond all comparison the greatest general port on the continent, it actually handles more wheat, coal, and timber than any other—all bulk commodities requiring special large-scale facilities. We will emphasize this absolute pre-eminence with a very few selected figures.

Customs District.	Value of Merchandise in Millions of Dollars. 1935.	
	Imports.	Exports.
New York	1,033 (50·6 per cent.)	790 (34·6 per cent.)
Massachusetts (Boston) . . .	110 (5·4 per cent.)	24 (1·0 per cent.)
Philadelphia	120 (5·9 per cent.)	62 (2·8 per cent.)
Maryland (Baltimore) . . .	55 (2·7 per cent.)	36 (1·6 per cent.)
All U.S.A.	2,039 (100 per cent.)	2,283 (100 per cent.)

[1] And oil.

Montreal, New York, and Vancouver, together ship more than three-quarters of the grain exports of the Continent.

But the work of the port is, of course, interrelated with the gigantic local market represented by its millions of people, and with the manufacturing development of this huge population. In spite of the great manufacturing development of New England, Pennsylvania, and the Lake States in particular, the value of the manufactures of the states of New York and New Jersey together is at least one-quarter of the total value for the U.S.A., and certainly most of the work is done near the mouth of the Hudson. New York City employs more people in clothing factories, machine shops, and foundries, printing and publishing, and tobacco factories, than any other city, and has a host of miscellaneous manufactures in addition. In New Jersey, Paterson has the greatest silk-works in the country. Camden has shipbuilding yards ; Bayonne, great oil refineries ; and Newark and Jersey City, many miscellaneous industries. The swamp sites about Newark Bay are being reclaimed and taken up for factory work. Trenton has big pottery works.

But though the bulk (possibly 60 to 70 per cent. of the value) of manufactures in New York State are developed at the Hudson mouth, the topography of the hinterland which made New York possible has defined a subsidiary zone of great industrial development. All the towns of over 50,000 inhabitants in New York State are on the Hudson-Mohawk route. The transport developments, which meant everything to the terminals of Buffalo and New York, were an asset to all places *en route*. Buffalo, with half a million people, is a great manufacturing centre, a port of coal shipment to Canada, a site for some of the biggest of the lake-side iron and steel plants, and a great milling centre.

East of Buffalo stretches, in the lake plains, the widest area of agricultural land in the state, and the influence of the Great Lakes in mitigating the season of early frost makes of the lake-side areas great fruit-growing centres. Further east, again, the basins of the Mohawk and Upper Hudson provide little room for agricultural expansion but much power—e.g. at Little Falls, where the Mohawk passes through a narrow gorge, and more important, at Cohoes Falls. In both these cases the falls are due to a deviation of the stream since glacial times. Then, again, the Adirondack tributaries of the Mohawk and Upper Hudson have much power. A number of villages used these power sites for factories in the pre-steam days, and in these days of hydro-electric distribution there is a recrudescence of these powers in competition with the Pennsylvanian coal.

Cohoes is the centre of the biggest hosiery industry in the

States. Troy has big linen factories. Buffalo is served, of course, by Niagara's power, which is certainly available as far east as Utica. Rochester, which has important electrical engineering works and factories making optical apparatus,[1] uses much hydro-electric power, and owes its original position to the Genesee Falls. Utica has cotton and foundry works. The Adirondack forests and streams gave rise to a great lumber industry, and, later, to paper and pulp factories. The whole valley, then, from Albany to Utica, forms an important manufacturing area subsidiary to New York, and based on the nearness of a great market, on great power resources, and on position on a great route-way.

The New York State Barge canal (the successor of the historic Erie canal) extends from the Hudson River at Troy to Tonawanda and Buffalo. Twelve feet deep, and with locks 311 feet by 45 feet, it is a fine piece of work, which up to the present has not been very successful in recapturing bulk traffic from the railways.

Philadelphia and Baltimore are fall-line cities near the head of the Chesapeake and Delaware respectively. In colonial times they flourished as colonial capitals, because of their considerable ingress to the country, and their situation on the narrow strip of generally fertile Cretaceous soils on the route joining them both to New York. Philadelphia as the metropolis of Pennsylvania had the advantage of serving a much greater territory, and one which expanded westward so as to include a great section of the Appalachians at their weakest, i.e. where the ridges were lowest and most gapped, and the valleys most accessible and most fertile. At Sparrow Point near Baltimore are large iron and steel works.

The falls on the Susquehanna at the fall line, and the early road and canal connection of Philadelphia with Middleton diverted the traffic of that river valley to Philadelphia rather than to the Chesapeake.

Neither city could compete with the great trans-Appalachian route of New York, while the distance of both from the open sea, and the relative ease of their land connection with New York, have made of them, and of intermediate cities, one great manu-facturing district subsidiary to New York itself. The line through Baltimore, Philadelphia, and Jersey City carries some of the heaviest traffic in the States. Both cities are now available for vessels up to 30 feet draught, and are important ports both for general commodities and in particular for grain (out), timber (in), and oil (in). They are even more important as coastal manu-facturing districts. Woollen, worsted, knit goods, foundries and machine shops, automobile factories, publishing and printing, and clothing, are among the most important of the industries of Philadelphia.

[1] Including Eastman's photographic and film apparatus.

Although the Cretaceous rocks of the coast plain, much of the Piedmont soils, and also the limestone valleys of the Appalachians, provide good agricultural land, a great deal of the peninsula of New Jersey and of Chesapeake consists of almost sterile sands and pine wastes. On the other hand, the dense population about the line of cities—Baltimore, Philadelphia, Jersey City, and New York—provides an immediate market for truck farming, so that, with the help of fertilizers, many light quick soils are intensively cultivated.

We have emphasized throughout this chapter the economic importance not only of New York itself, but also of the great subsidiary belts of industrial population which occupy :

(i) The Mohawk-Hudson valleys.

(ii) The Washington, Baltimore, Philadelphia, Newark corridor.

(iii) The coastal lowland of New England from New York to Boston.

South Atlantic States

In the large, the Atlantic States south of the Chesapeake entrance differ from those to the north in having (a) a compact block of the Coast Plain Province, (b) a length of growing season and intensity of summer temperature which allow of the growth of cotton, and above all (c) a hinterland limited by a very real mountain barrier.

The ports, Wilmington, Charleston and Savannah, Jacksonville, etc., are of more local importance than the great ports of the north, and the one notable industry (cotton manufacture) is of comparatively recent development (see p. 217, Chapter XIV).

The whole lies within the cotton belt and cotton occupies more cultivated land than any other crop. This production has already been treated in Chapter XIV. The coast has an even greater development of the sand-spit marine marsh type than that obtaining further north, and vast areas are susceptible to drainage here when the pressure on land becomes sufficiently great. The occasional patches of large-scale coastal truck farming provides products intermediate in date between those of the East Shore and those of Florida. Inside the coastal marsh area the greater part of the coast plain, with its prevailing sands and sandy loams, was forested with conifers, the long-leaf pine predominating and forming the most valuable timber. Timber and turpentine were important here in Colonial days, and still are so, and it is only in recent decades that the north-west Pacific States have wrested the premier position as lumber-producers from the coast-plain pine belt of the South Atlantic and Gulf States. The soils are light, yet if fertilizers are used, stock kept and legumes are in the rotation, economic farming is possible because of the relatively low price of land. Cotton, corn and beans, and in the north corn, peas and some winter wheat, are the chief crops both of coast plain and Piedmont. On the coast plain, however, there are still large areas of forest and cut-over land, and much of the latter is used as cattle range.

Charleston Harbour is on the coast of South Carolina and is formed by an almost landlocked bay at the mouth of the Cooper and Ashley rivers. The city is at the confluence at the head of the bay, 7½ miles from the ocean bar. There is a 30-feet channel over the bar. Four-fifths of the goods handled have a hinterland confined to the Carolina States. The chief exports are raw cotton, coal and lumber, and the chief imports are mineral oils and fertilizers. The chief coastwise shipments are lumber, oil and cotton, and the chief coastwise receipts are crude oil, sugar and miscellaneous merchandise.

Wilmington in North Carolina is on the east bank of Cape Fear River, 30 miles from its mouth ; the controlling depth on the bar is 26 feet. It is less of a general port than Charleston, its trade being almost confined to fertilizers and petroleum (in) and cotton and lumber (out).

Similarly Savannah, the chief port of Georgia, situated some 24 miles up the Savannah River, is a port of somewhat local hinterland for the great proportion of its traffic. The river is navigable for large traffic for 200 miles up to the fall line at Augusta. Again fertilizers form the chief of the imports, followed by sugar and crude oil. The chief exports are cotton, linters and cotton seed. The chief domestic shipments are cotton and lumber, and the domestic receipts are very varied manufactured goods. Thus the occupation with fertilizer, lumber and cotton is characteristic of the South Atlantic ports, yet this movement of bulk products, and of requirements of the immediate hinterland, has suffered some recent modification. The great development of the southern cotton industry has affected adversely the raw cotton shipment, and the tendency to work up lumber near its source gives products better dealt with by the railways. Moreover the facilities provided at a bulk-commodity port are not readily suitable to a more general type of traffic.

The Coast Plain regions of the Atlantic states and of Mexico exhibit respectively their greatest development in the twin blunt peninsulas of Florida and of Yucatan. An elevation of 100 fathoms would nearly double the area of both, and in each case the emerged mass would be almost wholly on the west or Gulf side, where now are the shallows of Campeche and of the Florida Bank. Both countries are nearly flat, and represent the slightly emerged surfaces of a great platform of Eocene limestone, extending from Florida to the Bahamas and Cuba and possibly at one time bridging the gulf between the peninsulas themselves. Both of them exhibit certain features of surface drainage characteristic of limestone regions, and both are areas of climatic transition.

Yucatan is politically a part of Mexico, and we will consider it in discussing that country.

In Florida, the Atlantic and Gulf Coast Plains unite in a southerly projection of some 350 miles, which nearly attains the tropics. Key West (lat. 24° 4′) in the temperate zone faces Havana (lat. 23° 8′) across the 100-miles strait of Florida. In climate and production, Southern Florida is of the West Indies, and yet only just so. We think of it as a country almost free from drought and frost, yet probably in no state of the Union have these twin evils done more damage—i.e., of course, relatively to the total value of the crops in the state. Florida is so nearly frost-free that it apes the cultivations of the tropics. Its soils are so often light and sandy that its crops cannot always combat the occasional drought periods which occur even in a region of heavy and fairly well-distributed rainfall.

The whole peninsula has within very recent times suffered oscillations which have slightly depressed it below sea-level and as slightly raised it above. It consists of a great crustal block of limestone partially and irregularly covered with sands of varying depths. The porosity and shallowness of much of the surface deposits, together with the heavy rainfall, have resulted in a very extensive and irregular solution of the limestone. Large-scale maps are required to illustrate the immense number of lakelets which occupy sink-holes in the limestone, or depressions in the cover caused by subterranean solution. In the centre and south there is much underground drainage, and many subterranean channels, many miles in length, have been traced. This fact, combined with the mildness of relief especially in the south, the shallowness of the water table, the influence of obstructive masses of vegetation and of fallen cavern roofs, make the drainage extremely irregular and variable. These conditions are not representative of the whole state, however. A belt of relatively high sand-lands runs from the north-western boundary (300 feet) and widens out in the north central peninsula so as to extend almost from coast to coast with a central elevation of 200 feet. This higher region sinks east, west, and south to the less well-drained flatwood area. South again, in the southern third of the peninsula, Lake Okechobee and its contiguous everglades and cypress swamp lands are only a few feet above sea-level, and quite uninhabitable save where reclaimed. The constant currents off the east coast have resulted in a development of sand-spit unusually continuous even for the Atlantic coast of North America. Within the sand-spit the usual narrow strip of shallow waterway exhibits a particularly complete development in what is known as the Indian River, which runs uninterruptedly from Palm Beach to Port Orange—some 150 miles. To the west of this comes another narrow coastal unit in a long belt of dune country, seldom more than 2 miles in width or more than 30 feet in height. This is the well-known pineapple belt. To the west again, this sinks to the wide belt of marsh or poorly drained country of the everglades. In the extreme south the mildness of the climate and the warmth of the sea-water is attested by a considerable development of mangrove swamp (especially about the Ten Thousand Isles) and of coral reefs about the Floridan Keys.

Sandy soils predominate, and the chief variations in the distribution of natural vegetation depend upon the depth of the water table. The high sand-belts of the north are apt to be very dry. Lower and still sandy land of the flatwood may often be waterlogged. In many districts the surface sands are interrupted by hard layers of fine material (sand and clay) cemented with iron oxides. The depth of these will obviously—unless broken up—be a factor in the possibility of crop development. The soils of the marsh country, when drained, are usually light, but covered with a mantle of rich humus. Clays and loams are rare.

Originally, probably nearly the whole state, save the permanent marsh land of the everglades, was pine-covered, and with a preponderance of the marsh-loving southern cypress. Florida cuts about 10 per cent. of the production of this wood in the U.S.A. It has about one-quarter of the total stand. The tree assumes rather different forms according to its location. In marsh country it develops basal thickenings or "knees," which serve both to assist transpiration and to attain a firm holding.[1] The wood is soft and easily worked, and the heart-wood is pre-eminently damp-resisting, as many examples of the long life of shingle and water troughs testify. In marsh surroundings the wood is expensive to log, for over a considerable distance neither firm road nor open waterway is available. Many miles of temporary light railway, or of channels for floating, have been cut through the dense undergrowth for the purpose of marketing this timber. Forests, too light soils, swamps, and an almost tropical climate,

[1] See U.S.A. Dept. of Agriculture Bulletin 272: "The Southern Cypress."

have been factors in the backward development of the state. Very little of the land was available for settlement, save by forest clearing or swamp draining. In the everglade area there still exist a few hundred Seminole Indians, who have no official existence in that their chiefs have never formally come to terms with the U.S.A. Government.

Central and Southern Florida has, however, climatic characteristics unexampled elsewhere in the States. It is the only state which approaches true Antillean conditions. South-western states attain higher summer temperature, but they are arid and their winters a little cooler. Few U.S.A. stations are more equable than Key West, with its very low daily range and its annual average range of 11° F. only. Even so, there is room for considerable variation in the 350 miles of the State. The passage of one of the deep winter cyclones to the north may be followed by temperatures below freezing almost as far south as Key West. No state combines equability and high average temperature to the same degree, and so Florida has been able to specialize in citrous fruits, in the production of which it is rivalled only by the irrigation products of South California. Even so, the early producing areas were located too far north, and the frost of 1894–5 in particular was so bad that most plantations were destroyed. The industry had to be built up afresh, and further to the south. 1886, 1899, and 1917 also were bad years.

The citrous fruit belt in Florida is wedged between the too cold north and too swampy south. And rainfall is usually sufficient for this growth. Florida, however, has slightly less well-distributed rain than occurs in the other East Gulf states. Like them, it gets rain (slightly greater in the west) from the north-eastward curving summer Gulf Lows. In winter it is too liable to come under the influence of an extension of the Bermuda High, and though rain is fairly frequent, a winter drought is not uncommon. The unusually mild winters allow of the growth throughout the winter months of vegetables (e.g. celery, potatoes, greens, etc.), and the placing of these upon the markets at times when they are otherwise unavailable. Much of the best land is used for this winter truck farming. For such production, a light soil is all to the good, provided it is heavily fertilized, and the high prices obtained renders this possible. As we have just seen, however, Florida is liable to winter drought, but as throughout the country water is seldom far below the surface, supplementary irrigation (by pumps and flowing wells) is extensively used. Twenty-five per cent. of the truck acreage is irrigated and 10 per cent. of the citrous and truck acreage combined. The most important single area is the Hastings potato sections where 10,000 acres are regularly irrigated. As frosts, though sometimes severe enough to do damage to the characteristic Florida productions, are yet always very transient, they have not time to cool any considerable bodies of water, and damage from frost can sometimes be actually avoided by irrigation. A sheltered situation (yet not at the lowest level in locally irregular country, for there cold air collects) is important in the case of

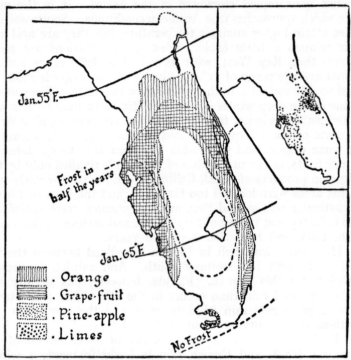

Jan. 55° F.

Frost in half the years

Jan. 65° F.

▥. Orange
▤. Grape-fruit
▦. Pine-apple
▨. Limes

No Frost

Fig. 99.—Florida.　Diagram showing climatic zones suitable for various fruits.
Inset : The actual quantitative representation of orange production.

citrus fruits. Warning of frost can often be given, and then wood and oil fires to heat the air to windward may prevent disaster. The pineapple is particularly susceptible to frost, and when cultivated in Florida occupies a long, narrow, raised coastal belt just to the west of the India River. Recently, however, the yield decreased through soil impoverishment, and the crop was almost ruined by frost in 1917, since when the famous belt has been almost uncultivated, for the soil is too light for citrus fruits.[1]　The belt is being restored, however.

[1] See U.S.A. Dept. of Agriculture, Farmers' Bulletin 1237 : " Pineapple Culture in Florida."

The following table will serve to set the foregoing facts in their right perspective :

PRODUCTION TABLE (IN MILLIONS)

	1920		1927		1935	
	Florida	California	Florida	California	Florida	California
	Boxes	Boxes	Boxes	Boxes	Boxes	Boxes
Oranges .	5·9	21·6	10·0	22·5	16·9	34·9
Grape Fruit	3·16	0·46	6·3	·7	10·5	2·3
Lemons .	0·03	6·5	—	6·4	—	8·0

In addition to these agricultural products proper, Florida contributes to the general well-being of U.S.A. agriculture by her production of phosphate rock. Next to nitrogen, phosphorus is the essential soil constituent most apt to be removed by prolonged cultivation, and it is less readily replaced. This fact gives great importance to the distribution of the world's phosphorus rock reserves. At present the largest world producers are French North Africa and Florida. Florida produces about three-quarters of the mineral phosphates of the U.S.A.

And we may notice in passing the shipping accessibility of this production. The U.S.A. is fortunate in having immense untouched reserves in Utah, Wyoming, and Idaho, but these are obviously relatively badly placed either for domestic agriculture or for export. The area occupied by the Florida deposits is shown in Fig. 100. Two types of deposit are distinguished—the hard rock phosphates and the pebble phosphates. Both occur near the surface, and often in swampy country or below the water table. Dry mining is the exception. The hard rock phosphate occurs in irregular beds under an overburden of sand or clay, which is removed by steam shovel or hydraulic pump. From the wet mines the hard rock is dredged, cleaned of adhering sand and clay, and dried for shipment. Much is exported. The pebble phosphate occurs in regular sheets of varying thickness. These are eaten into by forced jets of water, and the mulch removed by hydraulic pump and screened to retain the phosphatic pebbles. One-half is used within the U.S.A. In both cases separation of commercial phosphate involves the wastage of an even greater quantity of phosphate in the washing processes.

A railway map of Florida reveals the small development of the peninsula area as a whole. The only two important ports,

Jacksonville and Tampa, are connected with each other. Jacksonville is on the west bank of the St. John River, nearly 30 miles from the ocean. The harbour has been improved so as to be available for vessels drawing not more than 28 feet of water. Its imports consist largely of general merchandise from the northern states, and coal, oil, grain, and hardware. Its exports are lumber and phosphates. Tampa has a rather more specialized commerce,

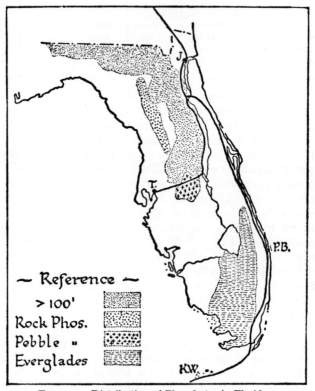

FIG. 100.—Distribution of Phosphates in Florida.
J, Jacksonville; P.B, Palm Beach; K.W, Key West; T, Tampa.

and deals with more of the shipped tobacco and phosphate of Florida than does Jacksonville. The Floridan peninsula adds a maximum of 700 miles to voyages from, say, Charleston to New Orleans. Four transpeninsula canal routes have been prospected, but it is not likely that any canal will be built. It would not take steamer traffic, for rounding the peninsula would be less expensive than two transhipments, and the interior local traffic would not warrant the expense of construction.

An interesting feature of the communications is the east coast railway line extension to Key West, which was hardly warranted by any very obvious advantage to be gained. True, the sea passage to Cuba is a little shortened, but in actual fact, since West Indian export produce has to put to sea, it is usually landed nearer to markets than South Florida ; and Key West has not enough traffic to warrant the enormous engineering works involved in carrying the railway over nearly 100 miles of key and intercepting water channels, and for keeping the great viaducts —one of them is 7 miles in length—free from the corrosive action of the warm salt water and the damage of the summer hurricanes. For these reasons the railway has now been closed and replaced by a road. At such places as Miami and Palm Beach, however, the warm, bright winter weather and magnificent firm beaches have led to the establishment of great winter resorts.

On the basis of these climatic attractions and the possibilities of success in extensive truck and fruit farming, a great Floridan land boom was engineered in 1924–5. The late-comers were left with areas of extensive swamp on their hands. Yet the results of the great gamble were not completely contemptible. A very real development of road-building accompanied the boom.

CHAPTER XXXI

MEXICO

IN Mexico occur the greatest complexity of structural detail, and the greatest contrasts of climatic and topographic phenomena ; yet in their broader relations to human activities the chief physical characteristics of the country are simple, effective, and clear-cut.

Any good atlas map will indicate the main elements of relief. Such a map shows that the greater part of the country consists of a vast horn-shaped tableland, narrowing and tilted up to the south. East and west marginal ranges border the tableland, rising with it to the south. That of the west is more compact and higher than the eastern one. Both approach the coasts to the south, leaving two triangular coastal plains, the more extensive of which is on the east. In the south these marginal ranges merge with an east-to-west series of mountains, forming a complicated mountain plexus having several high intermont plains surrounded by gigantic mountain ranges and peaks. To the south of this plexus the land drops rapidly to the lowland isthmus of Tehuantepec, and rises again to the east-and-west ranges of the Chiapas highland of Central America. All this can be read from the ordinary atlas map, and though a more detailed description will be necessary if we are to realize the significance of the topographic control, the main elements of relief above indicated can be related to the main elements of structure.

Whatever its previous history, the land of Mexico was beneath the sea and receiving deposits in Cretaceous times. At the close of this period the land emerged and the uplift was accompanied by much north-to-south close-folding and faulting. This upraised mountain mass was worn down to a peneplain in early Tertiary times. The raising and tilting of this peneplain and the accompanying extensive volcanism have resulted in the Mexico of to-day. W. N. Thayner,[1] in his account of the physiography of Mexico, has divided the country into physiographic regions, and these, with some slight modifications, appear in Fig. 101. They are worth consideration in a general geographical account, for

[1] " Journal of Geology," vol. 24, 1916, pp. 61–94.

they correspond closely to the main topographic divisions, and these again to the main climatic areas. For once the " physiographic division " is the " Natural Region."

We will give, presently, a brief description of the geography of each region, but before doing so let us assume a knowledge of the main elements of relief as portrayed in a good atlas map and relate thereto the climates of the country.

Mexico extends through 17° of latitude and far enough north to be reached by occasional winter cyclones of California, so that the *extreme north* of the Californian peninsula gets its tiny quota of precipitation in the winter months. The southern tip of this arid peninsula comes just far enough south to get a little summer tropical rain. The almost desert coast of Lower California, then, is the site of the change from the prevailing winter rain of the whole of the Pacific coast of the U.S.A., to the prevailing summer rain of the western coasts of Central and Southern Mexico. Summer is the rainy season for the bulk of the country. This rainy season is longer and more marked in the south than in the north, so that aridity is the main characteristic of the whole of the northern half of the country, and this aridity is intensified on the Central Mesa by the marginal ranges. In winter the Eastern Cordillera present an obstacle to the north-east Trades, and there is heavy rain on the windward sides of these mountains.

We have, then, in the main, a great arid tableland with a summer rainfall, increasing towards its higher and southern extremity. This is bordered by the ranges giving some extension of precipitation within their own limits to the north, but actually shielding the Central Mesa from rain. The western peninsula and the western mainland coast of Mexico are extremely arid as far south as Mazatlan, from which point summer rainfall increases towards Central America. There is little precipitation on this coast in winter. The eastern coast lands have a heavier and better distribution of rainfall. This is least in the north, where a rather dry belt of coast plain exists about the Lower Rio Grande, i.e. at the boundary between Mexico and Texas. To the south the precipitation increases rapidly, causing the rich tropical forests of the coasts in Southern Mexico and Central America.

With regard to temperature, apart from the coastal regions, the increasing elevation of the country to the south rather cancels the effect of lower latitude. Here a narrowing continental mass, a low latitude, high ground, small inland precipitation, and rapid radiation, combine to give a greater difference between day and night, and between sun and shade temperatures, than is discernible in any seasonal variation.

The southern *coast lands*, however, are hot, humid, and un-

healthy. Any further references to climate will occur in the
consideration of the separate natural regions, to which we will
now return.

Sierra Madre Occidental. Coming first into evidence at the
international boundary, this mountain barrier extends as far south
as the Rio Grande de Santiago, where it adjoins the volcanic
plexus of Southern Mexico. This western marginal cordillera
is not merely the upraised western edge of the Central Tableland.
Though in the main its physical history seems to have been the
same as that of the tableland, it was characterized by greater
uplift and a more general volcanism. A narrow, deeply dis-

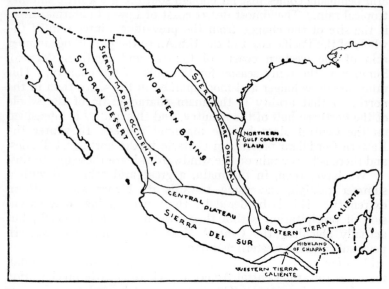

FIG. 101.—Physiographic Regions of Mexico.

sected tableland forms the highest mountain belt, and is almost
smothered in the igneous flows which accompanied its uplift.
These were irregular, and so the region hardly evinces the even
skyline expected in an old upraised peneplain. The region is
distinguished from its neighbours by greater height, and by the
fact of its more complete covering of igneous material.

Historically, its barrier nature should be emphasized.
Throughout the great length of the country its western scarp
edges form the political boundary between the states of Chihuahua and Durango on the east and Sonora and Sinaloa on
the west. As we saw in Chapter II, it divided the main stream
of Spanish advance to the north, and until recently the most

expeditious way of getting from, say, Mazatlan to Mexico City, was to follow the coast railway to the north into the U.S.A., to take the Southern Pacific to El Paso, and then return south by the Central Mexican. The margins of this narrow belt are irregular, but they rise, and usually sharply, in a fault scarp above both the jagged spur country of the west coast and the irregular tableland to the east. Along its borders the basalt layers have been removed by denudation, and the contact metamorphism with the older crystalline rocks here exposed has often resulted in an accumulation of metallic ores which have always made the country famous for its mineral production.

The great altitude of the range itself has ensured a heavier precipitation than occurs either on the coast or in the interior. It is covered by a belt of forest at present economically inaccessible from the coastal foothills, yet useful in its supply of mining timber. The greater precipitation, too, has afforded numerous streams which can be utilized by the mining camps, and for local irrigation. We should notice, too, that the precipitation on the western slopes is greater than on the eastern edges, and the western streams have cut back into the plateau ridge and have captured many streams formerly running north-west to south-east along the general strike of the structure. Again, as denudation has been accompanied by continuous uplift, these streams have maintained their courses in gigantic cañons, which hinder communication from north to south, as do the captured longitudinal valleys that from east to west. It is not the height alone—great though that is—which has made the Sierra Madre Occidental so formidable a barrier to movement.

The Sonora Desert. Physiographically, this includes the Mohave desert of Arizona, that is to say, it extends to the foot of the Colorado Plateau. It includes also the Gulf of California and its analogous lowlands, the Salton Depression and Colorado Delta, and lastly, the Lower California Peninsula. The main structural element of the whole is the great down-warp of the Gulf of California, from which the peninsula rises somewhat abruptly on the west and the mainland more gently to the east. This feature and the extreme aridity of the whole area serve to distinguish it from the other natural regions. The peninsula of Lower California is 750 miles in length, and of a width varying from 30 to 150 miles. Fighting his way northward against the constant northern winds (see Chapter II), the Spaniard could find neither food nor harbours, neither wood nor water. Some timber there is, but it lies inaccessible along the spine of the peninsula, which has greater precipitation in virtue of its height. A small quantity of guano is obtained from the coastal isles, and the Pacific fisheries are of some importance. Esemada is the only western point of any importance, and it only has a population of between 1,000 and 2,000 and some little importance as a mining centre. There is deeper water on the eastern coast of the peninsula, and La Paz (pop. 6,000), the seat of the government of Lower California, is on the most conspicuous inlet, though the port itself is encumbered with shoals and difficult to reach. Here we have the site of Cortez' attempted colonization, and the revival of the old Spanish pearl fisheries. The exports are pearl shell, hides, silver ore, and guano. Further north we have the desert mining station of Santa Rosalie (Camargo) (pop. 10,000), the seat of operations of the Bolea Copper Company (Fr.). This is an almost desert station, entirely dependent upon the port of Guaymas and upon the United States for all stores, and existing only because of the important copper mines.

The Colorado Delta is formed by the great silt-laden river, which in its summer flood carries more solid material than any river of the States, and has built up a delta which separates the Salton Sink (below sea-level) from its structural continuation, the Gulf of California. As the rainfall here is only about 3 inches per annum, the only settlement is based on the Imperial Canal Scheme, the intake of which is just on the U.S.A. side. The canal takes the water a few miles through Mexican territory, and then back again to develop what is known as the Imperial Valley in the States—an irrigated area continued over the border into Mexico. According to international agreement, 50 per cent. of the water goes to Mexico. The development and organization of the dual area is largely controlled from the U.S.A. side. Mexacali, in Mexico, is exactly opposite, and physically a part of, Calexico, in the U.S.A. In the latter are the chief offices, stores, and warehouses pertaining to this important irrigation settlement. Recently cotton has become the chief crop of the region (see Chapter XIV), but fruits, alfalfa, wheat, and barley are important irrigated crops. The Colorado Delta is of little use for navigation.

The western coast of the mainland of Mexico is interrupted by spurs of crystalline rock, separated and half-buried by smooth aggraded intermont plains. These spurs approach the coast most nearly in the south. The mainland coast bordering the Gulf of California is extremely arid, and only the longer rivers which rise highest in the Sierra persist throughout the year (e.g. the Sonora, Yaqui, and Fuerte), and then only with a very diminished winter flow. Apart from mining camps in the hills, population exists only along the streams of perennial flow, and is dependent upon irrigation. The most considerable of these settled areas is about the Rio Fuerte, where sugar and early fruits and vegetables are grown. The only collecting centres of any importance are Guaymas, in the arid region to the north, and Mazatlan, in a region of considerable summer rains, to the south. Both normally export mining produce brought from the west of the Sierra Madre, and though they are the only ports of any size in the whole region, to neither can vessels drawing more than 10 feet of water approach within half a mile.

The Northern Basins. Structurally, there is little to separate these from the Sierra Madre Oriental to the east save the greater elevation of the latter. The folded underlying Cretaceous sandstones and limestones are much exposed, for igneous material is less in evidence than in the Sierra Madre. It exists, however, in many areas, and these are often mining regions. Numerous ridges rise above the flat aggraded plains. In this region of drought, denudation is as much a matter of daily temperature range, which shatters the rock surface by alternate expansion and contraction, as it is due to the action of water. There is little surface drainage to carry away the loosened material, which is swept into the valleys by the wind, and is gradually burying the uneven topography. The set of such sharp hill ranges as occur is usually north and south. Communication is easiest in this direction. Broad, flat-topped basaltic masses are frequent in the western parts of the area, and sharper ridges with isolated volcanic intrusions occur more frequently to the east. In the centre and east are many shallow basins (*bolsoms*), some of which have no outlet to the sea.

Over the northern portion the annual rainfall is less than 15 inches, and occurs in short summer convectional showers. Many streams flowing east from the Sierra Madre Occidental never reach the Rio Grande, but lose themselves in the sands. Only the Rio Conchas effects a junction, and so a complete outlet to the sea.

The most important of the inland drainage basins, economically, is that of the Laguna, which is watered by irrigation works from the Rios Nazas and Nievas. Here there is only about 8 inches of rain. The rivers flow only in the flood season, yet rudimentary irrigation works have resulted in a fertile and productive basin which provides a large proportion of the Mexican cotton, and much maize, wheat, alfalfa, and beans. The distributing centre is the Americanized and growing town of Torreon. Further west and nearer the Sierra Madre Occidental is the mining collecting centre of Durango, which lies a little north of the famous iron mountain, where a large store of accessible high-grade iron ore exists, but is little worked at present. Apart from occasional mines and their attendant irrigation centres, the northern portion of this great Central Mesa is of little economic value, and the small population is concerned with the keeping of cattle on enormous estates. Even so, the semi-desert vegetation, though nutritious for stock, will support but few animals to the acre, and every possible use must be made of irregularities in the surface to build storm storage dams. Underground water can often be obtained by wind pumps. The older village settlements are usually situated near springs in the Cretaceous limestone. Towards Monterey and Saltillo, the rainfall increases a little and some wheat is grown without irrigation. Population and rainfall increase to the south, where Zacatecas, San Luis Potosi, and Guanajuato were, and remain, the chief collecting centres of a very rich mineral district. All these towns have a population of over 30,000.

The Central High Intermont Plains. The separate flat valley floors encircled by great ranges which support the population of this region, are but little higher than the southern limit of the Central Mesa to the north. Volcanism here was more extensive, and continued into later periods, than in any other part of Mexico. In particular a number of high volcanic cones dominate the topography. Some of the valley basins of the region were occupied by lakes during the more recent periods of volcanic activities, and are now covered with lacustrine deposits originating in part from volcanic ash and in part from denudation of the surrounding heights. From the standpoint of human geography, the chief characteristics of the area are:

(i) The physical isolation of the separate valley floors, and of the whole region relative to the outside world.

(ii) A number of flat, fertile intermont plains.

(iii) The height of these plains (e.g. Mexico City, 8,000 feet) is sufficient to ensure a temperate type of climate— maize, wheat, and barley are grown, but not the tropical products of the coastal plains.

(iv) A slight but generally sufficient precipitation—greatest in the summer months, but much less than that received by the coast-facing mountain barriers. Mexico City has 23 inches of rain a year.

In an article on the distribution of population in Mexico by the late Sumner W. Cushing,[1] the author publishes excellent population maps of Mexico, which, besides showing generally the concentration of much of the population in the south, show also a number of separate population groups in this region quite obviously based on the separate valley systems. We have here

[1] " American Geographical Review," April, 1921.

the only portion of Mexico at a habitable level, which avoids both the extreme aridity of so much of the country, and the tropical humidity of the southern coast lands.

The most important of these high valleys is that of Mexico City, which stretches north and south in a great oval, 60 miles by 30 miles. Much of the valley floor was covered by lagoons in Cortez' time. In one of these a small island provided the site of the city, which was connected with the valley sides by raised causeways. There was always danger of inundation from an excess of flood-water, in addition to difficulties of drainage, and these disadvantages were never satisfactorily overcome until the modern engineering work of a British firm connected the valley drainage with the Gulf drainage by a tunnel through the valley rim. To-day three lagoons (one salt and two fresh) are the only representatives of the old lake basin. Quite apart from the natural fertility and large agricultural population of the valley, Mexico City derives much importance from its position as capital city. It is at least as naturally accessible to all parts of the country as any point that could be found, and all modern lines of communication are focused there, as were the tracks and roads of old. The chief commercial concerns of the country, wherever the actual sites of their productive activities, have offices in the capital. Until acclimatized, some folk suffer from the rarefied atmosphere consequent upon the great height. Both night and shade temperatures are low, but the plateau has been free from the more deadly fevers of the coast districts. The population of these high valleys is mainly agricultural, and the chief food-stuff is maize. Indeed, maize and population maps of Mexico are almost indistinguishable. Yet there are some textile and mining centres of importance, and in this connection it is well to remember the resources of the district in water power. The heavy rainfall of the eastern coast-facing margin of the High Plateau, together with the steep gradient of some of the rivers, suggest considerable possibilities in this direction. Actually, the rather irregular régime of these streams, and the absence of natural reservoirs, render considerable storage works a necessity. The chief hydro-electric powers at present developed are the more important because of the high freightage on coal and fuel oil in so mountainous a country. The Necaxa River is a head-stream of the Tecolutha, which enters the Gulf of Mexico between Vera Cruz and Tuxpan. The two main falls are 460 feet and 740 feet sheer. An embankment 3 miles long and 157 feet high regulates the flow above the falls, and there are a number of subsidiary dams and reservoirs. The main generating station is at Necaxa, and the whole system provides 132,000 h.p. " The power supplies tramways, factories, lighting and heating of Mexico City, besides mining establishments at El Oro and Pachuca; it also serves pumping stations for irrigation near Mexico City, and machinery at Xochimilco in connection with the city water supply." [1]

The rivers Atoyac and Los Molinos in Puebla State, and also the Rio Blanco in Vera Cruz State, supply power for the cotton mills of Puebla and also for the towns of Tlaxcala, Santa Cruz, and many neighbouring sites. The chief power stations are at Tuapango and Portozuela. On the west, the large towns of Guadalajara and Guanajuato are supplied from neighbouring hill power stations. One other considerable station exists, viz. that at Boquilla, in Southern Chihuahua, where the Upper Conchos River is dammed back and provides the Parral mines with power.

These really quite extensive works have been erected largely with American and British capital and organization. They have a measure of protection in that coal, and even oil (because of the difficulty of pipe-line construction), are relatively dear on the Mexican uplands. Many of the works were initiated because of the power requirements of the mining industries. The total developed hydro-electric power in Mexico is more than 400,000 h.p.

The Gulf Coasts. The western limits of the Gulf Coast Plain are formed by the eastern scarp edges of the irregular Sierra Madre Oriental. The plain itself is of relatively undisturbed Tertiary material. It is broader and less interrupted by spurs from the Sierra than the western coast plain. An approach of the central hill masses to the coast about Vera Cruz divides the northern broad area from a narrower district to the south. The lowland widens again about the basin of the Papaloapam River. In the isthmus of Tehuantepec a broad lowland area extends from the Atlantic to the Pacific. Structurally, however, the central and western part of this lowland should be regarded as a dropped piece of the Central Plateau country, and the plain of Tertiary rocks is confined to the eastern portion only.

There is no part of the Gulf Coast Plain so arid as the northern Pacific coast of Mexico, yet on either side the Rio Grande there is only a rainfall of about 25 inches, decreasing rapidly inland. South of lat. 22° the rainfall increases rapidly and the vegetation becomes luxuriantly tropical. The Gulf coasts are low, flat, lagoon and sand-spit bordered, fever-ridden strips. The inshore waters are shallow, yielding few places where big vessels can approach the coast and no good natural harbours whatever. In the frequent winter storms (called Northers) of the Gulf, ships are safer in the open sea than in the unprotected roadsteads. The

[1] " A Handbook of Mexico." Admiralty I.D. (I.D. 1205), 1920.

bad and exposed anchorage and the suddenness and intensity of these winter storms constitute a serious geographical disadvantage to this coast. The great drop in temperature which gives warning of the Norther sends the people indoors, and the ships out into the safer deep water.

During 1918 they were thus distributed :—September (one, light) ; October (two) ; November (four) ; December (three). 1919—January (four) ; February (eight) ; March (four) ; April (three) ; May (one, light). And this is a fairly normal distribution. Seven vessels were lost near Tampico during the 1917 Norther season.[1] The Norther is usually accompanied by a southern winter cyclone in the U.S.A. of great intensity, and so situated as to interrupt the normal winter flow of the Trades.

Porto Mexico, Vera Cruz, and Tampico, because of the economic importance of their situation, have been developed into artificial harbours. The first two will take really large vessels. They are all difficult to make or leave in a Norther, and there are no other considerable ports on this coast. The Tampico oil loading is done by flexible pipe-lines to the tank steamers in an open roadstead.

From Tampico southwards the coastlands suffer rainfalls sufficient to give them a very dense cover of tropical vegetation, with many saline marshes and flood areas. The dense undergrowth is a difficulty in prospecting for oil, and causes an added expense in the laying of pipe-lines. From the time of the Spaniard's discovery, the low humid coasts have been notorious for their unhealthiness, and though from certain areas (e.g. about Vera Cruz) the most deadly disease of yellow fever has been practically eradicated by sanitary improvements and drainage, the coast as a whole is not considered healthy. This is the real " Tierra Caliente " of Mexico, and the term has passed into everyday speech. Better conditions obtain on the eastern margin of the mountainous zone which approaches Vera Cruz. Coastal population is largely confined to the three considerable ports. Porto Mexico is the port of the Tehuantepec lowland and of the trans-isthmus railway to Salina Cruz. Vera Cruz in the old days gave some protection from the Norther on the lee-side of the island of San Juan de Ulloa. The harbour now is largely artificial. From here we have always had the shortest route to the populous Central Plateau region. For general trade the port is far and away the most important in the country. Tampico has railway connections with San Luis Potosi and with Saltillo, but the chief business of the port is concerned with the important oil development of the immediate hinterland.

[1] " M.W.R.," July, 1919.

As in Central America, when the coast forests are cleared, bananas, cocoa, and coffee can be grown at successive altitudes on the foothills, and there is room for very great development here. Actually only a very small area of the coast lands is in agricultural use.

This southern Gulf coast about Tuxpan and Tampico is the site of some of the greatest oilfields of the world. The characteristics of the area from this point of view are dealt with in Chapter XXII. The Eastern Tierra Caliente are still largely forested, for they are too humid for extensive fires, and plantation clearings have only a small area in the aggregate. Where there are flood-streams free of high falls or subterranean passages, mahogany and cedar can be floated to the coast. Minatitlan and Laguna de Terminas are the chief ports for these tropical woods. Logwood will not float and must be shipped on streams navigable for small boats, or on rafts, or by roads or tramways. Sarsaparilla root and rubber (wild) are other exports of the Tierra Caliente.

The Western Tierra Caliente. This differs from the Southern Gulf Coast Plain in that its precipitation, though heavy, is more definitely a summer rainfall. The mountain spurs come nearer the coast and communication is difficult from one valley to another and also to the capital. Development here is likely to lag behind that of the Gulf region.

The Sierra del Sur. This may be separated from the Sierra Madre Occidental because of the greater denudation of its volcanic cover. The relief is irregular to a degree, and the whole mass is an exceptionally formidable barrier to communications. The harbour of Acapulco is the best on the Pacific coast of Mexico, but with such a hinterland there is little to stimulate modern development.

The Chiapas Highlands. The mountain mass of Western Guatemala sends out two great ranges to the west into Mexico, which enclose between them the valley of the Chiapas River. The southern of these, the Chiapas range, rises to over 7,000 feet within 30 miles of the Pacific. The northern and more irregular mountain mass slopes more gently to the Gulf of Campeche. Precipitation is heavy with a summer maximum. The mountains are forested and the Chiapas Valley is a savannah land. The usual zonal plantations of bananas, cocoa, coffee, maize, and cereals obtain.

The Yucatan Peninsula. Under settled conditions Mexico has three sources of considerable economic wealth—her precious metals, her oil, and her sisal hemp. These are the most valuable articles of export. It is to be noted that much of the capital and organization required for these productions is of foreign origin. All three are typical products of exploitation and employ few people in relation to their economic importance. One of these products—sisal hemp—is the staple of the peninsula of Yucatan. The modern towns, railways, and population of the north-west of this peninsula are completely dependent upon this very modern industry. Yet the developed area occupies less than one-fifth of the peninsula, and is isolated by physical circumstances to quite an extraordinary degree.

Yucatan is an extension of the Gulf Coastal Plain corresponding in structure, as well as in shape and position, to the peninsula of Florida. Both are developed on limestone and have the characteristics of a low karst region. The most striking difference is that whereas in Florida the most populous and developed parts of the country lie nearest and in good connection with the main continental mass, in Yucatan the developed area is as far remote as possible from the rest of Mexico, and separated from it by the very real physical barrier of the thick tropical forest which covers the southern four-fifths of the peninsula, and which continues, we may note, into the tropical regions of Central America. In Central and Southern Yucatan there are neither roads nor railways : only a few Indian tracks connect the few and scattered villages of this little-populated area. And nature has been little kinder in the matter of sea approach. There may be fair harbours on the east coast, but for the whole length of the peninsula this is densely forested and little inhabited. The northern and western coasts are extraordinarily shallow, lagoon- and spit-bordered, and unprotected. Small boats can navigate the sheltered lagoons, but have to put out to sea every few miles because of some obstacle. In the shallow waters of the Campeche Banks the Trade winds are usually fresh enough to make the landing of goods by boat a hazardous proceeding. Steamers have to stand out some distance, and there is no protection from the Norther storms of winter.

Now, it is just this isolated north-west corner of the Yucatan Peninsula which has become one of the most progressive parts of Mexico. The reason is partly climatic. There are few reliable meteorological data available for Yucatan, but from those existing and from descriptions of the vegetation it is abundantly evident that there is a very rapid diminution of rainfall to a minimum in the extreme north-west corner. Merida has a rainfall of 34 inches. Progresso and Sisal almost certainly have less than 20 inches ; Valladolid, much further to the east, almost certainly more than 50 inches. Rainfall, in fact, increases to the east and south as we move from Progresso. It also becomes better distributed throughout the year. Only about one-sixth of the rain of Merida falls in the six months December to May inclusive. Now, a rainfall of 20 inches in a tropical country, and that with a marked dry season, will give xerophilous vegetation. There is scrub land near Progresso ; the bushes become higher and isolated trees begin to appear about Merida : Valladolid is just within the tropical impenetrable forest. Ellsworth Huntingdon, in an article on Yucatan,[1] distinguishes clearly between the tropical jungle of the north-west and the tropical forest, with its tall trees, impenetrable shade, numerous evergreens, long and sinuous lianas, which occupies the rest of the peninsula. In the north-west the climatic conditions, and relative ease with which the ground may be cleared, make it an ideal area for the cultivation of the henequen. This is a variety of yucca, from the thick fleshy leaves of which the very valuable sisal hemp is obtained. The largest export is to the United States of America. Northern Yucatan is without hills, but there is a gradual rise to a low ridge over 500 feet in height which runs north-west to south-east parallel to the railway from Ticul to Peto. The even relief, however, is broken by innumerable cenotes, or limestone sink-holes—formed by the breaking in of the roofs of underground caverns. In this limestone country there are no surface streams, though a vast reservoir of water exists underground. The water in the cenotes is very near the surface near the coast (and only 20 to 40 feet deep in Merida), but becomes deeper with the rise of the land to the south. In some places in the shallow waters of the northern coast these cenotes have been submerged in a general change of surface level, and columns of fresh water rise from the sea bottom—only a few feet, of course—to the surface. Similar fresh-water " springs " in the salt waters of the Atlantic are known off St. Augustine, Florida. " The inhabitants of these coastal villages (in Northern Yucatan), in some cases, place hollow tree-trunks in the holes of the sea floor, through which the water gushes, thus leading it to the surface of the Gulf without commingling with the salt water." [2]

The old villages of the Mayas were situated near cenotes and dependent upon them for water supply. As the water is seldom more than 100 feet from the surface, the modern towns and settlements use wind or petrol pumps and wells. In the bigger towns—Merida (pop. 60,000)—many of the houses raise their own water from the underground supply by windmills on the roofs.

[1] " The Peninsula of Yucatan." " Bulletin of American Geog. Soc.," vol. 44, p. 801.

[2] " The Caverns and People of Northern Yucatan," by Leon J. Cole, " Bulletin of American Geog. Soc.," vol. 42, p. 321.

Progresso is the chief port of Yucatan, and the most important in the world for the export of henequen. It lies on a sand-spit backed by a narrow lagoon. Ocean vessels have to lie 3 to 5 miles out, and discharge, or take up, from lighters. Plans exist for the completion of a deep-water artificial harbour. The port is connected with Merida, the capital of the henequen district, and with the little network of lines of North-western Yucatan.

Campeche is a much older port, if one can so designate a spot where the 3-fathom line is 10 miles from the coast, and which is only accessible to shallow-draught lighters. Progresso takes most of the modern trade.

CHAPTER XXXII
£ASTERN CANADA AND NEWFOUNDLAND
(Population maps of Canada appear on pages 565 and 566)

IN 1897 the International Congress of Geologists met at Montreal, and Professor Dawson, the Chief Geologist of the Dominion Government, outlined a division of Canada into physiographic regions which has been little qualified by his successors. We shall refer to these divisions in detail in later sections. For the moment it may be stated that they are really subdivisions of those more obvious regions into which we can divide the whole continent north of Mexico, viz. eastern and western hill countries and an intermediate lowland. It is true that in Canada —and to a very limited extent in the U.S.A. also—the irregular rocky surface of the Laurentian Shield is added to the Appalachian folded hill region, thus materially limiting the extent of the intermediate lowlands proper. Canada, then—in the first instance—may be divided into three great areas :

(a) *Eastern Canada* including the whole of the Laurentian Shield, the Maritime Provinces, and extending, therefore, westward to Lake Winnipeg. The rocks here are almost without exception either pre-Cambrian or early Palæozoic. They are frequently—but with some notable exceptions—distorted and metamorphosed. Extending into this region from the U.S.A. we have embayments of almost horizontal Palæozoic (Ordovician-Devonian) rocks in the Ontario Peninsula and St. Lawrence Valley.

(b) *Intermediate Plains*, of usually undisturbed strata from older Palæozoic on the east to Tertiary in the west. They exhibit a general rise to the Rockies, but with some marked east and north-east facing escarpments, which divide the prairie area into a series of steps. The country south-west of a line from Winnipeg to Edmonton was, and is, almost unwooded.

(c) *The Western Cordillera*, where orogenic movements have broken through the regular horizontality of the strata, forming a complicated series of high parallel ranges. These are something of a barrier to east-and-west movement, and produce marked climatic differences as between coast, western and eastern hill-slopes, and interior valleys.

For two and a half centuries the European population of

Canada was almost confined to the Lower St. Lawrence and Maritime Provinces. Indeed, so recent has been the peopling of the country west of Montreal that the geographical controls shaping the distribution of population are sharp-cut and easily determined. Only a small fraction of the whole country has a population of over one person per square mile. Very much of it is *entirely* unpopulated. It is practically certain that, because of climatic and other reasons, a very large portion of the total area never will be continuously populated, so that figures indicating the immense area of the country have, by themselves, little significance. Nevertheless the Dominion could probably support many times its present population.

Once transport was available, the open fertile prairie, ready for the plough, proved more attractive to the immigrant than the scattered and more difficult patches of farm lands in the eastern provinces outside the St. Lawrence Valley. For a time, and in spite of the forest clearing to be done, the fertile lands, long growing-season, and relatively mild climate of the Ontario Peninsula stayed the western tide. But once the Laurentian Shield country north and west of Lake Superior had been breached by the Canadian Pacific Railway, and the open prairie connected with Montreal, then indeed the St. Lawrence system and its attendant railway acted but as a narrow connecting funnel between the rapidly extending fan of population in the north-west prairies and its origin—Europe.

The best and most accessible farm lands in the north-west are rapidly being taken up. Very shortly the prairie farmer will forsake his " wheat-madness " system—a one-crop system which supports but a thin population on a land of lessening fertility—and will adopt, more and more, a mixed system of farming. As the best and most accessible prairie land becomes taken up, more attention will be given to those large but scattered areas of fertile land in the east which, till now, have been neglected.

A further major distinction between the three main regions is to be found in the forest wealth of East and West Canada and the timberless southern intermediate plains (Fig. 102). The northern plains are forested, it is true, but at present this timber is economically inaccessible. So also in water-power resources,[1] and for the present at any rate in mineral production, except coal, the eastern and western divisions are far ahead of the intermediate one.

[1] There are great powers in the Mackenzie basin on Devonian rocks, e.g. Alexandra Falls on the Hay River, but these are far north of any considerable present population.

Region I.—The Laurentian Shield (Fig. 1)

This huge north-eastern quadrant of the continent is defined in the continuous exposure of pre-Cambrian rocks. Its boundary represents the transition to Cambrian or later Palæozoic material. The palæozoic seas which washed the shore of this old protaxis have had varying shore lines, but much of the whole area has been above water since pre-Cambrian times, and by the denudation of its mountain masses has provided material for building much of the surrounding continent. It must not be supposed that this great area has in all parts the same geological history, or exhibits always the same characteristics of relief, structure, and rock composition. Yet if we except a few large, and many scattered small areas, we can apply to it the following generalized description.

The greater portion of the whole consists of huge batholiths [1] of granite-gneiss, breaking partly through yet older material, and now exposed by denudation.

We have not, then, a homogeneous Archæan fundamental matrix, but the scattered remnants of a pre-Cambrian continent, largely developed on stratified rocks now rent by granite-gneiss intrusions themselves of pre-Cambrian occurrence. Very great areas of the sedimentaries have been metamorphosed. Greater areas have been denuded exposing the batholiths. The whole has been an area of progressive uplift, just as the horizontal Palæozoic sedimentaries of the central plains to the south have been deposited in an area of progressive subsidence. The time duration of pre-Cambrian uplift and denudation was much longer than the sum of all succeeding epochs to the present. The area was a worn-out continent before even Cambrian times. Yet, from the point of view of geographic control, nothing is of more importance than the consequences of the relatively recent glacial periods.

We may summarize the geographical characteristics derived from this geological history as follows :

(a) The Laurentian Shield consists of an area of exposed pre-Cambrian rocks extending over about two million square miles. Denudation has accompanied uplift, and most of the area is under 2,000 feet. Actually the greatest elevations (over 6,000 feet) occur between Ungava Bay and the Atlantic Ocean, and

---

[1] " Great lenticular or rounded bosses of granite or granite-gneiss, which are found arching up the overlying strata through which they penetrate, disintegrating the latter, and displaying at the same time a more or less distinct foliation ; which is seen to conform in general to the strike of the invaded rocks when the latter have not been removed by denudation."—Canadian Dept. of Mines, Memoir No. 6, p. 12.

these must be regarded rather as a portion of the raised rim of the area than as mountain ranges. This raised rim is lower but still apparent along the rest of the coast of Labrador, and overlooks quite abruptly the St. Lawrence River lowlands, where it is about 1,500 to 2,000 feet high. In the west, towards Lake Winnipegosis, the rim is not pronounced, and the junction of pre-Cambrian and Palæozoic is masked by glacial deposits. From the Labrador and the St. Lawrence height of the land, the plateau sinks gradually to the shallows of Hudson Bay, on the south-west side of which is an area developed on Palæozoic material. Across the raised, rounded, plateau-like eastern and southern rim of the Shield, the rivers cut deep valleys to the Atlantic, to the Gulf of St. Lawrence, and to the St. Lawrence lowlands, yet still have a sufficiency of gradient to supply one of the most important water-power areas in the world. In general the relief is hummocky and irregular. There is some evidence of pene-planation in the uniformity of summit levels over large areas. The southern margin of the Shield forms a line of irregular hill country, in marked contrast to the level plains developed on the undisturbed Palæozoic strata of the St. Lawrence lowlands. That some of these Palæozoics at one time covered a portion of the already peneplained Shield, is shown by the existence of out-liers preserved from erosion in faulted depressions—e.g. as in the Lake St. John lowland.

(*b*) The results of the ice-sheet are of fundamental geographical importance. Much of the surface rock has been completely bared of its residual soil. Small declivities and hollows have been filled with drift material. The general result is that, in the aggregate, an enormous area is completely soilless or sterile. The patches of drift and old drift-filled valleys are scattered, often boulder-ridden, and set in difficult, irregular, ill-drained country. Another result of this glaciation appears in the enor-mous number of lakes and lakelets of glacial origin, the old pre-glacial drainage having been largely obliterated. Within the relatively small section (4,200 square miles) which has been the subject of detailed geological survey, and is represented in the Haliburton and Bancroft map sheets, there are 525 lakes of various sizes, from a fraction of a square mile to 22 square miles in extent. These are interconnected by a wonderfully intricate and irregular series of waterways, by which it is possible to travel in almost any direction *by canoe*, with frequent but short portages. The function which the Laurentian Shield lake system performs as a series of natural reservoirs regulating to some extent the flow of rivers to the St. Lawrence appears an important one from the point of view of water-power development. The soil areas, and sometimes the clefts in the bare rock, are occupied by timber in the southern half of the Shield. As the timber of the St. Lawrence lowland of the Ontario peninsula is all cut, the Laurentian Shield forests constitute the most considerable of Canadian reserves. North of the limit of " dense forest," as shown in Fig. 102, the species rapidly dwindle in number and size, and become confined to sheltered and favoured localities. Further north again is the moss, grass, lichen and stunted willow of the tundra, with its herds of caribou, and perennially frozen subsoil. The Labrador coast is completely bare of timber, though forest growth occurs in the more sheltered stream basins (e.g. that of the Hamilton River) leading to that coast. North of the St. Lawrence, conifers predominate, though a very small hardwood admixture continues right up to the height of the land. A sad feature is the enormous destruction wrought by forest fires, which have wiped out millions of acres of splendid timber.

The broad belt designated Southern Forest in Fig. 102 is, of course, susceptible of considerable subdivision. It is of the Mixed Hardwood and Softwood type and extends from some distance south of the boundary of the Shield to a line running roughly from the north-east corner of Lake Superior to the Saquenay River on the St. Lawrence.

This is still the chief lumber-producing area of eastern Canada. The white pine—a dominant member—has been now largely cut, and spruce, hemlock, yellow birch and maple have to some extent taken its place, and under undisturbed conditions " hardwood ridges " carrying chiefly maple and yellow birch occur throughout the belt. Large areas of an association of white spruce and balsam fir occur on well-drained ground. Black spruce, tamarack and white cedar are associated in the poorly drained areas.

Recently fired areas are covered by an undergrowth of poplar and white birch, intolerant of shade and nursing a future coniferous cover. Jack pine tends to take complete possession of fired sandy or gravelly areas.

North of this Mixed Hardwood-Softwood type, on the Shield, is the Northern Forest belt. This, apart from the poplar-birch association, is coniferous. There is less pine than to the south, and white spruce, black spruce (on the vast areas of poorly drained land) and Jack pine (dry sandy areas) are the chief cover. North of the Northern Forest is the sub-arctic belt. The trees get smaller and balsam fir, Jack pine, poplar and white birch drop out successively, leaving the spruces, tamarack and willow in sparse, stunted groups, becoming less frequent as the tundra is reached. Of the trees above mentioned, white pine provides the best constructional timber, though less is now available and white spruce is taking its place. The latter is, besides, an excellent pulp wood. Black spruce is a pulp wood. In the last few decades nearly all mature tamarack has been destroyed by Saw Fly. It was much used for railway ties. Poplar is used and paper birch may be used as pulp woods. Yellow birch is the most valuable hardwood in the Dominion : extensively used for flooring, interior work and furniture, and for distillation products.

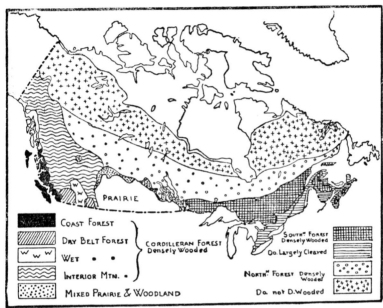

FIG. 102.—Forest Belts of Canada.

Tundra not shaded.

(c) *Mineral Wealth.*[1] It is to the segregations incident upon fusion that we owe many of the more important accumulations of metalliferous deposits, and so it is in the proximity of rocks of igneous origin (of many epochs) that we find the chief world deposits of precious metals and of many others not so designated (e.g. of copper). The rapid development of mining in the Laurentian Shield area is one of the most striking economic features of Canada today (1953). In this connection, too, we must remember that much of it is still geologically unexplored. We shall confine ourselves to actual and important producing centres.

With regard to gold production, this region is third in order

[1] Expansion of mineral production, Canada.

	Values million $	Index of volume	
1940 .	500	100	Dominion Bureau
1950 .	1,000	148	of Statistics

of world production, being surpassed only by South Africa and the U.S.S.R. In silver production it stands fourth after Mexico, U.S.A. and Peru. It produces well over 80 per cent. of the world's nickel and over 50 per cent. of the cobalt. All this in Canada, but the same region west of Lake Superior and in the U.S.A. has by far the most important iron production of the world (see Chapter XIX).

Nickel and Copper. Of nickel, the whole of the Canadian production and 90 per cent. of that of the world comes from the Sudbury area. The ore body is " connected with a single great sheet of eruptive rock roughly boat-shaped, with a blunt bow to the south-west and a square stern to the north-east." Only the upturned edges of the sheet are exposed, since it is basin-shaped (36 m. × 16 m.) and has its interior filled with sedimentaries. Without, the basin is the hilly rock and forest wilderness of the Shield : within, the topography is that of an agricultural plain. At the edge are the ore bodies, worked along the south-east margin. The reserves are enormous. For long the problems were first to smelt these compound sulphides of copper and nickel, and then to find a market for the nickel.[1]

There is a wide market for nickel in connection with alloys and nickel steels—particularly in motor manufacture. Sudbury (9,000 inhabitants) is the business centre a few miles from the nearest mines, and is a great railway junction. The ores are roasted—formerly all in the open, with dire results to the vegetation—smelted at Copper Cliff and Coniston, near the mines, and the matte refined at Port Colborne (Ont.) and Clydach (Wales).

Silver and Cobalt. Just as the building of the Canadian Pacific brought to light the nickel copper ores of Sudbury, so the Timiskaming and North Ontario line led to the discovery of the ores of the Cobalt district. This district includes a stretch of country some 70 miles in length, scattered over which are ore bodies similar to those of Cobalt itself—for long the only producing area. New South Lorraine township, 16 miles south-east of Cobalt, and Gowganda, 55 miles to the north-west, are important producing areas. The silver occurs chiefly native in narrow intricate veins of very high-grade material. The adjacent wall-rocks are impregnated with silver for a considerable distance, and it is actually from this lower-grade material that the bulk of the supply is obtained to-day. The ores are concentrated at the mines, whereby the milled ore is reduced to but $2\frac{1}{2}$ per cent. of its weight, and the concentrates are sent to Deloro and Orilila (Ontario), or abroad for smelting. The cobalt is used largely for colour purposes, and production is controlled because requirements are somewhat limited.

---

[1] The most recent development is the opening up of the rich copper-nickel ores of Lynn Lake, 200 miles north of Flin Flon.

Iron Ore. The most productive iron-ore districts of the world belong to this region, but unfortunately for Canada they are situated on one of those extensions which the pre-Cambrian makes into U.S.A. territory (see Chapter XIX). Rich deposits of iron-ore, estimated at 1,000 million tons, with an iron content as high as 69 per cent. and averaging 58·5 per cent., are in process of development at Burnt Creek on the Quebec–Labrador frontier 360 miles north of the port of Seven Islands on the St. Lawrence. These deposits may rival those of Lake Superior. Power can be obtained from nearby falls.

Gold. Districts where gold has been worked on the Shield are widely scattered and there are promising areas awaiting development. The chief present areas are as follows :—

(*a*) In Quebec, the *Rouyn Field*—a stretch of country about 100 miles long and of indefinite width, running along the southern fringe of that part of the Clay Belt which lies in Quebec. It includes the eastward extension of the zone of gold-bearing rocks which have given rise to the Kirkland Lake and Larder Lake gold camps in Ontario. The chief producing district is in the Township of Rouyn and is of recent development.

(*b*) In Ontario are the Porcupine and Kirkland Lake areas. Of these the Porcupine with its great Hollinger mine is first. Timmins (15,000 inhabitants) is the business and commercial centre, and is situated on a branch of the Temiscaming and Northern Ontario Railway. The district was discovered through prospectors moving northward from the Cobalt silver area in 1908. Forest fires destroyed the mine buildings in 1911. Hollinger, Dome and McIntyre are at present the chief mines. This district produces two-thirds of the Canadian production. Kirkland Lake district lies 60 miles south-west of the Porcupine district. It has about one-fifth the production of the latter.

(*c*) In Manitoba gold mining has begun in the promising Manigatogan river district some 20 miles east of Lake Winnipeg, and a railway line which leaves the Hudson Bay line near The Pas runs 80 miles northward to reach the promising copper districts of Flin Flon (copper, zinc) and Mandy.

All this mining activity has placed Canada's Laurentian Shield high among the world producers of precious and valuable metals. The districts mentioned make use of large amounts of electrical energy produced from the falls with which the Shield abounds, and in all of them the mining and treatment of the ores are large-scale, elaborate, scientific, expensive, and highly capitalized industries.[1]

It remains to refer to the distribution of population of this great natural region. Only a small proportion of the people of Canada live actually on the Laurentian Shield. Yet its forests,

---

[1] The extensive use of aircraft has greatly facilitated the mapping and rapid development of the mining activities of the Shield.

its minerals, and its water power are tributary to the cities of the St. Lawrence lowland. The aggregate of bare rock, the scattered soil areas, the irregular boulder-strewn uplands, the clearing necessary for farm land—all have rendered the whole region relatively unattractive to the immigrant, who prefers to take up land in the open fertile prairie plains with assured market organization and means of communication. From the point of view of ultimate expansion also, it is undoubtedly true that *latitude for latitude* as we proceed northwards, the intensity of the summer temperature is more marked and the *length of the effective growing season* is longer in the north-west prairie than in this region. Apart altogether from economic possibilities, it would always be physically possible to grow wheat further north in the north-west provinces. In this connection, however, we must note that the southern rim of the Shield country extends in Ontario actually a little south of lat. 45° N. Even Lake Abitibi and the Grand Trunk Railway about Cochrane are only at the latitude of the very centre of the wheat belt of the western provinces.

Against this we have to set a greater relative humidity and a less effective insolation. The table following compares Cochrane near the " clay belt " with western wheat areas.

MEAN SHADE TEMPERATURES (° F.) AND PRECIPITATION (INCHES)

	J.	F.	M.	A.	M.	J.	J.	A.	S.	O.	N.	D.
Edmonton :												
Lat. 53·35 N. i.e. North of Alberta	6	11	23	41	51	57	61	59	50	42	24	16
Wheat Area	0·76	1·07	0·67	2·2	1·86	3·36	3·56	2·47	1·40	0·74	0·73	0·75
Lethbridge :												
Lat. 49·43 N. i.e. South of Alberta	15	12	28	43	51	58	65	64	53	47	30	26
Wheat Area	0·68	0·54	1·02	1·07	3·39	2·76	2·86	1·85	1·39	0·71	0·61	0·53
Cochrane :												
Lat. 49·4 N. Nr. the	0	1	16	33	46	58	64	59	51	38	24	8
" clay belt "	1·86	1·09	1·40	1·37	2·72	2·39	3·54	3·41	3·92	2·84	2·32	2·73

Note the relatively low March, April, May and October temperature figures for Cochrane.

These figures are worth some attention. They show that the average July temperature varies with the latitude : Lethbridge 65, Cochrane 64, and Edmonton 61. More important than the extreme heat of summer and the extreme cold of winter is the length of growing period available. Here we notice that Edmonton has 5 months and Lethbridge 6 months over 46°. Cochrane has only 4 months. Cochrane has a much shorter growing period, and a much heavier precipitation than the wheat-belt places. Oats and potatoes, vegetables, and dairy produce do well.

Now it is around the Cochrane district on the Grand Trunk Pacific and extending towards Lake Timiskaming, just north of the water parting on the Timiskaming and North Ontario line, that a very big and fairly continuous area is covered by soil. This is the Great Clay Belt of Ontario and Quebec. The clay belt has subsoils of glacial lacustrine deposits derived in part from Palæozoic limestones which here cover part of the pre-Cambrian. The flat clay lands are interrupted by occasional ridges of pre-Cambrian material. There are considerable areas which require draining and almost all the belt requires clearing. The better drained land when cleared has proved entirely suitable for dairying and mixed farming.

The north shore of the St. Lawrence below the Saguenay, where, save for very occasional patches of Palæozoic rocks, the Laurentian Shield extends right to the shore line, becomes increasingly bare, bleak, and unpopulated towards the Strait of Belle Isle and beyond to the north-west in the bare mountain and fiord coast of Labrador. Here, when the fiords are free from ice (June to September), they shelter many hundreds of Newfoundland schooners which visit the coast for the cod fisheries. There are a number of small summer seasonal fishing stations and some Moravian mission stations. A few thousand Eskimos visit the coasts for the summer fishing, but winter inland. The coastal district washed by the Labrador current with its stream of southward-moving icebergs has too short a growing season for agriculture. It is unforested and is indeed even more barren than the land a few miles inland. The vegetables raised at the mission stations are grown partly under glass.[1]

REGION II.—THE CANADIAN APPALACHIAN REGION

Nova Scotia, Prince Edward Island, New Brunswick, and Quebec south-east of the Champlain fault zone, form a block of country mainly formed of Palæozoic rocks (but with *some* pre-Cambrian and Triassic), and having for the most part marked structural similarities to the New England region of the Appal-

[1] For the conditions of life in Labrador, see Dr. Grenfell's most interesting books.

achian Province (Fig. 103). Exposed over the surface are outcrops of the older Palæozoic rocks, most of them folded and
some crushed and metamorphosed. In general, the folds conform to the general north-east and south-west strike of the
Appalachians. Accompanying these disturbances were intrusions
of igneous material over large areas. The more active movements
did not continue into later Carboniferous times. The rock of
this period in Nova Scotia and New Brunswick, and the permo-
Carboniferous of Prince Edward Island, are exceptional to the
area in being very little disturbed. The whole area must have

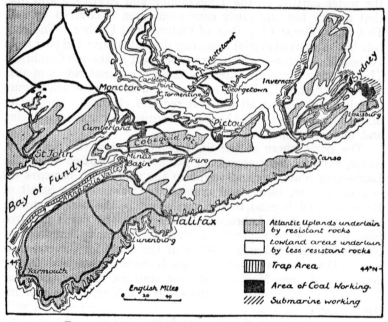

FIG. 103.—Nova Scotia and a part of New Brunswick.

been at one time occupied by high mountains, and, like the
rest of Appalachia, have suffered peneplanation in Cretaceous
times. Subsequent uplift has produced differential erosion,
giving a rugged, hilly topography with a marked north-east to
south-west development of hill-mass and valley plain. This
is particularly noticeable in Nova Scotia, which is essentially
a dissected peneplain dipping towards the sea and consisting
of a number of relatively broad infertile plateau masses developed
on the more resistant outcrops and covered with swamp and
forest, alternating with deeply-trenched valleys, developed chiefly
on softer material and forming the sites of practically the whole

farming development. Fig. 103 brings out the main facts of relief and structure. Geographically, then, we are concerned with an area of bold rocky shores having many indentations, of which the most marked exhibit the general north-east to south-west strike of the rocks (e.g. Bay of Fundy, Gulf of Minas). Inland lies a hilly and rugged but not really mountainous country, if we except the Notre Dame and Shickshock Mountains, parallel ridges, often over 2,000 feet high, which border the St. Lawrence Gulf. These border hills give way a little opposite Quebec and again about the river Matapedic, where the lowland affords a passage-way for the railway from Moncton to Quebec. For the rest there are extensive areas over 1,000 feet in the Gaspé peninsula, in North New Brunswick about Bold Mountain, and in the western peninsula of Cape Breton Isle. The remainder is under 1,000 feet in height but by no means flat. The mildest relief is developed on the softer unmetamorphosed mainly horizontal strata of the Carboniferous rocks to the north, on the permo-Carboniferous of Prince Edward Isle, and in the long, narrow, Triassic basin of the Annapolis and Cornwallis Valleys.

In Carboniferous times an immense thickness of rock seems to have accumulated to the north of the—at that period— great mountain mass of Nova Scotia and New Brunswick. This material was laid down between the north-east extending ridges of the northern coast and out into the Gulf of St. Lawrence. Thus, the older Carboniferous rocks are found towards the southern limit of the outcrop ; the newer and coal-bearing strata towards the present north coasts, where they dip gently seawards, the actual coal basins (e.g. at Sydney) being separated—at any rate on land—by intervening north-eastern extensions of older material. True Carboniferous rocks probably underlie the undisturbed red Permian rocks of Prince Edward Island.

The Magdalen Islands are of Carboniferous age, as also is a portion of South-west Newfoundland. It is not improbable that a great Carboniferous basin extends under the lower Gulf of St. Lawrence from Northern New Brunswick and Nova Scotia to Newfoundland.

Climatically the Maritime Provinces differ little from New England. The shores are bathed by cold water and the prevailing winter winds are north-west from the cold interior. There is thus only a little oceanic amelioration of the continental type of the interior. Precipitation is heavy and well distributed throughout the year with actually an almost imperceptible winter maximum in Nova Scotia. The snowfall is much heavier and the spring less sudden than in Western Canada. The growing season is not long enough for the growth of maize, but the climate is excellently suited to the temperate cereals (wheat, barley and oats) and fruits (apples and cherries and strawberries).

In a country, still relatively undeveloped and admittedly (like New England) containing large areas of negative land (rocky uplands, swamp, areas of poor soil, etc.), agricultural development has proceeded only in the favourable spots. These are for the most part valleys and narrow lowland belts developed on the softer rock material, and certain coastal basins. We will enumerate the chief of these farming areas.

(i) The Cumberland, Pictou, Herts-Colchester and Antigonish-Guisborough (see Fig. 103) lowlands are all developed on carboniferous sedimentaries, relatively soft compared with the great granite and quartzite area of the Southern Upland or the metamorphic Palæozoics of the Cobequid Upland. The lowlands about the Minas Basin are continued without topographic break into the Annapolis-Cornwallis valley developed on Triassic sandstones eroded between the triassic trap of North Mountain and the granite northern edge of South Mountain.

About the Minas Basin, and the lower parts of the rivers tributary to it and to Chignecto Bay—a region of very high tides —much land has been reclaimed by dyking and a marine marsh has been converted into magnificent hayfields. The Annapolis-Cornwallis valley has specialized in apple production, though the holdings usually combine hay lands in the valley bottoms with the orchards on the slope. Most of the apple crop is exported in barrels to England from Halifax.

(ii) In New Brunswick a broad upland belt of resistant intrusive material runs north-east to south-west of the Province from Chaleur Bay to near the mouth of the Penobscot in Maine. It is breached by the St. John River, but above the breach forms a water parting between that river and the river Merimachi to the east. This is the highest land in the Province (1,000 feet to 1,700 feet, with individual heights over 2,000 feet), a rough, forested country.

A second massive negative area of infertile upland is formed rather near the coast between St. John and the head of Chignecto Bay. A great △-shaped lowland of undisturbed carboniferous strata lies between the uplands with the shoreline facing Northumberland Strait as base and its apex near Fredericton. This lowland, especially about Bathurst and Moncton, together with the valley of the St. John where it is developed on silurian limestones above Fredericton, are among the best farm lands of the Province. Oats, hay and potatoes (middle St. John valley) are the chief crops.

(iii) Many minor river valleys have strips of valuable alluvial land, some of which is occupied.

(iv) All the coastal valley inlets of the Maritime Provinces have a fringe of farming-fishing settlements. Oyster fisheries are important on the West Coast of C. Breton Isle and lobster on the New Brunswick St. Lawrence Coast. There are many canneries. In-shore fishing obtains along all the coasts, but from the larger fishing ports of Nova Scotia, e.g. Lunenburg, Canso and Yarmouth, fishing schooners (line fishing from dories), and more recently, trawlers ar.d drifters, visit the Nova Scotia and Newfoundland banks.

In order of value the chief fish are cod, lobster, haddock, mackerel, herring, halibut, hake and salmon.

Lumber products are important except in Prince Edward Island.

In Prince Edward Island there is almost no hilly land, a fine, red, fertile soil, abundant fisheries and a climate suitable for north temperate fruits and cereals. It is the only portion of the Appalachian region of Canada which is predominantly in farms, and even so could support a very much greater population. There is also much dairy-farming and stock-breeding. A modern and interesting activity is the breeding of the fox (black and silver) for peltries. This was begun in 1914, and is rapidly becoming a very considerable activity owing to the high prices for this type of fur in the London market.[1] Communication with the mainland across the narrow Northumberland Strait is maintained in winter by ice-breakers.

The island is without mineral wealth. If coal measures underlie it, they probably do so at depths too great for working. Boreholes of over 2,000 feet have failed to find them. A notable product is the winter-dredged oyster-mud—from old oyster and mussel beds—which the farmers are using to apply to their land when it requires liming.

Fig. 103 shows the position of the chief coal areas in the Maritime Provinces. For the most part, these occupy coastal basins more or less surrounded by older rock material. The most important fields are those of Cape Breton Island. During recent years these have averaged 81 to 84 per cent. of the Nova Scotia production, and 44 to 47 per cent. of the total Canadian production of coal. The measures here are little disturbed, though the Sydney field " is separated into four subordinate basins coinciding with the arms of the sea, chief among these being the commodious harbour of Sydney. The intervening older rock ridge separates the seams on land, and it is not known whether the basins coalesce under the sea." There is an aggregate of

[1] This industry has spread so rapidly to other parts of Canada that the breeders of Prince Edward Island concentrate mainly on raising foxes for sale for breeding purposes.

some 40 feet of coal distributed in seven workable seams.   There
are many seams too thin for working.   Only the thicker seams
have been worked as yet, and these are now being followed
several miles under the sea to the north, but there is a limit to
the distance which men can be taken to their work from pit-
head and to which mine ventilation and transport is effective
and economic.   Progress must now be made with some of the
thinner seams.   The Sydney field, like its namesake in Australia,
and like so many of the British Isles fields, has the very great
advantage of coastal position.   Its situation is suitable for coaling
St. Lawrence vessels.   The configuration of the coast, too, is
such that Sydney is nearer to eastern parts of South America than
are the Gulf ports of the U.S.A.   Louisburg, 20 miles from Sydney,
and with coaling facilities, is the nearest port to Great Britain
which has continental rail connections.

In spite of the competition of the greatest and most economically worked coal area of the world—that of Pennsylvania—
the Sydney field is sure of the St. Lawrence markets as far as
Montreal, and actually exports a little coal to the U.S.A. on the
coasts of Maine and Massachusetts.   During the navigation season
many large colliers of 8,000 tons capacity are kept busy taking
Sydney coal to Quebec, Montreal, and other St. Lawrence ports.
Mining is continued in the winter months, and a feature of the
district is the gigantic coal-bank which is then formed awaiting
shipment with the opening of the navigation season.

More than one-half of the Cape Breton output, however, is
used in the manufacture of iron and steel—the one great industry
of the area.   Here we have a history similar to those of so many
other steel industries.   At first local ores were used, and these
are plentiful but scattered.   To-day, it is more economical to
bring the water-side, high-grade, phosphoric ores of Belle Isle,
Newfoundland, to the coastal blast-furnaces at Sydney.   Good
coke is produced in modern by-product ovens, and limestone
quarries are available within a few miles.   There is thus an
unusual concentration of raw materials in a coastal position.
The great steel companies concerned own blast-furnaces and
steel plants, coal mines, ore mines, harbour facilities at Louisburg, Sydney, and many other ports, and a fleet of transport
vessels.

On the western side of Cape Breton Island is Inverness County,
with four detached basins dipping steeply under the sea to the
west.   There are also two important fields on the mainland of
Nova Scotia—the Cumberland and Pictou fields (Fig. 103).   The
Cumberland fields are more inland, and more irregular and of
less good quality, than those of Sydney.   The Pictou coals are

very fiery. Both supply local needs, and are little used for export or for iron and steel. There remains the New Brunswick area, in which there is only one seam (of 2 feet) worked, and that about Grand Lake. It is used by the Grand Trunk Transcontinental, which crosses the field.

* * * * *

The ports of Halifax and St. John offer some interesting comparisons and contrasts based on their respective situations. Both are ice-free—Halifax because of its oceanic situation, St. John because its tides forbid the obstruction of ice. Both have deep-water harbours and are nearer to Liverpool than is New York, Halifax by 616 miles, St. John by 400 miles. Halifax harbour is being extensively improved in the matter of terminal facilities. Its special advantages are that it is practically on the route from the north-west Europe ports to New York, and that passengers and mails for interior points, e.g. Chicago or Montreal, could reach their destinations most rapidly if landed at Halifax.

St. John is nearer Montreal, but further from Liverpool. It is developing as a Canadian bulk freight port.

NEWFOUNDLAND

The island of Newfoundland is now part of the Dominion of Canada. Structurally and economically it is intimately related to the Appalachian Province of the Canadian mainland.

The island blocks the very entrance to the Gulf of St. Lawrence, leaving only narrow passage-ways in Cabot Strait (60 miles wide) and Belle Isle Strait (10–15 miles wide). The island is a little smaller than England and has an estimated population of 290,000 (1934). We have seen that it was visited every summer for many decades before there was any permanent settlement of Europeans in North-Eastern America. It was claimed for Henry VII by Cabot on his first voyage, and holds the sites of our earliest permanent settlements in the New World. It would seem then that there must be particular reason for the smallness of its population, though it may be noticed at once that no part of Eastern Canada in the same latitude is at all thickly populated. In general it may be stated that both soil and climate conditions are adverse to agricultural pursuits, as it is estimated that not more than 2 million acres in all are suitable. Very much less is at present used. It is true that the country as a whole does not suffer the persistent fogs characteristic of its eastern fishing banks, nor does it have quite such cold winters as are experienced on the Eastern mainland in similar latitudes. It is however surrounded by the cold waters of the Labrador current, its summer maxima are low, and its growing season is short, e.g. at St. Johns (lat. 47° 30′) the climatic data are as follows :—

	Jan.	Feb.	Mar.	Apr.	May	June	July	Aug.	Sept.	Oct.	Nov.	Dec.
Temp. . .	24·2	23·3	28·5	35·4	42·7	49·7	58·9	59·3	53·7	45·4	37·6	28·9
Ppt. . .	6·3	5·7	4·7	4·3	3·2	3·9	3·6	3·7	3·5	6·2	6·0	5·4

cp. London (England) (lat. 51° 30′).

	Jan.	Feb.	Mar.	Apr.	May	June	July	Aug.	Sept.	Oct.	Nov.	Dec.
Temp. . .	38·7	40·0	42·5	47·4	52·6	59·2	62·8	61·7	57·1	49·2	43·5	39·3
Ppt. . .	1·8	1·7	1·7	1·7	1·8	2·3	2·6	2·4	2·0	2·7	2·3	2·1

We see at once that Newfoundland will never be an important agricultural country and that the climate is especially unsuitable for the growth of cereals.

Soil conditions are as little favourable. Though only the Long Range in the extreme west has areas over 2,000 feet, yet most of the island is well over 1,000 feet, and most of it too is developed on old crystalline rocks stripped of most of their soil. There are in the aggregate great areas of bare rock or of ill-drained upland. The mountains, the peninsulas, the fiords, the great lakes and the main river channels all conform to the general north-east–south-west strike of the rocks and proclaim the island to be an extension of Appalachia. The surface is almost wholly of pre-Cambrian material, though Silurian and Carboniferous rocks form the western coastlands, and Silurian rocks occupy much of the basins of the Exploits and Gander rivers. These Palæozoic areas also, save where mountainous, provide the best soil ; e.g. dairy-farming is developed and could be much extended in the extreme south-west, and the Exploits and Gander River basins contain the most valuable forest areas of the interior.

Throughout its history the economic life of the country has been based on the fisheries of the Banks. For long, the home authorities positively discouraged permanent settlement as likely to interfere with the seasonal fishing from Europe. There was further the long-standing difficulty of the French claim about Placentia Bay. One-fifth of the inhabitants live in the capital of St. Johns, and almost all outlying settlements are coastal fishing stations which draw their general supplies from the wholesale merchants of the capital. The fishing trade has maintained its general nature and direction since its origin, and consists largely of the export of dried fish (chiefly cod) to Southern Europe and South America. The fisheries are divided into the Shore fisheries, the Banks fisheries, and the summer Labrador fisheries. Fish are exported to Brazil, Portugal, Italy and Spain.

Considerable quantities go to Canada. There is an important export of fish oil for medicine and for leather dressing. There is also short-season seal fishing (for oil and skins only) off the north-east coast, and this provides an interesting export. Apart from the fisheries the only other very important economic activities are concerned with pulp and paper manufacture and iron mining. The best timbers (spruce, balsam, fir, and pine) are found about the great interior lakes and along the river valleys. The Anglo-Newfoundland Development Company Ltd. has big pulp and paper mills at Great Falls. The heavy precipitation and many natural lake reservoirs ensure large water-power possibilities, and these are of special interest in connection with the timber industries.

Newfoundland has great iron-ore resources, but the only workings are of the hæmatites of Wabana, Belle Isle, in Conception Bay. These can certainly yield at least 1,000,000 tons per annum for several generations. The chief iron ore market is the coastal Nova Scotia industry (see page 488), but occasionally ore goes to Great Britain.

There is coal in the younger rocks of the island, viz. the carboniferous of the extreme south-west coastlands. The resources have been much over-estimated and the deposits are not likely to lead to any considerable developments.

* * * * *

The Maritime Provinces and New England are frequently compared as to physical features, and contrasted as to economic development, and the matter is worthy of some consideration. Physically they have much in common in climate as in structure. Perhaps the Canadian side has the advantage in lowlands readily fit for agriculture, but New England (e.g. the Connecticut Valley) has longer growing seasons and slightly higher summer temperatures. Nova Scotia and New Brunswick have coalfields. New England has not. The economic contrasts are by no means inexplicable. Physically the two areas are similar, and so to a limited extent was the fishing, boat-building, trading sequence of development. Yet the Maritimes only advantages were some coal and a shorter run to Europe. What of comparative disadvantages ?

New England did not owe its early manufacturing and trading development to itself alone, but to the (i) differentiated requirements of plantation settlement to the south, and to these New England was nearer than the Maritimes. (ii) New England had the advantage of proximity to the New York and Philadelphia population and routes to the interior.

There were indeed similarities. The Maritime Provinces

marketed salt fish, lumber, potatoes and wooden ships to the southern states, and to some extent did a carrying trade for them, but in these respects they were gathering up of New England's superfluity. The U.S.A. tariff prevented a manufacturing rivalry.

In the decade culminating in the Civil War, these provinces achieved the height of their prosperity. They had a market for their boats, freights were very high, and they exported foodstuffs to the New England industrial centres. Their seamen ran the blockade of the Southern ports and shipped fish in and cotton out—both at large prices.

But the Civil War came to an end, and at about the same time these Provinces entered—somewhat reluctantly—into Confederation with the rest of Canada and had to drop their reciprocal tariff with New England. The day of the iron ship came. With bad trade there was a loss of population to the States, and the immigrant from Europe passed by on his way to the Western Prairies. Yet there is much fine, attractive and low-priced land to be had—especially in New Brunswick—and there are symptoms that point to a development of farming activity once more. With increased settlement will come a revival of prosperity.

REGION III.—THE ST. LAWRENCE LOWLANDS

These consist (Fig. 104) of narrow stretches of low country from a little below Quebec to Lake Huron, i.e. some 600 miles, with varying width, and a total area of about 35,000 square miles. They represent—apart from the Nova Scotia coast settlements —the Pre-railway Canada. To-day they contain the densest population of the Dominion. Structurally, this area is developed upon drift-covered, little-disturbed Palæozoic rocks (Ordovician-Devonian), in marked contrast to the Canadian Shield. Less significant from a geographical point of view is the structural boundary on the south-east. This is formed by a fault zone running north-east from the foot of Lake Champlain to the city of Quebec, along which, and accompanying lines of dislocation, were relieved the stresses and strains due to the action of the mountain-building forces that, to the east, folded and faulted the strata, and at times thrust great blocks up and over westerly-lying beds. The rocks of the St. Lawrence lowlands largely escaped these disturbing forces through the yielding of the strata of this fault zone.

A subdivision of the lowlands is advisable both from the point of view of climate and of structure.

(i) From Quebec the river lowlands widen until at Montreal

the nearly level country is about 120 miles wide. About 50 miles above Ottawa, however, an extension of the Shield crosses the Ottawa River and, spreading to the south-east, crosses the St. Lawrence in the region of the Thousand Isles, between Brockville and Kingston. Thus the two pre-Cambrian regions of Laurentia and the Adirondacks are joined by a neck of pre-

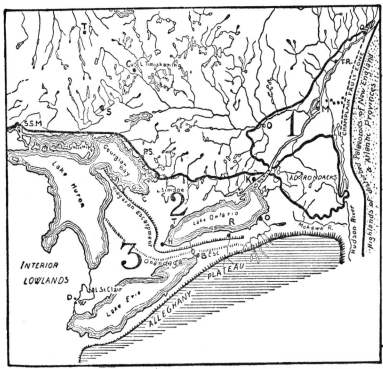

FIG. 104.—Diagram to show relation of St. Lawrence Lowlands to neighbouring physiographic regions.

1, 2, 3, Chief subdivisions of the Lowlands.
** Monteregian Hills.

T, Timmins (gold area) ; Co, Cobalt ; S, Sudbury ; S.S.M, Sault Ste. Marie ; P.S., Parry Sound ; K, Kingston ; T, Toronto ; H, Hamilton ; D, Detroit ; W, Windsor ; B, Buffalo ; O, Ottawa ; M, Montreal ; T.R, Three Rivers ; Q, Quebec.

Cambrian material which cuts off the first division of the St. Lawrence lowlands. This division is almost entirely underlain by drift-covered, horizontal Ordovician strata. It is less than 200 feet in height, save where interrupted by the isolated Monteregian hills. Apart from these, the plain seems to the casual observer perfectly flat.

The other divisions form the Lake Peninsula of Ontario itself, and are usually divided into two portions, viz. (ii) a triangular area of little disturbed Ordovician rocks bordered by the Shield to the north, by Lake Ontario to the south-east, and by the Niagaran escarpment on the south-west. (iii) South of this escarpment the peninsula is developed on undisturbed Silurian and Devonian rocks. The Onondaga escarpment is often imperceptible, but the Niagaran usually presents a bold edge 200 feet to 300 feet in height.

These three divisions together form a narrow belt of structurally simple lowland in marked contrast, both as to relief and structure, to the Laurentian Shield to the north-west or to the Appalachian provinces to the south-east.

Since the St. Lawrence lowlands run through some 5 degrees of latitude and 10 degrees of longitude, and include in the lake peninsula an area almost surrounded by large water bodies, we should expect some differences of climate.

Oak, ash, hickory, elm, maple, walnut, tulip-tree, and sycamore abounded south of the Niagara escarpment. The north divisions, with a generally poorer drift soil and a more rigorous climate, saw the elimination of the three last and a gradually increasing admixture of conifers. All three areas have long been deforested.

Only in the extreme south-west of the peninsula (Kent, Lambton and Essex counties) is corn grown for husking, though it is considerably grown for ensilage anywhere above Montreal. Almost every southern Ontario farm has its apple orchards, but the apples grown for shipment on a large scale are all produced near the lakes, particularly in the central counties bordering Ontario (Northumberland and Prince Edward) and those bordering Lake Huron (Bruce, Huron and Greys).

The very considerable production of peach and of vine is strictly limited to lakeside sites : the vine in the Niagara peninsula—especially under the scarp edge itself—and the peach in the same district and at lake shore areas in the western counties bordering Lake Erie (Norfolk, Elgin, Kent, Essex and Lambton).

AVERAGE TEMPERATURES FOR SELECTED PLACES IN THE ST. LAWRENCE
LOWLANDS

	Jan.	Feb.	Mar.	Apr.	May	June	July	Aug.	Sept.	Oct.	Nov.	Dec.
Windsor . .	24	24	33	46	57	66	71	69	63	51	38	29
Kitchener .	20	18	28	42	54	64	68	64	58	46	35	24
Ottawa . .	11·8	12·8	24·8	42·0	55·6	64·4	68·8	65·8	58·2	46·1	32·4	17·0
Montreal .	13·2	13·7	25·4	41·0	55·5	64·7	69·4	65·2	58·3	46·5	33·5	19·9
Quebec . .	10·0	10·8	22·3	37·5	51·4	60·9	66·6	62·9	55·2	43·4	29·9	15·7

An important lake-side influence, only brought out in a comparison of actual frost incidence, is the higher minima recorded, in any particular cold wave, at lake-side, as compared with points only a few miles inland—a point of special importance to the fruit industry in spring.

In our brief account (see Chapter III) of the stages in the evolution of the Great Lakes, we noticed that as the ice finally retreated from the north-eastern quadrant of the continent, the land rose relatively to the sea, somewhat irregularly, and by stages. Thus after the retreat of the ice an arm of the sea extended right up the lowland between the rim of the Laurentides on the north and the folded Appalachian hills to the south-east. The two chief results of this episode are, first, that the St. Lawrence Lowlands to-day have a veneer of marine sands and silts and clays right up to the point where the great river leaves Lake Ontario ; thus distinguishing this section from the Ontario peninsulas which are covered with morainal material, or with glacial lake deposits.

The various stages of the retreat of this sea are marked by a very large number of terraces on either side of the St. Lawrence. They often form the site of roads, or of land boundaries in the cultivated strips which border the river. The Champlain Sea, too, invaded the Lake St. John basin, and the Ottawa Valley, which also are covered with marine deposits. Thus in the nature of the subsoils, as well, as we have seen, in the climate, and in the predominance of the French race and language, the lowlands below the Great Lakes may be distinguished from the lake peninsulas. The latter, too, have the further distinguishing characteristic of more intimate connection with the very populous and industrially developed portion of the United States which lies just to the south of the Lakes Erie and Ontario.

THE LAKE PENINSULA OF ONTARIO

(a) *Above the Niagaran Escarpment* (3 in Fig. 104). This is a triangular-shaped area, lying between the escarpment itself, and Lakes Huron and Erie developed on Silurian and Devonian strata and covered with glacial drift and lake deposits. The present lakes are respectively 581 and 572 feet above sea-level, but the peninsula rises to a little more than 1,000 feet in the north-central part of the triangle. Some relatively rough topography is found along the line of the escarpment, and on the borders of Lake Huron, but the southern portion of this region is of markedly smoother topography than the area lying to the east of the escarpment. This becomes particularly so towards the south-west, as one approaches the Detroit River and the St.

Clare River and lake ; and this most southerly part of the whole
of Canada has also the warmest summers. The few south-western
counties here may almost be said to belong to the corn belt. It
is noticeable that the Canadian shores of Lake Erie have no
considerable towns, and main road and rail keep well north of
the shore line, yet the south shore of Erie has some of the greatest
connurbations in the United States. The position is reversed
in the case of Lake Ontario. In this we can perhaps see an
historic influence of the Hudson-Mohawk Gap, and of the barrier
of Niagara, which together made effectively of each lake a
terminal.

This part of the peninsula is more completely in farms and in
crops than any other major region of Canada. There is mixed
farming, with emphasis on dairy production. The influence of
the lakes on the climate of specialized fruit areas has already been
noticed. Fall wheat, oats, and corn are all grown, the latter
especially as a fodder crop. The region is within reach of the
hydro-electric energy of Niagara but there are few big towns.
Windsor, Walkerville, and Sandwich, make up a large con-
nurbation on the Detroit River, which is almost an overflow of
the motor district of Detroit on the American side. Chemical
works based on salt deposits have some importance here too.
A number of scattered urban centres, of which London, Brant-
ford, and Guelf, are the largest, have hardware and cotton
industries. The land is laid out in the rectangular township plan
usual in the interior of the United States.

(b) *Below the Niagaran Escarpment* (2 in Fig. 104). This
escarpment, unlike the Onandagan outcrop, is clearly marked
all the way from Niagara, to where it overlooks Georgian Bay in
the Saugeen peninsula. The Laurentian Shield forms the north-
eastern shores of this bay, and continues eastward, interdigitating
with Ordovician limestones through a chaplet of lakes, from the
northern extremity of Lake Simcoe, to reach the St. Lawrence
a little below Gananoque, opposite the stretch of the Thousand
Isles, where the pre-Cambrian, contracted to a narrow neck,
crosses the St. Lawrence to reaffirm itself in the Adirondacks.
At the junction with the Shield the sedimentary limestones form
a ragged low minor scarp, facing northwards, and on the other
hand, just south of the boundary, inliers of pre-Cambrian stand
up above the sedimentaries as islands of rugged infertile country.
The eastern portion of this region from Trenton to a little below
Kingston, is almost drift-less, with shallow but quite fertile soils
just covering the limestone. Beginning just west of Trenton a
major composite moraine, running westwards, near to the lake,
forms the most conspicuous unit of relief, and a major water

parting. From the south of this roughish strip of country, short streams flow to Lake Ontario, often in narrow valleys through the thick glacial drift. One may instance the sharp little gullies which are used as public parks on either side of Toronto. North of this composite moraine, on the land bordering the Shield, e.g. about Peterborough, Lindsay and Orillia, north–south running drumlins are the chief feature of relief. While the isthmus of the Shield which lies between the Ottawa lowland and the lower peninsula maintains its negative characteristics, it is yet so close to considerable centres of population as to be influenced by them. Toronto, Trenton, and especially Kingston and Ottawa, are within a quite short motor ride of this area, and so its lakes are become studded with summer bungalows and camps ; and occasional clearings, and a few farms are to be seen.

There is good land fully occupied by farms in the lower peninsula of Ontario, but as compared with the upper peninsula, it has a rather larger proportion of rough moraine and drumlin land, and thus a larger proportion still in wood and permanent pastures. Dairy farming, and cheese making, are features of the agriculture. Maize is grown as a fodder crop. There are no large towns except on the lake-side, where Toronto and Hamilton overshadow all the others. Hamilton is situated at the western end of Lake Ontario, just where the little Dundas creek breaks through the Niagara escarpment, upon which indeed the upper town is built. The harbour is completely cut off from the lake by a sand-spit representing a former lake level. This is breached by an artificial opening to allow the entrance of lake vessels. A parallel spit at a higher level occupies a crescentic position at the upper end of the bay.

Hamilton with over 155,000 population is one of the most important engineering centres of Canada, and like Sydney in Nova Scotia, has iron and steel works. In this instance, however, like the American lake-side industry, they work with Lake Superior ores, and with Appalachian coal. Hamilton is also a centre of both the cotton and the woollen industry.

A few miles to the east, and also protected by a sandspit, is the harbour and city of Toronto (pop. 631,000). Here are a great diversity of hardware and engineering works, and in particular one of the greatest factories of agricultural machinery on the continent. The textile and rubber industries are also represented, and there is a large amount of miscellaneous manufacture, including printing, publishing, and the manufacture of clothing. It has an important shipping trade with the United States. Here is centred the government of Ontario, and in happy proximity to the government buildings, one of the most important universities in the Empire. Toronto was originally Fort York, a strong royalist centre after the American War of Independence. At the eastern extremity, just where Lake Ontario is narrowing to the river, is the site of the old French Fort Frontenac, and adjacent, the city of Kingston, a beautifully situated university town, of moderate size, with boat-building, hardware, and textile factories.

THE ST. LAWRENCE VALLEY AND ESTUARY (1 in Fig. 104). The third region of the St. Lawrence lowlands might be termed the lowland of the Champlain Sea, for all the lower portions of it were once covered by this post-glacial inundation. To the south, the United States boundary continues along the river as far as Cornwall. Beyond this point the international boundary runs due East to Lake Champlain, and thence to the water parting between Maine and the St. Lawrence—an upland and little occupied region of the Appalachian structure. Below Montreal the Shield begins to close in on the lowland, and a little below Quebec it forms the north shore of the river ; while the lowland strip on the right bank of the river, which is 44 miles wide opposite Montreal, contracts to less than 15 miles east of Quebec, and becomes a mere shore terrace as we approach the Gaspé peninsula. With the gradual change in climate we have already dealt. In all except the extreme south-west of this region, French becomes the dominant language and racial ingredient. Even in the eastern townships, where formerly there were a preponderance of British, much land has passed to the rapidly increasing French Canadians ; and of course the original belt of settlement between Montreal and Quebec was entirely French. Much of the original land grants were aligned at right angles to the St. Lawrence, and to the Ottawa, and the lay-out of the farmlands to-day reflects this fact in most conspicuous fashion. The lands of an individual farm lie at right angles to the waterway, upon which, or upon some parallel road, they have usually a very narrow frontage, though the extent at right angles may be very considerable. The white farm buildings are actually on the roadway, which thus presents the appearance for miles at a time, of almost contiguous settlement, swelling at intervals into a village group dominated by a huge church. The soils are often light and require fertilizers, and the better land is fully occupied ; but there are large areas of very sandy, or ill-drained land, which remain in timber, or as cut-over land. Maize becomes less prominent as a fodder crop below Montreal, oats and potatoes are grown everywhere, and there is much dairy produce. Just opposite the north-eastern extremity of the Isle of Orleans, the pre-Cambrian Laurentides come right down to the water's edge, and continue, usually as a steep cliff, down stream. Thus some miles below Quebec the north shore ceases to be occupied at all, except where, as at Murray Bay and Malbaie, a rift valley in the pre-Cambrian has preserved some Palæozoic cover in a lowland, subsequently to be covered by marine deposits of the Champlain Sea. Murray Bay is a well-known holiday resort, and the railway from Quebec, often blasted out of the cliff front, follows the north bank to this point. There are important pulp mills at Clarke City, and a number of summer fishing stations even farther down-stream. Otherwise the north shore below the Isle of Orleans is practically unoccupied, neither topography nor climate being propitious.

The Lake St. John basin, at the head of the Saguenay gorge, is rather an oasis of settlement on the Shield than a St. Lawrence settlement. The Saguenay itself is an ice-deepened, fault-guided, fiord in the pre-Cambrian, completely barren on either side. Lake St. John is a shallow fresh-water lake, occupying a part of a smooth lowland which lies between well-marked fault scarps aligned roughly parallel to the Saguenay gorge.[1] The lowland was invaded by the Champlain Sea, and has a veneer of terraced marine silts. Both it and the surrounding Shield were of course forested.

Better soils, and a slightly warmer summer than obtains on the north shore of the St. Lawrence itself in these latitudes, together with the navigability of the Saguenay in the gorge, led to this region becoming occupied by French Canadians, lumber men and agriculturists, in the fifth decade of last century. A railway was built from Quebec in 1880, and to-day there is, as well, road connection. The gorge of the Saguenay is navigable as far as Chicoutimi, but the Saguenay River between this point and Lake St. John, from which it flows, is interrupted by rapids. This is especially so as it leaves the lake, and branches on either side of Isle de Maligne. A few miles farther down are the Caron Rapids. The lake was to some extent a natural regularizer of the flow, which in this climate has a severe winter minimum. The outlets around Maligne have been dammed, and the lake above thus deepened and extended, and a great power-house established at one of the dams. Similarly down-stream great dams and great power-stations have been constructed at Caron Rapids and at the junction of the Shipshaw River. These, with smaller developments on tributaries of the Saguenay (the Rivière au Sables and the Chicoutimi), have given to the Lake St. John region one of the greatest hydroelectric power developments in Canada, totalling about 2 million h.p.

[1] This lowland according to Griffith Taylor is a typical " graben."

A tremendous capital expenditure was called for and the motive was twofold. First pulp and paper works, and secondly the establishment at Arvida of great aluminium works. The bauxite comes chiefly from tidal water in British Guiana, and is brought in ocean-going steamers right up the Saguenay gorge ; not to Chicoutimi, the old limit of navigation, but to Port Alfred on Ha Ha Bay, which has a better approach. Production of aluminium here was greatly stimulated by the requirements of the second world war.

On the east shore, opposite Quebec, the lowlands extend back some 15 miles before the Appalachian fold mountains are reached, but this agricultural plain narrows to only a few miles a short distance below Quebec, though this shore, unlike the northern coast, has a fringe of farming, fishing, and lumber settlements right round the Gaspé peninsula, to widen into the coastal settlements of New Brunswick. Railway and road follow the whole way round, though a short cut is made by both rail and road across the gap formed by the river Matapedia. The Shickshock Mountains, forming the core of Gaspé, are forest covered, and like the Shield on the opposite side of the gulf, exhibit two main peneplanation levels, at about 1,500 feet and 2,500 feet. A narrow silt-covered shore terrace, and a rather warmer summer, and longer growing season, have made settlement possible farther downstream than is the case on the north shores of the Gulf of St. Lawrence. The farms become slightly more diversified as we go up-stream towards the markets of Quebec ; but oats and potatoes are always the chief crops, and dairy herds are usually kept.

Between its exit from Lake Ontario, and Montreal, the St. Lawrence falls 226 feet compared with the fall of 326 feet between Erie and Ontario (Fig. 105). Thus it is clear that if this very considerable fall is at all concentrated enormous powers (over 5 million h.p.) on this strip of the river are available. Actually there is very little fall in level from the exit of Lake Ontario to Prescott. Between this point and Cornwall there is a fall of about 90 feet accounted for in part by the following sets of rapids : Galop (8 feet), Rapide Plat (11 feet) and Long Saulte (30 feet). The river then broadens out to form Lake St. Francis. Four canals below Prescott, each of 14 feet depth, and with locks 250 feet long, render this stretch of the river navigable. There is little fall through Lake St. Francis, but between this widening and Lake St. Louis, there is a further drop of 83 feet in 16 miles, made up of the Coteau, Cedars, Split Rock, and Cascades rapids. These, too, are passed by canals of the same dimensions. The river hardly falls at all in the 12 miles across Lake St. Louis, but between this lake and Montreal, swift water and the actual

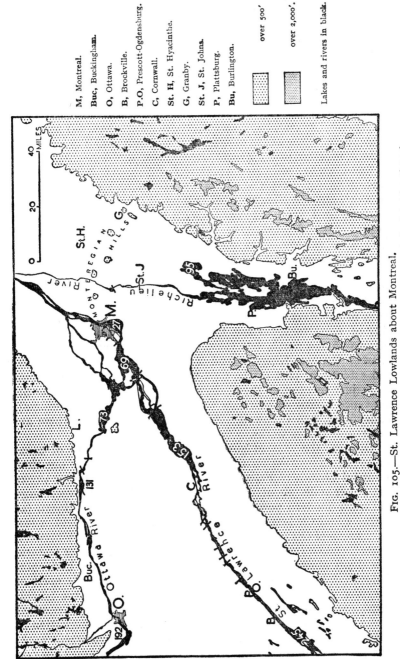

FIG. 105.—St. Lawrence Lowlands about Montreal.
Numbers represent height of rivers above sea-level. Short lines across the rivers represent terminals of stretches of canal.

M, Montreal.
Buc, Buckingham.
O, Ottawa.
B, Brockville.
P.O, Prescott-Ogdensburg.
C, Cornwall.
St. H, St. Hyacinthe.
G, Granby.
St. J, St. Johns.
P, Plattsburg.
Bu, Burlington.

over 500'
over 2,000'.

Lakes and rivers in black.

Lachine rapids, account for another 47 feet. Montreal Harbour is only 27 feet above sea-level, and is well above tidal influence, which dies out at Three Rivers. The Lachine canal is of the same dimensions as the others, and thus a 14 feet depth is available from Montreal to Lake Erie. We may notice also that the Grenville rapids on the Ottawa River are avoided by a canal, so that Montreal has canal communication with Ottawa also. Since the old Welland canal by which Niagara was avoided has been deepened to 27 feet, big lake vessels are able to proceed from the head of the lakes as far as Prescott, but only small ones can at present proceed to Montreal. In spite of the deepening of the Welland, exchange to smaller vessels still usually takes place on Lake Erie (at Port Colbourne or at Buffalo) rather than at Prescott, and the New Welland will hardly fulfil its true function until the St. Lawrence below Prescott has been improved to take large vessels. A deep section has already been engineered around the Soulanges group of rapids by a great canal which invades the south shores of the St. Lawrence. It has been constructed in connection with the very great water-power development on the St. Lawrence at this point. Most of the canals to which reference has been made are cuts in, or embankments against, the north bank of the river. The edge of the Shield, represented here by hills of 1,000 to 1,500 feet in height, comes close down to the Ottawa to the north, but the triangle of lowland lying roughly between Ottawa, Kingston and Montreal is part of the lowlands, and essentially part of the hay and dairying belt. Apart from those just mentioned there are no really large towns. The St. Lawrence is crossed by roads and rail at Montreal (two bridges), Valleyfields, and Cornwall. At the last-named centre there are paper and rayon works.

Ottawa, the seat of government, lies at the head of canal improved navigation on the river of that name. The one-time beautiful Chaudière Falls are almost hidden in the power works and paper mills about the river at this point. Two very large and quite modern power developments are on the Gatineau (at Farmers and Chelsea Rapids), just as it leaves the Shield, a few miles north of Ottawa. The Ottawa forms the boundary between Quebec and Ontario, and the city stands on the south or Ontario side, high above the river on a platform of nearly horizontal Ordovician limestone. This plane extends a little to the north of the river, but soon gives way to the rugged edge of the Shield. Ottawa and Hull, its north-shore neighbour, are chiefly concerned in the pulp and paper industry, but a considerable proportion of the population of Ottawa itself are employed in government work. The plexus of natural waterways between Ottawa and Kingston

have been linked up by the Rideau Canal, but actually, this takes
to-day almost no commercial traffic.

Montreal (Fig. 105) (pop. 818,000), the largest city of Canada,
has a most interesting geographical position. In the first place
it was the head of unimproved navigation, for just above Montreal
were the Lachine rapids. Nevertheless, navigation was difficult
and dangerous above Quebec. In particular the channel through
Lake St. Peter was shallow and winding, and the head of the lake
is encumbered by a maze of low islands. Then at the site of
Montreal itself the river is over-rapid, and so the immediate
approach was difficult for sailing ships. Quebec would be now,
as it was for long, the chief port of Canada, if there had not been
drastic dredging particularly through Lake St. Peter, and elaborate harbour works at Montreal itself. Even improved as it is to
30 feet, the channel is, in part, still unduly narrow and requires
careful navigation. Work is in progress for a deepening to 35
feet. It should be remembered that even the St. Lawrence,
most regular of rivers, exhibits some slight variation of flow below
the Great Lakes, for an increasing proportion of flow is then
derived from great tributaries, such as the Ottawa and the St.
Maurice, which have a decreased flow in the autumn. Thus a few
feet less depth is available at this season. The winter minimum
is unimportant because the navigation is closed. We should
remember also that any increase in depth gives an altogether
disproportionate increase in the possible tonnage of a vessel using
the waterway. Actually only a very small proportion of commercial vessels draw more than 27 feet of water.

These great improvements were forced on Montreal just
because in all other respects the site was so superior. Quebec is
essentially at the entrance to the St. Lawrence lowlands, Montreal
is in the midst of them, and is, too, much better placed for communication with the rest of the continent, and particularly via the
Richelieu and Lake Champlain route to the Hudson Gap and so to
New York. The city is on one of the large islands at the junction
of the Ottawa and the St. Lawrence. The surrounding country
is quite flat except for the Monteregian Hills. These are a series
of ancient denuded plutonic intrusions which rise suddenly from
the surrounding plains. They are Mounts Johnson (875 feet),
Brome (1,755 feet), Shefford (1,775 feet), Yamaska (1,470 feet),
Rougemont (1,250 feet), Beloeil (1,437 feet), and Mount Royal
itself (750 feet), the last the site of a fine public park in the heart
of the city.

There is no tide at Montreal so that closed docks are not
necessary ; but the basin, quay and warehouse space is large.
There are huge grain elevators.

In addition to the great port activities, Montreal is the chief railway and route centre of Canada. Canada has little of the localization of industry as we know it in the British Isles ; and in Montreal, or in the vicinity, are great engineering works (including railway works) as well as textile factories, sugar refineries, boot and shoe factories, and clothing factories.[1] The agricultural plain north of the St. Lawrence narrows somewhat rapidly to Quebec, but to the south of the river it is more considerable. Here St. Hyacinthe has textile factories, and farther east still where the plain gives way to the folded mountains, water power was early developed and Sherbrooke, a considerable railway route junction on the St. Francis River, has important textile, engineering, and leather factories, while farther north in the eastern townships, is Thetford, with some of the chief asbestos mines in the world. In this section of the St. Lawrence basin very large hydro-electric developments are available, on the Ottawa, the Gatineau, at Cedars rapids and Beauharnois on the St. Lawrence itself, and to a lesser but considerable extent in the hilly parts of the eastern townships, at Sherbrooke itself, at Coaticoke, and Windsor Mills.

About half-way between Montreal and Quebec, the St. Maurice River enters on the left bank at Three Rivers. The edge of the Laurentian Shields is here about 20 miles to the north, and near its junction with the lowland, at Grandmère, and at Shawinigan Falls, have been developed two of the larger powers of Canada. These two considerable towns are important centres of the paper and pulp industry. So also is Three Rivers at the mouth of the St. Maurice, and it, and Shawinigan, have textile factories as well.

Below Three Rivers the tide becomes just perceptible, and 17 miles farther down-stream at Batiscan, the range is still only 2 feet, but on nearing Quebec it increases rapidly to reach 19 feet off the city itself. A few miles above Quebec the river narrows considerably and cuts sharply into the rocks of the surrounding plain. Opportunity is taken to bridge it just above Quebec, and at a height which allows of the passage of vessels below. Quebec itself lies just at the point at which the river widens from a minimum of 3,500 feet to a width of some ten miles. Just below Quebec most of this width is occupied by the Isle of Orleans, which is separated from the north shore by a shallow strait, and connected to it by a bridge. Shipping then passes to the south

---

[1] In 1949 Montreal was the chief manufacturing centre of Canada with a gross output valued at nearly $2,000,000,000 ; Toronto coming second with a gross output of $1,500,000,000. Many new light industries developed in both centres as well as elsewhere in Canada during the war.

of the island, and entering Canada by this route, a sharp turn brings Quebec suddenly into view. The upper city is magnificently situated on the rocky extremity of a small plateau, which itself is almost cut off by a wide trench, the lower portion of which is occupied by the mouth of the Charles River. The Charles estuary, however, is very shallow and was in fact never important as a shelter for shipping. For this there was plenty of sheltered water beneath the cliffs of Quebec itself, and the lower town grew up on a narrow terrace just above the water-level. The upper level presented a magnificent defensive site, however, and soon became the fortified city of the French colony. The present great ramparts which give to the city so much the appearance of some fortified city of Europe, date, in reality, chiefly from the mid-nineteenth century. Ease of fortification at Quebec, difficulties of navigation above it—these were factors in its early development. Montreal depends, as a port, almost entirely on the river improvements above Quebec—should these ever become inadequate Quebec would renew its dominance. Docks have been engineered out of the tidal flats at the mouth of the Charles River, but much of the traffic passes on to Montreal. Passenger liners drawing up to about 26 feet (including, e.g. the Duchess class of the C.P.R., 20,000 tons) can make Montreal. A new quay constructed at the base of the rock face about one mile above Quebec is connected with the C.P. Ry. by a tunnel and will accommodate vessels up to 40 feet draught and too large to use the docks. For a few miles below Quebec the navigable channel is narrow, and with the increasing size of vessels some deepening has had to be done. A little below the Isle of Orleans a depth of over 60 feet is available to the sea. Quebec City, and the St. Lawrence below Quebec, are almost entirely French Canadian. In the upper town are the government buildings of the province, and a considerable portion of the residential and business quarters. In the St. Charles lowland are factories and warehouses, and some of the poorer residential districts.

Great pulp and paper works adjoin the dock area, and the city has as well both engineering and textile factories.

We cannot leave this treatment of Eastern Canada without emphasizing once more the importance of the paper and pulp industry, the manufactured products of which often exceed in value the Canadian production of wheat. Abundant spruce forest—not necessarily of large timber—abundant water-power, and the gigantic demand in the United States for newsprint are circumstances favourable for this development. Canada produces more pulp and paper than either Scandinavia or Finland,

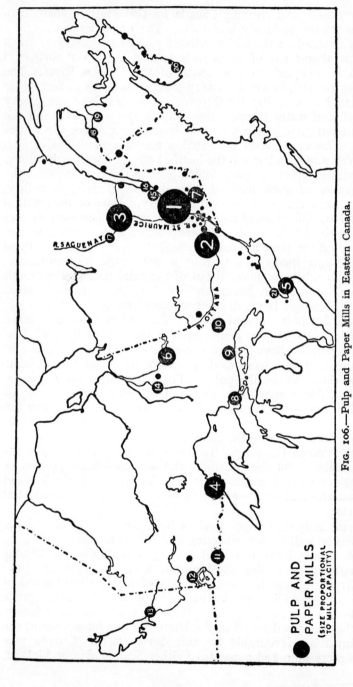

Fig. 106.—Pulp and Paper Mills in Eastern Canada.

The names of the ten chief districts are: 1. Grandmère, Shawinigan Falls and Three Rivers, all on the St. Maurice river. 2. Ottawa. 3. Saguenay and L. St. John. 4. Ft. William, Pt. Arthur. 5. St. Catherines, etc. 6. Iroquois Falls. 7. Windsor Mills, etc. 8. Sault Ste. Marie. 9. Espanola. 10. Sturgeon Falls.

and exports great quantities, but principally to the United States. Fig. 106 gives the distribution of pulp and paper mills.[1] This great industry, so prominent in the French-speaking parts of Canada, tends rather to break up the traditional economy of the *habitant* of the typical French Catholic village. The lumber industry with its winter cutting fitted in well enough. The *habitant* was farmer or fisherman or both in the summer, and a lumberman in the winter ; but the great pulp and paper mills attract permanent labour from both farm and village.

The St. Lawrence is entered either by Cabot Strait or by the Strait of Belle Isle. The approaches are rendered impassable by ice in winter, and often difficult by fog in summer. With fog outside the Gulf we have already dealt. Within the Gulf it will suffice to say that it decreases rapidly westwards, and is most prevalent in early summer. Navigation even in the Gulf and lower estuary is by no means straightforward. In times of fog ships have to take frequent soundings. In Cabot Strait fogs accompany almost all easterly wind-drifts from May to October, and were present in 20 to 30 per cent. of the observations taken in these months from 1891 to 1905.[2] West of long. 60° W. they rapidly decrease in frequency.

Cabot Strait is never completely frozen over, but is accessible only from May to December for boats not built for ice. Sometimes in April or May escaping St. Lawrence ice becomes wedged between St. Paul Isle and Cape Ray, and hundreds of vessels may be held up. The harbours and bays of the lower Gulf all close by the end of December. With regard to the date of the closing of the St. Lawrence, we must remember that the principal traffic is through traffic, or coal from Sydney, and that if any considerable part of the St. Lawrence is closed, it is virtually all closed. Although Montreal is 4 degrees south of the Gaspé peninsula, yet the dates of first closing on the Upper St. Lawrence and in the Gulf tend to approximate, because of the different degrees of salinity of the water. Cabot Strait is open May to December, i.e., on the average a little longer than Montreal, but Quebec is unsafe between the limits mid-November to mid-April. Actual limits vary considerably year by year, and shipping is informed accordingly. Belle Isle Strait in lat. 52° begins to suffer drift-ice in mid-December. This increases in thickness through the winter, and is followed in spring by bergs which float into the St. Lawrence, usually hugging the north shore. These begin in

[1] In 1953 Canada produced 5,687,000 short tons of newsprint and shipped 4,835,000 tons to the U.S.A. The U.S.A. production was 1,147,000 tons. The Canadian production is five times that of any other country.
[2] " St. Lawrence Pilot," p. 39.

April, and the route is not used by steamers until early June, when it forms part of the shortest route from Great Britain to the St. Lawrence.

Montreal is the real effective head of navigation (save for the largest liners), and in explaining Montreal the river improvements must be taken into consideration with the fact that immediately above the town, the Lachine rapids set an absolute limit to anything but canoe traffic in the pre-canal days, and that the St. Lawrence canals between Montreal and Lake Ontario are under 14 feet deep. Further, a smaller type of craft must be used than that available on the upper lakes, so that a change of bulk must occur above Niagara. The present small size of the St. Lawrence canals is then effective, not only in adding enormously to the importance of Buffalo and the U.S.A. route to the Atlantic, but in diverting lake traffic to rail at Georgian Bay ports, or at Lake Erie ports, if bound for the St. Lawrence. The very configuration of the Great Lakes is of importance here, Georgian Bay ports (e.g. Parry Sound, Midland, etc.) being much nearer to Montreal by land than by water.

We have seen that since the construction of the new Welland canal a depth of 27 feet is available from the Head of the Lakes to Prescott below Lake Ontario. Below this there is a limiting depth of 14 feet—the general depth of the canals which by-pass the series of rapids on the lower river.

The provision of a waterway deep enough to take large ocean-going vessels (27 feet) from Lake Superior to the Atlantic has long been discussed. Such an undertaking has the support of the middle-west and of central and western Canada, but is opposed by Atlantic interests, e.g. Montreal, New York.

It is indeed possible that even if the Deep Waterway were completed it would not be generally used by sea-going vessels, and it is true also that the present great bulk traffic—wheat— might at no very distant date diminish in importance ; but we must remember that with the scheme goes the development of some 5 million h.p. for hydro-electric generation, and that in a populous area some distance from coal supplies.

The engineers have prepared the fullest plans, and at last it seemed that the scheme was to be put into operation. The U.S.A. Senate has now refused to ratify an agreement to that effect, and though for the time (1945) the scheme is in abeyance, it is difficult to believe that it will not ultimately be carried out.[1]

We have already noticed the gradual climatic changes in the St. Lawrence lowlands from Quebec to Montreal—the lengthening

[1] The agreement was ratified in 1954.

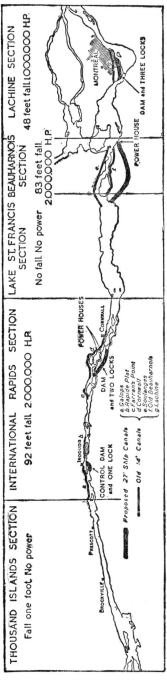

FIG. 16A.—Plan of St. Lawrence Deep Waterway Scheme.

growing season, and ultimately the greatly increased frost-free period at lake-side. This and also the generally better soils make the lake peninsula the most valuable of the lowlands for general farming and for soft-fruit production. There is another general difference between the lake peninsula and the Montreal–Quebec lowland to be noticed. The one is set opposite one of the most populous and productive areas of the U.S.A., in lake communication with it, and that by big lake vessels. The other is somewhat cut off from the U.S.A. by the little-populated Eastern Highlands, and partly isolated, too, over the waterway, by the Niagara obstacle, which necessitates change of bulk. We may take as instances of this effect the lake-side iron and steel industry of Canada. There are about twenty blast-furnaces in Canada, about half of which are usually in blast. The most important plants are in Cape Breton Island (Sydney) and Nova Scotia ; these work with Newfoundland ore and local coal, i.e., with supplies independent of the U.S.A. The remainder are at Hamilton (L. Ontario), Parry Sound, and Midland. These lake-side furnaces work with Pennsylvanian coal and Lake Superior ores, and therefore follow the state of the U.S.A. industry. Again, the proximity of the much greater blast-furnace plants of the U.S.A. lake-side (see Chapter XIX) results in a ready export of pig-iron to Canada. This is used in steelworks and foundries at Sault Ste. Marie, Toronto, Hamilton, and Welland. Such plants, however, are dependent upon the conditions of the U.S.A. iron industry for their raw material.

With regard to coal, too, the Sydney fields can compete to Montreal ; after that the change of bulk caused by the shallow St. Lawrence canals and the absence of large-scale terminal facilities for coal-handling prevent further ingress. The lake peninsula is largely dependent upon U.S.A. coal. Much of the domestic heating is done with U.S.A. anthracite, but the demand for this is so high in the U.S.A. that export is likely to dwindle. Coke may prove a useful competitor if the anthracite prices rise much more.

One natural resource the St. Lawrence lowlands possesses to an extraordinary degree, viz. water power. The proximity of the rim of the Laurentian Shield along the whole line of the lowlands, the heavy precipitation, and the lake storage, all make for abundant power resources. Fig. 107 brings out this fact, for it gives the location of the power stations, and is also to some extent quantitative. Among the largest of these plants are Cedar Rapids (St. Lawrence River), 130,000 h.p. ; Shawinigan Falls (St. Maurice River, 21 miles up), 150,000 h.p. ; Grand Mère Rapids (St. Maurice River, 28 miles up), 120,000 h p. ; Niagara

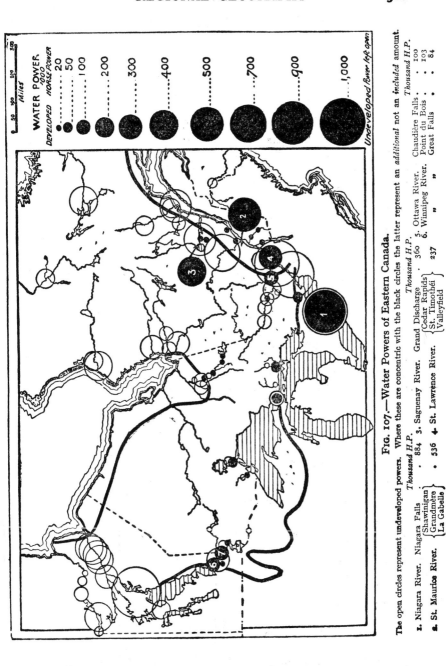

FIG. 107.—Water Powers of Eastern Canada.

The open circles represent undeveloped powers. Where these are concentric with the black circles the latter represent an additional not an included amount.

	Thousand H.P.			Thousand H.P.			Thousand H.P.
1. Niagara River.	Niagara Falls	884	3. Saguenay River. Grand Discharge	360	5. Ottawa River.	Chaudière Falls	100
					6. Winnipeg River.	Point du Bois	103
2. St. Maurice River.	Shawinigan		4. St. Lawrence River.	Cedar Rapids		" "	Great Falls	84
	Grandmère	536		St. Timothéi	237		
	La Gabelle			Valleyfield			

Thick black line indicates edge of Shield.

Falls (Canadian only), 500,000 h.p. ; and a host of smaller plants as shown. The total horse-power for Canada actually developed has increased enormously in the last decade. A larger proportion is undeveloped in Canada than is the case in the States, but nevertheless progress has been very rapid, and Canada is actually second among the countries of the world in installed horse-power. The greatest possibilities, and the greatest developments, are in the fuelless provinces of Quebec and Ontario, which together have 80 per cent. of the developed horse-power of the country. Here in the St. Lawrence lowland are the greatest manufacturing and population centres, while on the shield to the north are the pulp, paper, and mining activities—all requiring gigantic power supplies.

The location of the chief sites—developed and undeveloped —are shown in Fig. 107. Since this was drawn, however, the following very considerable additions have been made to the actual developments. On the Gatineau River at Chelsea and Farmers rapids near Ottawa, some 200,000 h.p., 150,000 h.p., at Beauharnois on the St. Lawrence, and nearly 200,000 h.p. at the cañon on the Atibiti River. Nearly 2,000,000 h.p. have been installed on the Saguenay. 88 per cent. of the horse-power installed is in Central Electric stations which produce solely for sale. 7·7 per cent. is used in pulp and paper factories, but these as well take about 40 per cent. of their requirements from the Central Electric stations. 4·4 per cent. is in other industries, most of which buy also from the Central stations.

AVAILABLE WATER POWER IN EASTERN CANADA AND POWER DEVELOPED UP TO JANUARY, 1943

Development	Undeveloped Estimate at 80 per cent. Efficiency	
Turbine Installation in h.p. 10^6	Ordinary Minimum Flow, h.p. 10^6	Dependable for six months, h.p. 10^6
Ontario . . . . . . 2·673	5·3	6·9
Quebec . . . . . 5·847	8·5	13·0
New Brunswick . . . . 0·133	0·07	0·2
Nova Scotia . . . . 0·133	0·02	0·1
Prince Edward Island . . 0·003	0·003	0·005
Total for Eastern Canada only 8·789	13·893	20·205
Total for whole of Canada . 10·214	20·3	33·6

Far and away the greatest single consumer is the paper and pulp industry. More than half the power required in this—the greatest industry of its kind in the world—is used in electric boilers producing process steam. This requirement can be confined to off-peak hours, and can therefore be supplied by the Central stations at much below the usual rates. Now all these eastern developments are so situated as to be within effective distance of the St. Lawrence lowlands, no part of which is without an abundant and cheap source of power. Already Canada (and chiefly Eastern Canada) has developed more hydro-electric power than any other country, save the U.S.A. In the absence of very abundant and well-distributed supplies of fuel in the east, this is a factor of great and increasing importance. Town and village lighting ; street transport ; timber, pulp, paper, and grain mills, and many other factories, are using hydro-electric power. In the last two years there has also been an enormous increase in its use for domestic cooking purposes, and it is likely to take the place of all other methods.

CHAPTER XXXIII

THE PRAIRIE PROVINCES OF CANADA

MANITOBA, Saskatchewan, and Alberta are usually called the Prairie Provinces. Fig. 114 shows that only the southern portions are unforested, and though the present population is almost confined to these portions, the title cannot be considered satisfactory. Nor are the boundaries of these three provinces coterminous with any—even the largest —physiographic division of Canada. Manitoba includes large areas in the north and east belonging to the Laurentian Shield, albeit much of these areas are of lower relief and sufficiently covered with drift to lack some of its characteristic features as exemplified farther east. Alberta includes a narrow portion of the Pacific Cordillera province, where the character of the relief and the disturbance of the strata are in marked contrast to the plain and plateau developed on horizontal strata which cover most of the prairie provinces. But these are but marginal zones. The northern boundary (lat. 60°) separating the three provinces from north-west territory and the southern (lat. 49°) have little physiographical significance, though the latter indicates a zone of climatic change as between the land in Southern Alberta and Saskatchewan, where there is just enough moisture for farming, and the lands in Northern Montana and the western third of North Dakota, where it is insufficient.

The economic development of the region under consideration is the work of little more than half a century. The Prairie Provinces produce from half to two-thirds as much wheat as the States and export more than any other country. They supply about one-third of our own loaf, to which we can contribute less than one-sixth. They have the second greatest coal reserves of the world, and a wealth of pulp wood, water power, and metallic ores not popularly associated with them. Of the 200 million acres in the prairie provinces classed officially as possible agricultural land, one quarter is actually under crops. The wheat crop—varying chiefly with the season's weather—has been, from 1932–1936 inclusive, 423, 263, 264, 264, and 212 million bushels, and of the last figure, Alberta, the latest to develop, contributes 67 million bushels, and Manitoba but 28. Since 1932 the production, and price obtained, have been far below the averages for the last 15 years, which have been 348 million bushels, and 1·07 dollars per bushel, respectively. In this great farming area one-fifth of the population live in towns of over 20,000 inhabitants, and manufactures of great variety are increasing.

The area between the limit of the Shield in the east and the upturned strata of the Rocky Mountain foothills in the west, that is to say, the extreme south-west of Manitoba and nearly all of Saskatchewan and Alberta, has a certain unity based on structure and on climate. On structure, because the rocks everywhere are stratified and little disturbed ; on climate, because these provinces, considered in relation to the rest of the continent, exhibit a marked extension of summer warmth to the north, and of summer precipitation to the west. The important point is not merely that, latitude for latitude, the July temperature is higher in the Prairie Provinces than in Eastern Canada, but that the effective growing period is longer.

In the Prairie Provinces we have, in general, a vast plateau developed on Cretaceous rocks (with some tertiary residuals), sloping from South-west Alberta northwards and eastwards ; overlooking in a sharp but dissected scarp the Lake Winnipeg and Red River lowland to the east, and the Mackenzie lowland to the north, both developed on Palæozoic sedimentaries. The general slope upwards from this eastern and northern outer edge to the extreme south-west of Alberta meets the mighty Rocky Mountain front, almost—at this point—without the customary intervention of foothills. This very general slope is interrupted by a secondary, less regular, and usually much less perceptible scarp, which is really a continuance north-eastward of the Missouri côteau. The latter runs from Estevan north-westwards in the direction of Battleford. The whole plateau region, though flooring the greater part of Alberta and Saskatchewan, as well as south-western Manitoba, is spoken of as the Alberta plateau.

This classical division of the Prairie Provinces into three steps formed by two scarp lines interrupting a general rise south-west-wards, requires considerable amplification if it is to be of use, or, indeed, if it is not to be misleading. The general rise is interrupted in addition by many isolated residual plateaux ; and the second step has an almost continuous intermediate belt of relatively high country running north-west to south-east, and including the Touchwood, Beaver, and Moose Mount plateaux. The advance and recession of ice sheets have left the usual symptoms in glacial lakes, lacustrine deposits, ground and terminal moraines, a re-arranged drainage system, and a general smoothing of relief.

Let us, beginning in the east, and working westwards, describe the area in rather greater detail. The eastern boundary of Manitoba lies well beyond the western limit of the Laurentian Shield—that vast pre-Cambrian unit whose innumerable lakes are only now yielding the details of their outline to the superior resources of air survey; whose intricate hummocky outcrops of bare scraped rock are placed irregularly about the basins of present and past lakes of all shapes and sizes.

On either side of the great transcontinental lines which bring us to the gate of the prairies at Winnipeg, one is seldom for long out of sight of the recently burnt forest, looking for all the world like the shell-stricken woods of France; or, if the fires be less recent, the old coniferous forest area is now occupied by quickly growing poplar and silver birch, intolerant of shade, enlivening the colour scheme, but much less valuable than the conifers they have temporarily replaced.

From the standpoint of agricultural settlement the whole Shield forms a negative area, incapable of cultivation, save where, far to the east, in the great Clay Belt of Ontario and Western Quebec, and again round Lake St. John in Quebec, old glacial lakes have left lacustrine deposits of clay, enriched from occasional remnants of Palæozoic limestones. It was this great North-Eastern Laurentian Shield which confined Canadian development to the St. Lawrence lowlands for so long, and which even to-day largely separates Eastern from Western Canada. Only lately has it become possible to motor from Ottawa or Toronto to Winnipeg without traversing U.S.A. territory.

Western Canada was acquired for the Confederation by a single line of rails which traversed the wilderness of the Shield for more than 1,000 miles. For long it depended precariously on this same miracle of human initiative, courage and faith. Gradually, almost imperceptibly, as the traveller proceeds westwards, the hummocky surface becomes smoother; the bare rock outcrop, still frequent, less obtrusive; the forest-cover more patchy, and improved land more frequent; until at last we emerge on the now un-forested, flat expanse of the Red River Valley, where most land is cultivated, and where the turned sod reveals a friable heavy loam of incredible blackness.

We are now on the so-called first prairie step, the lowest (800 feet) and flattest of the prairie regions, with a very gradual rise eastwards, but with its western limits quite sharply defined by the scarps of a succession of flat-topped hill masses, each of which, followed westward, after rising to a summit level set a little back of the scarp edge, sinks gently somewhat before conforming again to the general rise of the second prairie step. These are successively from the International Boundary northwards—Pembina Mountain (1,500 feet), Riding Mountain (2,000 feet), Duck Mountain (2,400 feet), and Porcupine Mountain (2,400 feet), all overlooking the first step, which averages about 800 feet only. All but the first and lowest were originally wooded, with the density of timber and the percentage of spruce increasing northwards and the percentage of poplar southwards. Breaking this wall in well-marked gaps and tributary to the Red River Plain are, from south to north, the Pembina, Assiniboine, Swan, and Red Deer Rivers.

With the advance of the ice sheet the whole lowland was covered with a till, largely derived from the underlying limestone, but partly also from the pre-Cambrian to the east and the Cretaceous Shales of the west. With the final retreat of the ice northwards of the water parting between the Upper Minnesota (Mississippi drainage) and the Red River (Arctic drainage), lake waters were impounded by this water parting itself to the south, by the gradual rise to the Laurentian Shield eastwards, by the Cretaceous scarp westward, and by the ice front in the north. Thus was formed glacial Agassiz, and so, above the glacial till of the first prairie step, are deposits of stratified lacustrine clays, forming the subsoil of much of the area, and derived from the streams entering the lake loaded with material assorted from the surrounding glacial till or parent rock. Lakes Winnipeg and Winnipegosis are the remnants of this vast lake.

The first prairie step as structurally defined is by no means all prairie, is not absolutely flat, and is not coterminous with good agricultural land. Only the smaller southern part is thickly settled, and within this area there are many negative spots. No single physical control in the development of the north-west has so far been more important than the line of heavy bush. On the inner side of this lies the grove belt of scattered willow and poplar, only of local importance in development. These parallel belts fringe the whole prairie region in the three provinces. Actually they correspond roughly to a zone of increasing effective precipitation, for if we make allowance for a rather greater amount incident upon isolated plateau-like elements of relief in the south, then an isohyetal map shows us that precipitation increases westwards, northwards, and eastwards, from a semi-arid zone in South-east Alberta.

Returning, then, to our first prairie step, and with the general conspectus of forests and precipitation in mind, we notice first of all that the bush limits come to the southern borders of lakes

Winnipeg and Winnipegosis, and that the grove approaches
from the east almost to Winnipeg. Only a small part of South-
west Manitoba displayed those characteristics of entirely open,
rich, agricultural land, which were to attract not only a host of
immigrants from Europe, but also, as in the case of the United
States, settlers from the older eastern parts of the continent.
Settlers are now clearing the bush from agricultural land west of
Edmonton and in the Peace River district, yet still, dense settlement in Manitoba has not pushed far north and east from the
original prairie and grove belt.

Forest has been the chief limiting control—small trees, of
small value before the days of pulp, and when cut and the land
cultivated, exposing usually soils less fertile than the dark loams
of the prairie proper. But there were concurrent factors. There
is a rapid decrease in the length of growing season, eastward and
northward from Winnipeg and upon the western plateaux (Duck
Mountain, Riding Mountain, etc.).

Precipitation is adequate. Indeed, it is more favourable than
any other part of the provinces. As in all the prairie provinces,
more than 60 per cent. is in the growing period May–September,
and the percentage increases, fortunately, with the diminution
of total precipitation westward into South Saskatchewan and
Alberta. The true prairie with a growing season of more than
120 days is very limited in Manitoba. And there were yet other
controls. The slight relief is usually favourable to agricultural
activities, but the complete flatness of portions of the first step
has made of drainage a serious problem, and considerable areas
still require drainage, even in the true prairie area. North of
this we have the Big Grass Marsh just west of Lake Manitoba, and
innumerable lesser swamps. To the east of Winnipeg on the
border of the Shield is a north-and-south belt of sand-hills. The
most considerable topographic irregularities of the first step are
the glacial-lake deltas and beaches. The Cheyenne in Dakota
(U.S.A.), the Pembina, and, above all, the Assiniboine, with its
temporarily increased drainage basin and flow, in glacial times, all
formed considerable deltas on the western side of Lake Agassiz.
The first Pembina Mountain is such a one. The fine material was
scattered well out over the area, but much of the delta surface of
the Assiniboine is now a land of very sandy loams, and on its
central area, of barren sand-dune.

The political-group mind, groping for some decades now after
a Hudson Bay outlet, represents perhaps an inherited instinct !
Hudson Bay—the shorter route to Liverpool, the route which was
independent of the French occupation of the St. Lawrence, was
an effective influence in the seventeenth and eighteenth century

traffic of the Hudson Bay Company. The North-West Company was formed later, by a group of fur traders who operated westwards from Lake Superior. Agricultural settlement began near Winnipeg, and only with the maturing of the purposeful scheme of Lord Selkirk. Hunters have ever resented the invasion by settlers of their domain. The opposition of the North-West Fur Company did not stop short of bribery, of interruption of supplies, and of armed raids. The early settlers, with a beautiful regard for the dictates of modern geography, strung their farms along the waterside at the junction of the two navigable streams of the area, and just within the prairie. Here even to-day the sectional map offers in the comparative irregularity of the riverside land boundaries a welcome relief to the prevailing checker-board arrangement of the West. Floods, locusts, and mice devastated the crops in successive years. Since the farmers had at first no outlet for their surplus products, many of them turned to hunting, to traffic with the Indian, or took part in the seasonal buffalo round-up of the Western Plains. Though we must not stop to describe the evolution of this settlement and its checkered and rebellious career under the ægis of the Hudson Bay Company, yet it is vital to our subject to point out one of the major geographical factors which affected it. Communications eastward were on portage and canoe lines to the Hudson Bay, or on the intricate series of waterways which led past Rainy Lake and Lake of the Woods to Lake Superior. A more local and easier line was the Red River itself, but this led to the head of navigation of the Red River in the States. Soon, in spite of the order to the contrary, this became an outlet for illicit fur trade. At the time of the origin of the Red River Settlement, the bordering territory of the States was little occupied, but the general movements westward in Canada and in the U.S.A. were very differently conditioned. Before the railway era, the Great Lakes provided a magnificent route westward, but one which favoured American territory ; for the great terminal lake of Superior is situated some 300 miles within the confines of the Laurentian wilderness, while the southern lobe of Lake Michigan safely attains the prairie.

The Canadian Red River Settlement had only a population of about 20,000 in 1860, including French and Half-Breed, and no railway had as yet connected Lake Superior with Winnipeg. About this time an American line was completed from Chicago to St. Paul. By all the rules of geography the North-West should have become American. Steamers connected Belmont in U.S.A. and Winnipeg, and U.S.A. lines were approaching the Canadian

boundary from the south. In 1879 there was rail communication from Winnipeg to St. Paul. Artificial restraints were put
upon this natural outlet. There were discontent, rebellion, and
threats of secession. Only just in time—in 1883—was the C.P.R.
driven through to the prairies, saving them for the Empire,
opening them for the immigrant, and inaugurating that great
stream of Canadian wheat eastward.

As the attraction of the prairies was dependent upon a European wheat market, an efficient transport connection, and on the
peculiar physical conditions which here favour wheat production,
any considerable settlement was in general preceded by railway
development. More than 20 to 30 miles from farm to railway
formed as a rule a barrier to settlement, which thus tended to
spread along the extending lines and their branches.

To-day at least three-fourths of the true prairie territory is
within 20 miles of the railway, and though some major lacunæ in
the general density of settlement are still due to distance from the
station elevator, yet a map of settlements begins to show also
certain areas of lesser natural productivity. Some of these are
so obvious that they have been simply avoided by the railway,
others are within reach of the rail, but have a relatively sparse
population.

Let us proceed westward then with our description, noting as
we go these less attractive regions. Riding, Duck, and Porcupine
Mountains, all rise at least 1,200 feet above the Lake plain, and
are developed on Cretaceous rocks chiefly of two formations ; an
under one, the Benton shales (non-calcareous) of Middle Cretaceous age, and an upper one, the Niobra shales, with occasional thin beds of limestone. A shorter growing season, a forest
cover, a rougher topography, and often poorer soils make of the
scarps and summits of these plateaux, areas to be avoided. Cultivation has proceeded up their gentle south-western slopes to the
limits of the forest reserves which protect their summits. The
same is true of Turtle Mountains, the only Tertiary remnant in
Manitoba—set back of the Cretaceous scarp, and rising 700 feet
above the surrounding country—a rough bush-covered irregular
hill mass rising out of the second step. If we proceed westward
by the southern (and later) branch of the C.P.R., that which
heads for Lethbridge and the Crow's Nest Pass, we have to the
south the northward-facing scarps of similar tertiary plateaux—
increasing in area and importance to the west.

These are, in order, the Wood, Cypress, and Milk River plateaux ; all developed on cretaceous and tertiary sandstones and
clays, and usually gravel-topped. In the drier South-west Saskatchewan and South-east Alberta parts of these plateaux there is

little forest cover, but a grass or scrub covered gravelly soil with some bad land development about the scarps of circumdenudation. There are considerable areas of fair ranch country, but these southern plateaux, left well to the south of railways requiring easy gradients, have remained somewhat negative areas because of their rougher topography, usually poor soils, and towards their tabular summits, their shorter growing season. On the other hand, they present irregular but large areas of fair grazing.

The contoured sectional maps (1 inch to 3 miles) of the south-western parts of Alberta are published, and from these we see that everywhere within 10 miles west of the Cardstone-McCleod-Calgary line there is an irregular but very marked rise of some hundreds of feet from the typical plateau and plain country of the prairies to a more intricate relief ; yet though the topography of this hill country is less tabular and more intricate, one has to proceed some miles farther west before the foothill zone proper is reached, with its forest, its parallel block-faulted ridges, and its more disturbed strata. The point is rather that a little west of a line from Lethbridge to Calgary there is a fairly definite topographic limit to the prairie plains and plateaux. West of this slope there is a rapid increase of precipitation. Less definitely, too, begins the western belt of grove land, patches of aspen and open parks of Douglas fir becoming more frequent as we move to the foothills and Rockies, where forest occupies most of the country under 7,500 feet, if topographically possible.

If we continue due north from Calgary to Edmonton the general level becomes lower ; the Rockies and their foothills strike away from us to the north-west, and the western limit to present (though not to future) farming occupation is set by the forest belt which parallels this line a few miles to the west of it. Thus the limit north of Calgary ceases to be a topographical one and becomes a forest line.

A line of slight convexity from a little north of Edmonton to Winnipeg has, all the time, bush to the north and north-east of it, while to the south and south-west runs a more irregular and much broader belt of grove country than that apparent in the west. If this demarcation is to receive any attention at all, it must be clearly understood that of the land designated grove land, only a small proportion was ever occupied by forest cover. Varieties of poplar predominate with an increase of black and white spruce towards the border of the real forest cover.

This great triangle of combined grove and prairie country, with Winnipeg, Edmonton, and Carstone at its apices, includes almost the whole of the large-scale developments of farm land

and of railway plexus. But it is not all equally productive. In addition to the southern tertiary plateaux there are a great number of lower scarp-faced plateau masses, scattered irregularly, more particularly in Alberta and Western Saskatchewan. These have usually a thinner cover of glacial till than that which occurs in the surrounding lowlands, and have often also a gravel or boulder strewn summit soil, and towards their edges areas of rough topography. Such, for example, are the Black Spring Ridge and Hand Hills of Alberta. Parts of the slightly elevated tracts already referred to as Moose Mountain, Beaver, and Touchwood Hills, are of rougher topography, too, with scattered areas of sandy soil and tree cover. Again in South-western Saskatchewan, just north of Maple Creek, there is a very considerable area of rough topography called The Great Sand Hills. Then, again, although the general effect of glaciation has been to smooth and fill up the original topography somewhat, stony and sandy morainal areas are frequent, especially along the border between South Alberta and Saskatchewan and about the eastern edge of the third prairie step. Vast areas between the deeply trenched main river valleys have a very indeterminate drainage, and in the driest part of the prairie, form scattered basins of inland drainage.

In these areas the surface is dimpled with multitudes of small, irregularly distributed, shallow lakes—some of them in the drier areas with an encrusted surround of saline material. Under more favourable conditions they form a water supply for stock and a fringe of luxuriant grass for hay.

Much of the country due south of Edmonton to the Red Deer River is riddled by such lakes, some of them, such as Beaver Hill Lake and Buffalo Lake, being of considerable extent. But apart altogether from these bigger manifestations of relief and cover, the general prairie country is seldom perfectly level. The smooth curves over large areas are apt to be interrupted by belts riddled with small depressions, with ponds and marshes, with hummocks and gullies too small to show even on a detailed map ; breaking the monotony of the foreground, but themselves repeated as each new landscape comes to view.

No single topographical feature on the prairie proper is so well marked, so abrupt, as are the steep sides of the trenches formed by all the large streams along their whole course across the Alberta plateau. Though over considerable areas, almost every farm has its little piece of rough topography, and of marsh or lake ; these are not such as to effect ultimate close settlement. A much more vital factor is the gradual decrease in effective precipitation in the plains of South-east Alberta and South-west

Saskatchewan. This minimum rainfall area is indicated on the map shown (Fig. 108). The rainfall here is less than 13 inches on the average, and it is irregular. E.g., at Medicine Hat it reached a minimum of 6·9 in. in 1907 and a maximum of 17·9 in. in 1916. In the period 1905–22 the average annual precipitation was 11·4 in. In detail this semi-arid land has small areas of white alkali soil ; small areas almost barren of vegetation ; and a few areas of real sand-dune ; while large areas are grassed so sparsely as to be easily over-stocked. In a good year some of the best wheats of Canada are produced here. The area, like the enclosing hills to west and south, was once

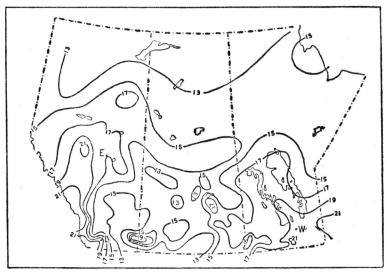

FIG. 108.—Average Annual Total Precipitation in the Prairie Provinces.
E, Edmonton. L, Lethbridge. W, Winnipeg.

ranch country, and apart from irrigation, should revert to this use.

The standing difficulty of the ranchers was winter feed for the cattle. When the ranch was not over-stocked the sun-cured grass provided a meagre sustenance. The snow cover was light and disappeared quickly under the chinook influence. In spite of the frequent severe frosts, the cattle were often without shelter, save for such as nature provided in gullies and brushwood. The first farmers entered to help the big cattle men, farmed for themselves and their work-animals, and gradually, with patchy irrigation, began to provide winter feed crops. Then the numbers became too great for this function, and the climate of a cycle of years too dry for unirrigated wheat farming. Many farms here have been abandoned, and the grass country has not been improved by the drifting soils and weed development which marks this neglected arable land. For future development we may look to this, and to some of the better watered surrounding foothill country, as a ranch land once more, supplemented by irrigated lands on which fodder crops will have the most impor-

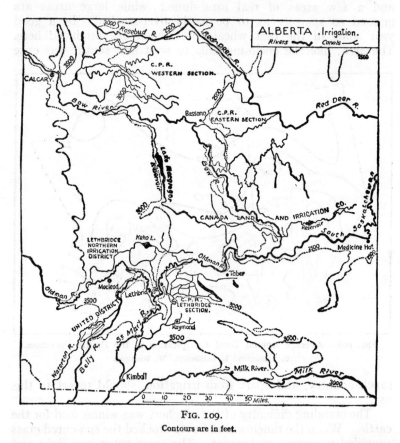

FIG. 109.

Contours are in feet.

tant place. And this brings us to the subject of irrigation in the Prairie Provinces (Fig. 109).

The areas irrigable by present works lie for the most part between and about the great **V** of land in Western Alberta formed by the Bow and Old Man Rivers, which unite to form the South Saskatchewan, and derive their supplies from the heavier precipitation of the Rockies and foothills. Fig. 109 shows the offtake

on the rivers concerned, and the main canal systems. There are
no storage works in the mountain zone, the maximum flow corresponding to the opening of a short growing season.
The two C.P.R. irrigation sections are among the biggest
works on the continent, and their completion has entailed a very
large expenditure. Most of the land of the western district is
occupied, but there is still much for sale in the eastern area.
When we examine the area actually irrigated in any year, we
find a considerable discrepancy between what is irrigable with
the present works, and what is irrigated ; and we find also that
there are very large variations from year to year in the amount
put under the ditch. The fact is that the preparation of the land
for irrigation is laborious and expensive. The farmers in the
western C.P.R. area are apt to pray for rain, and to take their
chance of growing wheat without irrigation. In the eastern district it is naturally drier, and farmers do not wait for a dry cycle
of years to make use of the water.
The price at which this land is available is certainly not un-
reasonable, yet it is not merely nominal, as it has been for much
homesteading in the country. There are other difficulties, by no
means insuperable, in the way of rapid development. The labour
which can manage an all-wheat farm of 320 acres unirrigated,
can hardly use one-fourth to one-third of that area for intensive
irrigation farming. The newcomer, again, lacks experience in
the use of water. Then there is the provision of a market for
the bigger range of rotation crops which should be grown if the
best use is to be made of the land. Spring wheat is still the chief
crop even under irrigation. But alfalfa, timothy, and oats, are

IRRIGATION TABLE

Project	Source	Irrigable Area. Acres	Irrigated Area, 1935. Acres
C.P.R. Western . . .	Bow River	218,980	19,109
C.P.R. Lethbridge . .	St. Mary River	100,000	70,000
Canada Land	Bow River	130,000	22,694
Taber	St. Mary River	21,499	19,471
Lethbridge Northern . .	Oldman River	96,871	73,022
United	Belly River	34,166	12,000
Eastern	Bow River	250,000	143,997
Raymond	St. Mary River	15,130	13,000
Others	Bow, St. Mary and Highwood Rivers	14,631	6,366
Total	. . . .	881,277	379,659

usual crops, and in the extreme south-west of Alberta on the St. Mary River irrigation systems, the production of cantalupe and water melons gives some idea of the climatic possibilities.

Thus about 40 per cent. of the land at present rendered irrigable is under the ditch. A gigantic scheme to irrigate about 1½ million acres by use of the North Saskatchewan has not yet reached the stage of practical politics.

A certain historical, economic, and geographical setting has made the prairie a farm area still predominantly devoted to wheat. It was begun early enough to serve the then expanding British market, and late enough to take over in some measure

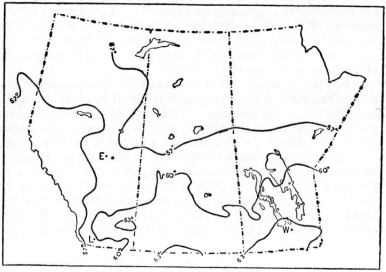

FIG. 110.—Mean Summer (June, July and August) Temperature of Prairie Provinces.
E, Edmonton. L, Lethbridge. W, Winnipeg.

the rôle of exporter from the U.S.A., whose supply was limited at times by bad seasons, and a growing home market. The policy of land settlement—by no means perfect—meant at any rate for the initially unmoneyed settler large farms at extraordinarily low prices, and the possibility of a modest competence. Of course, farms have since changed hands, especially after the war, at prices which leave the new tenants in difficulties; yet much good land still remains on a homesteading basis in outlying districts for any who are not work-shy.

Geographically there was the level, open surface, the good soil, a climate in general more favourable to high-grade wheat

than to any other crop, and adversely, what in any other age,
would have been a quite insuperable difficulty of outlet. With the
general topography we have already dealt. What of soil ? We
have come to regard climate as the chief agent controlling the
character of the soil. Climate will not in any immediate sense
put lime, potash, phosphorus, and nitrogen into a soil ; but it
may, through its controlling effect on natural vegetation, induce
a humus condition which will render and keep these elements
available ; will conserve moisture ; and will favour tilth. Climate, vegetation and soil do not co-operate quite as a co-equal
trinity ; for with climate is the initiative. Whatever the basis

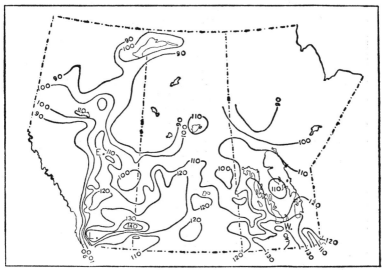

Fig. 111.—Average Length in Days of Frost-free Period in the Prairie Provinces.
E, Edmonton. L, Lethbridge. W, Winnipeg.

of the future generalized soil classification, it will certainly not
be one which will diminish the significance of the major climatic
region in geography.

The general facts of the severity of prairie winters are too well
known to keep us here. The generally extremely low winter
temperature, however, is liable to sudden breaks, the incidence
and intensity of these increasing to the west. The July shade
averages in Southern Alberta are 5–7 degrees higher than that
of London, but the sun temperatures are proportionately higher
still, and the periods of sunlight more prolonged. Over most
of the area 75 per cent. of the precipitation falls between April 1

tion to any other crop, and adversely, what to any other use would have been a quite unappreciable difficulty. . . . With the

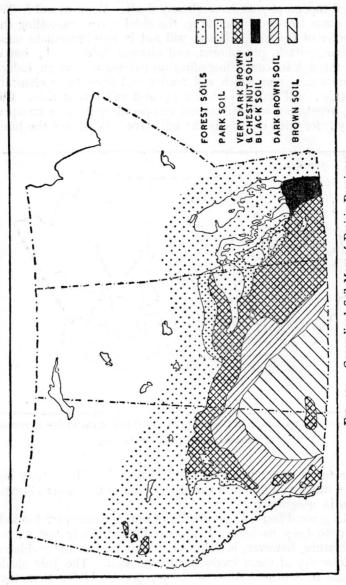

FIG. 112.—Generalized Soil Map of Prairie Provinces.

FOREST SOILS

PARK SOIL

VERY DARK BROWN & CHESTNUT SOILS
BLACK SOIL

DARK BROWN SOIL

BROWN SOIL

and October 31. To quote Mr. Wyatt, the soil chemist of Alberta, "the climatic conditions favour intensive and rapid growth for a period of the year coinciding with the greatest rainfall, followed by dry, cold weather which delays and often almost immediately prevents the decomposition and loss of organic matters and plant foods until the following spring, when temperature and moisture again permit the rapid preparation of food for plants at a time when they are in greatest demand."

Such conditions have been responsible for the vegetation covering these plains, and this native vegetation has been responsible for the nitrogenous and organic content of the soils.

The Great Plains soil belt and its members, from black to brown, extends and widens to the Rockies in the prairie provinces. The soil over very large areas has been developed on unreassorted glacial till, derived from the local, largely calcareous, shales and sandstones, and to a much less extent from the Rockies in the west, and the Laurentian elements in the east. Much of the lower lands have been occupied by evanescent glacial lakes, the more permanent of which, such as Lake Agassiz and Lake Saskatchewan, were to the east, where are the largest areas of lacustrine subsoils.

Now just as we have been at some pains to emphasize the local variation in topography, so we must insist on a great variety of soils ; often exhibited, as the soil analyses of Shutt and Wyatt clearly show, within quite small areas. However, in all three. provinces by far the greater proportion of the land has soils which set the region very high among the large-scale farming areas of the world. The usually high available N content is the most important, and the most characteristic quality. Available P and K contents are usually up to the general standard of fertile soils. Acidity and alkalinity are more variable, and there are scattered moist spots which drained and limed would give excellent results.

A whole set of influences promoted wheat production. Wheat is admirably suited to a short sunny growing season, to a light rainfall, and to the extensive unskilled machine-farming of a sparse population of immigrants, and was the only crop which would bear the transport charges. Even so, areas of production waited on the railways, and if we except some Peace River developments, very little is now hauled more than 20 miles to the railway. Save for a very recent slight resuscitation of the South-west Alberta winter wheat area, nothing but spring wheat is grown. The climate favours the production of hard, strong, glutinous wheats, admirable for mixing with the bulky starchy

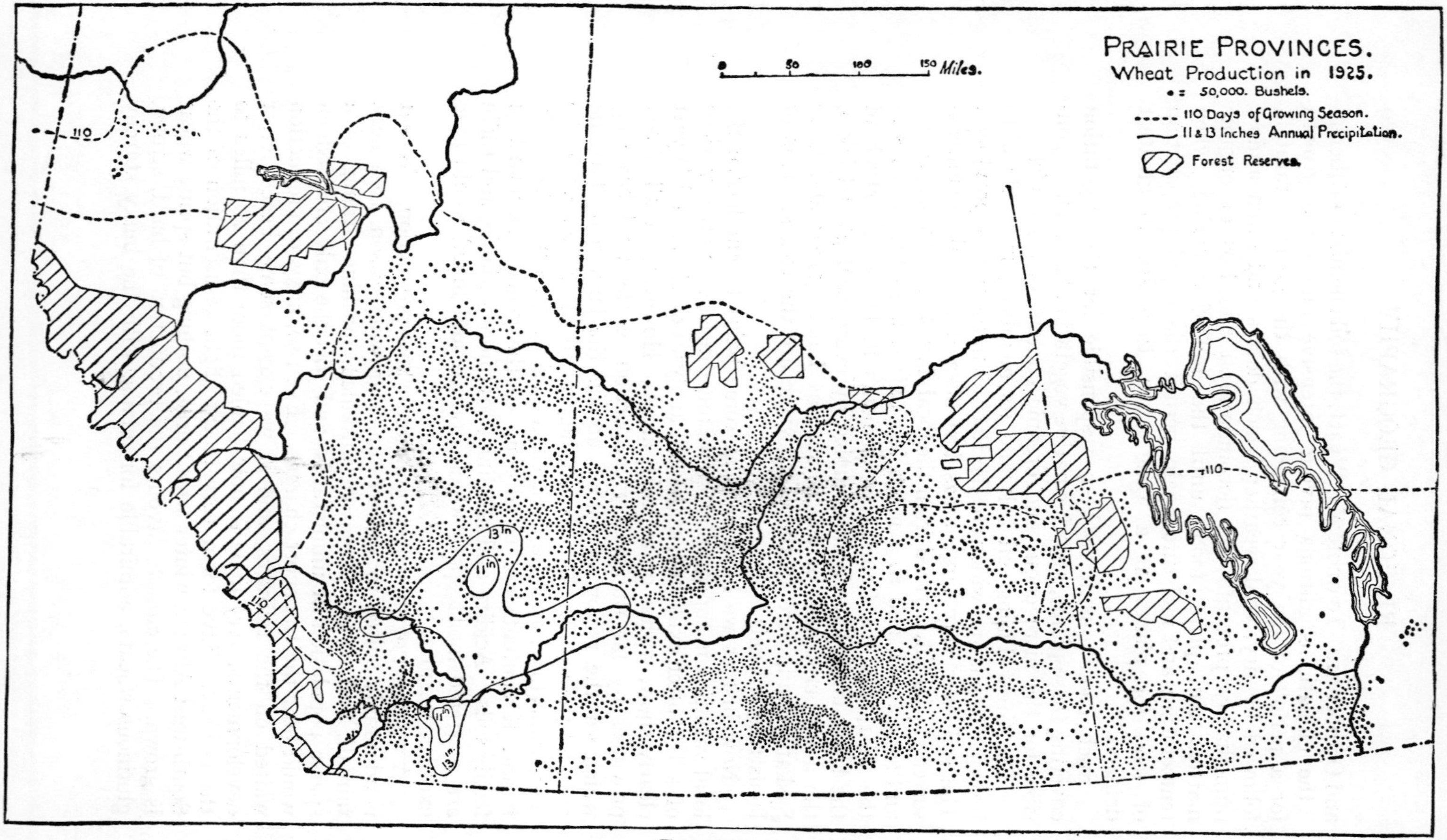

PRAIRIE PROVINCES.
Wheat Production in 1925.
• = 50,000. Bushels.
- - - - 110 Days of Growing Season.
———— 11 & 13 Inches Annual Precipitation.
▨ Forest Reserves.

0   50   100   150 Miles.

FIG. 113.

The forest reserves are under Government management, all the Indian tribes and the northern zones.

grain of milder and wetter regions. Nevertheless the growing season is short and much of the safe extension of the wheat area has gone step by step with the production of ever quicker varieties. Red Fife, Marquis, Ruby, and now Garnet, show progress in this respect, and reflect great credit on the laboratories concerned. In an area of marginal rainfall the crop shows greater correspondence with precipitation than with any other climatic element. The weather is not always favourable. A dry late spring ; the summer furnace winds of the dry belt ; hail storms which reduce a wheat-field to a pitted black puddle ; night frost in early August which shrivels the grain in the milk— all and each are capable of wrecking hopes in what had promised to be a good season. Happy the farmer who has got a bumper harvest of No. 1 grain to the station elevator or loading platform and with the price still high at Liverpool. Often the farmer grows nothing but wheat, uses motor machinery, or ekes out his horses on the prairie wool, a little hay, and some bought feed to strengthen them before the great spring push. For motors by no means do all the work. The horse is still an economic animal, more particularly when there are 6–8 of him with a modern plough or combined harvester behind.

What are the penalties of wheat-mining ? Diminishing fertility ; soil drifting ; weeds ; a dependence on one product ; and perhaps, a too specialized skill are all promoted by the practice. As to fertility, this diminishes at first rapidly, then more slowly, to a dead level, which would be very low indeed in some of the poorer forest soils. Yet there are Red River soils of thirty years' cropping which are still classed as very good. With the light rainfall of the prairie, summer fallow and cultivation are necessary to conserve moisture. Strong winds, dry weather, and loss of humus, result in soil drifting, exaggerated sometimes by careless cultivation. The lack of crop variety, and of intertilled crops, favours alike wheat disease and weeds. The Manitoba Ministry of Agriculture has a department of Weeds and Publications. It needs it. Fig. 114 is a Land Utilization map. Note the wheat area fringed by a mixed farming area of greater effective precipitation, of usually shorter growing season and slightly lesser temperatures. Here oats, barley, rye, rotate or take the place of wheat, most of the two former being grown for stock. Inside this belt wheat and fallow still predominate, and wheat is often the sole crop. Let us remember that the farmer, like most of the rest of us, works for what he supposes to be his more or less immediate economic advantage, and if rotations are such as to produce an excess of utility crops, for which he cannot find a farm use or a market, he is not likely to adopt them merely from a scientific anxiety as to the welfare of posterity. The aridity, too, of much of the area limits the adoption of some

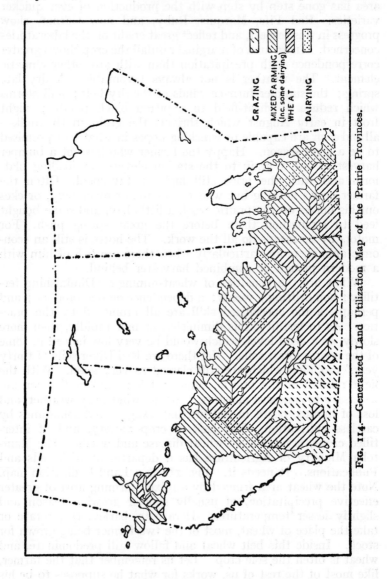

FIG. 114.—Generalized Land Utilization Map of the Prairie Provinces.

GRAZING

MIXED FARMING
(inc. some dairying)

WHEAT

DAIRYING

rotations that would be otherwise attractive. The greatest divergence from purely wheat farming is favoured in three areas, (i) by the age of development, the big city population, and the greater moisture, in the Winnipeg district ; (ii) by a climate generally more suitable for other crops, in the grove lands ; (iii) by irrigation, in the south-west.

In the whole of the Provinces and throughout their history, one economic question looms large ; that of transportation, and particularly of outlet. It has ever been a political question. Lord Selkirk's settlement was, in minor degree, an agricultural oasis in a land of huntsmen. It had at first no outlet for agricultural produce, and later when such produce was shipped, its first water and rail connections were with Minnesota and the U.S.A. Lake ports. The present routeing is shown in Fig. 115. The Hudson Bay railway from The Pas to Port Churchill was opened in 1929. Churchill is 978 miles from Winnipeg, and as near to Liverpool as is Montreal. Navigation is possible for from three to four months each year, i.e. in the late summer and autumn, and so at a time to relieve the peak shipment of wheat. An elevator has been constructed at Churchill, but so far the wheat shipment has been rather disappointing. The line passes near a number of recently opened mining camps on the Laurentian field, and is rendering possible the exploitation of these. Surveying and prospecting over the difficult country of the Shield has been enormously facilitated by the use of aeroplanes and, in this country of innumerable lakes, of motor boats. From The Pas a branch line has opened up the important Mandy and Flin Flon mining camps. Since 1921 Vancouver has entered the lists as a competing outlet, and with success. Panama, a growing Asian market, and a period of low ocean freights favoured the initiation of this movement, which has made Vancouver the second wheat port of the continent.

The economic weakness of dependence on one crop was tragically demonstrated during the 1930's when wheat prices were often below the cost of production. The prairie wheat farmer is handicapped by having to depend on a cash crop which, in such a climate, is of very variable yield, and of having to sell in the world market in which the price of wheat is also very variable.[1] The world market is supplied from such widespread sources that a low yield in any particular exporting country is by no means modified by a corresponding increase in price, and the running costs of the farm are much the same whatever the variation in yield and price. Nor in such a climate and with so limited an immediate urban market is diversification an easy matter.

The Prairie Provinces are often thought to fall between Laurentian and Cordilleran stools in the matter of mineral production and water power. To some extent, perhaps—excepting the case

[1] Apart from war conditions.

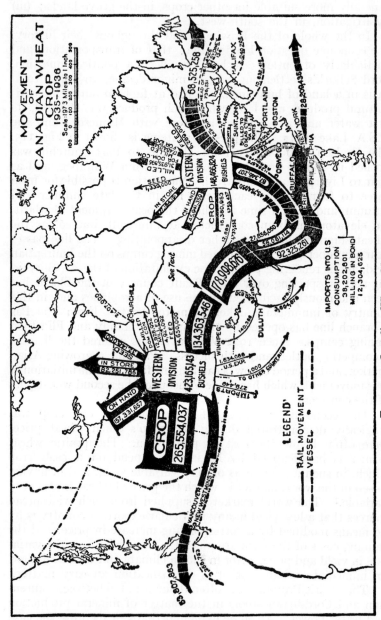

Fig. 115.—Canadian Wheat Movement.

(From the "Grain Trade of Canada," 1936. Ottawa.)

of sub-bituminous coal—this is true of the prairies proper, but not of the area covered by the provinces themselves, which extends to include on either side portions of the Shield and of the Cordillera.

We can give the matter but a moment's consideration. The characteristics of forest, mineral and power wealth, by which the Shield attracts capital and on which it depends for development, are evinced in that part of this physiographic division which lies in North-eastern Manitoba. A line built 80 miles north from near The Pas on the H.B. Railway reaches the great Flin Flon and Mandy copper and zinc ore bodies ; while 20 miles east of Lake Winnipeg the Manigatagan Valley is a very promising gold district. Manitoba has developed 390,000 h.p. practically all from the Winnipeg River. On the Lower Churchill and Nelson, too distant at present, are the greatest undeveloped powers on the continent, estimated at 3,000,000 h.p.

In the Cretaceous cover of the western and south-west prairie provinces, at three horizons, the conditions of deposition favoured coal formation. These horizons are the Lower Division of the Edmonton, the Upper of the Belly River, and much lower down, the Kootenay of the Lower Cretaceous. With regard to the two former, east of the foothill zone, a major broad syncline, on an axis from Edmonton southwards, buries the Edmonton formation under a thick cover of barren (Paskapoo) strata. The mining belts flank this syncline, as also the broad anticline which succeeds it to the east, from the summit of which the coal formations have been denuded.

The coal passes from sub-bituminous through bituminous to some anthracite as we move westward to the mountain mining areas. Only when we are well within the Cordilleran area does the Kootenay series of the Lower Cretaceous come to the surface ; not continuously, or with little deformation, but in basins of deformed strata, preserved in the angles between one great fault block and the next.

A string of such isolated, elongated basins of Kootenay coal-bearing rocks, each surrounded by Palæozoic material, runs nearly but not quite parallel to the interprovincial boundary and nowhere far from the Front Range itself. It is this Rocky Mountain foothill zone which produces the best coals. Yet they present greater mining difficulties. The seams are more disturbed and communications are more difficult than on the prairie, where large areas with shallow, undisturbed and persistent seams compensate for the low quality of the coal—a coal frequently containing much ash and moisture, and which crumbles on prolonged exposure, and has a low calorific value. Of the western best-quality coals the railways take the greater part, and use them until they run within the range of American coals landed at Port Arthur. The lower-grade prairie coals are used particularly when they are accessible in the neighbourhood of big centres, such as Edmonton and Lethbridge, or are present under exceptionally favourable mining conditions, as when they outcrop about the river gorge at Drumheller, 80 miles east-north-east of Calgary.

In 1936 the Prairie Provinces (chiefly from Alberta) produced 6·7 million tons, i.e., nearly 50 per cent. of the total Canadian production of that year. They now receive little from the U.S.A., but Alberta sends large quantities to the other two provinces.

Coal mining is predominantly a winter occupation. In Alberta it employs twice as many men in January as in July. There are 341 mines, yet nearly all the coal is produced from about a dozen large electrically equipped plants with, of course, railway connections. Small mines without railway connections provide a few tons to the carts of farmers in the locality.

An increase in bituminous mining will further militate against U.S.A. imports. At big population centres, Edmonton, Lethbridge and Calgary, for instance, power stations will increasingly use the prairie coal ; and lastly, if political influence can be sufficiently brought to bear, Albertan coal may enter populous Southern Ontario at freight prices very possibly below the cost of transport ; for this mode of indirect taxation is within the competency of a Board of Railway Commissioners and a National Railway.

The most striking development of power resources in the prairies during the past decade was the bringing in of the Imperial Leduc No. 1 oil well south-west of Edmonton in 1947. Subsequent drilling proved extensive reserves and by 1952 some 2,800 wells were in production. Prior to this discovery there was a small production from the Turner Valley in Southern Alberta and from a field at Lloydminster to the east.

In 1950 a pipeline over 1,000 miles in length was built from Edmonton to Lake Superior and the oil is taken by tanker to the refineries at Sarnia. A 700-mile pipeline is under construction from Edmonton to Vancouver. The output to-day (1953) represents about 40 per cent. of Canada's consumption.

Winnipeg is old enough to have had its siting affected by similar geographical conditions to those operative in the cases of so many cities of the American plains. The site of the present city was known as Les Fourches to the French voyageurs, and for many years after the establishment of Lord Selkirk's Scottish colonists (1811–15) it was still known as the Forks. It is, in fact, at the junction of two navigable streams, the Red River and the Assiniboine, in that narrow gap of relatively open country between the thick bush which extends from the north to the southern extremities of Lake Winnipeg, and the international boundary. During the period when the settlement was under the ægis of the Hudson Bay Company, their local head-quarters were at Fort Gary within the confines of the present city. When the Canadian Government took over the North-west Territory from the Hudson Bay Company there were about 200 inhabitants of Winnipeg (then called Fort Gary) which became Government head-quarters. Growth became rapid after the junction effected in 1883 by the C.P.R. between Winnipeg and the Great Lakes. From that time the Prairie Provinces had an effective outlet and development conformed to the fan-like expansion of the prairie belt west of Winnipeg ; thus the Winnipeg railway plexus became a point of concentration for all that passed in or out of the prairies. To-day the city has a quarter of a million inhabitants and is a very important wholesale distributing and manufacturing centre with a large electric power supply generated on the Winnipeg River and with American coal imported from the head of the lakes. Here the great train-loads of box cars (each car carrying from 1,000 to 1,600 bushels of wheat) are marshalled for inspection before proceeding to the lakes. There are great flour mills, meat-packing and car-repairing industries, and a host of minor ones.

Edmonton and Calgary at the other extremity of the prairies are considerable and rapidly growing cities. Calgary, on the Bow River, is almost at the junction of prairies and foot-hill country, on a river whose upper valley leads to the gap in the Rockies used by the C.P.R. West of Edmonton the prairies are limited by heavy bush rather than by topography, and the Yellowhead Pass of the Rockies is far away to the west.

Edmonton was the site of important forts of the Hudson Bay Company and North-West Fur Company, built in 1808, when forts a little lower down had been destroyed by the Indians. From these forts the trappers began their journeys into the northern wilds, and the North Saskatchewan, though swift, was navigable from this point down-stream. Rapid growth came only with the railways in 1905, and Edmonton is now a very important junction, with a population practically the same as that of Calgary, which the C.P.R. reached in 1883-4.

Edmonton (capital and university town of Alberta) is a coal-producing centre (see Fig. 116), and uses natural gas piped from wells at Viking, 80 miles to the east. It maintains its historic connection with the North-West, but now by railways connecting with the great northern navigable stream of the Mackenzie Basin, and with the Peace River mixed farming country. Meat packing, milling, dairy factories, are among its chief industries, the range and variety of which is rapidly extending.

Calgary, at the confluence of the Bow and Elbow rivers, had its origin in a fort of the Royal Canadian Mounted Police

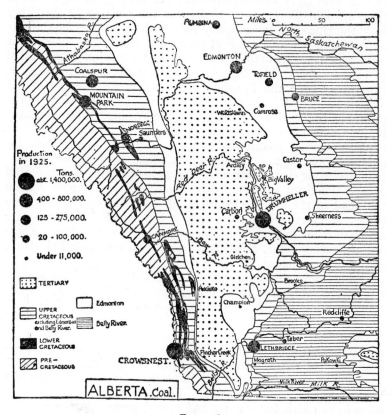

FIG. 116.

established in 1876. It is at the meeting zone of foothill ranch, of prairie, and of irrigated country, and at a gateway to the Rockies. Coal mines are near, but not actually in the vicinity as at Edmonton. Natural gas is piped from Bow Island, 160 miles away. Cereal preparation, meat packing, flour milling, saddlery are among the more important of a very varied and growing list of manufactures. Regina (capital of Saskatchewan) and Saskatoon (on the South Saskatchewan) are distributing centres for the surrounding prairies and are rapidly developing local manufacture. Considerable recent farming development has taken place in what is known as the Peace River country. The Peace River leaves the Rocky Mountains through a cañon country terminating at Hudson's Hope, from which point it is navigable to Vermillion Chutes. Between Hudson's Hope and Peace River Crossing, there are considerable areas, not far from the river on either side, of good agricultural land, some of which is open prairie or grove land. The growing season is rather longer than immediately to the north or south and there is less muskeg swamp. The chinook influence is frequently felt and the precipitation suffices for general agriculture. This district is at present reached by the line running from Edmonton, first due northward, and then westward, skirting Lesser Slave Lake. It then branches to Peace River Crossing to the north and Grand Prairie to the west. It is estimated that in the aggregate there are some twelve million acres of land about the Middle Peace basin, which is suitable for agriculture, though from 70 to 80 per cent. of it would require fairly heavy clearing. Much of the oases of prairie land have already been taken up. Farming here is mixed and dairy, though some wheat is grown. The difficulty lies in the relative inaccessibility of the region. There is no network of railway and few roads. Produce is sometimes hauled 60–70 miles to the railway, and then there is the handicap of 300–400 miles by rail before Edmonton is reached. A western outlet is being seriously considered, either due west past Hudson's Hope to the valley of the Parsnip River, or south-west via Pine Pass to the same valley.

The settlements in the main natural divisions of Canada— The Maritime Provinces, The French St. Lawrence, The Ontario Peninsula, The Prairie Provinces, and British Columbia—have each suffered a well-defined system of geographic influences. These have been, and are, quite obviously reflected in the politics of the various provinces. This is particularly true of the Prairie Provinces where, naturally enough, low tariffs and low freights are ever to the fore among political questions. Problems peculiar to the Prairie Provinces are likely to arise also, because a very large proportion of recent immigrants are of Eastern and South-Eastern European origin. There is some tendency too for the Canadian, American and British-born farmers to migrate to the growing towns leaving their farms to such immigrants.

CHAPTER XXXIV

BRITISH COLUMBIA AND MACKENZIE RIVER BASIN

BRITISH COLUMBIA is the cordilleran province of Canada. From the international boundary to lat. 54° the eastern limit of the province is the Rocky Mountain watershed. From about lat. 54° northward, however, it is the meridian of 120° W. long. Lat. 60° N. forms the northern boundary between the province and Yukon and the North-West Territory. Important areas east of the Rockies, then, about the Upper Liard and Upper Peace River, are included in British Columbia. The Alaskan panhandle occupies a coastal strip as far south as 55° N. lat. So delimited British Columbia has an area of 355,855 square miles, an area equal to that of the British Isles, France, Belgium, and Holland combined—all coastal countries in similar latitudes, which together support a population of about 100 millions. But North-west Europe and North-west North America are really very unlike, even climatically. With its great succession of parallel ranges set across the path of the prevailing westerlies, British Columbia experiences variations in climate—as from place to place—quite unknown in Western Europe.

As we shall see, the province as a whole is extraordinarily rich in minerals, in lumber, and in power resources. It is very largely undeveloped, and will support many times its present insignificant population ; yet its maximum possible population will bear little relation to its actual area, for very large portions of the province are mountainous, while others lack a sufficiency of precipitation.[1]

Let us examine a little its relief. An orographical map (Fig. 117) indicates at once that the main physiographical features of the Pacific Cordillera in the Northern U.S.A. are continued into British Columbia. We note the high barrier in the east—the Rocky Mountains proper—and the high Coast Range [2] of British

---

[1] An official estimate gives 22 million acres as the land suitable for agricultural development, i.e. about one-tenth of the whole area of the province.

[2] Structurally, quite distinct from the Coast Ranges of Washington, Oregon, and California.

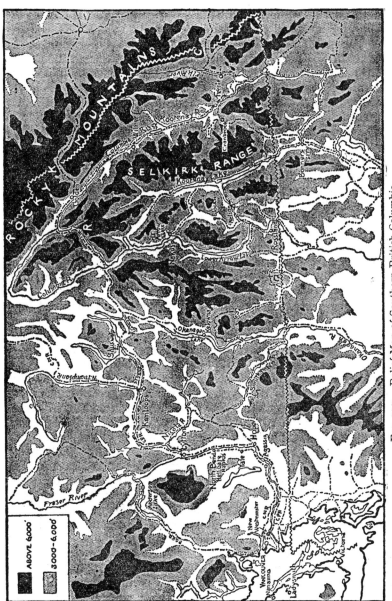

Fig. 117.—Relief Map of Southern British Columbia.
K, Kicking Horse Pass ; R, Roger's Pass ; C, Crow's Nest Pass.

Columbia, corresponding to the Cascades of Washington. The Queen Charlotte Sound and Straits of Georgia are the analogues of Puget Sound and the Willamette-Cowlitz Valley. Vancouver and Queen Charlotte Isles correspond to the Coast Ranges of Washington. Then the mountainous country between the Coast Range and the Gold Range is lower than either, and its hill summit masses have generally accordant levels, so that we have something corresponding to the Interior Plateaux of the U.S.A.

Though we can recognize this continuity of the physical divisions, we should notice in British Columbia, as compared with the States—

    (i) the decreasing width of the whole cordilleran system ;
    (ii) the decreasing height of the system as we go north ;
    (iii) the extraordinarily continuous great trough-like longitudinal river valleys.

Rocks of all ages occur within the province, and their strike is generally parallel to the present mountain ranges, which have resulted from foldings, fracturings, and uplift induced by pressures from the west. This is not to suggest that the present structure and the geological history are simple—in few regions are they more complicated.

The most striking topographical features—and the most important in this mountain province—are the great valley trenches. These supply—in the aggregate—a large area of fertile irrigable land. They supply also a succession of cross-routes between the few—there will never be many—routes which cross the province from east to west, i.e. against the grain of the land. The Rocky Mountain Trench is the most remarkable of these features. It stretches for more than 1,000 miles from the Flathead River valley in Montana to Yukon territory, and carries in different portions, at different levels, the upper waters of the Columbia, Kootenay, and Fraser rivers. It follows a gigantic fault west of the Rocky Mountains.[1] This great range to the east is not to be considered a single mountain mass. It consists of ridge after ridge separated by high valleys in sympathy with the general north-to-south strike of the rocks. Above the forest line are exposed bare jagged limestone edges. In a dozen or more localities the mountains rise above 10,000 feet, and the whole range forms the first and most formidable of the many barriers to east-west communication in British Columbia. " The serrated nature of their crest lines, the massive pyramidal and roughly prismatic forms of certain isolated peaks, and the impressive alternation of the colours in their relatively thick component strata, distinguish them from the other western mountains."

[1] Canada, Department of Mines. Memoir 23, p. 12.

Between the Rocky Mountains (i.e. the mountains east of the great Rocky Mountain Trench) and the Coast Range, the country is blocked out in a series of great river bends in echelon. Thus the bend of the Fraser forms the apex of a great triangle bounded by the Fraser River itself on the west, and by the Rocky Mountain Trench in the east. The Thompson River and Lake Okanagan form an irregular western side of an inner triangle having its apex opposite the Yellowhead Pass. Within this again is a third valley triangle, of which the western side is the Columbia River and Arrow Lakes, and the apex is the Great Bend of the Columbia. The Upper Columbia, the Upper Kootenay, and Lake Kootenay almost divide off a fourth triangular unit. Roger's Pass in the Purcell Range, the east and west tributaries of the Columbia about Revelstoke, the Shuswap Lake and Thompson Rivers, and Kamloops Lake, provide a line of weakness by which the Canadian Pacific Railway cuts right across the series of ranges, to the Fraser at Lytton.

The student should make himself familiar with these major valley systems (see Fig. 117), for in the mountainous country of Southern British Columbia they define alike the possible routes, and the areas of agricultural development. The Columbia River rises in Columbia Lake in the Rocky Mountain Trench. At the southern end of the lake is a settlement called Canal Flats. At this point only a few miles of low-lying gravel separates the lake from the Kootenay River, which here enters the Rocky Mountain Trench from the east, after a course of some 80 miles in one of the Rocky Mountain inter-range valleys. The subsequent course of the two great rivers is such that a canal connecting them here would make of the whole Kootenay country an island including within its valley limit the gigantic ranges of the Purcell and Selkirk systems. This was actually done for a period, and in a very rough way, but as the whole valley from Beavermouth to the international boundary is now threaded by the railway, it is unlikely that a modern work will be undertaken, especially as the navigation of both the rivers is very inferior, and becomes impossible on the Columbia in the rapids of the little-known Big Bend country, and on the Kootenay in its mountain gorge excursion into Montana. The Rocky Mountain Trench forms a convenient route for a line joining the Canadian Pacific Railway, which enters British Columbia via the Kicking Horse Pass (5,332 feet), and the southern branch, which breaches the Rockies in the Crow's Nest Pass (4,453 feet) (Fig. 117). It is a deeply cut trough with forested sides and open, park-like, flat valley bottom. Of the major inhabited valleys of British Columbia it is the highest—everywhere over 2,000 feet,

18

and closely enclosed by mountains which rise everywhere to over 6,000 feet. Although warm summer temperatures are experienced (av. July > 62), the growing season is noticeably shorter than in the great fruit valleys farther west (e.g. Thompson River, Okanagan, etc.). The mid-winter temperatures (e.g. Jan., 12° F. at Wilmer) are also much lower. Precipitation increases to the north, but is only 13 inches at Wilmer and 18 inches at Golden. The open park-like valley of the Kootenay gives way to " gloomy defiles through a maze of rugged mountains "[1] in Montana. Kootenay Lake is a deep fiord-like depression with little room for agricultural land. The evolution of the rail system in this great lake area of British Columbia suggests—what is a fact—the linking up of lake steamer routes.

West of the Gold Ranges, and east of the Coast Range, we have the region of Interior Plateaux of British Columbia. It includes not one plateau, but several. The generally accordant broad summit levels suggest peneplanation, and the present deep valleys a subsequent uplift. The valleys of this district, e.g. the Thompson River, the Nicola, the Okanagan, the Similkameen, are famous for their fruit production. The temperatures are the highest reached in British Columbia, the growing season is longer than in the more easterly valleys and the winter's cold less intense. Irrigation is everywhere necessary, however, for the precipitation is usually under 13 inches per annum, with a tendency to a winter maximum. The hill masses are often forested, but with a smaller and sparser timber than that of the Coast Range. The lowlands have a semi-arid vegetation of sage-bush, cactus, and bull-pine. The uplands have scattered areas of open grass lands, and of open yellow pine forest.

We have given *average* climatic figures elsewhere, so perhaps local differences may be illustrated by some *actual* figures (1926) for these fruit-growing valleys, and for a few other districts for purposes of comparison.

Dry-belt Fruit-growing Districts	Highest T. F.°	Lowest T. F.°	Ppt. Rain, In.	Snow, In.
S. Okanagan Valley (Penticton) .	104·0	2	8·07	10·8
Similkameen (Hedley) . .	103·0	–8	8·02	18·6

The West Kootenay valleys have similar temperatures but more rain and snow—irrigation is frequently unnecessary, though always beneficial.

West Kootenay (Nelson) . .	100·3	–1	19·02	81·4

---

[1] " The Kootenay Country," by W. A. Baillie Grolman, in " R.G.J.," 1918, p. 44.

Finally as an example of the Rocky Mountain Trench, where the winters are too long and too intense for fruit growing, yet the north-south valley so deep that the precipitation is small, i.e. :—

N. Columbia River (Golden) . 95·0 −29·0 9·38 56·4

It should be noticed that the Arrow Lake Country and the West Kootenay valleys are much moister than the hot, dry valleys of the premier fruit districts (Okanagan, Similkameen and Nicola) or than the Middle Fraser valley (Soda Creek nearly to Yale, below which town the Fraser valley has a heavy rainfall), or again than the relatively cool but dry Rocky Mountain Trench. In the hot, dry valleys, the irrigation water at convenient levels is somewhat limited. The chief fruit orchards in the Okanagan valley are on the bench lands and deltas of white silt which were formed in glacial times when the lake was much higher than at present. When water from lateral streams is available, these are irrigated for fruit and truck farming. Even in this one valley—the most important fruit-farming area in British Columbia—there are climatic differences which are expressed in character of fruit grown, and the season of ripening. The southward continuation of the valley, i.e. from Penticton to the international boundary, is the hottest driest part, and has the longest growing season. Here considerable irrigation works are in progress, and the district should develop because of its relatively early harvest. The lake is served by combined passenger and freight steamers, which go from Penticton to Okanagan Landing, whence a railway reaches the main line in the relatively moist and densely forested region about Sicamous.

After the Okanagan and Similkameen valleys, those of West Kootenay and the Boundary country are the most productive.

Apples are the most important fruit, but plums, prunes and cherries, and in the southern Okanagan, peaches and apricots, are produced to a considerable extent. There is a tendency to rely less on purely fruit farming and to develop truck farming. The production of tomatoes, onions, and celery is important. Also alfalfa is irrigated, and there is some dairy-farming. The very open woodland on the plateaux above the valleys of the dry belt provides excellent summer grazing.

The Middle Fraser is deeply incised as far as Soda Creek, but below the junction of the Chilcotin the neighbouring interior plateaux are lower than in the south of the Province. There are considerable areas between 1,000 feet and 3,000 feet in the basin of the Chilcotin, around Prince George, and in the tributary basin of the Nechako. The Chilcotin country is rather dry and is used as a ranch country, though areas in it are susceptible to dry farming.

The Prince George and Nechako basins have rather more pre-cipitation (e.g. Prince George 18 inches) and are wooded but with much park land. The July average temperatures are lower (Prince George 59° F., cp. Penticton 69° F.), and the growing season shorter. Oats, hay and vegetables do excellently, and these relative lowlands should make excellent dairying and mixed farming areas. Already much of the land near the railway in the Nechako valley is taken up. As one approaches Prince Rupert the country becomes definitely mountainous, and the precipitation heavy, though the Bulkely valley, also, is a very promising general-farming district.

Thus it is in North Central British Columbia that there are extensive areas suitable for general farming. The area has only been threaded by the Grand Trunk since 1914, and the war years were a serious drawback to development. The southern valleys of the interior have had the C.P.R. since 1885.

Between the Skeena in the north and the Fraser in the south, no rivers completely breach the Coast Range system, and practic-able routes are few. Somewhere about the Fraser mouth was bound to occur the outlet of a developed Western Canada. At Prince George the Nechako joins the Fraser, which from this point southwards is navigable to Soda Creek. The cañon-like character of the valley increases to the south. The old Caribou road by which the miners gained the Caribou mining centre of Barkerville followed the Fraser route from New Westminster through Hope, Yale, and Lytton to Lillooet. Here it left the Fraser cañons and struck north-east to Clinton and crossed a flat-topped tableland divide to the La Hache lake and river, and so back to the Fraser at Soda Creek. Thence the river was navigated to Quesnelle, from which the road tracked north-east to Barker-ville. The Pacific Great Eastern follows much of this route now. We should notice, however, that the gorge-like valley of the Fraser between Lillooet and Lytton is not followed by any rail-way. The line after leaving Lillooet follows the Anderson Lake route to North Vancouver. Throughout its whole course from Prince George to Yale, the Fraser cuts deep into the tableland, but it is in the portion between Lillooet and Yale, in the notch between the Cascades and the Coast Range, that the gorge-like nature of the valley is best developed. Here the river frequently contracts and flows with enormous force between high cliff-like barriers. There are numerous rapids also, so that this portion of the great stream is quite useless for navigation. Its chief function is to provide a routeway—not easy to engineer—for the two great trunk lines from Lytton to Vancouver. Although the whole valley from Lytton to Yale is of the nature of a gorge, the term Fraser Cañon is applied to the particularly deep cutting between North Bend and Yale. The greatest constrictions are about Hell's Gate Rapids and Black Cañon. The whole of the mid-Fraser from Prince George to Lytton has a rainfall of less than 15 inches, and the river is generally too deep-cut to provide irrigation except on its terraces and from lateral streams. There is very much good ranch country on the surrounding plateau, however, and the precipitation is sufficient for cereals if dry-farming methods are adopted. From Hope to the sea the river is running in a gradually extending lowland. Agassiz is generally cited as the head of the delta region, which extends into U.S.A. territory. There are evidences of a great depression of the coast here in Pleistocene times, and the delta then formed —although a part of the Fraser mouth lowland—is at a greater height than the delta deposition now taking place. The Straits of Georgia have considerable tidal currents, and are not shallow, yet the strength of the river current (particularly in the early summer snow-melt) predominates over the sea currents, and more material is deposited than is removed. The difficulties of navigation of the Lower Fraser are concerned with the strength of the river current—the shallow river steamers which normally reach Hope are unable to do so in the months May, June, and July—the shifting of the river channel in its lower courses among the sandbanks, and the maintenance of the channel across the bar at Garry Point. At low water, there is only 14 feet of water between the entrance and New Westminster. At high tide, vessels of 23 feet may reach the city. Much of the recent delta deposit is inundated at the highest tides save when diked and reclaimed. The Fraser mouth deltaic lowlands (Fig. 118) are the most extensive areas of cultivated lands on the coast of British Columbia. They are in the rain-shadow of the Olympic Mountains (Washington) and have less rain and higher temperature than most of the coast. A very valuable truck, small-fruit, and dairying area, they have the advantage of the market of Vancouver near by. Burrard Inlet lies at the northern limit of the delta, and is the first of the rocky fiord-like inlets, so characteristic of the British Columbia coast, to be met with north of the 49th parallel. It is deep enough at low water to take the largest vessels, and the only difficulty of entrance is due to the periodic strong tidal currents of the First Narrows. The geographical factors in the development of Vancouver are sufficiently obvious. Difficult passage though it is, the Fraser River valley forms the only means of threading the southern Coast Range. In pre-railway days, and in the days of small vessels, the chief port was naturally on the river itself at New

Westminster. Big vessels required the better harbour of Vancouver, and railway communication gave the place all the advantages of the Fraser routeway with none of the disadvantages of the delta bars. It has, too, the general advantages of its local environment : the adjacent intensive farming area of the delta, and the calm waters of the Straits of Georgia. Like Victoria, on Vancouver Island, but to a much less extent, it is in the rain-shadow of the Olympic Mountains and the mountains of Van-

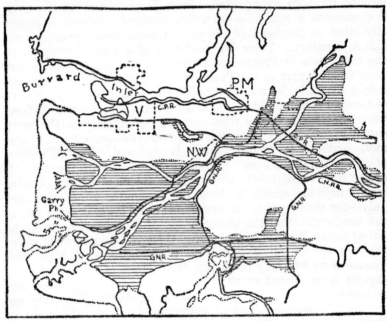

FIG. 118.—Showing position of Fraser Delta in relation to Vancouver and New Westminster.

Recent delta formation.   N.W, New Westminster.
V, Vancouver.   P.M, Port Moody.

couver Island, and though having more rain and less sun than the capital city, it does not suffer the intensely heavy falls of the west coast of Vancouver Island, or of the exposed mainland farther north. The Pacific Great Eastern, the Canadian Pacific Railway, and the Canadian National Railway, as well as the American coast lines from Washington and Oregon, all concentrate on the city. There are many lumber, pulp, and fishing stations on the British Columbia coast, but it looks more and more as if Vancouver is going to attract not only the local traffic to itself for concentration, but an increasing amount of traffic destined for, or originating in, the interior. Like most Pacific ports, it has received a great impetus to development in the opening of the Panama Canal. Viewed as a port of Canada, and not merely of British Columbia, we should note that the whole of Canada west of Winnipeg is nearer to Vancouver than to Montreal, and that though Vancouver is nearly three times as far from Liverpool (8,512 miles) as Montreal, yet even in traffic for Europe it may pay to ship via Vancouver in cases where there is a serious diminution of the rail journey. The route, too, would be independent of the great lake traffic, with its tranship-ments, and winter stoppage. Wheat, from the Prairie Provinces, and lumber, from the Coast Range, are the chief exports.

Vancouver Island is 280 miles long, mostly mountainous, with a fiord west coast. An area of lowland in the south-east has a warmer summer, more sun, and less rain than any other part. For these reasons, and because of the east coastal coalfield, the popula-tion of the island is almost confined to the south-east. Victoria is the capital city of British Columbia. It is not accessible to the largest vessels. The adjoining Esquimalt is a magnificent deep, sheltered harbour. Victoria has regular daily steamer connection with Vancouver, Seattle, and Tacoma. Comax, Cumberland, Nanaimo and Ladysmith, are all colliery harbours on the eastern coalfield, and are connected with Victoria by railway. The better steam coals come from the northern parts of the coalfield.

North of the Fraser the British Columbia Coast Range is dissected into high rugged blocks by gigantic fiords, and is densely forested save where the slope is not too precipitous. The summers are cool, the annual daily temperature range very small, and the precipitation extremely heavy. Like the Southern Alaskan and Northern U.S.A. Pacific coastlands, that of British Columbia is important chiefly for its enormous production of fish (especially salmon and halibut) and of timber. The heavy precipitation and mild climate give rise to thick forests of big trees. The most important cut is from the Douglas fir, but there is much pulp-wood, and the splendid water powers available are creating a lumber, pulp, and paper industry. Particularly noticeable are the pulp and paper mills at Ocean Falls, a very large, very modern plant with the advantage of a coastal situation and local water power.

The fiords and skerry coast of British Columbia make it an ideal fishing-ground. The British Columbia salmon never return to the sea after spawning once, but die at the head-waters of the rivers. The sockeye variety is chiefly used in the canneries because of its richness in oil, and its even colour. That of the Fraser River is most plentiful every fourth year. The U.S.A. fishermen intercept this fish in Puget Sound, and so there is some fall in the Fraser production. The Spring Salmon is more plentiful in the Skeena river fisheries and in the water about

Queen Charlotte Island. There are now about 100 canneries in British Columbia, the most important of which are about the Fraser and Skeena Inlets.

The enormous water powers consequent upon the great relief and precipitation of the Coast Range are in process of rapid development.[1] The Goldstream and Jordan Rivers, near Victoria, now provide about 30,000 h.p., and Coquiltan and Slave Falls, near the Fraser mouth, provide 123,000 h.p. near Vancouver. There are smaller plants near Nanaimo and Prince Rupert.

Minerals. British Columbia, like the rest of the vast cordilleran area of North America, is rich in minerals. Some of the earliest settlements and much of the early development of transport were in connection with mining. The Fraser River, Caribou, Quesnel, and Cassiar districts have each experienced a " gold rush."

There is little placer mining to-day, and Barkersville and Quesnel are comparatively deserted towns, though there is still a little hydraulic mining. The gold production at present is not important, but the Province leads Canada in the production of lead, zinc, and silver. Often several metals are obtained from one mine. No purpose would be served by enumerating here the very many promising areas awaiting development, or any of the smaller developed areas. The great proportion of the metal production came from a few great concerns—in 1935 :

Copper production of British Columbia was 39 million lb. The chief mines are, Britannia at Britannia Beach, 28 miles north of Vancouver city, on Howe Sound, the Hidden Creek and Outside mines, 90 miles north of Prince Rupert and near the great Anyox smelter (Portland Canal Region), and Copper Mountain (south of Princeton) in the Similkameen valley.

Lead production, 337 million lb. Most of this came from the Sullivan mine, 2 miles north of Kimberley, with 19 miles railway connections to the Southern C.P.R. at Cranbrook.

Zinc production, 255 million lb. Most of this is from the Sullivan and other mines in the Fort Steele mining district near Cranbrook.

Silver production, 9 million ozs. Here again the Sullivan, the Premier mine (connected by a 12-mile aerial tramway with its shipping point Steward at the head of the Portland canal), and Slocan (Kootenay) were the chief producers.

[1] The waters of the Nechako River and a chain of lakes 400 miles north of Vancouver have been diverted by a dam and tunnel 10 miles long through the backbone of the Coast Range and dropped nearly 3,000 feet through penstocks to a power station at Kemano, which will generate eventually 1,670,000 h.p. This power will be used to smelt up to 500,000 tons of aluminium annually at a smelter 50 miles to the north on tide-water at Kitimat.

The Britannia and Premier mines ship the bulk of their products as concentrates to American smelters. Anyox smelts the immediate Hidden Creek and Outside mines production. Most of the mines of the southern interior of the Province (Sullivan, Slocan, Copper Mine and many smaller ones) concentrate their ores locally and deliver to one of the world's largest metallurgical plants at Trail for final treatment. Power is supplied (60,000 h.p.) from Bonnington Falls, 30 miles away on the Kootenay River.

The province is rich, too, in coal, chiefly in beds of Cretaceous age. In the Rocky Mountains there are fields of the Kootenay (Cretaceous) coals preserved in elongated basins, which, beginning in British Columbia, with the Crow's Nest and Elk River basins, are continued over the border into Alberta about Banff, and northwards. There are a number of scattered basins about the Interior Plateaux, and coastal areas in South-east Vancouver Island, the Fraser River lowlands, and Queen Charlotte Island. We will add a few notes to an enumeration of the chief producing and explored areas. The total annual production is about 1¼ million tons.

Crow's Nest. This field is just west of Crow's Nest Pass, and its northern tongue is crossed by the Canadian Pacific Railway. It is one of the most accessible and valuable of Canadian reserves. It is in basin form, covering 230 square miles. Here are 100 feet of workable coal in about 2,000 feet of measures, much of it in thick seams, and all of good quality. Several short lines run from the Canadian Pacific Railway to mining centres on the field.

Flathead River Basin, just south-east of the Crow's Nest, contains several small basins containing good-quality coal in thick seams.

Elk River Basin. This is due north of the Crow's Nest basin in the same river valley. This is a large field with 100 to 150 feet of good coal in thick seams. It is only awaiting railway development.

These South-east Rocky Mountain areas contain the greatest reserves of good-quality coal in British Columbia ; reserves much greater than those of the Sydney fields of Cape Breton Island, and of quality better than almost all of the prairie province coal.

Other fields which are worked because of their railway communications are :

The Nicola Valley Field about Nicola. This area is of Tertiary rocks, and the coals are sub-bituminous and non-coking. The area is deeply drift-covered, and prospecting is difficult.

Similkameen River. There is a small production from Tertiary beds of lignitic coal near Princetown.

More valuable but quite untouched areas occur in the north about the Upper Peace River, near Hudson's Hope, near Hazleton (G. T. Pac.), and above all, in the great Ground Hog field of the Upper Skeena valley, where there is anthracitic coal.

The area of greatest present production (after the Crow's Nest) is the coastal field of South-eastern Vancouver Island. Here two narrow coal-belts are separated by a 12-mile interval of crystalline rocks at Nanoose. There is thus the northern or Comax field, and a southern one with Nanaimo and Ladysmith as its shipping points. There are fair-quality bituminous coals in seams of very varying thickness. The situation has been the main factor in development.

Opposite this field and in the Fraser mouth lowlands are extensive beds of lignitic coal at present untouched. The probable resources of the more important of the British Columbia fields are given in the table following.[1]

		Actual Reserve. (Million tons.)	Probable.
South District			
Flathead River ⎫	All Bituminous ⎰	—	600
Crow's Nest ⎬	⎱	22,600	20,000
Elk River ⎭		—	15,200
Princetown			
(Similkameen River). Lignitic		—	310
Nicola River. Sub-bituminous		—	195
Northern British Columbia			
Groundhog. Anthracitic		—	1,200
Peace and Prince Rivers. Bituminous and lignitic		—	6,800
Skeena River Tributaries			
Monico, Selkuc, and Bulkeley Fields. Bituminous		—	340
Vancouver Island. Bituminous		1,178	6,370
Queen Charlotte Isle			
Cretaceous. Anthracitic and Bituminous		6	293
Tertiary. Lignitic		60	1,000

These reserves place the British Columbian high among the world coal resources. The actual production is small at present, and is used chiefly for the railways, the coast ports, and for mineral smelting.

The Mackenzie River Basin. North of lat. 60° the cordilleran areas of North America are arbitrarily divided between Yukon territory and the U.S.A. province of Alaska.

East of the Rocky Mountains and north of this latitude we have the Northern Territories. Most of this country lies within

[1] See Canada, Dept. of Mines, Geological Survey Memoir 59, 1915: "Coal Resources of Canada."

the Laurentian Shield province, but between this latter and the Rockies we have a wedge of relatively little disturbed sedimentaries, narrowing northward, and occupied by the River Mackenzie and its tributaries (Fig. 119). The head-waters of the three great tributaries—the Liard, Peace, and Athabasca Rivers—all lead to important breaches in the Rocky Mountain system ; in the case of the Liard and Peace, to rather wide lowland corridors ; in the case of the Athabasca, to the narrow Yellowhead Pass near the meeting-point of four important rail routes—to Edmonton, to Prince Rupert, to Vancouver, and to the East Kootenay Valley.

The Mackenzie is one of the eight great rivers of the world. Its basin occupies about one-fifth of the whole of Canada. Its greater eastern tributaries leave the Laurentian Shield via three of the greatest fresh-water bodies in the world—Great Bear Lake, Great Slave Lake, and Lake Athabasca. Apart from the possibilities of mineral wealth, both the Rocky Mountains and the Laurentian margins are unlikely to be of outstanding economic importance, but the central belt is structurally a continuation north-westwards of the great central plains of the continent, and experiences, too, a notable extension of the hot summers and relatively long (compared with Laurentian posts in the same latitude) growing season.

Owing to greater cloudiness, a shorter growing season, slightly lower summer maxima, and, more than all, to its typical topographical and soil characteristics, it does not seem probable that any of the Laurentian Shield north of lat. 55° will be occupied in agricultural settlements. On the other hand, there seems every likelihood that much of what has been termed the Alberta Plateau country may yield fair agricultural land. This is so, at any rate, as far north as the east-to-west line formed by the Liard River and the Great Slave Lake.

" So far as our incomplete knowledge of the country will allow us to draw any conclusions, it may be said that the northern limit to which cultivation of the land may proceed in a large way, is the line formed by Great Slave Lake, Mackenzie River to the mouth of Liard River, and Liard River up to the mountains. This is approximately along the line 61° N." [1] North of this line, apart from specially favoured localities, " the greater part of this portion of the basin, inland from the stream, is made up of spruce muskegs with little or no drainage, and a permanent frost only a few inches below the surface, which would make farming impossible." South of this area is the Alberta Plateau,

[1] Canada, Dept. of Mines, Geological Survey Memoir 108 : " The Mackenzie River Basin," by C. Camsell and Wyatt Malcolm, 1919, p. 41.

SELECTED CLIMATIC DATA FOR BRITISH COLUMBIA

Temperatures in Degrees Fahrenheit. Rainfall in Inches.

Region	Station	J.	F.	M.	A.	M.	J.	J.	A.	S.	O.	N.	D.	Total
Vancouver Island, S.E.	Victoria	39 / 4·39	40 / 3·09	44 / 2·31	48 / 1·23	53 / 1·01	57 / 0·83	60 / 0·42	60 / 0·64	56 / 1·62	50 / 2·79	45 / 4·54	41 / 4·78	27·65
Vancouver Island, E. Coast.	Nanaimo	36 / 5·90	38 / 4·22	42 / 2·83	47 / 1·66	53 / 1·52	58 / 1·45	63 / 0·75	63 / 1·01	57 / 2·18	49 / 3·04	43 / 6·94	39 / 5·96	37·46
Vancouver Island, W. Coast.	Clayoquot	39 / 14·30	40 / 12·27	42 / 11·86	45 / 8·70	50 / 6·20	54 / 4·19	57 / 2·20	58 / 3·42	55 / 7·36	50 / 13·11	45 / 18·78	41 / 16·74	119·13
North Coast.	Prince Rupert	33 / 9·85	36 / 8·28	39 / 9·19	48 / 7·23	43 / 5·34	58 / 4·14	62 / 4·86	63 / 5·61	58 / 8·77	50 / 12·97	42 / 12·93	36 / 11·76	100·93
Lower Fraser.	Vancouver	36 / 8·34	38 / 5·90	42 / 5·13	47 / 3·25	54 / 2·94	59 / 2·57	63 / 1·31	62 / 1·74	56 / 4·12	49 / 5·83	42 / 9·68	38 / 7·95	58·76
Lower Fraser.	Hope	29 / 8·07	33 / 5·65	41 / 4·64	48 / 2·78	54 / 2·55	59 / 1·65	64 / 1·08	60 / 1·59	58 / 3·48	48 / 6·16	38 / 8·10	32 / 8·50	54·25
Middle Fraser. (Charleston River)	Big Creek	12 / 0·75	17 / 0·79	27 / 0·84	39 / 0·49	46 / 1·05	53 / 1·54	59 / 1·39	58 / 1·43	49 / 1·16	39 / 0·63	26 / 1·09	16 / 0·92	12·13
Upper Fraser.	Quesnel	13 / 1·36	18 / 0·95	30 / 0·51	43 / 0·45	51 / 1·06	58 / 1·84	62 / 1·69	61 / 1·59	53 / 1·62	42 / 1·48	29 / 1·27	21 / 1·09	14·91
Thompson River.	Kamloops	22 / 0·87	26 / 0·74	38 / 0·35	49 / 0·39	58 / 1·00	64 / 1·32	69 / 1·10	68 / 1·07	58 / 0·83	47 / 0·62	35 / 0·94	28 / 0·85	10·08
West Kootenay.	Nelson	25 / 3·18	28 / 2·01	36 / 1·84	46 / 1·61	53 / 2·31	60 / 2·55	66 / 1·70	64 / 1·51	56 / 1·96	48 / 2·17	36 / 3·09	28 / 2·93	26·86
East Kootenay.	Wilmer	14 / 1·20	21 / 0·61	31 / 0·52	43 / 0·63	51 / 1·20	58 / 1·64	64 / 1·29	61 / 1·53	52 / 1·10	41 / 0·78	27 / 0·88	16 / 1·15	12·53
Okanagan Valley.	Summerland	27 / 0·94	30 / 0·45	38 / 0·55	47 / 0·78	56 / 0·70	63 / 1·05	71 / 0·50	68 / 0·78	59 / 0·71	48 / 0·84	37 / 0·92	28 / 1·35	9·57
N. Columbia River.	Golden	12 / 2·55	17 / 1·04	29 / 0·81	42 / 0·56	50 / 1·03	57 / 1·76	62 / 1·42	59 / 1·65	50 / 1·55	41 / 1·45	28 / 1·97	16 / 1·97	17·76
Yukon.	Dawson	-22 / 0·83	-12 / 0·74	4 / 0·49	29 / 0·58	46 / 0·84	57 / 1·24	59 / 1·59	55 / 1·47	42 / 1·51	25 / 1·25	0 / 1·13	-13 / 1·06	12·73

which sinks to the north from Edmonton and terminates in a fairly well-marked escarpment running from Fort Smith on Salem River to the Liard River in long. 122° and thence probably south-westward along that river valley. This escarpment is formed of Devonian limestones overlying shales, and causes falls on the smaller rivers, but is more completely graded by the larger ones.

There are nearly 200,000 square miles of this plateau in the Central Plain area and within the Mackenzie basin. In the south it is a continuation of the Cretaceous area of the prairie provinces. It is relieved by higher plateaux rising 1,000 to 2,000 feet above the general level, e.g. the Birch Mountains, Caribou Plateau, Buffalo Head Hills, and Clear Hills. This high land—in these latitudes—is unfit for agriculture. There is much of the lower areas which is low-lying, ill-drained spruce muskeg, and much, too, is rather thickly forested.

About the Upper Peace River, however, eastward of where it emerges from the Rocky Mountain Cañon at Hudson's Hope, and again about the Smoky River tributary basin, there are extensive areas of park-like, well-drained land with a rainfall of about 15 inches, and temperature conditions entirely suitable to cereal cultivation. It is in these areas that settlement is proceeding, as this area is now opened up by the railway north-west of Edmonton.

The Mackenzie basin—where it is in the Central Plain province —is forested, save in the park-like area of the south-west. The timber is usually small away from the river valleys, however, and much of it only suitable for pulp-wood. Also the Mackenzie is flowing in the wrong direction for economic transport. The chief economic products of the middle basin are to-day, as they have been for 100 years, connected with the fur trade. The only old settlements are the various " forts " of the great fur companies, at river and lake junctions, and at falls on the rivers.

The railway now reaches Fort McMurray and the Upper Peace River district, but for long the only means of transport was by river, and this is liable to considerable interruptions, the chief of which are summarized below.

The Athabasca River. The upper steamboat [1] limit is the junction of the McLeod River, and the river is navigable, but with many minor rapids, to Grand Rapids, 325 miles. Here there is a fall of 50 to 60 feet in half a mile, and no possible navigation. Below Grand Rapids the river is interrupted repeatedly by rapids as far as Fort McMurray. Thence to Athabasca Lake it is a slow-moving river, and navigable for river steamers.

Peace River. There is boat navigation of the Parsnip and

[1] i.e. stern paddle and 3 to 4 feet of water.

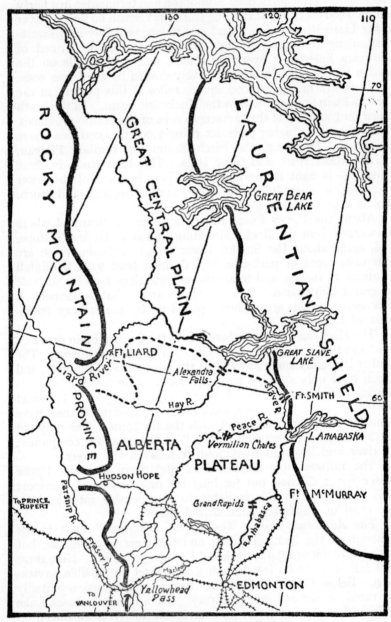

FIG. 119.—Mackenzie River Basin.

Upper Peace Rivers from the Fraser bend in British Columbia to Hudson's Hope Cañon, but it is then interrupted by a number of rapids entailing portages. Hudson's Hope is the upper limit of steam-boat navigation, which extends 500 miles to Vermillion Chutes, near the mouth of the Mikkwa River. The valley is cut about 800 feet into the plateau in its upper portion, but only about 100 feet at the Chutes. There is a direct drop of 15 feet here. Thence the river is navigable again for steam-boats to its junction with Slave River.

Slave River is navigable to the series of rapids about Fort Smith, which is the upper limit of navigation from the mouth of the Mackenzie. Locks here would entail 1,630 miles open navigation from Fort McMurray on the Athabasca to the Arctic Sea.

Hay River is interrupted by magnificent falls about 20 miles direct from its junction with Great Slave Lake. Here, at the Alexandra Falls, the river, 130 yards wide, has a sheer drop of 105 feet.

Below Fort Liard the *Liard River* is a slow-moving stream, probably suitable for steamer navigation. A series of rapids 30 miles from its junction with the Mackenzie would form a serious barrier, however.

The whole of these river systems are only open at a maximum from May to October. There are fairly regular river steamer services from Peace River Crossing to Fort McMurray, and less frequently to Hudson's Hope.

There are promising indications of mineral wealth in the Mackenzie basin, but much prospecting remains to be done.[1] The bituminous Cretaceous coals of the Kootenay formation known in the foothill regions of Alberta have been discovered farther north in the Smoky River basin. The Lower Cretaceous Athabasca sandstone is often impregnated with bitumen, and there has been much recent exploration of the Middle Peace and Athabasca River basin for oil. Paying wells have not yet been encountered. There are signs of oil, too, in some of the Devonian strata farther north about Great Slave Lake.

Great undeveloped water powers exist at the various rapids to which attention has just been called, and at many others, especially those occurring in streams draining to the south of Great Slave Lake, and at those on the edge of the Laurentian Plateau.

[1] Canada ranks high as a source of uranium products. The chief centre is Port Radium at the eastern end of Great Bear Lake. A secondary centre is being developed near Lake Athabaska at Uranium City. Transport is provided mainly by the use of aircraft. For security reasons details of output are not available.

CHAPTER XXXV

ALASKA

ALASKA, the most northerly of U.S.A. territories, separated from the parent body, and inhabited by but 56,000 souls, has suffered more than its share of popular misconception. Until the last decade there was little official material available for study. That is no longer the case. The territory is popularly conceived of as an Arctic region, yet less than one-third of it lies within the circle : as an area wholly remote, yet the great circle from Washington (D.C.) to Tokio passes through it in crossing Behring Straits ; as barren tundra and ice-fields, yet its ice-fields are in the relatively warm south, and cereals are grown regularly in the interior ; as of no great extent, yet in area it equals that of any eight adjacent central states of the Union.

Of course, the fact is that so large an area has many different climates, and a general subdivision must preface the simplest study. Much of the region has not yet been the subject of detailed survey, but quite sufficient is known of the relief to justify the division (common to the whole Pacific Cordillera) into an interior plateau country set between great mountain masses. The strike of these ranges follows the curvature of the coast, and becomes almost east and west in Central and Western Alaska. Mr. A. H. Brock, of the U.S.G.S., distinguished five principal physiographic regions, viz. (i) Pacific Mountains ; (ii) Interior Plateau ; (iii) Rocky Mountains ; (iv) Arctic Mountains ; (v) Arctic Slope. Structurally, the Arctic Mountains are not a continuation of the Rockies of Canada, and indeed such continuation in Alaska is inconsiderable, so that (iii) above is unessential. The essential elements of relief are the two east-and-west mountain systems, the more southerly a continuation of the fiord-indented Coast Range of British Columbia, the more northerly terminating in a bold scarp-land overlooking the Mackenzie delta (Fig. 120).

The broad Arctic slope, with its subdivision into Piedmont and coast plain, is condemned ever to be a barren tundra region. The interior is a plateau only in the sense that the term is applied to that of British Columbia. It is hilly, but the hills are lower than the border ranges, and are often rounded and of an accordant summit level. Wide stretches of river bench lands surround the Middle Yukon (e.g. about Fort Yukon). This great river, and the smaller Kuskokwim to the south, form extensive delta lands bordering the Behring Sea. From the standpoint of economic geography, we are concerned only with the two great regions

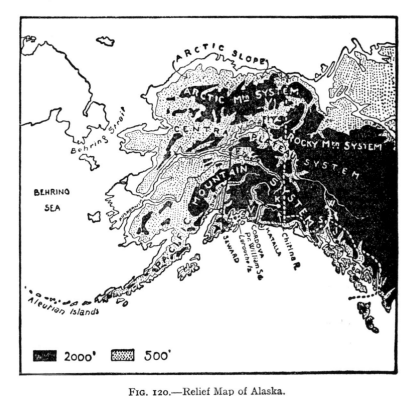

FIG. 120.—Relief Map of Alaska.

F, Fairbanks; W, Whitehorse; S, Skagway; J, Juneau; Ft.Y, Ft. Yukon; V, Valdes; K, Kennicott.

of the Interior Plateau and the Pacific bordering mountains; two regions as strongly opposed in climate as in relief. Like the corresponding coasts of British Columbia, the Pacific mountains have a very heavy precipitation, with a well-marked winter maximum in the Panhandle country. There is no real summer drought, however, and the distribution throughout the year is more uniform as we go north-westwards. The winters on this coast are mild for the latitude, the harbours open, and the occasional lowlands and lower slopes well forested. The great snowfall on the mountains, however, is consolidated into ice, and there are many great glaciers, some of which reach to the water's edge. This phenomenon is the combined result of a high relief, a heavy precipitation, and a high latitude. The most extensive glaciers are those of the Great Elias Range, the summits of which are over 15,000 feet—e.g. Mount Elias, 18,000 feet ; Mount Logan, 19,540 feet. The Alaska Range, which lies more inland, has some even greater heights (Mount McKinley, 20,000 feet), but much less extensive glaciers.

To the north of these great coast mountains the lower irregular country of the Interior Plateau has an entirely different climate. The precipitation is usually less than 16 inches (i.e. less than one-fifth of that of the coast ranges). The winters are long and very cold. The July temperatures are equal to those of London, and the month seldom passes without daily maxima above 85° F. being registered. Hard frosts are liable to occur, however, in May and in September, so that the growing season is distinctly shorter than that of the Canadian wheat prairies. This is in part counterbalanced by the long days of summer, and the cloudless skies of this interior region of low precipitation.

The table following will serve to distinguish the coastal and the interior climates.

MEAN MONTHLY TEMPERATURE AND PRECIPITATION (1918–20)—AV.

		J.	F.	M.	A.	M.	J.	J.	A.	S.	O.	N.	D.	
Juneau, S.E.Coast Extension.	° F.	28·2	30·8	29·1	39·0	45·7	52·9	57·6	54·5	50·9	41·3	35·0	32·1	
	Ins.	11·4	6·3	4·4	5·6	5·5	4·1	3·5	9·0	10·6	12·4	10·2	8·0	90·9
Seward, S. Coast.	° F.	13·2	24·9	23·9	33·4	42·5	49·0	53·3	50·9	45·6	38·2	28·0	22·1	
	Ins.	5·8	3·8	0·8	2·3	1·2	1·6	2·9	8·2	14·0	11·3	4·5	7·8	64·4
Fairbanks, Central Plateaux.	° F.	−11·7	5·4	4·1	28·9	44·9	55·7	62·7	55·7	46·3	24·2	2·2	−5·3	
	Ins.	0·3	0·7	1·2	0·4	1·0	1·4	2·0	1·5	0·7	0·6	0·6	0·5	10·9

The coastal zone will never be of much agricultural value. The winters are comparatively mild, but that is unimportant from the point of view of agriculture. The summers are not hot enough for cereal production, as the precipitation and cloudiness are too great. Also, of course, there is little lowland available. Garden vegetables are grown for the coastal mining and fishing stations.

In the southern interior, however (e.g. in the Tanana Valley), wheat is grown successfully every year. The famous Marquis wheat of Canada will not mature, but an acclimatized Eastern Siberian type does well. As far as climate is concerned, wheat, oats, barley, can be and indeed are grown. It would be a great mistake, however, to conclude that we have anything in Alaska at all comparable with the Canadian wheat prairie region. Almost everywhere in the interior, the line of permanent frost is not far below the surface. This prevents adequate drainage. Muskeg swamps result, and the presence of moss vegetation itself, through its non-conductive properties, facilitates the near approach of the frost layer to the surface even in summer. Stripping of the moss cover, drainage, and liming, would be required to make most of the land of any use for crops, and even then precipitation is on the low side. However, the crops produced at the experimental stations, and the actual farming production of the Fairbanks district, make it quite clear that Alaska should at any rate be quite independent of imported grain, and remain so even with many times its present insignificant population. The tundra of the Arctic slope form a belt also on the coasts of Behring Straits and Behring Sea. The milder Pacific influences do not occur until the Aleutian peninsula is crossed to the south. The Alaskan peninsula and Aleutian islands are grass land on the south, tundra on the north.

Timber. The snow-line of the Pacific mountains is low, but the lower mountain country and coastal valleys are forested with coniferous trees, smaller, less dense, and less valuable than the reserves of British Columbia and of Washington and Oregon, yet a really important supply nevertheless.

There is abundant water power available for saw-mills and pulp-mills. Much of the southern interior is forested, but with a distinctly smaller growth, and the cut is chiefly for firing.

Salmon. At present the industry in Alaska of greatest value is that of the salmon fisheries. The fiord coast of the Pacific Alaska is as much frequented by this fish as those of British Columbia and of Washington and Oregon. Almost every considerable inlet has its cannery, and more fish are landed than in any other state or province of North America. Alaska yearly produces more than three-fifths of the enormous salmon catch of Pacific America.

As is the case in all the cordilleran country, the rocks are extensively mineralized. Gold-mining, as usual, caused the first rush to the country, and the production is still important. Copper is abundant, and forms the most important mineral production at present.

Copper. Many ore bodies have been located, but productive mining is limited to those having communications. The chief areas at present are in the Chitina River valley, where are the most productive mines of Kennicott, now reached by a railway giving access to the coast at Cordova. The only considerable area of production in South-eastern Alaska is in the Ketchikan, which has the advantage of coastal situation and abundant timber and open harbours.

Another important centre of production is the Beatson-Bonanza mine, in Latouche Island. Here there is the advantage of open water and small annual climatic range.

The copper reserves in *present* mining areas are small, but many new areas await exploitation.

Gold. Gold is obtained from the auriferous gravels of the Yukon River, e.g. at Fairbanks, and from lode-mining about Juneau, Willow Creek, and Prince William Sound.

About one-third of the total gold is obtained from lode-mining and two-thirds from placers.

Coal. The two pre-eminent fields are the Katalla field and the Matanuska field.

The first lies 25 miles east of Cordova and is drained by the Behring River. The coal is anthracitic, and occurs in thick but much contorted and faulted seams. This deformation makes the coal recovery a serious problem. The Matanuska coalfield lies along the river valley of that name, with its western end 25 miles from the sea at Knik Arm. The coals are sub-bituminous to bituminous, and much faulted and folded.

The great coal reserves of Alaska are of sub-bituminous coal, and in the interior. The coals more obviously set for exploitation are those near the Pacific coast, especially as some of this coal is of better steaming quality than any other Pacific coal. We have, however, the long-standing shipping facilities of Vancouver, of the Nanaimo coalfield, and of Washington competing with a more easily mined but lower-grade article. There is also the competition of Californian oil and Pacific water power generally to consider. In fact, the richness of the Pacific regions—whether they be in British Columbia or in the U.S.A.—in the very products which Alaska can produce, is somewhat of a hindrance to rapid development.

Communications. The mining developments in·part of Alaska have entailed a certain amount of railway construction, viz. the Copper River and north-western mineral line which runs from the Kennicott mines in Wrangle Mountains along the Copper River valley to the ice-free port of Cordova. To assist entrance to the Yukon gold districts a railway exists from Skagway over White Pass (2,888 feet), and down to the navigable River Yukon at Whitehorse. Then there is the Government railway from Seward via the Susitna Valley to Fairbanks, with a branch line to Chickaloon along the Matanuska Valley coalfield.

The Yukon is a splendid stream, whose value is diminished by the fact that it can be entered only from the Behring Sea, and it is closed by ice for all but three months of the year. The delta channels, too, are shallow. In the season there is through navigation for river steamers to Whitehorse in Yukon, i.e. more than 2,000 miles. Its tributary, the Tanana—the most promising valley for cereal agriculture in Alaska—is navigable nearly to Fairbanks. There is a Government road from Fairbanks to Valdez, on Prince William Sound. Morass is apt to hinder cross-country movement in summer.

During the second world war the Alaskan Highway has been constructed. This runs from Edmonton through the occupied Peace River country and thence northward, keeping to the east of the main Pacific Cordillera, through the forests and swamps of virgin country to Alaska. Its war purpose was to make ground communication with Alaskan airfields—so important in global warfare. In peace it may lead to settlement, mining, and the development of parts of the route for tourist traffic.

It seems likely that communication with Alaska will remain largely by sea (as to bulk commodities) and by air (for passengers and light but valuable goods).

APPENDIX

POPULATION AND LAND USE IN THE UNITED STATES

Total population of the Continental U.S.A..   150 million (1950 Census)

                      .   161   „   (1954 Estimate)

Total area of the Continental U.S.A. .   .   3   „   sq. mls.

REGIONAL POPULATION AND LAND USE

*Region	Gross Area (Thousand sq. mls.)	Population (millions), 1954 Estimate	Crop-land	Wheat	Oats	Hay	Barley	Potatoes	Corn
						Million acres, 1954			
1. New England . .	66·6	9·8	2·8	—	0·1	2·3	0·2	0·1	0·1
2. Middle Atlantic .	102·7	31·4	12·2	11·8	1·4	5·6	—	0·1	2·2
3. East North Central	248·2	32·5	53·5	5·5	10·0	13·0	0·1	0·1	21·8
4. West North Central	517·2	14·5	133·3	25·4	20·7	26·7	5·3	0·1	33·8
5. South Atlantic. .	278·9	23·0	25·0	0·8	1·6	3·7	0·1	0·1	8·1
6. East South Central	181·9	11·6	22·4	0·4	0·6	3·1	} 0·4	—	7·7
7. West South Central	438·8	15·5	49·0	7·9	2·1	3·7		—	3·4
8. Mountain . . .	863·8	5·7	24·5	7·3	0·7	6·9	} 5·3	0·2	0·4
9. Pacific	323·8	16·7	15·4	3·2	0·4	3·5		0·1	0·1

     * States included in these regions are—
       1 = Maine, N.H., Vt., Mass., R.I.
       2 = N.Y., N.J., Pa.
       3 = Ohio, Ill., Ind., Mich., Wis.
       4 = Minn., Iowa, Mo., N.Dak., S.Dak., Nebr., Kans.
       5 = Del., Md., Va., W.Va., N.C., S.C., Ga., Fla.
       6 = Ky., Tenn., Ala., Miss.
       7 = Ark., La., Okla., Tex.
       8 = Mont., Idaho, Wyo., Colo., N.Mex., Ariz., Utah, Nev.
       9 = Wash., Ore., Cal.

POPULATION AND LAND USE IN CANADA, 1955

	% Area of Canada	Population (millions)	Field Crops	Wheat	Oats	Hay	Barley	Rye	Potatoes
					Million acres				
P. Edward Isle . .	0·1	0·1	0·43	—	0·09	0·20	—	—	0·04
Nova Scotia . .	0·6	0·6	0·43	—	0·05	0·35	—	—	0·01
New Brunswick .	0·8	0·5	0·66	—	0·13	0·45	—	—	0·04
Quebec	16·1	4 3	5·54	0·01	1·13	3·72	0·06	—	0·09
Ontario . . .	11·1	5·0	8·28	0·60	1·70	3·40	0·14	0·06	0·05
Manitoba . . .	6·7	0·8	6·85	1·95	1 48	0·52	2·09	0·08	0·01
Saskatchewan . .	6 8	0·8	23·10	13·14	3·65	0·63	3·84	0·45	0·01
Alberta . . .	6·9	1·0	14·43	5·71	2·64	1·42	3·70	0·17	0·01
B. Columbia . .	9·9	1·2	0·58	0·06	0·08	0·32	0·07	—	—
TOTAL . . .	100	*15·19	60·15	21·50	11·17	11·05	9·93	0·78	0·30

     * Populations of—North-west Territories   .   .   . 0·017
                   —Yukon   .   .   .   . 0·010
                   —Newfoundland   .   .   . 0·398

AGRICULTURE: U.S.A. AND CANADA
PRODUCTION OF SELECTED CROPS

Wheat. Canada. 1953

Province	Million bushels
P. Edward Isle	0·07
Nova Scotia	0·02
New Brunswick	0·07
Quebec	0·24
Ontario	26·94
Manitoba	46·00
Saskatchewan	375·00
Alberta	163·00
B.C.	2·60
TOTAL	613·96

Wheat and Corn. U.S.A. 1954

	Million bushels	
	Wheat	Corn
New England	—	7·3
Middle Atlantic	31·2	92·3
East North Central . . .	164·5	1,174·8
West North Central . . .	386·5	1,263·3
South Atlantic	26·1	164·1
East South Central . . .	10·6	162·8
West South Central . . .	103·1	58·3
Mountain	139·5	19·4
Pacific	106·6	4·9
TOTAL	969·7	3,192·4

Cotton. U.S.A. (*In order of rank for 1955 harvest*)
Running Bales in thousands

Texas	3,936
Mississippi	1,998
Arkansas	1,646
California	1,215
Alabama	1,024
Arizona	725
Georgia	695
Tennessee	615
Louisiana	569
S. Carolina	567
Oklahoma	453
Missouri	424
N. Carolina	355
Other States	279
TOTAL, U.S.A. . . .	14,542*

* Includes 41,516 bales of American-Egyptian.

LIVESTOCK ON FARMS, CANADA AND U.S.A.

	All Cattle	Milk Cows	Sheep	Swine
		Thousands		
CANADA, 1953				
P. Edward Isle	114	44	38	57
Nova Scotia	202	88	95	39
New Brunswick	193	95	64	56
Quebec	1,919	1,016	360	867
Ontario	2,982	1,040	414	1,450
Manitoba	654	195	65	287
Saskatchewan	1,435	285	170	469
Alberta	1,910	289	432	1,180
B.C.	352	94	81	42
Yukon	—	—	—	—
TOTAL, CANADA	9,762	3,146	1,721	4,447
U.S.A. 1955				
New England	1,242	785	69	190
Middle Atlantic	4,538	2,724	428	880
East North Central	14,759	6,145	3,233	16,824
West North Central	28,723	5,394	6,261	24,602
South Atlantic	7,154	2,158	764	4,935
East South Central	7,516	2,496	1,120	3,869
West South Central	14,955	2,416	5,693	2,355
Mountain	10,367	837	10,278	638
Pacific	6,179	1,453	3,085	709
TOTAL, U.S.A.	95,433	24,408	30,931	55,002

TOTAL STAND OF TIMBER, EQUIVALENT VOLUME OF SOLID WOOD CUT AND REFORESTATION, CANADA

	Accessible Equiv. Vol. Saw Timber (estimated 1953), millions cu. ft.		Equiv. Volume of Solid Wood Cut (1952), millions cu. ft.	Reforestation (Total area planted to March 1954), acres
	Conifer	Broadleaf		
Newfoundland	3,337	—	107,531	—
P. Edward Island	61	24	17,034	38
Nova Scotia	2,939	708	137,980	59
New Brunswick	6,100	2,850	251,058	—
Quebec	45,928	17,773	1,158,746	—
Ontario	54,589	19,562	709,413	22,667
Manitoba	1,004	1,949	87,761	1,093
Saskatchewan	5,147	5,582	86,739	425
Alberta	7,724	3,476	164,008	—
B. Colombia	88,248	1,075	845,339	6,090
N.W.T.	3,109	1,499	—	—
Yukon	1,769	815	—	—
TOTAL	219,995	55,313	3,565,609	30,372
TOTAL Inaccessible	107,871	14,184	—	—

FOREST LAND AREA AND TIMBER PRODUCTION. U.S.A., 1953

Region	Total Forest Land (million acres)	Volume of Saw Timber (million board feet)*		Lumber Production (million board feet)†	Lumber Production per cent. distribution
		Softwood	Hardwood		
New England .	31·0	33,263	24,934	} 2,334	6·4
Middle Atlantic	44·2	14,017	48,028		
Lake	55·7	15,670	35,040	293	—
Central . . .	44·9	2,418	41,329	} 2,111	5·7
Plains . . .	35·8	468	5,262		
South Atlantic .	43·8	59,326	37,815	3,858	10·5
South-east . .	91·8	76,992	58,895	} 7,416	20·2
West Gulf . .	51·1	57,472	47,487		
Pacific N.W. .	53·8	626,941	3,953	} 17,284‡	47·0
California . .	45·5	227,565	—		
North Rocky Mt.	53·2	126,293	936	} 2,624	7·1
South Rocky Mt.	72·6	55,952	916		
TOTAL . .	623·8	1,296,377	304,595	36,742	

* Listed as available.
† Based on sample surveys.
‡ Includes Nevada (included under S. Rocky Mt. in other figures).

AVAILABLE AND DEVELOPED WATER POWER. CANADA, 1953

Province	Thousands H.P. Available 24-hr. Power at 80% Efficiency		Turbine Installation (includes water wheels and hydraulic turbines installed)
	At Ordinary Minimum Flow	At Ordinary 6 months Flow	
Newfoundland . . .	958·5	2,754·0	311·1
P. Edward Island . . .	0·5	3·0	1·9
Nova Scotia	35·5	156·0	162·4
New Brunswick . . .	123·0	334·0	164·1
Quebec	10,896·0	20,445·0	7,719·0
Ontario	5,407·0	7,261·0	4,006·6
Manitoba	3,333·0	5,562·0	716·9
Saskatchewan	550·0	1,120·0	109·8
Alberta	508·0	1·258·0	207·9
B.C.	382·5	814·0	1,496·5
Yukon and N.W T. . .	7,023·0	10,998·0	32·4
TOTAL	29,207·0	50,705·0	14,929·0

CAPACITY AND PRODUCTION OF HYDRO-ELECTRIC POWER
U.S.A., 1953

Region	Installed Capacity (thousands Kw.)		Power Generated (million Kw. hs.)	
	Electric Utilities and Industrial	Electric Utilities	Electric Utilities and Industrial	Electric Utilities
New England . . .	1,282	996	4,915	3,780
Middle Atlantic . .	1,704	1,625	9,767	9,424
E. North Central . .	938	875	4,098	3,730
W. North Central . .	682	631	2,887	2,622
S. Atlantic	3,212	2,744	10,349	8,382
E. South Central . .	3,532	3,524	14,741	14,716
W. South Central . .	842	839	1,227	1,222
Mountain	3,438	3,434	14,989	14,980
Pacific	7,425	7,378	46,643	46,377
Total	23,055	22,045	109,617	105,233

PETROLEUM. WORLD PRODUCTION, 1955
(Thousands of Metric Tons)

Country	Production	Country	Production
U.S.A.	362,700	Austria	3,700
Venezuela	113,200	Trinidad	3,600
*U.S.S.R. (including		Western Germany . .	3,200
Sakhalin)	70,000	Peru	2,400
Kuwait	54,800	Egypt	1,800
Saudi Arabia	47,500	Bahrein	1,500
Iraq	33,700	*Hungary	1,500
Canada	17,600	Kuwait/Saudi Arabia	
Persia	16,200	neutral zone . . .	1,400
Mexico.	12,900	Netherlands	1,000
Indonesia	11,700	France	900
*Rumania	8,000	*China	500
Colombia	5,700	New Guinea	500
Qatar	5,400	Ecuador	500
British Borneo . . .	5,400	Other countries . . .	3,500
Argentina	4,500	Total	795,300

* Estimated.

Petroleum Information Bureau, 1957.

MINERAL PRODUCTION, INCLUDING FUELS. CANADA, 1953

	Cobalt (million lb.)	Copper (million lb.)	Iron Ore (million tons)	Nickel (million lb.)	Gold (thousand oz. troy)	Coal (million tons)	Nat. Gas (million cu. ft.)	Crude Petroleum (Thousand barrels)
Newfoundland.	—	5,627	2·686	—	7	—	—	—
Nova Scotia .	—	1,576	—	—	3	5·787	—	—
New Brunswick	—	—	—	—	—	0·721	177·122	14
Quebec . .	—	109,839	—	—	1,021	—	9,708,969	299
Ontario. . .	1,602	261,164	2·832	287·385	2·182	—	—	653
Manitoba . .	—	18,822	—	—	131	—	1,422,128	2,797
Saskatchewan .	—	61,176	—	—	88	2·021	89,651,605	76,816
Alberta . .	—	—	—	—	—	5·917	—	—
B.C. . . .	—	48,295	0·991	—	264	1·443	—	316
N.W.T. . .	—	—	—	—	289	—	26·109	—
Yukon . . .	—	—	—	—	66	0·01	—	—
CANADA TOTAL	1,602	506,504	6·509	287·385	4,055	15·900	100,985,923	80,839

Canadian Imports of Anthracite = 2·9 million tons, bituminous coal = 20·2 million tons.

MINERAL PRODUCTION, INCLUDING FUELS. U.S.A., 1953

COAL. Leading producers, millions of tons (short tons)

W. Virginia	134·1	Indiana	15·8
Pennsylvania		Alabama	12·5
Anthracite	30·9	Utah	6·5
Bituminous	93·9	Tennessee	5·4
Kentucky	65·0	Wyoming	5·2
Illinois	46·0	Colorado	3·5
Ohio	34·7	N. Dakota	2·8
Virginia	19·1	U.S.A. TOTAL . . .	483·2

NATURAL GAS AND PETROLEUM. Leading producers, million cu. ft. and million barrels

	Petroleum (million barrels)	Natural Gas (million cu. ft.)
Texas	1,019·1	4,383,158
California . . .	365·0	531,346
Louisiana . . .	256·6	1,293,644
Oklahoma . . .	202·5	599,955
Kansas	114·5	420,607
Wyoming . . .	82·6	76,262
New Mexico . .	70·4	399,086
Illinois	59·0	9·282
Colorado . . .	36·4	—

IRON ORE. Million tons (long tons)

Lake Superior	85·6	Western	8·8
South-eastern	7·6	Undistributed (by-product	
North-eastern	5·1	ore)	0·6
		U.S.A. TOTAL . . .	117·9

LEAD and COPPER. Leading producers, thousand short tons

	Copper	Lead		Copper	Lead
Arizona . .	393·5	9·3	Tennessee .	7·8	—
Utah . .	269·4	41·5	Colorado .	—	21·7
Montana .	77·6	19·9	Idaho . .	—	74·6
New Mexico	72·4	2·9	Washington	—	11·0
Nevada . .	61·8	4·3	Missouri .	—	125·8
Michigan	24·0	—	U.S.A. TOTAL	926·4	341·8

MANUFACTURING INDUSTRY. CANADA, 1952

Net value of products, million $

	Food and Beverages	Textiles (less clothing)	Wood Products	Iron and Steel Products	Non-ferrous Metal Products	Chemicals
Newfoundland . .	10·973	0·502	3·425	0·958	—	0·545
P. Edward Island .	3·521	0·303	0·465	0·224	—	—
Nova Scotia . . .	28·673	3,546	13·299	26,279	—	2·758
New Brunswick .	29,163	4·658	13·964	5·939	—	1·279
Quebec	279·540	167·980	108·265	254·097	146·155	124·797
Ontario	474·898	129·388	143·919	753·139	249·564	237·757
Manitoba . . .	64·584	3·101	13·036	30·520	1·947	5·505
Saskatchewan . .	38·004	0·308	6·550	3·569	—	0·714
Alberta	63·557	0·505	24·052	15·029	0·562	6·609
B.C.	98·963	2·331	206·830	44·284	4·561	33·595
Yukon and N.W.T. .	0·063	—	0·344	—	—	—
TOTAL	1,091·944	312·627	534·155	1,134·043	414·920	414·087

MANUFACTURING INDUSTRY. U.S.A., 1953

GENERAL STATISTICS

Region	Employees (average for the year) (thousands)	Value added by Manufacture (million $)
New England.	1,588·8	9,904·7
Middle Atlantic	4,498·0	31,654·9
East North Central . .	5,134·8	39,926·4
West North Central . .	999·9	7,050·3
South Atlantic . . .	1,816·6	10,686·2
East South Central . .	747·1	4,666·9
West South Central . .	739·7	5,464·8
Mountain	187·0	1,501·6
Pacific	1,381·3	10,620·9
TOTAL	17,093·0	121,659·1

TEXTILES. COTTON AND WOOLLEN MANUFACTURES

State	Cotton Spindles (thousands) 1954	Woollen Spinning Spindles (thousand) 1953	Woollen and Worsted Looms (thousand)
Alabama . . .	1,755	a ,	a
Connecticut . .	350	128·5	2·0
Georgia . . .	3,198	a	a
Maine	598	138·3	3·4
Massachusetts . .	1,781	279·7	8·8
New York . . .	67	173·8	1·8
N. Carolina . .	6,078	a	a
R. Island . . .	487	48·8	3·9
S. Carolina . .	6,268	a	a
Tennessee . . .	514	a	a
Texas	228	a	a
Virginia . . .	650	a	a
New Hampshire .	—	112·0	2·6
Vermont . . .	—	42·2	0·8
New Jersey . .	—,	53·9	2·3
Pennsylvania . .	—	111·7	3·9
Other States . .	731	334·2	7·6
TOTAL . . .	22,694	1,423·8	37·4

a = Included in " other States " figure.

PIG IRON PRODUCTION. U.S.A., 1953

Million short tons

Massachusetts } New York }	4·9	Ohio . . . . 15·1
		Indiana . . . . . . 8·3
Pennsylvania	20·7	Illinois . . . . . . 6·5
Maryland } West Virginia }	5·6	Michigan } Minnesota } . . . . . 3·1
Kentucky } Tennessee }	1·7	Colorado } Utah } . . . . . . 3·8
Texas }		California }
Alabama	4·0	U.S.A. TOTAL . . . 74·9

STEEL PRODUCTION. U.S.A. BY TYPE

Million short tons

	Capacity (Jan. 1st)	Total	Production		Electric
			Open Hearth	Bessemer	
1950	99·1	96·8	86·2	4·5	6·0
1953	117·5	111·6	100·4	3·8	7·2
1954	124·3	88·3	80·3	2·5	5·4

Regional production not available.

EXPORTS AND IMPORTS. U.S.A. AND CANADA, 1953

By continents

Continent	Total Exports		Total Imports	
	Canada %	U.S.A. %	Canada %	U.S.A. %
Rest of North America . .	61·4	29·0	75·6	34·4
South America	3·4	9·7	5·7	21·9
Europe	25·6	18·2	14·3	21·5
Asia	6·3	12·7	2·6	15·0
Australia and Oceania . .	1·3	1·1	1·0	1·9
Africa	2·0	3·2	0·8	5·3
Special category goods excluded from figures .	N/A	26·1	N/A	N/A

N/A = Not applicable

TOTAL VALUES OF IMPORTS AND EXPORTS BY CUSTOMS DISTRICTS. U.S.A., 1953

Customs District*	Million $	
	Exports	Imports
New York	3,450·3	4,133·0
New Orleans	825·2	618·5
Philadelphia	249·0	719·2
Boston, Mass	51·9	517·9
Galveston	706·6	337·5
San Francisco	370·0	361·8
Baltimore	430·7	443·4
Seattle, Washington	249·9	221·2
Savanah	36·5	55·8
Sabine	146·4	3·9
Mobile	83·1	79·1
Michigan	1,071·7	643·4
Buffalo	597·2	423·0
Los Angeles	269·9	261·4
Duluth-Superior	73·7	141·9
TOTAL	15,773·6	10,778·9
(including remaining districts)	(including special category commodities)	

* Where the Customs District embraces an entire State, the headquarters post is given

CARGO LOADED AND UNLOADED AT CERTAIN CANADIAN
PORTS, 1953

Port	Millions of tons (nearest)		
	Inward	Outward	Total
Montreal	8·40	8·49	16·89
Vancouver	5·98	5·84	11·83
Halifax	2·49	1·91	4·40
Quebec	2·19	1·05	3·25
Three Rivers	2·39	0·65	3·04
St. John	0·99	1·47	2·47

INDEX